The Family Book of Humor

The Family Book of Humor

Edited by Helen Hoke

Hanover House, Garden City, New York

For Franklin,
who kept his sense of humor all through my three years
of collecting the material for this book.

CONTENTS

DATE OF BIRTH:

PLACE OF BIRTH:

SCHOOLS ATTENDED:

SPECIAL APTITUDES:

SINGLE . . . :

. . . OR MARRIED:

NUMBER OF DEPENDENTS:

PETS:

WILL YOU TRAVEL?

ANY FURTHER REMARKS?

INTRODUCTION

Why an introduction to this book at all? Well, for one thing, introductions are customary. Or perhaps some introductions just happen because the publisher expects one and leaves blank pages for it. But perhaps a book of humor most of all challenges the compiler with that so-tempting opportunity: the occasion to explain his or her sense of humor. Heaven knows, practically everyone is touchier about this particular and nebulous property than about any other of his spiritual possessions. (Just try casting any aspersions or doubts on it!)

Probably anthologists are born, not made. If that is difficult to substantiate, I maintain at least it is likely they are developed at an early age . . . *This* book, for instance, really started when I was a child in California, Pennsylvania (yes, Reader, there *is* a California in Pennsylvania), and my first indoctrination into what you might call "organized" humor was with "boiler plate," as I trudged around helpfully and happily in my father's busy newspaper-and-job-printing shop.

Boiler plate—in case it's a new item to you—is that wonderful silver-colored flood of shiny intaglioed plates from various syndicates and press associations which used to land (and likely still does) on editors' desks in small-town and county-seat newspapers—the answer to prayer for last-minute "fillers." For example: if Coatsworth's Meat Market decided at the last minute to withdraw its customary two-column-wide-eight-inch-deep ad this week and to substitute a full page next week just before a big holiday—well! that empty space had to be filled, quickly—and exactly. And something humorous or educational was always sure-fire—in that order.

For ten or so years *I* filled those empty spaces: and it was humorous *and* educational to me—in that order.

For boiler plate held a wealth of delectable, selectable tidbits and odds and ends of data knowingly calculated to please the widest possible range of ages and funny bones. Long pieces, short ones, simple, sophisticated (never *too*)—here also were jokes and funny narratives;

short romantic stories; oddments about various customs of the Sandwich and Tahiti and Tulagi islanders; wonderfully corny riddles to add to one's repertoire—an unbeatable mélange.

Yes, boiler plate was wonderful. You filled up columns with it. You patched up holes in the pages with it. For one thing, you read much of it upside down and backwards—and that in itself almost made it seem funnier.

I was marked in several ways that are revealed in this volume: the first is an abiding lifelong conviction that it is by humor that we are unwound, that life without laughter is unthinkable. And I lived in a large family in a small town: the kind of humor that releases the American family was the standard I grew up with. The hilarity, the everyday calamities, the bristling and the making up, the kids who outflank us, the lovely literature of the home-style eccentrics—most of the great American humorists are in this group: the boisterous, the tender, and the sly.

Another way in which I was marked was that from that early age on I became not only a more avid reader than before, but began collecting clippings—bales of them—tore stories out of magazines, and accumulated books of humor, everything I did not want to forget and hoped someday to share with others. (And I never let them go! I bundled and toted them from California, Pennsylvania, to the real California, and back again—bales and years later—to New York.)

Our writers of humor to this day have been consistently brash, devilish, and unintimidated. The material in this book, from the choice things I found in books and almanacs and magazines like *Godey's Lady's Book* to tomorrow's science-fiction humor, reveals that our humorists have ever been knocking the legs out from under the chairs we sit up straight in. We are scuttled by laughter.

There are many stories and articles here that have never been anthologized before. Many of these are new, and some are very, very old; they were found through the happiest, dirtiest search of old files and books and ancient magazines imaginable.

Some, on the other hand, are so new that the world has not yet quite caught up with their ambitious young authors. And, too, many authors and agents were very helpful and interested indeed: they allowed me to use new book and magazine material still in manuscript form. Also, some of the material herein was written especially for this book.

A lot of wind has whistled past our ears in the last century, and we have the impression of having come at high speeds a long distance. Perhaps this is an illusion, however, in terms of family humor. The cast of characters remains much the same: "Cure of a Hypochondriac," written by Seba Smith in 1840, is as funny and subtle and knowing as the next story you will read about the Freudian couch. Adolescents seem always to have begrudged the air their parents breathe, the sexes still eternally tiptoe through their abrasive minuet, girls beguile boys, boys bedevil girls, children are underfoot and overprivileged, and you never earn as much as you spend.

The organization of the book into a standard questionnaire was chosen as a definition of the state we are in: we are an application-happy people. Before we do anything—buy, charge, wed, travel, get drafted, be sick, have a baby, go to school, *anything*—we must fill out a form. In this slight spoof of the Application Age, we can all look ourselves up. And look each other up. In doing so, we find the American family, past and present, united in recognition and identity. Which, I believe, is the purest fun of all.

Helen Hoke

Name:

HOW WE KEPT MOTHER'S DAY

As Related by a Member of the Family

STEPHEN LEACOCK

Of all the different ideas that have been started lately, I think that the very best is the notion of celebrating once a year "Mother's Day." I don't wonder that May the eleventh is becoming such a popular date all over America and I am sure the idea will spread to England too.

It is especially in a big family like ours that such an idea takes hold. So we decided to have a special celebration of Mother's Day. We thought it a fine idea. It made us all realize how much Mother had done for us for years, and all the efforts and sacrifice that she had made for our sake.

So we decided that we'd make it a great day, a holiday for all the family, and do everything we could to make Mother happy. Father decided to take a holiday from his office, so as to help in celebrating the day, and my sister Anne and I stayed home from college classes, and Mary and my brother Will stayed home from High School.

It was our plan to make it a day just like Xmas or any big holiday, and so we decided to decorate the house with flowers and with mottoes over the mantelpieces, and all that kind of thing. We got Mother to make mottoes and arrange the decorations, because she always does it at Xmas.

The two girls thought it would be a nice thing to dress in our very best for such a big occasion, and so they both got new hats. Mother trimmed both the hats, and they looked fine, and Father had bought four-in-hand silk ties for himself and us boys as a souvenir of the day to remember Mother by. We were going to get Mother a new hat too, but it turned out that she seemed to really like her old grey bonnet better than a new one, and both the girls said that it was awfully becoming to her.

Well, after breakfast we had it arranged as a surprise for Mother that we would hire a motor car and take her for a beautiful drive away into the country. Mother is hardly ever able to have a treat like that, because we can only afford to keep one maid, and so Mother is busy in the house nearly all the time. And of course the country is so lovely now that it would be just grand for her to have a lovely morning, driving for miles and miles.

But on the very morning of the day we changed the plan a little bit, because it occurred to Father that a thing it would be better to do even than to take Mother for a motor drive would be to take her fishing. Father said that as the car was hired and paid for, we might just as well use it for a drive up into the hills where the streams are. As Father said, if you just go out driving without any object, you have a sense of aimlessness, but if you are going to fish, there is a definite purpose in front of you to heighten the enjoyment.

So we all felt that it would be nicer for Mother to have a definite purpose; and anyway, it turned out that Father had just got a new rod the day before, which made the idea of fishing all the more appropriate, and he said that Mother could use it if she wanted to; in fact, he said it was practically for her, only Mother said she would much rather watch him fish and not try to fish herself.

So we got everything arranged for the trip, and we got Mother to cut up some sandwiches and make up a sort of lunch in case we got hungry, though of course we were to come back home again to a big dinner in the middle of the day, just like Xmas or New Year's Day. Mother packed it all up in a basket for us ready to go in the motor.

Well, when the car came to the door, it turned out that there hardly seemed as much room in it as we had supposed, because we hadn't reckoned on Father's fishing basket and the rods and the lunch, and it was plain enough that we couldn't all get in.

Father said not to mind him, he said that he could just as well stay home, and that he was sure that he could put in the time working in the garden; he said that there was a lot of rough dirty work that he could do, like digging a trench for the garbage, that would save hiring a man, and so he said that he'd stay home; he said that we were not to let the fact of his not having had a real holiday for three years stand in our way; he wanted us to go right ahead and be happy and have a big day, and not to mind him. He said that he could plug away all day, and in fact he said he'd been a fool to think there'd be any holiday for him.

But of course we all felt that it would never do to let Father stay home, especially as we knew he would make trouble if he did. The two girls, Anne and Mary, would gladly have stayed and helped the maid get dinner, only it seemed such a pity to, on a lovely day like this, having their new hats. But they both said that Mother had only to say the word, and they'd gladly stay home and work. Will and I would have dropped out, but unfortunately we wouldn't have been any use in getting the dinner.

So in the end it was decided that Mother would stay home and just have a lovely restful day around the house, and get the dinner. It turned out anyway that Mother doesn't care for fishing, and also it was just a little bit cold and fresh out of doors, though it was lovely and sunny, and Father was rather afraid that Mother might take cold if she came.

He said he would never forgive himself if he dragged Mother round the country and let her take a severe cold at a time when she might be having a beautiful rest. He said it was our duty to try and let Mother get all the rest and quiet that she could, after all that she had done for all of us, and he said that that was principally why he had fallen in with this idea of a fishing trip, so as to give Mother a little quiet. He said that young people seldom realize how much quiet means to people who are getting old. As to himself he could still stand the racket, but he was glad to shelter Mother from it.

So we all drove away with three cheers for Mother, and Mother stood and watched us from the verandah for as long as she could see us, and Father waved his hand back to her every few minutes till he hit his hand on the back edge of the car, and then said that he didn't think that Mother could see us any longer.

Well, we had the loveliest day up among the hills that you could possibly imagine, and Father caught such big specimens that he felt sure that Mother couldn't have landed them anyway, if she had been fishing for them, and Will and I fished too, though we didn't get so many as Father, and the two girls met quite a lot of people that they knew as we drove along, and there were some young men friends of theirs that they met along the stream and talked to, and so we all had a splendid time.

It was quite late when we got back, nearly seven o'clock in the evening, but Mother had guessed that we would be late, so she had kept back the dinner so as to have it just nicely ready and hot for us. Only first she had to get towels and soap for Father and clean things for him to put on, because he always gets so messed up with fishing, and that kept Mother busy for a little while, that and helping the girls get ready.

But at last everything was ready, and we sat down to the grandest kind of dinner—roast turkey and all sorts of things like on Xmas Day. Mother had to get up and down a good bit during the meal fetching things back and forward, but at the end Father noticed it and said she simply mustn't do it, that he wanted her to spare herself, and he got up and fetched the walnuts over from the sideboard himself.

The dinner lasted a long while, and was great fun, and when it was over all of us wanted to help clear the things up and wash the dishes, only Mother said that she would really much rather do it, and so we let her, because we wanted just for once to humor her.

It was quite late when it was all over, and when we all kissed Mother before going to bed, she said it had been the most wonderful day in her life, and I think there were tears in her eyes. So we all felt awfully repaid for all that we had done.

FRANK ADAMS, FAMILY CIRCLE MAGAZINE

I AM THE CORPORAL OF MY SOUL

MORRIS BISHOP

Life's askew
    In most regards;
But I can do
    Tricks with cards.

Men succumb
    To ennui.
Fleas bite some,
    Not me.

Songs are stilled,
    Teeth decay;
Mine were filled
    Yesterday.

'Mid the giggle
    Of the spheres
I can wiggle
    Both my ears.

Doom may smite,
    Fortune flee,
I'm all right;
    I've me.

YOUR BEST FRIEND IS YOUR FATHER

RALF KIRCHER

As I write this there is some doubt in my mind whether Father's Day was last Sunday or whether it will be next Sunday. This could be solved by looking in today's paper to see if the stores are still telling my family that there is nothing in the world I want so much as some underwear that will flatter my torso. However, there is an even simpler way to discover whether we fathers have been honored or are just about to be. After awhile I shall screw up the courage to look at my necktie. If I find that it should be singing bass in the Cossack Choir, then I shall know that Father's Day has come and gone, leaving me in its wake.

I suppose that Father's Day is a good idea, though there seems something pretty pointed in the fact that no one thought of putting a red mark on the calendar for the Old Man until long after there had been a Mother's Day, an Arbor Day, a Labor Day, and a Ground Hog Day. Since I am a father myself it might appear immodest were I to suggest that fathers are often found superior to ground hogs—or, at least, more useful around the first of the month than ground hogs. However, such a suggestion might be taken as an indication that fathers are ungrateful for their blessings and this might, in turn, start a movement to abolish Father's Day until we learn humility.

For my part, however, I confess myself interested in fatherhood and I simply do not go along with those who contend that about the only time a father is worth having about is in the Spring when it is time to fertilize the flower beds. It has been my privilege to know a great many fathers and I have found them to be charming creatures. True, many of them are shy, particularly those that have large, noisy families, but they respond marvelously to kindness, and I am not exaggerating when I say that the average father will, if treated with tolerance and respect, become a fine companion and pet and may be readily trained to retrieve balls, short sticks, and other small objects.

There are many things to bear in mind in the raising of a good, reliable father. It is well to remember that many of them are proud, sensitive animals, that they bruise easily, and that they thrive on peace and quiet.

Feeding is recognized by some of the most successful father fanciers as a problem deserving special attention. All too often the selection of his diet is left to the mother who, in most cases, insists on feeding father the sort of things which she prefers, which is to say, table scraps. A father can subsist just so long on salads, creamed side dishes, canned vegetables, gelatin desserts, and sandwiches with the crust cut off them. Then, unless something is done, he begins to sneak off at meal time. This is often confused with infidelity. Just remember that more marital discord is created by the absence of steak and French fries than by the presence of blondes and redheads.

Another common fault in the rearing of fathers is the tendency to educate them more than they want to be educated. It is a mistake to try to elevate a father's tastes because fathers are interested in creature comforts and, hence, do not like sopranos. A father, for instance, thinks of chairs only in terms of leaning back, and does not respond kindly to the information that he may, in the future, sit gingerly on the edge of an antique. He will doggedly refuse to believe that the antique is attractive and there is no use trying to educate him to any other point of view.

Similarly, efforts to teach fathers to discriminate between guest towels and the everyday variety usually fail. In fine, the sooner it is recognized that a father would rather be comfortable than socially acceptable, the quicker you will develop an animal which, while often disheveled and embarrassing in the presence of company, is a reliable creature to send downstairs late at night when it is believed that a burglar is at the Community Plate.

There is so much to be said on this topic that one is tempted to go on forever. I notice that it is almost dark, however, and I have been instructed to sprinkle the grass as soon as the sun is down, so I will have to quit. Incidentally, if you are really interested in producing a better father, sprinkle the darned grass yourself sometime. I'm not the only person in this family who can nurse a nozzle.

The point of all this is really quite simple. Just bear in mind, particularly around Father's Day, that the more fathers are treated like people the more they act like people. Whether this is worth all the trouble that is involved is something for you to decide.

City, Town, or Post Office:

YVONNE

FRANK SULLIVAN

Every afternoon at three o'clock a little girl with a deep bass voice appears at the corner of Beekman Place and Fifty-First Street and shouts "Yvonne!" for an hour and a half. On Saturdays she starts in the morning.

Apparently she wants to get in touch with another little girl named Yvonne, although I admit this is only one man's opinion. Up to now, Yvonne has not, to the best of my knowledge and belief, given any sign of responsiveness, and, frankly, I am worried.

At first I didn't care whether Yvonne answered or not. Then I hoped she wouldn't, just to spite the little girl. But now I want her to answer. More than anything else in the world I want Yvonne to answer that little girl, so that I can pick up the threads of my disordered life and try to make a new start.

I do not know how long the little girl with the bass voice has been on that corner shouting "Yvonne!" This is my third winter in this neighborhood and I do not think she was shouting it the winter of 1930–1931, although I wouldn't want to say for sure, because that was the winter the little boy was shouting "Glurk!" and I was working on the glurk case to the exclusion of all other interests. She might have been shouting "Yvonne!" and it just might not have registered with me. Your ear does acquire a certain selectivity about noises after you have lived in New York since January 6, 1919, and particularly after you have worked in newspaper city rooms from January 7, 1919, to February 27, 1931.

My guess would be that she has been at it a considerable length of time, judging from the obvious condition of her vocal chords. Because even the fact that she is out on that corner in all kinds of weather shouting "Yvonne!" could not account for her present voice. Even if her mother had been frightened by a fire siren, it wouldn't account for it. A little girl certainly not more than ten or eleven does not develop a voice like Bert Lahr's unless she has been shouting "Yvonne!" or something for a long time.

Furthermore, it is plain she is no novice at shouting. She has a technique that would do credit to a Wagnerian soprano. When she shouts "Yvonne!" she accents the first syllable and holds it, crescendo, for as long as thirty seconds. (I've clocked her on this.) Then she gives you the "vonne," in pear-shaped tones audible for about two of our city blocks.

The little boy who glurked had no particular technique. He just traveled up and down Beekman Place shouting "Glurk! Glurk! Glurk!" in a voice which, although of a treble appropriate to his years (he was about seven), had a curiously carrying quality. Now I defy anybody with a spark of curiosity in his makeup to sit by idly without wondering why even a *little* boy should want to spend the better part of his waking hours shouting "Glurk!" I dropped everything and went out gunning for the little codger. After several unsuccessful forays, I found him one day, lurking in the wake of a vasty beldame who came sailing down East Fifty-First Street laden to the gunwales with groceries.

He had a stick, whittled into something approaching a resemblance to a rifle. He would aim the stick at her, cock an eye, make a trigger motion with his finger, and say "Glurk!"

"Playing, little boy?" I asked, pleasantly.

He regarded me suspiciously.

"Is that a gun?" I pursued ingratiatingly.

"Yes," he conceded. He was pretty short with me, too.

"My goodness, don't tell me you're shooting that lady with it!"

"Aw, she's my mother."

"But don't you know you must never shoot your mother in the back? You should fight fair, and give Mummy a chance to defend herself. Why do you say 'Glurk'?"

"Aw, that's the noise when the gun shoots," he explained, with impatience.

"Did you ever hear of a Maxim silencer?" I asked.

He hadn't. I explained that it was a gadget that eliminated the glurk in guns. Then I asked him if he thought it would be worth while to accept a retainer of fifty cents a week to put a Maxim silencer on his gun. He accepted.

"But there's one condition," I warned him. "When I'm up there in that apartment, trying to work to keep body and soul together, every time I hear a glurk out of you, off comes three cents from the fifty. Remember, now."

The first week he owed me sixteen cents. The second week he wiped that out and made two cents. The third week he made twenty-three cents. The next week he collected the full half-dollar, and the week after that he demanded a raise of ten cents.

Thus, at a trifling cost, I had not only abolished glurking on our block, but I had also taught that little shaver a lesson in self-control and thrift, and at a formative age when it was apt to do him the most good. Not to mention the fact that when he grows up, if he should decide to take up a career of crime, he will, thanks to me, know how to use a Maxim silencer.

I would like to be of some similar service to the little girl who shouts "Yvonne!" but, damn it all, I can't *catch* her.

Every afternoon when school is out, I make ready to dart down to the corner at the first shout of "Yvonne!" but no matter how fast I get down those twelve flights, she's gone when I reach the street. As soon as I get back to the apartment, she's at it again.

She's a fool to elude me because, if she only knew it, I'd be an eager and valuable lieutenant. She's got me completely sold on the idea of locating Yvonne. I never was so bent on anything in my life. I'll bet you Carnegie would snap me up if he were alive and on the corner of Beekman Place and Fifty-First Street shouting "Yvonne!" Carnegie was a canny old party. The secret of his success was his ability to pick the right lieutenants.

I could help the little girl in lots of ways. I could help her shout "Yvonne!" and I could shout it at hours when she does not have access to the corner, such as three o'clock in the morning. How does she know that three o'clock in the morning isn't the very time to reach Yvonne? I tried it at half-past two the other morning, but when I stood on the corner and called for Yvonne, two taxicab-drivers, a doorman, and a cop responded and none of them would admit he was Yvonne.

Maybe it would help if we organized Beekman Place to help in the search for Yvonne. I could do that and it would not be difficult, because, thank God, the old husking-bee spirit has not disappeared from our little community. No Beekmanite in distress is suffered to go for long unaided. Outsiders may call it parochialism, but we have another name for it. We call it Loyalty. We of Beekman Place are a simple, rugged people without any frills. Life is no bed of roses for us. The soil is rocky, the climate none too salubrious, and the East River, which is our outlet to the sea (and the secret of our greatness), is full of floating tomato cans. But we eke out an existence on our little rock over here. It was good enough for our grandfathers, and at least we can look any man in the face, which is more than most of our critics from the effete tribes of western Manhattan can do. And we have given three Presidents to the country: Millard Fillmore, Guthrie Mc-Clintic, and Katharine Cornell.

But enough of braggadocio.

I thought that if everybody on Beekman Place would gather *en masse* on the Fifty-First Street corner on a day to be known as Find Yvonne for the Little Girl Day and then, at a given signal, set up a community roar for Yvonne, the resulting hullabaloo might fetch her, because I'm sure that with all our talent over here, we must have some mighty good Yvonne-shouters among us. If that uproar didn't fetch Yvonne, then I think we could fairly assume that nothing ever will; that she is a myth. We can then take her little friend aside and explain gently that there is no use shouting "Yvonne!" any more; that, in fact, it is henceforth taboo on Beekman Place.

After that, if she shouts for Yvonne again, we can throw her into the East River for breaking the taboo. This may seem harsh, but it is the law of the tribe and it will be for the common good.

GAHAN WILSON, COLLIER'S

"The map ends here, too."

CONCERNING A POUND OF BUTTER

ANONYMOUS

(About 1875–1900)

One winter evening, a country store-keeper in the Green Mountain state, was about closing up for the night, and while standing in the snow outside putting up the window-shutters, saw, through the glass, a lounging, worthless fellow within, grab a pound of fresh butter from the shelf and conceal it in his hat.

The act was no sooner detected than the revenge was hit upon, and a very few minutes found the Green Mountain store-keeper at once enjoying his appetite for fun to the fullest extent, and paying off the thief with a facetious sort of torture, for which he would have gained a premium from the old Inquisition.

"I say, Seth," said the store-keeper, coming in and closing the door after him, slapping his hands over his shoulders and stamping the snow off his feet. Seth had his hand on the door, his hat on his head, and the roll of butter in his hat, anxious to make his exit as soon as possible.

"I say, Seth, sit down; I reckon, now, on such a cold night as this, a little something warm would not hurt a fellow."

Seth felt very uncertain; he had the butter, and was exceedingly anxious to be off; but the temptation of something warm sadly interfered with his resolution to go. This hesitation, however, was soon settled by the right owner of the butter taking Seth by the shoulders and planting him in a seat close to the stove, where he was in such a manner cornered in by the boxes and barrels that, while the grocer stood before him, there was no possibility of getting out, and right in this very place, sure enough, the store-keeper sat down.

"Seth, we'll have a little warm Santa Cruz," said the Green Mountain grocer; so he opened the stove door and stuffed in as many sticks as the place would admit; "without it, you'd freeze going home such a night as this."

Seth already felt the butter settling down closer to his hair, and he jumped up, declaring he must go.

"Not till you have something warm, Seth; Seth, come, I've got a story to tell you," and Seth was again rushed into his seat by his cunning tormentor.

"Oh! it's so hot here," said the petty thief, attempting to rise.

"Sit down; don't be in such a hurry," replied the grocer, pushing him back into the chair.

"But I've got the cows to fodder, and the wood to split, and I must be going," said the persecuted chap.

"But you mustn't tear yourself away, Seth, in this manner. Sit down, let the cows take care of themselves, and keep yourself cool; you appear to be a little fidgety," said the roguish grocer, with a wicked leer.

The next thing was the production of two smoking glasses of hot toddy, the very sight of which, in Seth's present situation, would have made the hair stand erect upon his head, had it not been well oiled and kept down by the butter.

"Seth, I will give you a toast, now, and you can butter it yourself," said the grocer, with an air of such consummate simplicity that poor Seth believed himself unsuspected. "Seth, here's a Christmas goose, well roasted, eh? I tell you it's the greatest eating in creation. And Seth, don't you never use hog's fat, or common cooking butter, to baste it with; come, take your butter—I mean, Seth, take your toddy."

Poor Seth now began to smoke as well as melt, and his mouth was hermetically sealed up as though he had been born dumb. Streak after streak of the butter came pouring from under his hat, and his handkerchief was already soaked with the greasy overflow. Talking away as if nothing was the matter, the fun-loving grocer kept stuffing wood into the stove, while poor Seth sat upright, with his back against the counter and his knees touching the red-hot furnace in front.

"Cold night, this," said the grocer. "Why, Seth, you seem to perspire as if you were warm? Why don't you take your hat off? Here, let me put your hat away."

"No," exclaimed poor Seth at last. "No, I must go; let me out; I ain't well; let me go."

A greasy cataract was now pouring down the poor man's face and neck, and soaking into his clothes, and trickling down his body into his boots, so that he was literally in a perfect bath of oil.

"Well, good night, Seth," said the humorous Vermonter, "if you will go"; and adding, as the man darted out of the door, "I say, Seth, I reckon the fun I have had out of you is worth ninepence, so I sha'n't charge you for that pound of butter in your hat."

THE RANSOM OF RED CHIEF

O. HENRY

(1907)

It looked like a good thing: but wait till I tell you. We were down South, in Alabama—Bill Driscoll and myself—when this kidnaping idea struck us. It was, as Bill afterward expressed it, "during a moment of temporary mental apparition"; but we didn't find that out till later.

There was a town down there, as flat as a flannel-cake, and called Summit, of course. It contained inhabitants of as undeleterious and self-satisfied a class of peasantry as ever clustered around a Maypole.

Bill and me had a joint capital of about six hundred dollars, and we needed just two thousand dollars more to pull off a fraudulent town-lot scheme in Western Illinois with. We talked it over on the front steps of the hotel. Philoprogenitiveness, says we, is strong in semi-rural communities; therefore, and for other reasons, a kidnaping project ought to do better there than in the radius of newspapers that send reporters out in plain clothes to stir up talk about such things. We knew that Summit couldn't get after us with anything stronger than constables and, maybe, some lackadaisical bloodhounds and a diatribe or two in the Weekly Farmers' Budget. So, it looked good.

We selected for our victim the only child of a prominent citizen named Ebenezer Dorset. The father was respectable and tight, a mortgage fancier and a stern, upright collection-plate passer and forefoncloser. The kid was a boy of ten, with bas-relief freckles, and hair the color of the cover of the magazine you buy at the news-stand when you want to catch a train. Bill and me figured that Ebenezer would melt down for a ransom of two thousand dollars to a cent. But wait till I tell you.

About two miles from Summit was a little mountain, covered with a dense cedar brake. On the rear elevation of this mountain was a cave. There we stored provisions.

One evening after sundown, we drove in a buggy past old Dorset's house. The kid was in the street, throwing rocks at a kitten on the opposite fence.

"Hey, little boy!" says Bill, "would you like to have a bag of candy and a nice ride?"

The boy catches Bill neatly in the eye with a piece of brick.

"That will cost the old man an extra five hundred dollars," says Bill, climbing over the wheel.

That boy put up a fight like a welter-weight cinnamon bear; but, at last, we got him down in the bottom of the buggy and drove away. We took him up to the cave, and I hitched the horse in the cedar brake. After dark I drove the buggy to the little village, three miles away, where we had hired it, and walked back to the mountain.

Bill was pasting court-plaster over the scratches and bruises on his features. There was a fire burning behind the big rock at the entrance of the cave, and the boy was watching a pot of boiling coffee, with two buzzard tail-feathers stuck in his red hair. He points a stick at me when I come up, and says:

"Ha! cursed paleface, do you dare to enter the camp of Red Chief, the terror of the plains?"

"He's all right now," says Bill, rolling up his trousers and examining some bruises on his shins. "We're playing Indian. We're making Buffalo Bill's show look like magic-lantern views of Palestine in the town hall. I'm Old Hank, the Trapper, Red Chief's captive, and I'm to be scalped at daybreak. By Geronimo! that kid can kick hard."

Yes, sir, that boy seemed to be having the time of his life. The fun of camping out in a cave had made him forget that he was a captive himself. He immediately christened me Snake-eye, the Spy, and announced that, when his braves returned from the warpath, I was to be broiled at the stake at the rising of the sun.

Then we had supper; and he filled his mouth full of bacon and bread and gravy, and began to talk. He made a during-dinner speech something like this:

"I like this fine. I never camped out before; but I had a pet 'possum once, and I was nine last birthday. I hate to go to school. Rats ate up sixteen of Jimmy Talbot's aunt's speckled hen's eggs. Are there any real Indians in these woods? I want some more gravy. Does the trees moving make the wind blow? We had five puppies. What makes your nose so red, Hank? My father has lots of money. Are the stars hot? I whipped Ed Walker twice, Saturday. I don't like girls. You dassent catch toads unless with a string. Do oxen make any noise? Why are oranges round? Have you got beds to sleep on in this cave? Amos Murray has got six toes. A parrot can talk, but a monkey or a fish can't. How many does it take to make twelve?"

Every few minutes he would remember that he was a pesky redskin, and pick up his stick rifle and tiptoe to the mouth of the cave to rubber for the scouts of the hated paleface. Now and then he would let out a war-whoop that made Old Hank, the Trapper, shiver. That boy had Bill terrorized from the start.

"Red Chief," says I to the kid, "would you like to go home?"

"Aw, what for?" says he. "I don't have any fun at home. I hate to go to school. I like to camp out. You won't take me back home again, Snake-eye, will you?"

"Not right away," says I. "We'll stay here in the cave a while."

"All right!" says he. "That'll be fine. I never had such fun in all my life."

We went to bed about eleven o'clock. We spread down some wide blankets and quilts and put Red Chief between us. We weren't afraid he'd run away. He kept us awake for three hours, jumping up and reaching for his rifle and screeching: "Hist! pard," in mine and Bill's ears, as the fancied crackle of a twig or the rustle of a leaf revealed to his young imagination the stealthy approach of the outlaw band. At last, I fell into a troubled sleep, and dreamed that I had been kidnaped and chained to a tree by a ferocious pirate with red hair.

Just at daybreak, I was awakened by a series of awful screams from

Bill. They weren't yells, or howls, or shouts, or whoops, or yawps, such as you'd expect from a manly set of vocal organs—they were simply indecent, terrifying, humiliating screams, such as women emit when they see ghosts or caterpillars. It's an awful thing to hear a strong, desperate, fat man scream incontinently in a cave at daybreak.

I jumped up to see what the matter was. Red Chief was sitting on Bill's chest, with one hand twined in Bill's hair. In the other he had the sharp case-knife we used for slicing bacon; and he was industriously and realistically trying to take Bill's scalp, according to the sentence that had been pronounced upon him the evening before.

I got the knife away from the kid and made him lie down again. But, from that moment, Bill's spirit was broken. He laid down on his side of the bed, but he never closed an eye again in sleep as long as that boy was with us. I dozed off for a while, but along toward sun-up I remembered that Red Chief had said I was to be burned at the stake at the rising of the sun. I wasn't nervous or afraid; but I sat up and lit my pipe and leaned against a rock.

"What you getting up so soon for, Sam?" asked Bill.

"Me?" says I. "Oh, I got a kind of pain in my shoulder. I thought sitting up would rest it."

"You're a liar!" says Bill. "You're afraid. You was to be burned at sunrise, and you was afraid he'd do it. And he would, too, if he could find a match. Ain't it awful, Sam? Do you think anybody will pay out money to get a little imp like that back home?"

"Sure," said I. "A rowdy kid like that is just the kind that parents dote on. Now, you and the Chief get up and cook breakfast, while I go up on the top of this mountain and reconnoitre."

I went up on the peak of the little mountain and ran my eye over the contiguous vicinity. Over toward Summit I expected to see the sturdy yeomanry of the village armed with scythes and pitchforks beating the countryside for the dastardly kidnapers. But what I saw was a peaceful landscape dotted with one man plowing with a dun mule. Nobody was dragging the creek; no couriers dashed hither and yon, bringing tidings of no news to the distracted parents. There was a sylvan attitude of somnolent sleepiness pervading that section of the external outward surface of Alabama that lay exposed to my view. "Perhaps," says I to myself, "it has not yet been discovered that the wolves have borne away the tender lambkin from the fold. Heaven help the wolves!" says I, and I went down the mountain to breakfast.

When I got to the cave I found Bill backed up against the side of it, breathing hard, and the boy threatening to smash him with a rock half as big as a cocoanut.

"He put a red-hot boiled potato down my back," explained Bill, "and then mashed it with his foot; and I boxed his ears. Have you got a gun about you, Sam?"

I took the rock away from the boy and kind of patched up the argument. "I'll fix you," says the kid to Bill. "No man ever yet struck the Red Chief but what he got paid for it. You better beware!"

After breakfast the kid takes a piece of leather with strings wrapped around it out of his pocket and goes outside the cave unwinding it.

"What's he up to now?" says Bill, anxiously. "You don't think he'll run away, do you, Sam?"

"No fear of it," says I. "He don't seem to be much of a home body. But we've got to fix up some plan about the ransom. There don't seem to be much excitement around Summit on account of his disappearance; but maybe they haven't realized yet that he's gone. His folks may think he's spending the night with Aunt Jane or one of the neighbors. Anyhow, he'll be missed to-day. To-night we must get a message to his father demanding the two thousand dollars for his return."

Just then we heard a kind of war-whoop, such as David might have emitted when he knocked out the champion Goliath. It was a sling that Red Chief had pulled out of his pocket, and he was whirling it around his head.

I dodged, and heard a heavy thud and a kind of a sigh from Bill, like a horse gives out when you take his saddle off. A niggerhead rock the size of an egg had caught Bill just behind his left ear. He loosened himself all over and fell in the fire across the frying-pan of hot water for washing the dishes. I dragged him out and poured cold water on his head for half an hour.

By and by, Bill sits up and feels behind his ear and says: "Sam, do you know who my favorite Biblical character is?"

"Take it easy," says I. "You'll come to your senses presently."

"King Herod," says he. "You won't go away and leave me here alone, will you, Sam?"

I went out and caught that boy and shook him until his freckles rattled.

"If you don't behave," says I, "I'll take you straight home. Now, are you going to be good, or not?"

"I was only funning," says he sullenly. "I didn't mean to hurt Old

Hank. But what did he hit me for? I'll behave, Snake-eye, if you won't send me home, and if you'll let me play the Black Scout to-day."

"I don't know the game," says I. "That's for you and Mr. Bill to decide. He's your playmate for the day. I'm going away for a while, on business. Now, you come in and make friends with him and say you are sorry for hurting him, or home you go, at once."

I made him and Bill shake hands, and then I took Bill aside and told him I was going to Poplar Cove, a little village three miles from the cave, and find out what I could about how the kidnaping had been regarded in Summit. Also, I thought it best to send a peremptory letter to old man Dorset that day, demanding the ransom and dictating how it should be paid.

"You know, Sam," says Bill, "I've stood by you without batting an eye in earthquakes, fire and flood—in poker games, dynamite outrages, police raids, train robberies and cyclones. I never lost my nerve yet till we kidnaped that two-legged skyrocket of a kid. He's got me going. You won't leave me long with him, will you, Sam?"

"I'll be back some time this afternoon," says I. "You must keep the boy amused and quiet till I return. And now we'll write the letter to old Dorset."

Bill and I got paper and pencil and worked on the letter while Red Chief, with a blanket wrapped around him, strutted up and down, guarding the mouth of the cave. Bill begged me tearfully to make the ranson fifteen hundred dollars instead of two thousand. "I ain't attempting," says he, "to decry the celebrated moral aspect of parental affection, but we're dealing with humans, and it ain't human for anybody to give up two thousand dollars for that forty-pound chunk of freckled wildcat. I'm willing to take a chance at fifteen hundred dollars. You can charge the difference up to me."

So, to relieve Bill, I acceded, and we collaborated a letter that ran this way:

Ebenezer Dorset, Esq.:

We have your boy concealed in a place far from Summit. It is useless for you or the most skillful detectives to attempt to find him. Absolutely, the only terms on which you can have him restored to you are these: We demand fifteen hundred dollars in large bills for his return; the money to be left at midnight to-night at the same spot and in the same box as your reply—as hereinafter described. If you agree to these terms, send your answer in writing by a solitary messenger to-night at half-past eight o'clock. After crossing Owl Creek, on the road to Poplar Cove, there are three large trees about a hundred yards apart, close to the fence of the wheat field on the right-hand side. At the bottom of the fence-post, opposite the third tree, will be found a small pasteboard box.

The messenger will place the answer in this box and return immediately to Summit.

If you attempt any treachery or fail to comply with our demand as stated, you will never see your boy again.

If you pay the money as demanded, he will be returned to you safe and well within three hours. These terms are final, and if you do not accede to them no further communication will be attempted.

Two Desperate Men.

I addressed this letter to Dorset, and put it in my pocket. As I was about to start, the kid comes up to me and says: "Aw, Snake-eye, you said I could play the Black Scout while you was gone."

"Play it, of course," says I. "Mr. Bill will play with you. What kind of a game is it?"

"I'm the Black Scout," says Red Chief, "and I have to ride to the stockade to warn the settlers that the Indians are coming. I'm tired of playing Indian myself. I want to be the Black Scout."

"All right," says I. "It sounds harmless to me. I guess Mr. Bill will help you foil the pesky savages."

"What am I to do?" asks Bill, looking at the kid, suspicious.

"You are the hoss," says the Black Scout. "Get down on your hands and knees. How can I ride to the stockade without a hoss?"

"You'd better keep him interested," said I, "till we get the scheme going. Loosen up."

Bill gets down on his all fours, and a look comes in his eye like a rabbit's when you catch it in a trap.

"How far is it to the stockade, kid?" he asks, in a husky manner of voice.

"Ninety miles," says the Black Scout. "And you have to hump yourself to get there on time. Whoa, now!"

The Black Scout jumps on Bill's back and digs his heels in his side.

"For Heaven's sake," says Bill, "hurry back, Sam, as soon as you can. I wish we hadn't made the ransom more than a thousand. Say, you quit kicking me or I'll get up and warm you good."

I walked over to Poplar Cove and sat around the postoffice and store, talking with the chaw-bacons that came in to trade. One whisk-erando says that he hears Summit is all upset on account of Elder Ebenezer Dorset's boy having been lost or stolen. That was all I wanted to know. I bought some smoking tobacco, referred casually to the price of black-eyed peas, posted my letter surreptitiously, and came away. The postmaster said the mail-carrier would come by in an hour to take the mail on to Summit.

When I got back to the cave Bill and the boy were not to be found. I explored the vicinity of the cave, and risked a yodel or two, but there was no response.

So I lighted my pipe and sat down on a mossy bank to await developments.

In about half an hour I heard the bushes rustle, and Bill wabbled out into the little glade in front of the cave. Behind him was the kid, stepping softly like a scout, with a broad grin on his face. Bill stopped, took off his hat and wiped his face with a red handkerchief. The kid stopped about eight feet behind him.

"Sam," says Bill, "I suppose you'll think I'm a renegade, but I couldn't help it. I'm a grown person with masculine proclivities and habits of self-defense, but there is a time when all systems of egotism and predominance fail. The boy is gone. I have sent him home. All is off. There was martyrs in old times," goes on Bill, "that suffered death rather than give up the particular graft they enjoyed. None of 'em ever was subjugated to such supernatural tortures as I have been. I tried to be faithful to our articles of depredation; but there came a limit."

"What's the trouble, Bill?" I asks him.

"I was rode," says Bill, "the ninety miles to the stockade, not barring an inch. Then, when the settlers was rescued, I was given oats. Sand ain't a palatable substitute. And then, for an hour I had to try to explain to him why there was nothin' in holes, how a road can run both ways and what makes the grass green. I tell you, Sam, a human can only stand so much. I takes him by the neck of his clothes and drags him down the mountain. On the way he kicks my legs black-and-blue from the knees down; and I've got to have two or three bites on my thumb and hand cauterized.

"But he's gone"—continues Bill—"gone home. I showed him the road to Summit and kicked him about eight feet nearer there at one kick. I'm sorry we lose the ransom; but it was either that or Bill Driscoll to the madhouse."

Bill is puffing and blowing, but there is a look of ineffable peace and growing content on his rose-pink features.

"Bill," says I, "there isn't any heart disease in your family, is there?"

"No," says Bill, "nothing chronic except malaria and accidents. Why?"

"Then you might turn around," says I, "and have a look behind you."

Bill turns and sees the boy, and loses his complexion and sits down plump on the ground and begins to pluck aimlessly at grass and little sticks. For an hour I was afraid for his mind. And then I told him that my scheme was to put the whole job through immediately and that we would get the ransom and be off with it by midnight if old Dorset fell in with our proposition. So Bill braced up enough to give the kid a weak sort of a smile and a promise to play the Russian in a Japanese war with him as soon as he felt a little better.

I had a scheme for collecting that ransom without danger of being caught by counterplots that ought to commend itself to professional kidnapers. The tree under which the answer was to be left—and the money later on—was close to the road fence with big, bare fields on all sides. If a gang of constables should be watching for anyone to come for the note they could see him a long way off crossing the fields or in the road. But, no, sirree! At half-past eight I was up in that tree, as well hidden as a tree toad, waiting for the messenger to arrive.

Exactly on time, a half-grown boy rides up the road on a bicycle, locates the pasteboard box at the foot of the fence-post, slips a folded piece of paper into it and pedals away again back toward Summit.

I waited an hour and then concluded the thing was square. I slid down the tree, got the note, slipped along the fence till I struck the woods, and was back at the cave in another half an hour. I opened the note, got near the lantern and read it to Bill. It was written with a pen in a crabbed hand, and the sum and substance of it was this:

Two Desperate Men.

Gentlemen: I received your letter to-day by post, in regard to the ransom you ask for the return of my son. I think you are a little high in your demands, and I hereby make you a counter-proposition, which I am inclined to believe you will accept. You bring Johnny home and pay me two hundred and fifty dollars in cash, and I agree to take him off your hands. You had better come at night, for the neighbors believe he is lost, and I couldn't be responsible for what they would do to anybody they saw bringing him back. Very respectfully,

EBENEZER DORSET.

"Great pirates of Penzance!" says I; "of all the impudent——"

But I glanced at Bill, and hesitated. He had the most appealing look in his eyes I ever saw on the face of a dumb or a talking brute.

"Sam," says he, "what's two hundred and fifty dollars, after all? We've got the money. One more night of this kid will send me to a bed in Bedlam. Besides being a thorough gentleman, I think Mr. Dorset is a spendthrift for making us such a liberal offer. You ain't going to let the chance go, are you?"

"Tell you the truth, Bill," says I, "this little he ewe lamb has somewhat got on my nerves, too. We'll take him home, pay the ransom and make our get-away."

We took him home that night. We got him to go by telling him that his father had bought a silver-mounted rifle and a pair of moccasins for him, and we were going to hunt bears the next day.

It was just twelve o'clock when we knocked at Ebenezer's front door. Just at the moment when I should have been abstracting the fifteen hundred dollars from the box under the tree, according to the original proposition, Bill was counting out two hundred and fifty dollars into Dorset's hand.

When the kid found out we were going to leave him at home he started up a howl like a calliope and fastened himself as tight as a leech to Bill's leg. His father peeled him away gradually, like a porous plaster.

"How long can you hold him?" asks Bill.

"I am not as strong as I used to be," says old Dorset, "but I think I can promise you ten minutes."

"Enough," says Bill. "In ten minutes I shall cross the Central, Southern and Middle Western States, and be legging it trippingly for the Canadian border."

And, as dark as it was, and as fat as Bill was, and as good a runner as I am, he was a good mile and a half out of Summit before I could catch up with him.

HUCKLEBERRY FINN JOINS TOM SAWYER'S GANG

MARK TWAIN

The Widow Douglas, she took me for her son, and allowed she would civilize me; but it was rough living in the house all the time, considering how dismal regular and decent the widow was in all her ways; and so when I couldn't stand it no longer, I lit out. I got into my old rags and my sugar-hogshead again, and was free and satisfied. But Tom Sawyer he hunted me up and said he was going to start a band of robbers, and I might join if I would go back to the widow and be respectable. So I went back.

The widow she cried over me, and called me a poor lost lamb, and she called me a lot of other names, too, but she never meant no harm by it. She put me in them new clothes again, and I couldn't do nothing but sweat and sweat, and feel all cramped up. Well, then, the old thing commenced again. The widow rung a bell for supper, and you had to come to time. When you got to the table you couldn't go right to eating, but you had to wait for the widow to tuck down her head and grumble a little over the victuals, though there warn't really anything the matter with them. That is, nothing only everything was cooked by itself. In a barrel of odds and ends it is different; things get mixed up, and the juice kind of swaps around, and the things go better.

After supper she got out her book and learned me about Moses and the "Bulrushers"; and I was in a sweat to find out all about him; but by-and-by she let it out that Moses had been dead a considerable long time; so then I didn't care no more about him; because I don't take no stock in dead people.

Pretty soon I wanted to smoke, and asked the widow to let me. But she wouldn't. She said it was a mean practice and wasn't clean, and I must try to not do it any more. That is just the way with some people. They get down on a thing when they don't know nothing about it. Here she was a-bothering about Moses, which was no kin to her, and no use to anybody, being gone, you see, yet finding a power of fault with me for doing a thing that had some good in it. And she took snuff too; of course, that was all right, because she done it herself.

Her sister, Miss Watson, a tolerable slim old maid, with goggles on, had just come to live with her, and took a set at me now, with a spelling-book. She worked me middling hard for about an hour, and then the widow made her ease up. I couldn't stood it much longer. Then for an hour it was deadly dull, and I was fidgety. Miss Watson would say, "Don't put your feet up there, Huckleberry"; and, "Don't scrunch up like that, Huckleberry—set up straight"; and pretty soon she would say, "Don't gap and stretch like that, Huckleberry—why don't you try to behave?" Then she told me all about the bad place, and I said I wished I was there. She got mad, then, but I didn't mean no harm. All I wanted was to go somewheres; all I wanted was a change, I warn't particular. She said it was wicked to say what I said; said she wouldn't say it for the whole world; *she* was going to live so as to go to the good place. Well, I couldn't see no advantage in going where she was going, so I made up my mind I wouldn't try for it. But I never said so, because it would only make trouble, and wouldn't do no good.

Now she had got a start, and she went on and told me all about the good place. She said all a body would have to do there was to go around all day long with a harp and sing for ever and ever. So I didn't think much of it. But I never said so. I asked her if she reckoned Tom Sawyer would go there, and she said, not by a considerable sight. I was glad about that, because I wanted him and me to be together.

Miss Watson she kept pecking at me, and it got tiresome and lonesome. By-and-by everybody came in the parlor and we had prayers, and then everybody was off to bed. I went up to my room with a piece of candle and put it on the table. Then I set down in a chair by the window and tried to think of something cheerful, but it warn't no use. I felt so lonesome I most wished I was dead. The stars was shining, and the leaves rustled in the woods ever so mournful; and I heard an owl, away off, who-whooing about somebody that was dead, and a whippowill and a dog crying about somebody that was going to die; and the wind was trying to whisper something to me and I couldn't make out what it was, and so it made the cold shivers run over me. Then away out in the woods I heard that kind of a sound that a ghost makes when it wants to tell about something that's on its mind and can't make itself understood, and so can't rest easy in its grave and has to go about that way every night grieving. I got so downhearted and scared, I did wish I had some company. Pretty soon a spider went crawling up my shoulder, and I flipped it off and it lit in the candle; and before I could budge it was all shrivelled up. I didn't need anybody to tell me that was an awful bad sign and would fetch me some bad luck, so I was scared and most shook the clothes off of me. I got up and turned around in my tracks three times and crossed my breast every time; and then I tied up a little lock of my hair with a thread to keep witches away. But I hadn't no confidence. You do that when you've lost a horse-shoe that you've found, instead of nailing it up over the door, but I hadn't ever heard anybody say it was any way to keep off bad luck when you'd killed a spider.

I set down again, a-shaking all over, and got out my pipe for a smoke; for the house was all as still as death, now, and so the widow wouldn't know. Well, after a long time I heard the clock away off in the town go boom—boom—twelve licks—and all still again—stiller than ever. Pretty soon I heard a twig snap, down in the dark amongst the trees—something was a-stirring. I set still and listened. Directly I could just barely hear a "me-yow! me-yow!" down there. That was good! Says I, "me-yow! me-yow!" as soft as I could, and then I put out the light and scrambled out of the window on to the shed. Then I slipped down to the ground and crawled in amongst the trees, and sure enough there was Tom Sawyer waiting for me.

(*Huck and Tom are nearly discovered by Jim, a Negro servant to Miss Watson; but they manage to get away.*)

When Tom and me got to the edge of the hill-top, we looked away down into the village and could see three or four lights twinkling, where there was sick folks, maybe; and the stars over us was sparkling ever so fine, and down by the village was the river, a whole mile broad, and awful still and grand. We went down the hill and found Jo Harper, and Ben Rogers, and two or three more of the boys, hid in the old tanyard. So we unhitched a skiff and pulled down the river two mile and a half, to the big scar on the hill-side, and went ashore.

We went to a clump of bushes, and Tom made everybody swear to keep the secret, and then showed them a hole in the hill, right in the thickest part of the bushes. Then we lit the candles and crawled in on our hands and knees. We went about two hundred yards, and then the cave opened up. Tom poked about amongst the passages and pretty soon ducked under a wall where you wouldn't a noticed that there was a hole. We went along a narrow place and got into a kind of room, all damp and sweaty and cold, and there we stopped. Tom says:

"Now we'll start this band of robbers and call it Tom Sawyer's Gang. Everybody that wants to join has got to take an oath, and write his name in blood."

Everybody was willing. So Tom got out a sheet of paper that he had wrote the oath on, and read it. It swore every boy to stick to the band, and never tell any of the secrets; and if anybody done anything to any boy in the band, whichever boy was ordered to kill that person and his family must do it, and he mustn't eat and he mustn't sleep till he had killed them and hacked a cross in their breasts, which was the sign of the band. And nobody that didn't belong to the band could use that mark, and if he did he must be sued; and if he done it again he must be killed. And if anybody that belonged to the band told the secrets, he must have his throat cut, and then have his carcass burnt up and the ashes scattered all around, and his name blotted off the list with blood and never mentioned again by the Gang, but have a curse put on it and be forgot, for ever.

Everybody said it was a real beautiful oath, and asked Tom if he got it out of his own head. He said, some of it, but the rest was out of pirate books, and robber books, and every gang that was high-toned had it.

Some thought it would be good to kill the *families* of boys that told the secrets. Tom said it was a good idea, so he took a pencil and wrote it in. Then Ben Rogers says:

"Here's Huck Finn, he hain't got no family—what you going to do 'bout him?"

"Well, hain't he got a father?" says Tom Sawyer.

"Yes, he's got a father, but you can't never find him, these days. He used to lay drunk with the hogs in the tanyard, but he hain't been seen in these parts for a year or more."

They talked it over, and they was going to rule me out, because they said every boy must have a family or somebody to kill, or else it wouldn't be fair and square for the others. Well, nobody could think of anything to do—everybody was stumped, and set still. I was most ready to cry; but all at once I thought of a way, and so I offered them Miss Watson—they could kill her. Everybody said:

"Oh, she'll do, she'll do. That's all right. Huck can come in."

Then they all stuck a pin in their fingers to get blood to sign with, and I made my mark on the paper.

"Now," says Ben Rogers, "what's the line of business of this Gang?"

"Nothing only robbery and murder," Tom said.

"But who are we going to rob? Houses—or cattle—or——?"

"Stuff! Stealing cattle and such things ain't robbery, it's burglary," says Tom Sawyer. "We ain't burglars. That ain't no sort of style. We are highwaymen. We stop stages and carriages on the road, with masks on, and kill the people and take their watches and money."

"Must we always kill the people?"

"Oh, certainly. It's best. Some authorities think different, but mostly it's considered best to kill them. Except some that you bring to the cave here and keep them till they're ransomed."

"Ransomed? What's that?"

"I don't know. But that's what they do. I've seen it in books; and so, of course, that's what we've got to do."

"But how can we do it if we don't know what it is?"

"Why blame it all, we've *got* to do it. Don't I tell you it's in the books? Do you want to go to doing different from what's in the books, and get things all muddled up?"

"Oh, that's all very fine to *say*, Tom Sawyer, but how in the nation are these fellows going to be ransomed if we don't know how to do it to them? That's the thing I want to get at. Now, what do you *reckon* it is?"

"Well, I don't know. But per'aps if we keep them till they're ransomed, it means that we keep them till they're dead."

"Now, that's something *like*. That'll answer. Why couldn't you said that before? We'll keep them till they're ransomed to death—and a bothersome lot they'll be, too, eating up everything and always trying to get loose."

"How you talk, Ben Rogers. How can they get loose when there's a guard over them, ready to shoot them down if they move a peg?"

"A guard. Well, that *is* good. So somebody's got to set up all night and never get any sleep, just so as to watch them. I think that's foolishness. Why can't a body take a club and ransom them as soon as they get here?"

"Because it ain't in the books so—that's why. Now, Ben Rogers, do you want to do things regular, or don't you?—that's the idea. Don't you reckon that the people that made the books knows what's the correct thing to do? Do you reckon *you* can learn 'em anything? Not by a good deal. No, sir, we'll just go on and ransom them in the regular way."

"All right. I don't mind; but I say it's a fool way, anyhow. Say—do we kill the women, too?"

"Well, Ben Rogers, if I was as ignorant as you I wouldn't let on. Kill the women? No—nobody ever saw anything in the books like that. You fetch them to the cave, and you're always as polite as pie to them; and by-and-by they fall in love with you and never want to go home any more."

"Well, if that's the way, I'm agreed, but I don't take no stock in it. Mighty soon we'll have the cave so cluttered up with women, and fellows waiting to be ransomed, that there won't be no place for the robbers. But go ahead, I ain't got nothing to say."

Little Tommy Barnes was asleep, now, and when they waked him up he was scared, and cried, and said he wanted to go home to his ma, and didn't want to be a robber any more.

So they all made fun of him, and called him cry-baby, and that made him mad, and he said he would go straight and tell all the secrets. But Tom give him five cents to keep quiet, and said we would all go home and meet next week and rob somebody and kill some people.

Ben Rogers said he couldn't get out much, only Sundays, and so he wanted to begin next Sunday; but all the boys said it would be wicked to do it on Sunday, and that settled the thing. They agreed to get together and fix a day as soon as they could, and then we elected Tom Sawyer first captain and Jo Harper second captain of the Gang, and so started home.

I clumb up the shed and crept into my window just before day was breaking. My new clothes was all greased up and clayey, and I was dog-tired.

Well, I got a good going-over in the morning, from old Miss Watson, on account of my clothes; but the widow she didn't scold, but only cleaned off the grease and clay, and looked so sorry that I thought I would behave a while if I could. Then Miss Watson she took me in the closet and prayed, but nothing come of it. She told me to pray every day, and whatever I asked for I would get it. But it warn't so. I tried it. Once I got a fish-line, but no hooks. It warn't any good to me without hooks. I tried for the hooks three or four times, but somehow I couldn't make it work. By-and-by, one day, I asked Miss Watson to try for me, but she said I was a fool. She never told me why, and I couldn't make it out no way.

I set down, one time, back in the woods, and had a long think about it. I says to myself, if a body can get anything they pray for, why don't Deacon Winn get back the money he lost on pork? Why can't the widow get back her silver snuff-box that was stole? Why can't Miss Watson fat up? No, says I to myself, there ain't nothing in it. I went and told the widow about it, and she said the thing a body could get by praying for it was "spiritual gifts." This was too many for me, but she told me what she meant—I must help other people, and do everything I could for other people, and look out for them all the time, and never think about myself. This was including Miss Watson, as I took it. I went out in the woods and turned it over in my mind a long time, but I couldn't see no advantage about it—except for the other people—so at last I reckoned I wouldn't worry about it any more, but just let it go. Sometimes the widow would take me one side and talk about Providence in a way to make a body's mouth water; but maybe next day Miss Watson would take hold and knock it all down again. I judged I could see that there was two Providences, and a poor chap would stand considerable show with the widow's Providence, but if Miss Watson's got him there warn't no help for him any more. I thought it all out, and reckoned I would belong to the widow's, if he wanted me, though I couldn't make out how he was a-going to be any better off then than what he was before, seeing I was so ignorant and so kind of low-down and ornery.

Pap he hadn't been seen for more than a year, and that was comfortable for me; I didn't want to see him no more. He used to always whale me when he was sober and could get his hands on me; though I used to take to the woods most of the time when he was around. Well, about this time he was found in the river drowned, about twelve mile above town, so people said. They judged it was him, anyway; said this drowned man was just his size, and was ragged, and had uncommon long hair—which was all like pap—but they couldn't make nothing out of the face, because it had been in the water so long it warn't much like a face at all. They said he was floating on his back in the water. They took him and buried him on the bank. But I warn't comfortable long, because I happened to think of something. I knowed mighty well that a drownded man don't float on his back, but on his face. So I knowed, then, that this warn't pap, but a woman dressed up in a man's clothes. So I was uncomfortable again. I judged the old man would turn up again by-and-by, though I wished he wouldn't.

We played robbers now and then about a month, and then I resigned. All the boys did. We hadn't robbed nobody, we hadn't killed any people, but only just pretended. We used to hop out of the woods

and go charging down on hog-drovers and women in carts taking garden stuff to market, but we never hived any of them. Tom Sawyer
called the hogs "ingots," and he called the turnips and stuff "julery,"
and we would go to the cave and pow-wow over what we had done
and how many people we had killed and marked. But I couldn't see
no profit in it. One time Tom sent a boy to run about town with a
blazing stick, which he called a slogan (which was the sign for the
Gang to get together), and then he said he had got secret news by
his spies that next day a whole parcel of Spanish merchants and rich
A-rabs was going to camp in Cave Hollow with two hundred elephants
and six hundred camels, and over a thousand "sumter" mules, all
loaded down with di'monds, and they didn't have only a guard of
four hundred soldiers, and so we would lay in ambuscade, as he called
it, and kill the lot and scoop the things. He said we must slick up our
swords and guns, and get ready. He never could go after even a turnip-
cart but he must have the swords and guns all scoured up for it; though
they was only lath and broom-sticks, and you might scour at them till
you rotted, and then they warn't worth a mouthful of ashes more than
what they was before.

I didn't believe we could lick such a crowd of Spaniards and A-rabs,
but I wanted to see the camels and elephants, so I was on hand next
day, Saturday, in the ambuscade; and when we got the word, we
rushed out of the woods and down the hill. But there warn't no Spaniards and A-rabs, and there warn't no camels nor no elephants. It
warn't anything but a Sunday-school picnic, and only a primer-class
at that. We busted it up, and chased the children up the hollow; but
we never got anything but some doughnuts and jam, though Ben
Rogers got a rag doll, and Jo Harper got a hymn-book and a tract;
and then the teacher charged in and made us drop everything and
cut. I didn't see no di'monds, and I told Tom Sawyer so. He said
there was loads of them, there, anyway; and he said there was A-rabs
there too, and elephants and things. I said, why couldn't we see them,
then? He said if I warn't so ignorant, but had read a book called Don
Quixote, I would know without asking. He said it was all done by
enchantment. He said there was hundreds of soldiers there, and elephants and treasure, and so on, but we had enemies which he called
magicians, and they had turned the whole thing into an infant Sunday-
school, just out of spite. I said all right, then the thing for us to do
was to go for the magicians. Tom Sawyer said I was a numskull.

"Why," says he, "a magician could call up a lot of genies, and they would hash you up like nothing before you could say Jack Robinson. They are as tall as a tree and as big around as a church."

"Well," I says, "s'pose we got some genies to help *us*—can't we lick the other crowd then?"

"How you going to get them?"

"I don't know. How do *they* get them?"

"Why, they rub an old tin lamp or an iron ring, and then the genies come tearing in, with the thunder and lightning a-ripping around and the smoke a-rolling, and everything they're told to do they up and do it. They don't think nothing of pulling a shot-tower up by the roots, and belting a Sunday-school superintendent over the head with it—or any other man."

"Who makes them tear around so?"

"Why, whoever rubs the lamp or the ring. They belong to whoever rubs the lamp or the ring, and they've got to do whatever he says. If he tells them to build a palace forty miles long, out of di'monds, and fill it full of chewing-gum or whatever you want, and fetch an emperor's daughter from China for you to marry, they've got to do it—and they've got to do it before sun-up next morning too. And more—they've got to waltz that palace around over the country wherever you want it, you understand."

"Well," says I, "I think they are a pack of flatheads for not keeping the palace themselves 'stead of fooling them away like that. And what's more—if I was one of them I would see a man in Jericho before I would drop my business and come to him for the rubbing of an old tin lamp."

"How you talk, Huck Finn. Why, you'd *have* to come when he rubbed it, whether you wanted to or not."

"What, and I as high as a tree and as big as a church? All right, then; I *would* come; but I lay I'd make that man climb the highest tree there was in the country."

"Shucks, it ain't no use to talk to you, Huck Finn. You don't seem to know anything, somehow—perfect sap-head."

I thought all this over for two or three days, and then I reckoned I would see if there was anything in it. I got an old tin lamp and an iron ring and went out in the woods and rubbed and rubbed till I sweat like an Injun, calculating to build a palace and sell it; but it warn't no use, none of the genies come. So then I judged that all that stuff was only just one of Tom Sawyer's lies. I reckoned he believed in the A-rabs and the elephants, but as for me I think different. It had all the marks of a Sunday-school.

Occupation:

HOW TO BE HAPPY THOUGH FIRED

SYLVIA WRIGHT

When I first began to job hunt I always hoped I wouldn't get the job. I had to nag and bribe myself into office buildings: Go on in, you coward, I would say, go in, you slob, and when you get out you can have coffee and something fattening at the drugstore.

Because whenever I faced a prospective employer the prospect was utterly implausible. Had I been born, lived through chicken pox, measles, adolescence and a B.A. degree to spend the rest of my life in the office of the Better Bundling Blanket Company, shut up with this stranger and concentrating on his or her weird little preoccupations? I would be there forever—or a year, which amounted to the same thing. Could this type across the desk really give credence to such a fantastic notion?

This was not conceit. I knew I couldn't do most of the things they expected of me. It made me feel sincerely humble, in fact abysmal. And the last thing they wanted was *me*. They wanted something else, which, I gathered from reading magazines, was neat and alert in a linen-look, color-secured, Askron-and-Wonderlon, Stretcherized, Test-erized, crease-resistant, water-repellent, novelty-weave suit, which wore a light floral cologne and colorless nail polish and washed its hair, its girdle and its powder puff at least once a week. It had written a job-hunting letter saying it wasn't interested in money but in learning about the Better Bundling Blanket Company and how to promote its interests. But they might have to take me for some good reason such as they weren't offering enough money to get the something else, and if they did I knew they would gobble me up, snap their jaws shut, and I'd be lost forever.

Psychic states communicate themselves. It was not a bit surprising that without fail I didn't get the job. I helped. When they said, "Do you think you would be able to——?" I said, "No."

Out I would come, knowing I had failed again, happy as a clam in my relentless unemployability.

I might have made a life of never getting jobs if job hunting hadn't been so uncomfortable. It rained. My feet were tired. I had no place to go. People asked me and asked me if I had a job yet. I got broke.

There came a moment when my guard was down. Before I knew it, just like everybody else, I had a job.

The first week is awful, like being married but with nobody making love to you. You don't know what anybody is talking about or where anything is, or who the people are who call on the telephone who get mad if you don't, and your desk chair snags your stockings, and nobody is ever going to have lunch with you, and there you are, the lowest rung in the Better Bundling Blanket Company, and you are nothing, nothing, nothing.

But time passes. A certain ease creeps over you. You have a definite place to go when you get up in the morning. You begin to get mildly interested in that special high-ply wool they use in Better Bundling blankets. You're nothing, but so is everybody else.

This might be called Phase Two. Phase Two can last for years, and many people live out an entire life in it. Employers should do their very best to keep them there, even to getting them new desk chairs.

But sometimes, after a variable lapse of time, you switch to Phase Three. You begin to sense that your original instinct, like most original instincts, was right. Before you got into the Better Bundling Blanket Company you were Jane Doe, nothing special, but yourself. Now you are something else: Miss Doe in the New York Branch, or Miss Doe, J. B.'s secretary, or—the end—Our Miss D. In spite of social security, collective bargaining and the suggestion box; in spite of clean washrooms, the office Christmas party and the Billing Department Girls' Bowling Team—your employer owns your soul.

Don't argue. Of course he does. For instance, when does your day start? Not at 7:00, when the alarm rings, but at 5:00 P.M., when you leave the office. It's a very short day, which stops around 10:30, when, in the most uproarious gathering, something begins signaling to you and you realize it is the B.B.B. Co. needing your sleep. There are Saturdays and Sundays? Saturday you wash all those things you're supposed to wash if you're a nice, clean girl—I mean career woman.

Sunday is a day of rest, and besides you have all that ironing to do. So they give you two weeks' vacation? Anyone who has ever had a two-week vacation knows it is very cleverly timed: it takes at least one week to stop being Our Miss D. and another to get ready to be her again. There's barely time to sandwich a set of tennis in between.

And you really are Our Miss D. You think if you don't get those invoices typed by 4:31; if you don't make that phone call today; if you can't get Our Mr. R. on the afternoon plane to Kansas City— something frightful will happen to the Better Bundling Blanket Company. The B.B.B. Co. is the world and you hold it together. You have to believe this. Otherwise you might surprise yourself wondering who cares whether their blanket is a Better Bundling.

Time and the seasons are passing, and what is the passage of seasons in an office? Spring is Miss Jones, your colleague, just before Easter in a hat encrusted with flowers. Summer is Miss Jones deciding to stop wearing stockings and wondering if she'll bother with leg paint this year. Winter is Miss Jones on the first chill day coming in smelling of moth balls. It's like Plato's cave: life is a shadow on a wall of something going on outside.

What a soul needs to develop is some privacy in which it can try itself on to see how it looks. An office is the least private place in the world. They know everything. Finding out your age and your salary is elementary—they get those facts the first week, since they're the most important ones. They know what you are giving your grandmother for Christmas, that you broke your diet and had a chocolate fudge sundae for lunch, that you are fighting with your family, and what you said to the promotion department about what you think of the accounting department. They know all your symptoms of whatever you think you're coming down with—and you know theirs. If you come in wearing dark glasses and a breakable air, they ask if you have a hangover. But they don't need to ask—they know. You can't conceal going to a psychiatrist, even if you go at eight in the morning or six at night, because sometime you'll drop an unguarded "interpersonal relationship" and they'll guess. If you give a party and invite one person from the office, the next day all the others know you didn't invite them. If you think the new man in the advertising department is mildly attractive, they know, and don't think they won't tell him you think he's utterly divine. Then they'll tell you they told him. So before you know whether he's worth a dither, you're in one whenever you see him. This is hysterical love and is to real love as hysterical paralysis is to real paralysis, i.e., all the pain without any of the credit. If the office keeps at you, you may find yourself the mother of the advertising man's three children before you have a chance to decide this wasn't what you had in mind.

It's unnatural to spend as much time with anyone not related to you as you do with fellow office workers. In a curious way, it's like your family. Though their interest in your life is avid, you can't surprise them. You hold no mystery for them. If you try to get attention, their reaction is, There's that old shoe flapping its tongue again.

Phase Three doesn't mean you realize all these things consciously. Its immediate symptom is that you lose interest violently. For months you've been following the gruesome progress of the love life of that other old shoe, Miss Jones. Suddenly you wish she'd stop talking. However juicy, no further detail can intrigue you. You might throw something.

If you can restrain yourself at this point, you'll be safe—in your job. When the sun comes out or you get over your cold or Miss Jones starts confiding in someone else, Phase Two will reassert itself, briefly. But from now on you'll zigzag. At the most unexpected moments Phase Three will rear its ugly head. Your co-workers will feel you restraining yourself from one end of the office to the other and will begin to creep around. This is the time when you may overhear someone referring to you as "the old fiend."

But if, when you get into Phase Three, you don't restrain yourself; if you throw something, or worse, tell somebody something you've been polishing mentally for a month or two—eventually, which is what I am getting to, they will take you out for a couple of regretful Martinis and tell you that they're cutting down your department.

Here—though you won't think so after you've gone home and gloomily had two more Martinis—is the most beautiful moment of your life. Time, which has been racing along in skinny five-and-a-half-hour days, relaxes gloriously into huge, rounded, twenty-four-hour ones. Habits, so fixed that you wondered if you were prematurely old or just getting like your Aunt Susie, become irrelevant and immaterial. Life, losing its focus on Better Bundling blankets, becomes directionless: this means it has a million directions.

You don't have to get up. Half the people in the world love to get up in the morning, and they all work in offices, and this is as it should be. The other half finds getting up so intense a torture that someone should stand by and give them a gold medal every time they make it.

This is medically sound, but the first half thinks the second half is making it up and being difficult. If you are in the second half, and I suspect you are or you wouldn't have been fired, you will experience great bliss. There's one moment of death, when you think you're late to the Better Bundling Blanket Company. Then transfiguration, when you know that you can extend the process of getting up over such a long time that it will be barely perceptible. You'll have time to remember your dreams, and who knows what might come of that?

You can call your soul your own. For a while you'll call and it won't come: it's mad at you for burying it under Our Miss Doe. But when it sneaks out for a moment or two, don't pounce on it and tell it to go right out and find another job. Let it wander around and see what things are like. It may have entirely different ideas from yours. It doesn't think it's sinful to lie on the sofa and read detective stories all day. It may decide it could write a biting satire on life in offices. Or it may start to make an intricate stew that must be stirred every ten minutes. Sometime, when you're walking along the street at three o'clock in the afternoon, your soul will start saying, Oh, joy. Oh, life. Oh, infinite possibilities. This is silly, but why be a spoilsport? Your soul doesn't know what it's doing, but it might find out. It might find out something you lost sight of when you went to work for the Better Bundling Blanket Company: In spite of all the evidence to the contrary, life can change. Even you can change. You may be able to do some of those things Our Miss D. thought were impossible.

People in offices will do everything they can to make you feel that you are living in sin. They telephone at 9:15 A.M. and ask with superior solicitude if they woke you up—they've been up for hours and they'd forgotten you didn't have to be. They wonder if you aren't getting out of the swim. They remark kindly that it's all right for a while, but don't let it become a habit—people can become unemployable. If they come to dinner and eat your stew, they will say that it is delicious, but only somebody who has all the time in the world could bother with such a thing, and they must tell you the clever trick they've discovered with frozen cheese blintzes. If you visit them in their offices (this is a mistake), they become desperately indispensable: they type memos, telephone, summon messenger boys, ask your pardon for just a moment while they do something rather important, and they only relax when they suggest that with your experience you might be able to get a job at the Woolly Bear Blanket Company, where they know the personnel manager, though it probably wouldn't pay quite as much right away as your old job did.

Let them run on. They have to do something to bolster up their pathetic office-bound egos. And you can walk grandly out of there and into the sun, stroll down the street looking in shop windows, watch the seals in the zoo being fed and wonder what it would feel like to be a seal, take a bus ride to a strange part of town, and finally have a nice cup of tea and something fattening in a tearoom.

What does this remind you of? If I were you I wouldn't think about it. You're not going to make the same mistake again, are you? Or are you?

AND IF ELECTED, AND I THINK I WILL BE . . .

CASKIE STINNETT

This is the year of the big vaudeville show, with candidates resplendent in blue shirts, which absorb the glare from the spotlights, and pancake makeup, which artfully conceals both age and pallor and restores to weary politicians the ruddy vigor of a grade-B Western hero. There will be speeches, flags, music and, for the boys in the backroom, a bottle on the shelf. Promises will be made in good faith, and some in the rankest kind of hypocrisy. The din will be deafening, the television channels choked with argument, and ill will, we predict, will be in possession of the land.

To help you get your money's worth for your vote (a figure of speech; nothing more) we are offering a standard against which we ask that you check your candidate. The beauty of this standard is that it isn't scientific, and while your findings will not deliver you into a state of ataraxia they may bring your candidate into focus, perhaps even with devastating clarity. If so, good; and if you get any coins in change, strike them on the counter to check them for a hollow ring. In an election year, you can't trust anybody.

Just a few points for the politically alert to watch out for:

Keep your eye on the candidate who says ". . . and on the other hand" because he is arguing both sides of the question and hopes to get you going or coming. A candidate is entitled to work only one side of the street.

Look out for the candidate whose American Legion cap fits poorly. He just bought it.

Avoid the candidate who considers the hot lunch for school children about as controversial an issue as he cares to come to grips with.

Avoid the candidate who smiles too much. What's so blooming funny?

It may be hard to do, but keep your eye on the ball when one team claims all the patriotism.

Take a second look at the candidate whose voice falters at the end of each page of his speech. He doesn't know, any more than you do, what's coming next.

When the presidential candidate bestows his blessing upon the local official running for reelection, a ceremony somewhat comparable to Duncan Hines knighting a tearoom, require the presidential candidate to pronounce correctly the name of his good friend.

That's it, candidates. Now who among you hears cries from his country for succor?

JACK TYRRELL, THE SATURDAY EVENING POST

"If there's one song I hate, it's 'Tiger Rag.'"

THE BRIEFLESS BARRISTER

A Ballad

JOHN G. SAXE (1816–1887)

An attorney was taking a turn,
  In shabby habiliments drest;
His coat it was shockingly worn,
  And the rust had invested his vest.

His breeches had suffered a breach,
  His linen and worsted were worse;
He had scarce a whole crown in his hat,
  And not half a crown in his purse.

And thus as he wandered along,
  A cheerless and comfortless elf,
He sought for relief in a song,
  Or complainingly talked to himself:

"Unfortunate man that I am!
  I've never a client but grief:
The case is, I've no case at all,
  And in brief, I've ne'er had a brief!

"I've waited and waited in vain,
  Expecting an 'opening' to find,
Where an honest young lawyer might gain
  Some reward for toil of his mind.

"'Tis not that I'm wanting in law,
  Or lack an intelligent face,
That others have cases to plead,
  While I have to plead for a case.

"Oh, how can a modest young man
  E'er hope for the smallest progression,
The profession's already so full
  Of lawyers so full of profession!"

While thus he was strolling around,
　His eye accidentally fell
On a very deep hole in the ground,
　And he sighed to himself, "It is well!"

To curb his emotions, he sat
　On the curbstone the space of a minute,
Then cried, "Here's an opening at last!"
　And in less than a jiffy was in it!

Next morning twelve citizens came
　('Twas the coroner bade them attend),
To the end that it might be determined
　How the man had determined his end!

"The man was a lawyer, I hear,"
　Quoth the foreman who sat on the corse.
"A lawyer? Alas!" said another,
　"Undoubtedly died of remorse!"

A third said, "He knew the deceased,
　An attorney well versed in the laws,
And as to the cause of his death,
　'Twas no doubt for the want of a cause."

The jury decided at length,
　After solemnly weighing the matter,
That the lawyer was drownded, because
　He could not keep his head above water!

SKIMMING THE MILKY WAY

BILL NYE (1850–1896)

(From "Bill Nye's Red Book")

The comet is a kind of astronomical parody on the planet. Comets look some like planets, but they are thicker and do not hurt so hard when they hit anybody as a planet does. The comet was so called because it had hair on it, I believe, but late years the bald-headed comet is giving just as good satisfaction everywhere.

The characteristic features of a comet are: a nucleus, a nebulous light or coma, and usually a luminous train or tail worn high. Sometimes several tails are observed on one comet, but this occurs only in flush times.

Comets sometimes live to a great age. This shows that night air is not so injurious to the health as many people would have us believe.

Astronomers say that the tails of all comets are turned from the sun. I do not know why they do this, whether it is etiquette among them or just a mere habit.

Much fear has been the result of the comet's appearance ever since the world began, and it is as good a thing to worry about as anything I know of. If we could get close to a comet without frightening it away, we would find that we could walk through it anywhere as we could through the glare of a torchlight procession. We should so live that we will not be ashamed to look a comet in the eye, however. Let us pay up our newspaper subscription and lead such lives that when the comet strikes we will be ready.

Some worry a good deal about the chances for a big comet to plow into the sun some dark, rainy night, and thus bust up the whole universe. I wish that was all I had to worry about. If any respectable man will agree to pay my taxes and funeral expenses, I will agree to do his worrying about the comet's crashing into the bosom of the sun and knocking its daylights out.

The Sun

This luminous body is 92,000,000 miles from the earth, though there have been mornings this winter when it seemed to me that it was further than that. A railway train going at the rate of 40 miles per hour would be 263 years going there, to say nothing of stopping for fuel or water, or stopping on side tracks to wait for freight trains to pass. Several years ago it was discovered that a slight error had been made in the calculations of the sun's distance from the earth, and, owing to a misplaced logarithm, or something of that kind, a mistake of 3,000,000 miles was made in the result. People cannot be too careful in such matters. Supposing that, on the strength of the information contained in the old time-table, a man should start out with only provisions sufficient to take him 89,000,000 miles and should then find that 3,000,000 miles still stretched ahead of him. He would then have to buy fresh figs of the train boy in order to sustain life. Think of buying nice fresh figs on a train that had been en route 250 years.

The sun cannot be examined through an ordinary telescope with impunity. Only one man ever tried that, and he is now wearing a glass eye that cost him $9.

If you examine the sun through an ordinary solar microscope, you discover that it has a curdled or mottled appearance, as though suffering from biliousness. The spots on the sun vary from minute pores the size of an ordinary school district to spots 100,000 miles in diameter, visible to the nude eye. The center of these spots is as black as a brunette cat, and is called the umbra, so called because it resembles an umbrella. The next circle is less dark, and called the penumbra, because it so closely resembles the numbra.

The sun revolves upon his or her axletree, as the case may be, once in 25 to 28 of our days, so that a man living there would have almost two years to pay a 30-day note. We should so live that when we come to die we may go at once to the sun.

Regarding the sun's temperature, Sir John Herschel says that it is sufficient to melt a shell of ice covering its entire surface to a depth of 40 feet. I do not know whether he made this experiment personally or hired a man to do it for him.

The sun is like the star spangled banner—it is "still there." You get up tomorrow morning just before sunrise and look away toward the east, and keep on looking in that direction, and at last you will see a fine sight, if what I have been told is true. If the sunrise is as grand as the sunset, it indeed must be one of nature's most sublime phenomena.

The Stars

There is much in the great field of astronomy that is discouraging to the savant who hasn't the time nor the means to rummage around through the heavens. At times I am almost hopeless, and feel like saying to the great yearnful, hungry world: "Grope on forever. Do not ask me for another scientific fact. Find it out yourself. Hunt up your new-laid planets, and let me have a rest. Never ask me again to sit up all night and take care of a new-born world, while you lie in bed and reck not."

I get no salary for examining the trackless void night after night when I ought to be in bed. I sacrifice my health in order that the public may know at once of the presence of a red-hot comet, fresh from the factory. And yet, what thanks do I get?

Every now and then another astronomer comes to me and says: "Professor, I have discovered another new star and intend to file it. Found it last night about a mile and a half south of the zenith, running loose. Haven't heard of anybody who has lost a star of the fifteenth magnitude, about thirteen hands high, with light mane and tail, have you?" How can I discover whether he is or is not playing an old, threadbare star on me for a new one?

No serious accidents have occurred in the starry heavens since I began to observe and study their habits. Not a star has waxed, not a star has waned to my knowledge. Not a planet has season-cracked or shown any of the injurious effects of our rigorous climate. Not a star has ripened prematurely or fallen off the trees. The varnish on the very oldest stars I find on close and critical examination to be in splendid condition. They will all no doubt wear as long as we need them, and wink on long after we have ceased to wink back.

In 1866 there appeared suddenly in the northern crown a star of about the third magnitude and worth at least $250. It was generally conceded by astronomers that this was a brand new star that had never been used, but upon consultation of the star catalogue and price list it was found that this was not a new star at all, but an old, faded star of the ninth magnitude, with the front breadths turned wrong side out and trimmed with moonlight along the seams.

It is such things as this that make the life of the astronomer one of constant and discouraging toil. I have long contemplated, as I say, the advisability of retiring from this field of science and allowing others to light the northern lights, skim the milky way and do the other celestial chores. I would do them myself cheerfully if my health would permit, but for years I have realized, and so has my wife, that my duties as an astronomer kept me up too much at night, and my wife is certainly right about it when she says if I insist on scanning the heavens night after night, coming home late with the cork out of my telescope and my eyes red and swollen with these exhausting night vigils, I will be cut down in my prime. So I am liable to abandon the great labor to which I had intended to devote my life, my dazzling genius and my princely income. I hope that other savants will spare me the pain of another refusal, for my mind is fully made up that unless another skimmist is at once secured, the milky way will henceforth remain unskum.

THE WHISPERER

IRONQUILL (1841–1911)

He never tried to make a speech;
A speech was far beyond his reach.
  He didn't even dare to try;
  He did his work upon the sly.
    He took the voter to the rear
    And gently whispered in his ear.

He never wrote; he could not write;
He never tried that style of fight.
  No argument of his was seen
  In daily press or magazine.
    He only tried to get up near
    And whisper in the voter's ear.

It worked so well that he became
A person of abundant fame.
  He couldn't write; he couldn't speak,
  But still pursued his course unique.
    He had a glorious career—
    He whispered in the voter's ear.

DADDY'S A PRIVATE EYE!

SCOTT CORBETT

The day I am waiting for is the day the TV mystery shows run out of young bachelor-type private eyes and have to fall back on the family man. A typical caper will pick up Detective Luther Meeks sitting quietly at home fixing his youngest boy's roller skates when his partner, Herb Hodgkins, telephones.

"Got a hot tip on the electric ice-pick murders, Luther! Pick me up in five minutes."

"Gee, Herb, I wish I could, but Cora took the kids to a dance recital and I'm all alone with our youngest."

"But listen, Luther, this is hot!"

"Well, okay, I'll see if I can rustle up a baby-sitter somewhere. But Cora's got the car, so you'll have to pick me up."

"Can't, Luther—Junior had a date tonight."

"Oh. Well, be at your bus stop and watch for me. I'll try to make it in twenty minutes."

"Good. That'll give me time to finish my vacuuming. I promised Eloise I'd help her clean the spare room tonight—her mother's due in tomorrow, you know."

Luther has an awful time locating a baby-sitter and then he just misses a bus and has to wait 20 minutes for another one and when it does come he cannot get a seat by the window to wave at Herb. The tension mounts steadily as the bus nears Herb's corner. Will Luther be able to signal him? Will Herb let the bus go by without getting on?

At the last minute, by cleverly pretending to lose his balance, quick-thinking Luther falls across an elderly couple's lap and thrusts a hand out the window. Herb alertly catches the signal and leaps aboard.

After a while the crowd thins out and they get a seat. The man in front of them, a sinister, swarthy chap, is reading a tabloid with big black headlines which scream,

MURDER SUSPECT FOUND SLAIN ICE-PICK KILLER SOUGHT

Herb glances at the paper and gasps.

"What's the matter, Herb?" cries Luther.

"I just noticed the date—today's the fifteenth, the final day for mailing in deposits to Camp Hockamesset! Junior's been deviling us to send him there next summer, and we finally gave in, but I forgot to get my check off—and the camp folder made a great point of how it's got to be in the mail not later than tonight or they can't guarantee a place!"

Herb gets out his checkbook and frantically writes a check, and for a while it is really touch-and-go—they get to a stationer's shop just as the man is closing up, and after Herb stamps and addresses an envelope they reach the corner just as the mail truck pulls up beside the box to make the last collection of the evening!

Breathing a little easier, they walk the rest of the way to the deserted mansion which is involved in Herb's hot tip, and manage to force their way into the pitch-black living room through the French windows.

"Well, it figures," snaps Herb. "The secret button that opens the secret door that leads to the secret passage into the secret vault has to be here somewhere! Get out your flashlight, Luther."

"I am, Herb."

"You are? Gee! I thought that was a glimmer of moonlight. What's the idea of bringing a weak flash like that?"

"Listen, I can never keep a flashlight working around that house of mine! Someone's always borrowing it. Got any matches?"

Herb strikes a match, and Luther points to a desk.

"Look at that knife!" A polished wooden paper knife is lying on the desk. Luther picks it up and examines it intently. "Just as I thought. Some kid made this. Danny made one almost like it at school, only with a much fancier handle. You ought to see the scrollwork he carved out! Really darn good for a kid."

"Huh! You ought to see the book ends Junior made," says Herb. "Well, come on, let's find that secret button."

They find the button and the door and the passage and the vault and sure enough, the ice-pick killer is hiding there.

"Okay, Luther," snaps Herb, "put the cuffs on him."

"Never mind, fellows, you don't need no handcuffs," says the killer dispiritedly. "I'm harmless. I ain't got my ice pick with me—my kid borrowed it this morning to punch holes in his belt."

THE HEIGHT OF THE RIDICULOUS

OLIVER WENDELL HOLMES (1809–1894)

I wrote some lines once on a time
    In wondrous merry mood,
And thought, as usual, men would say
    They were exceeding good.

They were so queer, so very queer,
    I laughed as I would die;
Albeit, in the general way,
    A sober man am I.

I called my servant, and he came;
    How kind it was of him
To mind a slender man like me,
    He of the mighty limb!

"These to the printer," I exclaimed,
  And, in my humorous way,
I added (as a trifling jest),
  "There'll be the devil to pay."

He took the paper, and I watched,
  And saw him peep within
At the first line he read, his face
  Was all upon the grin.

He read the next: the grin grew broad,
  And shot from ear to ear;
He read the third; a chuckling noise
  I now began to hear.

The fourth; he broke into a roar;
  The fifth; his waistband split;
The sixth; he burst five buttons off,
  And tumbled in a fit.

Ten days and nights, with sleepless eye,
  I watched that wretched man,
And since, I never dare to write
  As funny as I can.

BUTCH MINDS THE BABY

DAMON RUNYON

One evening along about seven o'clock I am sitting in Mindy's restaurant putting on the gefillte fish, which is a dish I am very fond of, when in comes three parties from Brooklyn wearing caps as follows: Harry the Horse, Little Isadore and Spanish John.

Now these parties are not such parties as I will care to have much truck with, because I often hear rumors about them that are very discreditable, even if the rumors are not true. In fact, I hear that many citizens of Brooklyn will be very glad indeed to see Harry the Horse, Little Isadore and Spanish John move away from there, as they are always doing something that is considered a knock to the community, such as robbing people, or maybe shooting or stabbing them, and throwing pineapples, and carrying on generally.

I am really much surprised to see these parties on Broadway, as it is well known that the Broadway coppers just naturally love to shove such parties around, but here they are in Mindy's, and there I am, so of course I give them a very large hello, as I never wish to seem inhospitable, even to Brooklyn parties. Right away they come over to my table and sit down, and Little Isadore reaches out and spears himself a big hunk of my gefillte fish with his fingers, but I overlook this, as I am using the only knife on the table.

Then they all sit there looking at me without saying anything, and the way they look at me makes me very nervous indeed. Finally I figure that maybe they are a little embarrassed being in a high-class spot such as Mindy's, with legitimate people around and about, so I say to them, very polite:

"It is a nice night."

"What is nice about it?" asks Harry the Horse, who is a thin man with a sharp face and sharp eyes.

Well, now that it is put up to me in this way, I can see there is nothing so nice about the night, at that, so I try to think of something else jolly to say, while Little Isadore keeps spearing at my gefillte fish with his fingers, and Spanish John nabs one of my potatoes.

"Where does Big Butch live?" Harry the Horse asks.

"Big Butch?" I say, as if I never heard the name before in my life, because in this man's town it is never a good idea to answer any question without thinking it over, as some time you may give the right answer to the wrong guy, or the wrong answer to the right guy. "Where does Big Butch live?" I ask them again.

"Yes, where does he live?" Harry the Horse says, very impatient. "We wish you to take us to him."

"Now wait a minute, Harry," I say, and I am now more nervous than somewhat. "I am not sure I remember the exact house Big Butch lives in, and furthermore I am not sure Big Butch will care to have me bringing people to see him, especially three at a time, and especially from Brooklyn. You know Big Butch has a very bad disposition, and there is no telling what he may say to me if he does not like the idea of me taking you to him."

"Everything is very kosher," Harry the Horse says. "You need not be afraid of anything whatever. We have a business proposition for Big

Butch. It means a nice score for him, so you take us to him at once, or the chances are I will have to put the arm on somebody around here."

Well, as the only one around there for him to put the arm on at this time seems to be me, I can see where it will be good policy for me to take these parties to Big Butch, especially as the last of my gefillte fish is just going down Little Isadore's gullet, and Spanish John is finishing up my potatoes, and is dunking a piece of rye bread in my coffee, so there is nothing more for me to eat.

So I lead them over into West Forty-ninth Street, near Tenth Avenue, where Big Butch lives on the ground floor of an old brownstone-front house, and who is sitting out on the stoop but Big Butch himself. In fact, everybody in the neighborhood is sitting out on the front stoops over there, including women and children, because sitting out on the front stoops is quite a custom in this section.

Big Butch is peeled down to his undershirt and pants, and he has no shoes on his feet, as Big Butch is a guy who likes his comfort. Furthermore, he is smoking a cigar, and laid out on the stoop beside him on a blanket is a little baby with not much clothes on. This baby seems to be asleep, and every now and then Big Butch fans it with a folded newspaper to shoo away the mosquitoes that wish to nibble on the baby. These mosquitoes come across the river from the Jersey side on hot nights and they seem to be very fond of babies.

"Hello, Butch," I say, as we stop in front of the stoop.

"Sh-h-h-h!" Butch says, pointing at the baby, and making more noise with his shush than an engine blowing off steam. Then he gets up and tiptoes down to the sidewalk where we are standing, and I am hoping that Butch feels all right, because when Butch does not feel so good he is apt to be very short with one and all. He is a guy of maybe six foot two and a couple of feet wide, and he has big hairy hands and a mean look.

In fact, Big Butch is known all over this man's town as a guy you must not monkey with in any respect, so it takes plenty of weight off of me when I see that he seems to know the parties from Brooklyn, and nods at them very friendly, especially at Harry the Horse. And right away Harry states a most surprising proposition to Big Butch.

It seems that there is a big coal company which has an office in an old building down in West Eighteenth Street, and in this office is a safe, and in this safe is the company pay roll of twenty thousand dollars cash money. Harry the Horse knows the money is there because a personal friend of his who is the paymaster for the company puts it there late this very afternoon.

It seems that the paymaster enters into a dicker with Harry the Horse and Little Isadore and Spanish John for them to slug him while he is carrying the pay roll from the bank to the office in the afternoon, but something happens that they miss connections on the exact spot, so the paymaster has to carry the sugar on to the office without being slugged, and there it is now in two fat bundles.

Personally it seems to me as I listen to Harry's story that the paymaster must be a very dishonest character to be making deals to hold still while he is being slugged and the company's sugar taken away from him, but of course it is none of my business, so I take no part in the conversation.

Well, it seems that Harry the Horse and Little Isadore and Spanish John wish to get the money out of the safe, but none of them knows anything about opening safes, and while they are standing around over in Brooklyn talking over what is to be done in this emergency Harry suddenly remembers that Big Butch is once in the business of opening safes for a living.

In fact, I hear afterwards that Big Butch is considered the best safe opener east of the Mississippi River in his day, but the law finally takes to sending him to Sing Sing for opening these safes, and after he is in and out of Sing Sing three different times for opening safes Butch gets sick and tired of the place, especially as they pass what is called the Baumes Law in New York, which is a law that says if a guy is sent to Sing Sing four times hand running, he must stay there the rest of his life, without any argument about it.

So Big Butch gives up opening safes for a living, and goes into business in a small way, such as running beer, and handling a little Scotch now and then, and becomes an honest citizen. Furthermore, he marries one of the neighbor's children over on the West Side by the name of Mary Murphy, and I judge the baby on this stoop comes of this marriage between Big Butch and Mary because I can see that it is a very homely baby, indeed. Still, I never see many babies that I consider rose geraniums for looks, anyway.

Well, it finally comes out that the idea of Harry the Horse and Little Isadore and Spanish John is to get Big Butch to open the coal company's safe and take the pay-roll money out, and they are willing to give him fifty per cent of the money for his bother, taking fifty per cent for themselves for finding the plant, and paying all the overhead such as the paymaster, out of their bit, which strikes me as a pretty fair sort of deal for Big Butch. But Butch only shakes his head.

"It is old-fashioned stuff," Butch says. "Nobody opens pete boxes for a living any more. They make the boxes too good, and they are all wired up with alarms and are a lot of trouble generally. I am in a legitimate business now and going along. You boys know I cannot stand another fall, what with being away three times already, and in addition to this I must mind the baby. My old lady goes to Mrs. Clancy's wake tonight up in the Bronx, and the chances are she will be there all night, as she is very fond of wakes, so I must mind little John Ignatius Junior."

"Listen, Butch," Harry the Horse says, "this is a very soft pete. It is old-fashioned, and you can open it with a toothpick. There are no wires on it, because they never put more than a dime in it before in years. It just happens they have to put the twenty G's in it tonight because my pal the paymaster makes it a point not to get back from the jug with the scratch in time to pay off today, especially after he sees we miss out on him. It is the softest touch you will ever know, and where can a guy pick up ten G's like this?"

I can see that Big Butch is thinking the ten G's over very seriously, at that, because in these times nobody can afford to pass up ten G's, especially a guy in the beer business, which is very, very tough just now. But finally he shakes his head again and says like this:

"No," he says, "I must let it go, because I must mind the baby. My old lady is very, very particular about this, and I dast not leave little John Ignatius Junior for a minute. If Mary comes home and finds I am not minding the baby she will put the blast on me plenty. I like to turn a few honest bobs now and then as well as anybody, but," Butch says, "John Ignatius Junior comes first with me."

Then he turns away and goes back to the stoop as much as to say he is through arguing, and sits down beside John Ignatius Junior again just in time to keep a mosquito from carrying off one of John's legs. Anybody can see that Big Butch is very fond of this baby, though personally I will not give you a dime a dozen for babies, male and female.

Well, Harry the Horse and Little Isadore and Spanish John are very much disappointed, and stand around talking among themselves, and paying no attention to me, when all of a sudden Spanish John, who never has much to say up to this time, seems to have a bright idea. He talks to Harry and Isadore, and they get all pleasured up over what he has to say and finally Harry goes to Big Butch.

"Sh-h-h-h!" Big Butch says, pointing to the baby as Harry opens his mouth.

"Listen, Butch," Harry says in a whisper, "we can take the baby with us, and you can mind it and work, too."

"Why," Big Butch whispers back, "this is quite an idea indeed. Let us go into the house and talk things over."

So he picks up the baby and leads us into his joint, and gets out some pretty fair beer, though it is needled a little, at that, and we sit around the kitchen chewing the fat in whispers. There is a crib in the kitchen, and Butch puts the baby in this crib, and it keeps on snoozing away first rate while we are talking. In fact, it is sleeping so sound that I am commencing to figure that Butch must give it some of the needled beer he is feeding us, because I am feeling a little dopey myself.

Finally Butch says that as long as he can take John Ignatius Junior with him he sees no reason why he shall not go and open the safe for them, only he says he must have five per cent more to put in the baby's bank when he gets back, so as to round himself up with his ever-loving wife in case of a beef from her over keeping the baby out in the night air. Harry the Horse says he considers this extra five per cent a little strong, but Spanish John, who seems to be a very square guy, says that after all it is only fair to cut the baby in if it is to be with them when they are making the score, and Little Isadore seems to think this is all right, too. So Harry the Horse gives in, and says five per cent it is.

Well, as they do not wish to start out until after midnight, and as there is plenty of time, Big Butch gets out some more needled beer, and then he goes looking for the tools with which he opens safes, and which he says he does not see since the day John Ignatius Junior is born and he gets them out to build the crib.

Now this is a good time for me to bid one and all farewell, and what keeps me there is something I cannot tell you to this day, because personally I never before have any idea of taking part in a safe opening, especially with a baby, as I consider such actions very dishonorable. When I come to think things over afterwards, the only thing I can figure is the needled beer, but I wish to say I am really very much surprised at myself when I find myself in a taxicab along about one o'clock in the morning with these Brooklyn parties and Big Butch and the baby.

Butch has John Ignatius Junior rolled up in a blanket, and John is still pounding his ear. Butch has a satchel of tools, and what looks to me like a big flat book, and just before we leave the house Butch hands me a package and tells me to be very careful with it. He gives Little Isadore a smaller package, which Isadore shoves into his pistol pocket, and when Isadore sits down in the taxi something goes wa-wa, like a sheep, and Big Butch becomes very indignant because it seems Isadore is sitting on John Ignatius Junior's doll, which says "Mamma" when you squeeze it.

It seems Big Butch figures that John Ignatius Junior may wish something to play with in case he wakes up, and it is a good thing for Little Isadore that the mamma doll is not squashed so it cannot say "Mamma" any more, or the chances are Little Isadore will get a good bust in the snoot.

We let the taxicab go a block away from the spot we are headed for in West Eighteenth Street, between Seventh and Eighth Avenues, and walk the rest of the way two by two. I walk with Big Butch, carrying my package, and Butch is lugging the baby and his satchel and the flat thing that looks like a book. It is so quiet down in West Eighteenth Street at such an hour that you can hear yourself think, and in fact I hear myself thinking very plain that I am a big sap to be on a job like this, especially with a baby, but I keep going just the same, which shows you what a very big sap I am, indeed.

There are very few people in West Eighteenth Street when we get there, and one of them is a fat guy who is leaning against a building almost in the center of the block, and who takes a walk for himself as soon as he sees us. It seems that this fat guy is the watchman at the coal company's office and is also a personal friend of Harry the Horse, which is why he takes the walk when he sees us coming.

It is agreed before we leave Big Butch's house that Harry the Horse and Spanish John are to stay outside the place as lookouts, while Big Butch is inside opening the safe, and that Little Isadore is to go with Butch. Nothing whatever is said by anybody about where I am to be at any time, and I can see that, no matter where I am, I will still be an outsider, but, as Butch gives me the package to carry, I figure he wishes me to remain with him.

It is no bother at all getting into the office of the coal company, which is on the ground floor, because it seems the watchman leaves the front door open, this watchman being a most obliging guy, indeed. In fact he is so obliging that by and by he comes back and lets Harry the Horse and Spanish John tie him up good and tight, and stick a handkerchief in his mouth and chuck him in an areaway next to the office, so nobody will think he has anything to do with opening the safe in case anybody comes around asking.

The office looks out on the street, and the safe that Harry the Horse and Little Isadore and Spanish John wish Big Butch to open is standing up against the rear wall of the office facing the street windows. There is one little electric light burning very dim over the safe so that when anybody walks past the place outside, such as a watchman, they can look in through the window and see the safe at all times, unless they are blind. It is not a tall safe, and it is not a big safe, and I can see Big Butch grin when he sees it, so I figure this safe is not much of a safe, just as Harry the Horse claims.

Well, as soon as Big Butch and the baby and Little Isadore and me get into the office, Big Butch steps over to the safe and unfolds what I think is the big flat book, and what is it but a sort of screen painted on one side to look exactly like the front of a safe. Big Butch stands this screen up on the floor in front of the real safe, leaving plenty of space in between, the idea being that the screen will keep anyone passing in the street outside from seeing Butch while he is opening the safe, because when a man is opening a safe he needs all the privacy he can get.

Big Butch lays John Ignatius Junior down on the floor on the blanket behind the phony safe front and takes his tools out of the satchel and starts to work opening the safe, while Little Isadore and me get back in a corner where it is dark, because there is not room for all of us back of the screen. However, we can see what Big Butch is doing, and I wish to say while I never before see a professional safe opener at work, and never wish to see another, this Butch handles himself like a real artist.

He starts drilling into the safe around the combination lock, working very fast and very quiet, when all of a sudden what happens but John Ignatius Junior sits up on the blanket and lets out a squall. Naturally this is most disquieting to me, and personally I am in favor of beaning John Ignatius Junior with something to make him keep still, because I am nervous enough as it is. But the squalling does not seem to bother Big Butch. He lays down his tools and picks up John Ignatius Junior and starts whispering, "There, there, there, my itty oddleums. Da-dad is here."

Well, this sounds very nonsensical to me in such a situation, and it makes no impression whatever on John Ignatius Junior. He keeps on squalling, and I judge he is squalling pretty loud because I see Harry the Horse and Spanish John both walk past the window and look in very anxious. Big Butch jiggles John Ignatius Junior up and down and keeps whispering baby talk to him, which sounds very undignified coming from a high-class safe opener, and finally Butch whispers to me to hand him the package I am carrying.

He opens the package, and what is in it but a baby's nursing bottle full of milk. Moreover, there is a little tin stew pan, and Butch hands the pan to me and whispers to me to find a water tap somewhere in the joint and fill the pan with water. So I go stumbling around in the dark in a room behind the office and bark my shins several times before I find a tap and fill the pan. I take it back to Big Butch, and he squats there with the baby on one arm, and gets a tin of what is called canned heat out of the package, and lights this canned heat with his cigar lighter, and starts heating the pan of water with the nursing bottle in it.

Big Butch keeps sticking his finger in the pan of water while it is heating, and by and by he puts the rubber nipple of the nursing bottle in his mouth and takes a pull at it to see if the milk is warm enough, just like I see dolls who have babies do. Apparently the milk is okay, as Butch hands the bottle to John Ignatius Junior, who grabs hold of it with both hands and starts sucking on the business end. Naturally he has to stop squalling, and Big Butch goes to work on the safe again, with John Ignatius Junior sitting on the blanket, pulling on the bottle and looking wiser than a treeful of owls.

It seems the safe is either a tougher job than anybody figures, or Big Butch's tools are not so good, what with being old and rusty and used for building baby cribs, because he breaks a couple of drills and works himself up into quite a sweat without getting anywhere. Butch afterwards explains to me that he is one of the first guys in this country to open safes without explosives, but he says to do this work properly you have to know the safes so as to drill to the tumblers of the lock just right, and it seems that this particular safe is a new type to him, even if it is old, and he is out of practice.

Well, in the meantime John Ignatius Junior finishes his bottle and starts mumbling again, and Big Butch gives him a tool to play with, and finally Butch needs this tool and tries to take it away from John Ignatius Junior, and the baby lets out such a squawk that Butch has to let him keep it until he can sneak it away from him, and this causes more delay.

Finally Big Butch gives up trying to drill the safe open, and he whispers to us that he will have to put a little shot in it to loosen up the lock, which is all right with us, because we are getting tired of hanging around and listening to John Ignatius Junior's glug-glugging. As far as I am personally concerned, I am wishing I am home in bed.

Well, Butch starts pawing through his satchel looking for something and it seems that what he is looking for is a little bottle of some kind of explosive with which to shake the lock on the safe up some, and at first he cannot find this bottle, but finally he discovers that John Ignatius Junior has it and is gnawing at the cork, and Butch has quite a battle making John Ignatius Junior give it up.

Anyway, he fixes the explosive in one of the holes he drills near the combination lock on the safe, and then he puts in a fuse, and just before he touches off the fuse Butch picks up John Ignatius Junior and hands him to Little Isadore, and tells us to go into the room behind the office. John Ignatius Junior does not seem to care for Little Isadore, and I do not blame him, at that, because he starts to squirm around quite some in Isadore's arms and lets out a squall, but all of a sudden he becomes very quiet indeed, and, while I am not able to prove it, something tells me that Little Isadore has his hand over John Ignatius Junior's mouth.

Well, Big Butch joins us right away in the back room, and sound comes out of John Ignatius Junior again as Butch takes him from Little Isadore, and I am thinking that it is a good thing for Isadore that the baby cannot tell Big Butch what Isadore does to him.

"I put in just a little bit of a shot," Big Butch says, "and it will not make any more noise than snapping your fingers."

But a second later there is a big whoom from the office, and the whole joint shakes, and John Ignatius Junior laughs right out loud. The chances are he thinks it is the Fourth of July.

"I guess maybe I put in too big a charge," Big Butch says, and then he rushes into the office with Little Isadore and me after him, and John Ignatius Junior still laughing very heartily for a small baby. The door of the safe is swinging loose, and the whole joint looks somewhat wrecked, but Big Butch loses no time in getting his dukes into the safe and grabbing out two big bundles of cash money, which he sticks inside his shirt.

As we go into the street Harry the Horse and Spanish John come running up much excited, and Harry says to Big Butch like this:

"What are you trying to do," he says, "wake up the whole town?"

"Well," Butch says, "I guess maybe the charge is too strong, at that, but nobody seems to be coming, so you and Spanish John walk over to Eighth Avenue, and the rest of us will walk to Seventh, and if you go along quiet, like people minding their own business, it will be all right."

But I judge Little Isadore is tired of John Ignatius Junior's company by this time, because he says he will go with Harry the Horse and Spanish John, and this leaves Big Butch and John Ignatius Junior and me to go the other way. So we start moving, and all of a sudden two cops come tearing around the corner toward which Harry and Isadore and Spanish John are going. The chances are the cops hear the earthquake Big Butch lets off and are coming to investigate.

But the chances are, too, that if Harry the Horse and the other two keep on walking along very quietly like Butch tells them to, the coppers will pass them up entirely, because it is not likely that coppers will figure anybody to be opening safes with explosives in this neighborhood. But the minute Harry the Horse sees the coppers he loses his nut, and he outs with the old equalizer and starts blasting away, and what does Spanish John do but get his out, too, and open up.

The next thing anybody knows, the two coppers are down on the ground with slugs in them, but other coppers are coming from every which direction, blowing whistles and doing a little blasting themselves, and there is plenty of excitement, especially when the coppers who are not chasing Harry the Horse and Little Isadore and Spanish John start poking around the neighborhood and find Harry's pal, the watchman, all tied up nice and tight where Harry leaves him, and the watchman explains that some scoundrels blow open the safe he is watching.

All this time Big Butch and me are walking in the other direction toward Seventh Avenue, and Big Butch has John Ignatius in his arms, and John Ignatius is now squalling very loud, indeed. The chances are he is still thinking of the big whoom back there which tickles him so and is wishing to hear some more whooms. Anyway, he is beating his own best record for squalling, and as we go walking along Big Butch says to me like this:

"I dast not run," he says, "because if any coppers see me running they will start popping at me and maybe hit John Ignatius Junior, and besides running will joggle the milk up in him and make him sick. My old lady always warns me never to joggle John Ignatius Junior when he is full of milk."

"Well, Butch," I say, "there is no milk in me, and I do not care if I am joggled up, so if you do not mind, I will start doing a piece of running at the next corner."

But just then around the corner of Seventh Avenue toward which we are headed comes two or three coppers with a big fat sergeant with them, and one of the coppers, who is half out of breath as if he has been doing plenty of sprinting, is explaining to the sergeant that somebody blows a safe down the street and shoots a couple of coppers in the getaway.

And there is Big Butch, with John Ignatius Junior in his arms and twenty G's in his shirt front and a tough record behind him, walking right up to them.

I am feeling very sorry, indeed, for Big Butch, and very sorry for myself, too, and I am saying to myself that if I get out of this I will never associate with anyone but ministers of the gospel as long as I live. I can remember thinking that I am getting a better break than Butch, at that, because I will not have to go to Sing Sing for the rest of my life, like him, and I also remember wondering what they will give John Ignatius Junior, who is still tearing off these squalls, with Big Butch saying, "There, there, there, Daddy's itty woogleums."

Then I hear one of the coppers say to the fat sergeant:

"We better nail these guys. They may be in on this."

Well, I can see it is good-by to Butch and John Ignatius Junior and me, as the fat sergeant steps up to Big Butch, but instead of putting the arm on Butch, the fat sergeant only points at John Ignatius Junior and asks very sympathetic:

"Teeth?"

"No," Big Butch says. "Not teeth. Colic. I just get the doctor here out of bed to do something for him, and we are going to a drug store to get some medicine."

Well, naturally I am very much surprised at this statement, because of course I am not a doctor, and if John Ignatius Junior has colic it serves him right, but I am only hoping they do not ask for my degree, when the fat sergeant says:

"Too bad. I know what it is. I got three of them at home. But," he says, "it acts more like it is teeth than colic."

Then as Big Butch and John Ignatius Junior and me go on about our business I hear the fat sergeant say to the copper, very sarcastic:

"Yeah, of course a guy is out blowing safes with a baby in his arms! You will make a great detective, you will!"

I do not see Big Butch for several days after I learn that Harry the Horse and Little Isadore and Spanish John get back to Brooklyn all right, except they are a little nicked up here and there from the slugs the coppers toss at them, while the coppers they clip are not damaged so very much. Furthermore, the chances are I will not see Big Butch for several years, if it is left to me, but he comes looking for me one night, and he seems to be all pleasured up about something.

"Say," Big Butch says to me, "you know I never give a copper credit for knowing any too much about anything, but I wish to say that this fat sergeant we run into the other night is a very, very smart duck. He is right about it being teeth that is ailing John Ignatius Junior, for what happens yesterday but John cuts in his first tooth."

NED HILTON, LOOK

"Anything I can do to help? Want me to light the candles?"

JUD BROWNIN' HEARS RUBY PLAY

GEORGE W. BAGBY

(About 1870)

"Jud, they say you heard Rubinstein play when you were in New York?"

"I did, for a fact."

"Well, tell us all about it."

"What! Me? I might's well tell you about the creation of the world."

"Come now. No mock modesty. Go ahead."

Well, sir, he had the blamedest, biggest, catty-corneredest pianner you ever laid your eyes on—something like a distracted billiard table on three legs. The lid was heisted, and mighty well it was. If it hadn't, he'd a-tore the entire sides clean out, and scattered 'em to the four winds of heaven.

Played well? You bet he did. When he first sit down, he peared to care mighty little about playing, and wished he hadn't come. He tweedle-eedled a little on the treble, and twoodle-oodled some on the bass—just fooling and boxing the thing's jaws for being in his way.

I says to a man setting next to me, says I, "What sort of fool playing is that?" And he says, "Hesh!" But presently his hands commenced chasing one another up and down the keys, like a passel of rats scampering through a garret very swift. Parts of it was sweet, though, and reminded me of a sugar squirrel turning the wheel of a candy cage.

"Now," says I to my neighbor, "he's showing off. He ain't got no idea, no plan of nothing. If he'd play me a tune of some kind or other I'd—"

But my neighbor says, "Hesh!" very impatient.

I was just about to git up and go home, being tired of that foolishness, when I heard a little bird waking up away off in the woods, and calling sleepy-like, and I looked up and see Ruby was beginning to take some interest in his business, and I sit down again.

It was the peep of day. The light come faint from the east, the breezes blowed fresh, some more birds waked up in the orchard, then some more in the trees near the house, and all begun singing together.

People begun to stir at the house, and the gal opened the shutters. Just then the first beam of the sun fell on the garden and it teched the roses on the bushes, and the next thing it was broad day. The sun fairly blazed. The birds sung like they'd split their throats. All the leaves was moving and flashing diamonds of dew, and the whole world was bright and happy as a king. Seemed to me like there was a good breakfast in every house in the land, and not a sick child or woman anywhere. It was a fine morning.

And I says to my neighbor, "That's fine music, that is."

But he glared at me like he'd like to cut my throat.

By and by, the wind turned. It begun to thicken up, and a kind of gray mist come over things. I got low spirited directly. Then a silver rain begun to fall. I could smell the wet flowers in the meadow, but the sun didn't shine, nor the birds sing, and it was a foggy day, pretty but kind of melancholy.

Then the moonlight come, without any sunset, and shone on the graveyards, where some few ghosts lifted their hands and went over the wall. And between the black, sharp-top trees, there was fine houses with ladies in the lit-up windows, and men that loved 'em, but could never git a-nigh 'em, who played on gittars under the trees, and made me that miserable I could a-cried, because I wanted to love somebody, I don't know who, better than the men with the gittars did.

Then the moon went down, it got dark, the wind moaned and wept like a lost child for its dead mother, and I could a-got up then and there and preached a better sermon than any I ever listened to. There wasn't a thing left in the world to live for, not a blame thing, and yet I didn't want the music to stop one bit. It was happier to be miserable. I hung my head and pulled out my handkerchief, and blowed my nose to keep from crying. My eyes is weak, anyway, and I didn't want anybody to be a-gazing at me a-sniveling. It's nobody's business what I do with my nose. It's mine. But some several glared at me mad as Tucker.

All of a sudden, old Ruby changed his tune. He ripped out and he rared, he tipped and he tared, he pranced and he charged like the grand entry at a circus. Peared to me that all the gaslights in the house was turned on at once, things got so bright, and I hilt up my head, ready to look any man in the face, and not afraid of nothing. It was a circus, and a brass band, and a big ball, all going on at the same time. He lit into them keys like a thousand of brick. He give 'em no rest, day or night. He set every living joint in me a-going, and not being able to stand it no longer, I jumped spang onto my seat, and jest hollered—

"Go it, my Rube!"

Every blamed man, woman, and child in the house riz on me, and shouted, "Put him out! Put him out!"

"Put your great-grandmother's grizzly gray cat into the middle of next month!" I says. "Tech me if you dare. I paid my money, and you jest come a-nigh me!"

With that, some several policemen run up, and I had to simmer down. But I would a-fit any fool that laid hands on me, for I was bound to hear Ruby out or die.

He had changed his tune again. He hop-light ladies and tiptoed fine from end to end of the keyboard. He played soft and low and solemn. I heard the church bells over the hills. I saw the stars rise—then the music changed to water, full of feeling that couldn't be thought, and begun to drop—drip, drop—drip, drop, clear and sweet, falling into a lake of glory. It was too sweet. I tell you the audience cheered. Rubin, he kind of bowed, like he wanted to say, "Much obliged, but I'd rather you wouldn't interrupt me."

He stopped a moment or two to catch breath. Then he got mad. He run his fingers through his hair, he shoved up his sleeve, he opened his coat tails a little further, he drug up his stool, he leaned over, and, sir, he jest went for that old pianner. He slapped her face, he boxed her jaws, he pulled her nose, he pinched her ears, and he scratched her cheeks, until she fairly yelled. She bellered like a bull, she bleated like a calf, she howled like a hound, she squealed like a pig, she shrieked like a rat, and *then* he wouldn't let her up. He run a quarter stretch down the low grounds of the bass, till he got clean in the bowels of the earth, and you heard thunder galloping after thunder, through the hollows and caves of perdition. Then he fox-chased his right hand with his left till he got way out of the treble into the clouds, where the notes was finer than the points of cambric needles, and you couldn't hear nothing but the shadders of 'em.

And then he wouldn't let the old pianner go. He forward two'd, he crossed over first gentleman, he sashayed right and left, back to your places, he all hands'd round, ladies to the right, promenade all, here and there, back and forth, up and down, perpetual motion, double-twisted and turned and tacked and tangled into forty-eleven thousand double bow knots.

By jinks, it was a mixtery! He fetched up his right wing, he fetched up his left wing, he fetched up his center, he fetched up his reserves. He fired by file, by platoons, companies, regiments, brigades. He opened his cannon—round shot, shells, shrapnels, grape, canister, mines, and magazines—every living battery and bomb a-going at the same time. The house trembled, the lights danced, the walls shuck, the sky split, the ground rocked—heavens and earth, creation, sweet potatoes, Moses, ninepences, glory, ten penny nails, Sampson in a 'simmon tree—Bang!!! lang! perlang! p-r-r-r!! Bang!!!

With that bang! he lifted himself bodily into the air, and he come down with his knees, fingers, toes, elbows, and his nose, striking every single solitary key on the pianner at the same time.

The thing busted and went off into fifty-seven thousand five hundred and forty-two hemi-demi-semi quivers, and I knowed no more that evening.

A NEWSPAPER

ANONYMOUS

(About 1875–1900)

Organs that gentlemen play, my boy,
To answer the taste of the day, my boy;
    Whatever it be,
    They hit on the key,
And pipe in full concert away, my boy.

News from all countries and climes, my boy,
Advertisements, essays, and rhymes, my boy,
    Mixed up with all sorts
    Of flying reports,
And published at regular times, my boy.

Articles able and wise, my boy,
At least in the editor's eyes, my boy,
    A logic so grand
    That few understand
To what in the world it applies, my boy.

Statistics, reflections, reviews, my boy,
Little scraps to instruct and amuse, my boy,

And lengthy debate
Upon matters of State
For wise-headed folk to peruse, my boy.

The funds as they were and are, my boy,
The quibbles and quirks of the bars, my boy;
And every week
A clever critique
On some rising theatrical star, my boy.

The age of Jupiter's moons, my boy,
The stealing of somebody's spoons, my boy,
The state of the crops,
The style of the fops,
And the wit of the public buffoons, my boy.

List of all physical ills, my boy,
Banished by somebody's pills, my boy,
Till you ask with surprise
Why anyone dies,
Or what's the disorder that kills, my boy.

Who has got married, to whom, my boy,
Who were cut off in their bloom, my boy,
Who has had birth
On this sorrow-stained earth,
And who totters fast to their tomb, my boy.

The price of cattle and grain, my boy,
Directions to dig and to drain, my boy,
But 'twould take me too long
To tell you in song
A quarter of all they contain, my boy.

A NIGHT TO REMEMBER, OR
I'LL TRY TOMORROW

CASKIE STINNETT

The comment and news stories stirred up by Holiday Magazine's fire engine a short while ago set us to brooding about a bygone era in volunteer fire fighting, an era that we are concerned may shortly be lost to this and succeeding generations unless steps are taken by some of us elders to capture it in ballad or drama or narrative. To dissipate our own *angst* on this score, we have whipped up the following drama which we are offering to schools and amateur groups on a royalty-free basis. Motion-picture rights can be purchased, but it's only fair to warn the film companies that the price is understandably high.

> SCENE: *the headquarters of a volunteer fire company. The men appear to have just returned from a fire; they still have on their slickers and fire hats. They are sitting around uneasily, obviously getting a dressing-down from the Chief who stands facing them in front of the room. At curtain, the Chief is gazing about the room in silent contempt.*

CHIEF. Well, all I can say is another fire like that and we may as well disband. I don't think the fire was even given a chance.

WILSON. (*In a conciliatory tone*) Golly, Chief, sometimes a fire will just die out of its own accord, in spite——

CHIEF. (*Brusquely*) This one didn't. Some smart fireman put it out. And we hadn't even got to the dining room yet.

SIMPSON. (*Dreamily*) Did you see that china closet in the dining room? Packed with dishes?

CHIEF. Sure I saw it. And if I went back there again I'd still see it. Not a dish was broken.

(*The men cringe at this, and flush guiltily*)

WILSON. Curly did a good job on the piano in the living room. You got to give him credit for that——

CHIEF. Not according to my standards he didn't. (*Points finger at Curly*) Did you wet the felt? Did you wet the music rack so the sheets would stick together? Did you jam the pedals?

CURLY. (*Defensively*) Gee, Chief, I only got two hands.

CHIEF. Who was supposed to be working with you on the piano? One man is supposed to hold up the top while the other man hoses the felt.

SIMPSON. I was assigned to the piano, Chief, but when I saw the fire wasn't going to last long I thought I better start wetting down the books. He had a lot of books and—if I do say so myself—I got a little water on every one of them.

CHIEF. (*Rubbing hands*) Well, I didn't know that.

POMEROY. (*Eagerly*) And don't overlook my work on the radio. I was hacking at the cabinet right up until——

CHIEF. That's something I want to talk to you about, Pomeroy. You're new in the company and I should have told you this before. *Never* go to work on the outside of a radio—always get inside and crush the works first. Then—if you have time—you can attend to the cabinet. Got that?

POMEROY. Check, Chief.

CHIEF. Well, that's about all, fellows. Maybe we will learn from our mistakes. And bad as we were tonight, we didn't pull anything as raw as Company No. 3 did over in Glendale last week.

WILSON. What was that, Chief?

CHIEF. You won't believe it but I got it from good authority that they didn't even force the door. They just opened it and walked in.

(*Derisive laughter and murmurs of disbelief as The Curtain Falls*)

HOW TO ATTRACT THE ATTENTION
OF A SCHRAFFT'S HOSTESS

CLIFTON FADIMAN

Before setting down one or two methods which the writer has found practical, it may be helpful to explain how Schrafft's hostesses are selected. There are four basic tests. The applicant must secure a passing grade in Extension, Chin Inclination, Eye-Glazing, and Automatic Ear-Muffling.

Extension. The applicant must be sufficiently tall so that it will not be feasible for her to notice, without bending, the signal of any seated guest, male or female, of ordinary size.

Chin Inclination. Let us assume that the common or non-hostess chin is normally held out from the vertical line of the neck roughly at a right angle. Looking up from Thirty-fourth Street to the Empire State tower, one enlarges this angle considerably, approaching as a limit 180°, or a straight angle. The would-be hostess must either possess naturally or be able at will to assume a Chin Inclination striking a mean between these two angles—or, in other words, 135°, measured against the neckline. It is hardly necessary to point out the reason for this. I, for example, am five feet eight and three-quarters inches tall —about the stature of an average American male. Let us imagine that, wishing to attract the attention of a passing hostess, I suddenly rise from my seat directly in her path and look squarely into what I assume (as she is apt to be about my own height) will turn out to be her eyes. A 90° Chin Inclination would be fatal. She is sure to see me. But consider the 135° Chin Inclination. If I am not six feet one or over, I cannot meet the hostess's eye unless I have made an appointment in advance. Hence, she does not see me, performs that dreamy and graceful sidestep characteristic of her profession, and is off.

However, fully to protect the hostess against being successfully accosted or signaled by a guest, two other safe-guards are called into play. The first is the *Eye Glaze*. This physiological talent is used whenever, through ill chance, the glances of the hostess and the patron actually meet. Exactly at the split second of intersection, a sort of semi-opaque film is drawn over the eyes of the hostess and she undulates by.

It is at this point that the average or amateur guest will tend to utter some such salutation as "Miss," in accents ranging from an intimidated mutter to a strong clarion cry. Should the diner thus call out, the hostess reacts with another specialized physiological characteristic—the *Automatic Ear-Muffle*, which requires no further description.

The applicant who passes these four tests—Extension, Chin Inclination, Eye-Glazing, and Automatic Ear-Muffling—becomes a Schrafft's hostess and is ready to non-observe patrons professionally.

What is to be done? First, it is important not to be discouraged. The number of Schrafft's patrons who have successfully attracted the attention of a hostess is, despite the strength of the opposing forces, relatively large and, in my considered opinion, increasing. Indeed, I know of a case in which a patron suddenly held up his index finger, caught a hostess completely off guard before she had time to adjust Chin Inclination or Eye Glaze, and actually got her attention without more ado. This is known as a hostess-in-one.

I submit herewith a few sample suggestions. Each has been personally tested; none is infallible; all have proved successful at least once.

First, the elements. Tripping up a passing hostess is not good form. It has been done. I have done it myself, though only when wearing tennis shoes. But I do not advise it as a general mode of attack, for the entire maneuver is apt to be misunderstood by your fellow-diners, as well as by the management. A light kick on the shins, apparently accidental, as your hostess goes by, is excusable and often effective, though the average hostess shin tends to the osseous and must be approached with caution. Never, of course, pinch a hostess.

The sudden assumption of a grotesque mask as the hostess floats by, the wearing of luminous paint, and the use of various noise-producing machines, such as rattles, whistles, small cap pistols, and bull-roarers —all these have their points, but are tainted with a fatal defect. They are *outré*, hence easily remembered. Your competent hostess may stop once at the sight of a cut-out pumpkin quickly adjusted over the patron's face, but she will never do so again. Once conditioned to such obvious signals, she is as remote and unseizable as ever.

Nor is there much use in requesting your waitress to ask your hostess to stop by for a moment. A well-seasoned hostess pays no more attention to a waitress than to a patron. But a hostess—and this is her Achilles' heel—will gladly notice *another* hostess. In fact, hostesses are abnormally gregarious. At almost any time, but particularly during the height of the luncheon and dinner hours, a small, compact knot of hostesses may be observed in some inaccessible corner of the restaurant, busily devising plans for rendering the service in Schrafft's more homey. The existence of such hostess coveys provides the alert diner with, if I may be jocular, an attractive weapon. I call it the Divided Family Shift. If you are dining with your wife, place her at a table at one end of the dining room; yourself you place at the opposite end of the room, along the diagonal. This makes it impossible, of course, for you to dine with your wife and lays your behavior open to a certain amount of misinterpretation in case the two of you are noted by a friend; but omelets cannot be made without breaking eggs. Now wait until all the hostesses are congregated in or near your wife's corner. She is watching you. You pass her some simple, previously agreed upon signal. At once she tries to catch the attention of the hostesses conferring near her table. They, of course, obey an automatic tropism. They move rapidly in a body in such a manner as to get as far away as possible from your wife's signal. This, naturally, takes them in *your* direction. As they pass by, you get into action. You still have their individual resistances to overcome, but your chance of actually attracting their attention is multiplied by the number of hostesses. I have tried the Divided Family Shift many times, with an average to date of .250. I consider this quite decent.

The simplest of my methods, requiring no apparatus in the way of a wife, is the Contrary Act. Be oblivious of the entire world of Shattuck. Pay no attention to the waitress when she brings you any-

"Of *course* it's a police dog."

---

thing. Bury your nose in your Southern Bisque. With calculated abstraction allow your free hand to dabble gently in the butter. Within three minutes you will have a hostess at your side and a "Something you wanted?" dropped in your ear. And you have her—for the joke is that you *do* want something. During those years when I was first sowing my wild tables d'hôte, I spent many enjoyable moments watching the startled expression on a hostess's face as she fell like a perfect *fool* for the Contrary Act.

During this early period, too, I often resorted to the use of a small sign reading "Miss!" which I attached to a stick and raised above hostess-eye-level at a favorable moment. Napkin-flapping, hitting the tumbler with a knife, finger-snapping, or even dropping your chicken patty on the floor are all methods of a similar type. They are elementary but frequently successful in the case of an inexperienced and incompetent hostess, or one who has been poorly trained and really should have been a waitress.

My favorite tactic, however, is the Small Boy Decoy. To work this successfully, you are obliged to own a Small Boy, as I do (though he is rapidly growing too large for effective manipulation), and he must be a constant accessory whenever you eat at Schrafft's. The Small Boy Decoy method is based on my observation that a Schrafft's hostess, while paying no attention to the most frantic adult, will, upon noticing that a Small Boy is one of the party (a Small Girl will do in a pinch, but a Boy is the thing), at once bend over, smile, coo, be gracious, and offer him a plate of pink mints. At this point you have your hostess at an obvious disadvantage; she is bent over—Chin Angle gone, Eye Glaze forgotten, Muffle cut out. You address your request to her, and the thing is done. The Small Boy, once his work is over, may be stuffed under the table, together with the mints, and forgotten until you wish to attract the attention of the hostess again, at which point he is reproduced. A fairly tough Small Boy will last you a dozen meals before wearing out.

MOTHER MARRIED AN OBOE PLAYER

PAUL de VERGIE

The next time you see a symphony orchestra at work, look twice at the three men, second row center, who are getting plaintive notes from what look like undernourished clarinets. The instruments are oboes, and you are looking on haunted, hagridden, bedeviled men. The public likes to believe that all oboe players are crazy; the whole violin section hates them bitterly; their wives and children rejoice when they are not home; and a snake charmer with a sulky cobra on his hands doesn't have as much trouble as an oboe gives an oboist. Furthermore, these men are sore at themselves for taking up the oboe—the really good ones curse in their sleep when dreaming of the easy lives of other instrumentalists. But they can't get angry, for if they do, they'll sharp. Friend, have you got troubles? Then you'd enjoy knowing an oboist. Or an oboist's family.

I know, because I am the son of one of the best oboists in the country. Last winter while out in the Rockies I traveled about six miles on skis every Tuesday night to a mountain inn to hear the weekly broadcast of the Boston Symphony Orchestra, in which my father plays. My definitely battered appearance on the scene after bucking the mountain trails in the dark usually aroused some curiosity. When questioned, I would say I had come to hear my father play. "What does he play?" they asked with real interest. "Oboe," I said. "Oh," they said politely. As always, I drew inquiring and vaguely suspicious looks.

Tell people your father practices medicine, and they wonder where; say he practices law, and they wonder what kind; say he plays the oboe, and they just wonder. I'd like to testify, as an oboist's son, that oboists are Not necessarily crazy, but have every right to be. Furthermore, if it is true an oboist in Canada used to kick his wife out of bed and give her place to the oboe in cold weather, it is because oboes are even harder to keep in tune than the most temperamental of wives. The guy had a case, I mean. Lots of men have wives. Only a luckless few have oboes.

And a man with an oboe shouldn't get married anyway; it's a form of bigamy. If he is saddled with an oboe he's got all the wife and child any man needs; and he doesn't need a mother-in-law either. As a great conductor says, when trying to express the totally unsuitable, "It don't go, my friend; it don't go." Take morning in our house. Father had a stormy evening battling that oboe, and now he wants to make amends by being extremely pleasant. Only at breakfast does he see his family assembled, and he regards us lovingly. He sips his coffee. We are a picture of perfect peace. Suddenly father lets out a roar of anguish, as if he had just found carbolic acid in the bottom of his cup. He leaps to his feet. "Who knocked my best reed to the floor?" he bleats. Now we are getting back to normal.

You see, the kitchen table was covered, when mother began preparing breakfast, with small screw drivers, enough wicked little knives to perform all the surgery in the Mayo Clinic, and reeds. To an oboe player, his soul is not so important as his reed, nor does it give him so much trouble. He can never get it right. It starts out as a sturdy stalk of cane growing in the south of France and ends up as two fragile wisps, paper thin and about an inch long, bound tightly to a tiny copper tube ending in a cork tip. The secret of a successful reed lies in shaving it. This requires practice, a delicate sureness with the knife, and the patience of a saint. It also involves howls of exasperation, cursing, gnashing of teeth and agony of soul. Father is one of the few oboists with any hair left, but he started out with a luxuriant crop, and it is dwindling fast.

Just getting ready to play is a tough job in itself—a job any craftsman would watch with admiration. As for playing the darned thing, that is a remarkable physical feat approaching self-torture. Roughly,

"What do you mean, when is the slack season?"

---

what you do is this: you hold your breath for a full half minute at a time, letting it escape very, very gently through this fragile mouthpiece, which looks like the big brother of a trout fly; meanwhile you run your fingers ragged performing lovely arpeggios, all staccato, probably, and written in six flats.

An oboe player's home is full of little glasses of water in which reeds are soaking. You see, the poor beset man is trying to get one exactly soft enough for what he is sure they are going to play today. He is an expert at this—he has to be—and sure enough, he gets one into exactly the state that produces the round, soft, sweet tone he wants.

So what happens? They change the program on him, opening with music that requires a strong reed with a loud, brilliant tone, and he's cooked. He's always cooked. The reed that sounded so fine at home is sickly and weak in the concert hall or splits just when he needs it, or if none of this happens, then a key sticks and ruins a solo.

When the French National Orchestra was here recently, the same kind of accident befell the first oboe, but he was a fighter. Without losing a sixty-fourth note he snatched the instrument out of the hands of the astonished second oboe and played the solo perfectly. Without sharping, too, which was luck indeed, in his excited frame of mind. We try not to get father nervous for that very reason, and we have to try to keep him happy—or as happy as an oboe player ever can be—because a sad oboist plays flat. And if he's flat, everybody's flat. The orchestra, as you may know, tunes to the oboe. He is a frustrated perfectionist, and when he sounds his A, nothing under heaven will make him change it. The string players all hate his guts. They always want to sneak up a little sharper, for brilliance, and he never lets them. They never miss a chance at revenge. The great Jascha Heifetz paused during rehearsal to ask the oboe to sound another A. The A could hardly be heard. In a loud whisper, Heifetz asked the concertmaster, "Is your first oboe a Scot?"

A thousand devils of fear beset the oboist. Heat will crack his oboe from top to bottom; so will cold. Let it get damp and it may split; let it get a sudden jar and it may crack like a melon. On top of all this, he has to practice a great deal—the oboe is probably the most difficult of instruments and plays difficult music. In the Tomb of Couperin, by Maurice Ravel, the oboe solo is so tough that musicians in France have changed the name to the Tomb of the Oboist.

Furthermore, he knows every minute of his practicing that he has the unified hatred of the neighbors. It isn't mere suspicion. Shortly after an oboe player moves anyplace he can expect to find the first letter signed, "Indignant Neighbor." If it is an apartment, he has to smuggle the oboe in as you would smuggle a pet tiger. What really burns him is the letters passed along by his landlord which refer to "that damned piccolo player." He has to practice his trade as if it were a mild vice of some kind.

Father has worked out a system you have to admit is fairness itself. He practices one half hour in one part of the house and then moves to another room, until he has made a complete circuit. On the hottest day he keeps the windows tightly closed, and he has figured out scientifically just how much each neighbor can take. If somebody on the west is a little more sensitive than the others, then he, or she, doesn't get a full half hour. Our whole family keeps on the move, keeping one room ahead of father. Along the way he leaves a trail of reeds, screw drivers, corks and pieces of cane which no one dares to touch, much less move. One of the best cleaning women we lost swept an array of reeds into a desk drawer. Only by great self-control did father keep from strangling her. In turn, she said *he* was touched, and pointed out that it is hard to clean a house where every flat-topped piece of furniture is likely to have a glass of water with cane soaking in it. Father soaks many species of cane overnight, and some for a couple of days, before he makes reeds out of them. And there is no way in the world of telling what reed may be the good, the trouble-saving, the blessed one.

The cleaning woman had been suspicious of our family from the start; she may have thought we were involved in some form of voodoo. That's because the house is full of turkey feathers. My father gets gloomy every Thanksgiving, full of fear that turkeys will be eaten into extinction. He has to have turkey feathers; they are as important to an oboist as wax to a skier. He uses them to clean the oboe and to get its innards dry. No other feather will do it. But he's in good shape; he has a pupil whose mother runs a turkey farm. This pupil never arrives for a lesson without bringing another bundle. As a result, we have feathers enough to outfit a good-sized Indian tribe. It is a ten-year supply, my father believes happily. There are feathers in most of the bureau drawers; I find feathers mixed with my shirts and socks; mother finds feathers in the linen closet. Take a book from the bookcase and out spill more turkey feathers, and there are beautiful sprays of feathers in the flower vases. In moments of preoccupation mother has sometimes watered them.

Every time I hear my father take one of his oboes—every symphony oboist has several—and get sweet music out of it, instead of breaking it to pieces on the piano, my respect for his character increases. What a life! An oboist's career is in two neat movements; he takes up the oboe, he spends the rest of his life regretting it. A fiddle player who had to raise his own cats to get a reliable E string wouldn't have half the trouble an oboe player has on his quietest Monday.

Even in summer, when he doesn't have to worry about cold weather, an oboist watches the thermometer as anxiously as if he had his life savings tied up in a bed of orchids. Let an oboe get chilled, and if it doesn't crack it goes sour, and when warm again it sheds keys. Wherever we find an oboe in our house, there it stays. Nobody touches it; I just tiptoe around and make sure no smallest breeze is blowing on this mean-tempered chronic invalid. The other musicians think that story of the oboist who made his wife sleep on the floor in zero weather is funny. In our family we know how he felt. It was a choice between having trouble with his wife or trouble with his oboe, and he chose the lesser of two evils.

Date of Birth:

FAREWELL, MY LOVELY!

LEE STROUT WHITE

I see by the new Sears Roebuck catalogue that it is still possible to buy an axle for a 1909 Model T Ford, but I am not deceived. The great days have faded, the end is in sight. Only one page in the current catalogue is devoted to parts and accessories for the Model T; yet everyone remembers springtimes when the Ford gadget section was larger than men's clothing, almost as large as household furnishings. The last Model T was built in 1927, and the car is fading from what scholars call the American scene—which is an understatement, because to a few million people who grew up with it, the old Ford practically *was* the American scene.

It was the miracle God had wrought. And it was patently the sort of thing that could only happen once. Mechanically uncanny, it was like nothing that had ever come to the world before. Flourishing industries rose and fell with it. As a vehicle, it was hard-working, commonplace, heroic; and it often seemed to transmit those qualities to the persons who rode in it. My own generation identifies it with Youth, with its gaudy, irretrievable excitements; before it fades into the mist, I would like to pay it the tribute of the sigh that is not a sob, and set down random entries in a shape somewhat less cumbersome than a Sears Roebuck catalogue.

The Model T was distinguished from all other makes of cars by the fact that its transmission was of a type known as planetary—which was half metaphysics, half sheer friction. Engineers accepted the word "planetary" in its epicyclic sense, but I was always conscious that it also meant "wandering," "erratic." Because of the peculiar nature of this planetary element, there was always, in Model T, a certain dull rapport between engine and wheels, and even when the car was in a state known as neutral, it trembled with a deep imperative and tended to inch forward. There was never a moment when the bands were not faintly egging the machine on. In this respect it was like a horse, rolling the bit on its tongue, and country people brought to it the same technique they used with draft animals.

Its most remarkable quality was its rate of acceleration. In its palmy days the Model T could take off faster than anything on the road. The reason was simple. To get under way, you simply hooked the third finger of the right hand around a lever on the steering column, pulled down hard, and shoved your left foot forcibly against the low-speed pedal. These were simple, positive motions; the car responded by lunging forward with a roar. After a few seconds of this turmoil, you took your toe off the pedal, eased up a mite on the throttle, and the car, possessed of only two forward speeds, catapulted directly into high with a series of ugly jerks and was off on its glorious errand. The abruptness of this departure was never equalled in other cars of the period. The human leg was (and still is) incapable of letting in a clutch with anything like the forthright abandon that used to send Model T on its way. Letting in a clutch is a negative, hesitant motion, depending on delicate nervous control; pushing down the Ford pedal was a simple, country motion—an expansive act, which came as natural as kicking an old door to make it budge.

The driver of the old Model T was a man enthroned. The car, with top up, stood seven feet high. The driver sat on top of the gas tank, brooding it with his own body. When he wanted gasoline, he alighted, along with everything else in the front seat; the seat was pulled off, the metal cap unscrewed, and a wooden stick thrust down to sound the liquid in the well. There were always a couple of these sounding sticks kicking around in the ratty sub-cushion regions of a flivver. Refueling was more of a social function then, because the driver had to unbend, whether he wanted to or not. Directly in front of the driver was the windshield—high, uncompromisingly erect. Nobody talked about air resistance, and the four cylinders pushed the car through the atmosphere with a simple disregard of physical law.

There was this about a Model T: the purchaser never regarded his purchase as a complete, finished product. When you bought a Ford, you figured you had a start—a vibrant, spirited framework to which could be screwed an almost limitless assortment of decorative and func-

THE FAMILY BOOK OF HUMOR

tional hardware. Driving away from the agency, hugging the new wheel between your knees, you were already full of creative worry. A Ford was born naked as a baby, and a flourishing industry grew up out of correcting its rare deficiencies and combatting its fascinating diseases. Those were the great days of lily-painting. I have been looking at some old Sears Roebuck catalogues, and they bring everything back so clear.

First you bought a Ruby Safety Reflector for the rear, so that your posterior would glow in another car's brilliance. Then you invested thirty-nine cents in some radiator Moto Wings, a popular ornament which gave the Pegasus touch to the machine and did something godlike to the owner. For nine cents you bought a fan-belt guide to keep the belt from slipping off the pulley.

You bought a radiator compound to stop leaks. This was as much a part of everybody's equipment as aspirin tablets are of a medicine cabinet. You bought special oil to prevent chattering, a clamp-on dash light, a patching outfit, a tool box which you bolted to the running board, a sun visor, a steering-column brace to keep the column rigid, and a set of emergency containers for gas, oil, and water—three thin, disc-like cans which reposed in a case on the running board during long, important journeys—red for gas, gray for water, green for oil. It was only a beginning. After the car was about a year old, steps were taken to check the alarming disintegration. (Model T was full of tumors, but they were benign.) A set of anti-rattlers (98¢) was a popular panacea. You hooked them on to the gas and spark rods, to the brake pull rod, and to the steering-rod connections. Hood silencers, of black rubber, were applied to the fluttering hood. Shock-absorbers and snubbers gave "complete relaxation." Some people bought rubber pedal pads, to fit over the standard metal pedals. (I didn't like these, I remember.) Persons of a suspicious or pugnacious turn of mind bought a rear-view mirror; but most Model T owners weren't worried by what was coming from behind because they would soon enough see it out in front. They rode in a state of cheerful catalepsy. Quite a large mutinous clique among Ford owners went over to a foot accelerator (you could buy one and screw it to the floor board), but there was a certain madness in these people, because the Model T, just as she stood, had a choice of three foot pedals to push, and there were plenty of moments when both feet were occupied in the routine performance of duty and when the only way to speed up the engine was with the hand throttle.

Gadget bred gadget. Owners not only bought ready-made gadgets, they invented gadgets to meet special needs. I myself drove my car directly from the agency to the blacksmith's, and had the smith affix two enormous iron brackets to the port running board to support an army trunk.

People who owned closed models builded along different lines: they bought ball grip handles for opening doors, window anti-rattlers, and deluxe flower vases of the cut-glass anti-splash type. People with delicate sensibilities garnished their car with a device called the Donna Lee Automobile Disseminator—a porous vase guaranteed, according to Sears, to fill the car with a "faint clean odor of lavender." The gap between open cars and closed cars was not as great then as it is now: for $11.95, Sears Roebuck converted your touring car into a sedan and you went forth renewed. One agreeable quality of the old Fords was that they had no bumpers, and their fenders softened and wilted with the years and permitted the driver to squeeze in and out of tight places.

Tires were 30 x 3½, cost about twelve dollars, and punctured readily. Everybody carried a Jiffy patching set, with a nutmeg grater to roughen the tube before the goo was spread on. Everybody was capable of putting on a patch, expected to have to, and did have to.

During my association with Model T's, self-starters were not a prevalent accessory. They were expensive and under suspicion. Your car came equipped with a serviceable crank, and the first thing you learned was how to Get Results. It was a special trick, and until you learned it (usually from another Ford owner, but sometimes by a period of appalling experimentation) you might as well have been winding up an awning. The trick was to leave the ignition switch off, proceed to the animal's head, pull the choke (which was a little wire protruding through the radiator), and give the crank two or three nonchalant upward lifts. Then, whistling as though thinking about something else, you would saunter back to the driver's cabin, turn the ignition on, return to the crank, and this time, catching it on the down stroke, give it a quick spin with plenty of That. If this procedure was followed, the engine almost always responded—first with a few scattered explosions, then with a tumultuous gunfire, which you checked by racing around to the driver's seat and retarding the throttle. Often, if the emergency brake hadn't been pulled all the way back, the car advanced on you the instant the first explosion occurred and you would hold it back by leaning your weight against it. I can still feel my old Ford nuzzling me at the curb, as though looking for an apple in my pocket.

In zero weather, ordinary cranking became an impossibility, except for giants. The oil thickened, and it became necessary to jack up the rear wheels, which, for some planetary reason, eased the throw.

The lore and legend that governed the Ford were boundless. Owners had their own theories about everything; they discussed mutual problems in that wise, infinitely resourceful way old women discuss rheumatism. Exact knowledge was pretty scarce, and often proved less effective than superstition. Dropping a camphor ball into the gas tank was a popular expedient; it seemed to have a tonic effect on both man and machine. There wasn't much to base exact knowledge on. The Ford driver flew blind. He didn't know the temperature of his engine, the speed of his car, the amount of his fuel, or the pressure of his oil (the old Ford lubricated itself by what was amiably described as the "splash system"). A speedometer cost money and was an extra, like a windshield-wiper. The dashboard of the early models was bare save for an ignition key; later models, grown effete, boasted an ammeter which pulsated alarmingly with the throbbing of the car. Under the dash was a box of coils, with vibrators which you adjusted, or thought you adjusted. Whatever the driver learned of his motor, he learned not through instruments but through sudden developments. I remember that the timer was one of the vital organs about which there was ample doctrine. When everything else had been checked, you "had a look" at the timer. It was an extravagantly odd little device, simple in construction, mysterious in function. It contained a roller, held by a spring, and there were four contact points on the inside of the case against which, many people believed, the roller rolled. I have had a timer apart on a sick Ford many times, but I never really knew what I was up to—I was just showing off before God. There were almost as many schools of thought as there were timers. Some people, when things went wrong, just clenched their teeth and gave the timer a smart crack with a wrench. Other people opened it up and blew on it. There was a school that held that the timer needed large amounts of oil; they fixed it by frequent baptism. And there was a school that was positive it was meant to run dry as a bone; these people were continually taking it off and wiping it. I remember once spitting into a timer not in anger, but in a spirit of research. You see, the Model T driver moved in the realm of metaphysics. He believed his car could be hexed.

One reason the Ford anatomy was never reduced to an exact science was that, having "fixed" it, the owner couldn't honestly claim that the treatment had brought about the cure. There were too many authenticated cases of Fords fixing themselves—restored naturally to health after a short rest. Farmers soon discovered this, and it fitted nicely with their draft-horse philosophy: "Let 'er cool off and she'll snap into it again."

A Ford owner had Number One Bearing constantly in mind. This bearing, being at the front end of the motor, was the one that always burned out, because the oil didn't reach it when the car was climbing hills. (That's what I was always told, anyway.) The oil used to recede and leave Number One dry as a clam flat; you had to watch that bearing like a hawk. It was like a weak heart—you could hear it start knocking, and that was when you stopped and let her cool off. Try as you would to keep the oil supply right, in the end Number One always went out. "Number One Bearing burned out on me and I had to have her replaced," you would say, wisely; and your companions always had a lot to tell about how to protect and pamper Number One to keep her alive.

Sprinkled not too liberally among the millions of amateur witch doctors who drove Fords and applied their own abominable cures were the heaven-sent mechanics who could really make the car talk. These professionals turned up in undreamed-of spots. One time, on the banks of the Columbia River in Washington, I heard the rear end go out of my Model T when I was trying to whip it up a steep incline onto the deck of a ferry. Something snapped; the car slid backward into the mud. It seemed to me like the end of the trail. But the captain of the ferry, observing the withered remnant, spoke up.

"What's got her?" he asked.

"I guess it's the rear end," I replied, listlessly. The captain leaned over the rail and stared. Then I saw that there was a hunger in his eyes that set him off from other men.

"Tell you what," he said, carelessly, trying to cover up his eagerness, "let's pull the thing up onto the boat, and I'll help you fix her while we're going back and forth on the river."

We did just this. All that day I plied between the towns of Pasco and Kennewick, while the skipper (who had once worked in a Ford garage) directed the amazing work of resetting the bones of my car.

Springtime in the heyday of the Model T was a delirious season Owning a car was still a major excitement, roads were still wonderful and bad. The Fords were obviously conceived in madness: any car which was capable of going from forward into reverse without any perceptible mechanical hiatus was bound to be a mighty challenging thing to the human imagination. Boys used to veer them off the highway into a level pasture and run wild with them, as though they were cutting up with a girl.

Most everybody used the reverse pedal quite as much as the regular foot brake—it distributed the wear over the bands and wore them all down evenly. That was the big trick, to wear all the bands down evenly, so that the final chattering would be total and the whole unit scream for renewal.

The days were golden, the nights were dim and strange. I still recall with trembling those loud, nocturnal crises when you drew up to a signpost and raced the engine so the lights would be bright enough to read destinations by. I have never been really planetary since. I suppose it's time to say goodbye. Farewell, my lovely!

WHAT LACK WE YET?

ROBERT J. BURDETTE (1844–1914)

When Washington was president
   He was a mortal icicle;
He never on a railroad went,
   And never rode a bicycle.

He read by no electric lamp,
   Ne'er heard about the Yellowstone;
He never licked a postage stamp,
   And never saw a telephone.

His trousers ended at his knees;
   By wire he could not snatch dispatch;
He filled his lamp with whale-oil grease,
   And never had a match to scratch.

But in these days it's come to pass,
   All work is with such dashing done,
We've all these things, but then, alas—
   We seem to have no Washington!

YOUR TALK TELLS YOUR AGE

PERRY LAUKHOFF

Does your tongue sometimes have an urge to come out with a word like "depot"? Better watch it. *Depot* is a nice word and I'm fond of it myself but nowadays it's practically a dead giveaway that you're no longer a college freshman. Unless you're speaking of a bus terminal (or perhaps live in the South), *station* is what the new generation calls it. As a matter of fact, the language of travel has been extensively revised along with its means.

There are plenty of *buses* around but the *jitney-bus* is not among them. How could it be, when the *nickel* has given up its moniker of *jitney* along with its purchasing power?

Nowadays you go off for a ride on the *thruway* or the *expressway*, which are speedily replacing the mere *highways* which in their turn had succeeded the old-fashioned *pikes*. (But paradoxically, the *turn-pike* of great-grandfather's day is back.) As for the *klaxons* drivers used to sound at every curve, there's hardly any occasion to honk a *horn* any more.

Yes, it's quite plain that fashions change in words as well as clothes. *Shirtwaists* went out with the advent of the *blouse*, peasant or other-wise. In my boyhood I used to get my father his *carpet slippers* but now, of course, we wear *bedroom slippers* or *house slippers* or *loafers*.

The names for rainwear have become more drab by the generation, progressing from *oil-skin* (complete with *sou'wester*), to *slicker* to just plain *raincoat*. Mother's *lavaliere* is almost as forgotten as her shirt-waist but on occasion it is still put around the neck as a *pendant*. *Gaiters* gave way to *spats* and spats simply gave way, about the time the *picture show* became a *movie*.

At this point my mind is overcome with memories and begins to roam badly. In my boyhood we never *yawned* politely, we just plain *gaped*. People didn't die of *TB* or *tuberculosis*; they had *consumption*. Could anything sound more ominous?

That reminds me of a wonderful word which has gone straight into limbo: *gumption*. If a man had gumption he had everything you now have if you've got *backbone*, *guts* and *drive*.

Back in 1905 or so, I was taken out to a level field near Dayton to see the Wright brothers wobble around in their *flying machine*. This, of course, became *plane*, and now is getting shortened even further to *jet*.

In my boyhood, too, our neighborhood had various periodic visitors who enlivened the day. One was the *ragman*, with his melodious cry and rickety wagon. Another familiar figure was dearly beloved on a hot summer evening, dispensing his ice cream. He was known as the *hokey-pokey man*. You can still get rid of old clothes and buy ice cream, but to me it's not the same.

All this nonsense began when my wife asked me this morning to go to the *market* (yesterday it was a *grocery* and tomorrow it will be a *supermarket*). "How are the *muskmelons* today?" I asked the clerk. "Well," he replied, "we just don't happen to have had any since about 1925, but we have some good *cantaloupes* or *honeydews* or *Persian melons!*"

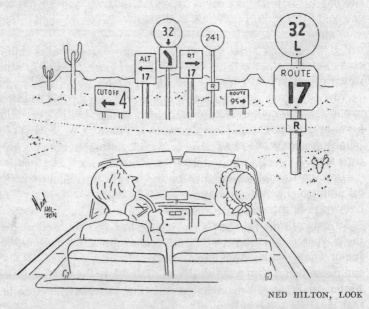

NED HILTON, LOOK

"Fifty years ago people would just have let the horse decide."

DOCTOR DOLL

INEZ ROBB

(From her World Telegram and Sun column, 1954)

Old-timers who weep into their beer because there is no longer saw-dust on the floor will have to weep without me. I want sawdust, all right, but I want my quota in a doll or dolls.

Ever since World War II, I have viewed with considerable alarm the Frankensteins who have obviously seized control of the doll fac-tories of America. They have been turning out little monsters that can cry real tears, wet their didies, drink, eat, burp, dance, walk, sing, talk back, and throw their cereal on the floor. And in my book there is enough back-talk today without having to take lip from a doll.

Nor is that all: their hair has been washed, set in pin curls or given a permanent, just like Mommy—whose work is never done, now that she has to fix a formula for and feed a doll on schedule. It ain't enough that she has to force spinach down Junior!

With this list of terrible achievements, I felt that doll manufacturers had gone about as far as they could go. But the above isn't a patch on two new models for which the United States Government has just issued patents.

Now dolls have built-in ailments and innards. The simpler of the two models has colic—obviously. After it is fed, it burps and then bel-lows—and goes right on bawling until Daddy walks the floor with it. (Probably next year's model won't shut up until Daddy tells it a bed-time story.)

However, the doll with the colic is a relatively uncomplicated medi-cal problem. The second model is a real hypochondriac with remova-ble viscera or innards.

Any parent with a strong stomach and an embryo doctor or nurse in the playpen need shop no further for a Christmas present for Sister or Junior. Once the tiny tykes have scrubbed up and sterilized their hands and instruments, they put this doll or cadaver on the operating table, administer an anaesthetic and open up the torso by removing laces that look like sutures.

One peek inside the yawning cavity gives the in-training Florence

Nightingales a lovely look at the small and large intestines, liver, heart, kidneys, appendix, stomach and lungs, but not necessarily in that order.

There is everything but blood. But any reasonably ingenious modern child should be able to find the real thing. And after the first attempt at a blood-transfusion, Rover will probably have sense enough to stay under the porch.

Dolly's vital organs are made of plastic and are suspended on pegs for easy removal and return. Squeamish as I am, I must confess that this is an improvement over the original model, and Nature could do worse than take note.

It strikes me that there will have to be one hard and fast rule about this dolly. No matter how serious the operation or how many of Dolly's vital organs have to be removed, they should be tucked away in a box when not tucked away in Dolly. Surely, nothing could be more unnerving to the Head of the House, after an evening out with the boys, than to return to his castle only to find liver and lights all over the place.

I suppose parents will be able to brace themselves for this new doll. I do not look for any real revolt until next year's model, capable of *talking* about its operations, hits the market.

WHAT EVER HAPPENED TO "PLOP!"?

EDWARD J. RIEBE

Boys' games today still have much the same requirements they had twenty-five years ago—a steady finger on the trigger, a keen eye, nerves of steel and a contemptuous smile when hopelessly outnumbered. But the sound track needs to be reshot and brought up to date to accommodate certain technical advances in homicide as well as the modern insistence on a more faithful reproduction of sound.

Here are a few of the most important, as they seemed to me the last time I examined them carefully—and I suppose they change by the year:

	1925	1950
Machine-gun fire:	Tat-tat-tat-tat.	Hahn-hahn-hahn-hahn.
Airplane ⎫ Jet ⎭ :	Bbrrrr-mmmm.	YeeeoooWWNNn
Pistol fire:	Bang.	Kahh.
Rifle fire:	BANG.	Kahh-ttwinngg.
Atom bomb:	——	KA-BLOOM—KHAAAAH.
Cops and robbers:	I arrest you in the name of the law.	O.K., Louie; we're coming in.
Secret Service ⎫ G-Man ⎭ :	Surrender or I'll shoot.	All right, Mr. Armstrong; throw in the tear gas.
Person being hit on head with blunt object:	Bop.	Boinnnggg.
Detection:	Chiggers, the cops.	Scram! It's Mr. Ferret, arch-foe-of-criminals.
The chase:	Officer, arrest that man!	Calling Car 82. . . . Get Joe Sluggo. . . . He is armed. . . . May be dangerous. . . . That is all.
Surrender:	I give up.	O.K. copper, put the gun down; I know when I'm licked. I can't fight your modern crime-detection laboratory.
Reply to mother's call to come in to dinner:	Aw, do I have to? Willie doesn't have to go in yet.	Aw, do I have to? Willie doesn't have to go in yet.

WOMAN'S WORK

JOHN D. WEAVER

Link Morley, when he heard the news from a passing squirrel hunter, came roaring down out of the hills and marched straight into Gus Falk's Cassville store, where Mrs. Falk told him indeed it was true, Slate had run off and married the little Thorne girl. Link fell back against the counter, as though struck a powerful blow, and Mrs. Falk cautiously shifted the glass candy jar against the probability he'd be seized by one of his fits to throw things.

"My other children I give up on long ago," Link said, bitter with the memory of the three married daughters who had deserted him and the oldest son who had moved to Richmond and married a city girl. "But Slate I had my hopes for."

"Rowena's a nice li'l thing," Mrs. Falk said.

"She's a Thorne."

Link's hands began to claw at the counter, and Mrs. Falk cleared a still broader area for his fumbling rage. One Saturday, arguing infant damnation with Jud Thorne, Link had picked up a crate of empty pop bottles and thrown it the length of the store. Usually he threw smaller things.

"There's no living with a Thorne," Link said, and Mrs. Falk said she reckoned you could get used to living with anybody. "It's just harder with a Thorne."

Link stalked out of the store, banging the screen door, and his trail home was marked by the rocks he threw at every living thing he saw and by the branches he ripped from trees along the way. He kicked open the door of his log cabin and grabbed Slate's five-dollar fishing pole, the first thing to catch his eye. He snapped it across his knees, and then, because his hands still itched with the aggravation of what Slate had done, he began to throw dishes. When Emmy was alive, she'd always kept her cracked plates within easy reach, but Emmy was dead now, and he threw what came handiest.

"I'm just an old plank the children walk across on their way outta the house," he told himself, as he moved restlessly through the cabin he'd built on the land Link, Jr., had bought for him after he'd been run off the Ridley place for throwing an organ stool through the front window.

"One of the girls could of stayed by me," he said, and it came to him how unfair it was that he should have had all the bother and expense of raising three girls, and then just as soon as they'd got some age on them and had learned to do about the house, they'd gone and got married. "I bring 'em up and strangers get the good of 'em."

He brought out the Mason jar of apple brandy he'd been saving against the first frost. He needed something to ease the pain of the great emptiness to which life had come—Emmy dead, the last of the children gone, and nobody to care for him in case he got sick, which he more than likely would, working as hard as he did.

"It was Link, Jr., that started it," he said, remembering how the boy, from his first day in town school, had lived for nothing except the time when he'd finish his schooling and get himself a town job and live in a town place. After two years in town Link, Jr., had moved to Richmond to work in the bag factory. He'd married a city girl who'd come to the hills only once, a holiday week end Link would never forget. The girl wouldn't eat fried cooking, had to have her washing water heated, and drove all the way to Royalton to go to the hotel bathroom.

"Link, Jr., married too high and now Slate's gone and married too low," Link grumbled, feeling certain that only trouble could come from a union with the Thornes. Unlike the Morleys, who were Democrats and Salvationists, the Thornes were all Republicans and Foot Washers, and a strain of contentiousness flowed in their blood.

At every election the number of Thornes who'd reached voting age was always the same as the number of votes recorded in Cassville against the Democratic Organization, and no matter what discussion arose at Gus Falk's store on a Saturday or a rainy weekday, a Thorne would take the opposite side. Only last Saturday, Link had said the deer from the national park would be the ruin of their crops, and everybody had agreed except Jess Thorne, who'd taken the deer's side.

"There's two sides to everything," Link had maintained, "but some things a man would have to be a lunatic to see the other side of it."

The Thornes had been run out of every church in Cassville for disputing doctrine, and finally old Saul Thorne had built his own church and brought in a Foot-Washing preacher who'd married a Thorne and kept a picture of Herbert Hoover in his parlor.

"A Thorne!" Link sent the empty Mason jar crashing against the far wall, and then, in the quiet which came with the darkness of evening he slumped in his chair, bowed low with the pitiful knowledge of what, through no fault of his, had brought his life to this great nothingness. "The trouble is none of the children took after me."

He sat in his big chair, night settling over him with the cries of whippoorwills, and when it came time to eat, he had to strike matches to light his way into the kitchen. The floor, sprinkled with broken china, made a frosty crunching sound beneath his shoes. "I deserve better'n this." He found the oil lamps where Slate always left them, lined up in a row beneath the hanging skillets. "I'll die thisaway, by myself, some night." He lighted a match to the wick of the big Aladdin lamp. It was dry. "The children will all come home to bury me and steal what they can from the house." The next lamp was dry, too. "It'll maybe make 'em see how they—Why—why—they're *all* dry!"

He flung a lamp chimney against the door and then, because no one would ever come tend for him again, he had to lug the five-gallon coal-oil can up to the table and fill the lamps himself. Emmy had always taken care of the lamps, and, after Emmy, Slate. The planting, hoeing, cooking, and what cleaning was unavoidable had also been done by Slate, and it rubbed Link raw to think of doing all these things himself.

"It's a sorry pass to come to," he said, splashing coal oil over the lamps, the table, and the floor. "Woman's work."

He was sweeping a path through the broken china when the front door opened and Slate came in with his head drawn into his shoulders, ready to duck in case something whizzed across the room at him. The Thorne girl edged in behind Slate, and it shamed Link that she should see him brooming up the floor like a hired girl.

"Whatta you want?" Link asked, and Slate began to back away.

"We wanta stay here," Rowena said, and it was the Thorne voice, no mistaking the quiet coolness of it.

"I got trouble enough keeping myself," Link said, "without I start taking in strangers."

"I'm not a stranger."

Slate cleared the dry fear from his throat. "She means we've got married."

"I know what you've did."

Link thrust the broom into the corner. Free of the broom, he felt more himself. He moved into the center of the room, eying the wiry, black-haired girl with the large dark eyes which looked like pure stubbornness melted down. She stood, like all the Thornes, straight and defiant, with the firmness of a young tree.

"We got no place to go," Rowena said, "but here."

Link snorted. "You ain't got here."

"We'll pay."

"Pay! 'Tween the two of you it wouldn't be enough to pay for a lickerish stick."

"Slate's got work."

Slate, from behind Rowena, nodded. "Picking apples."

"And what happens when the apples is picked?" Link asked.

"Mr. Miller said he'd keep me on," Slate said. "Trucking for him."

"I'll work out our first week's keep," Rowena said, "and then we'll pay."

"Well . . ." Link, at the mention of "work," hesitated, drawn by the pleasant prospect of having a woman do for him again. "I reckon we could try it out."

Rowena proved to be a quiet, capable girl who, to Link's surprise, never entered into an argument. Not since the first days of his marriage to Emmy had he enjoyed such hopping and tending, always without complaint. All he had to say was, "I'm thirsty," and Rowena came running, seeming to know by instinct whether he wanted a dipper of fresh spring water or a cup of hot coffee. She cooked and cleaned, weeded the garden, put out flowers around the house, and did up the beds every morning, as though company were coming.

"Music," Link would say of an evening, and Rowena would sit by the hour cranking the phonograph and playing his favorite records.

Link even overlooked Slate's pampering of the girl, figuring it was only natural he should make a great fuss over her, the way a young man does when the wonder of his woman is fresh upon him. Slate carried water to her kitchen, filled her lamps, even helped with the supper dishes. But when the boy insisted Rowena should sit at the table with them of an evening, Link decided it was time he spoke up. "A woman don't 'spect to eat with her men."

"She's tired."

"It's a fitten tiredness, somepun a woman's born to."

Rowena sat at the table anyway, and, afterward, when he had the boy alone, Link tried to straighten him out. "It's all new to you," he said. "You've had no way of knowing that nothing ever pleasures a woman so much as tending her men."

"I don't like to see her tired."

"I felt the same way when your mother come to me as a bride, but I rose up above it, and Emmy made me a good wife."

"She was old before her time."

"Thas when a woman gets at her best, when she's seasoned. A woman's like anything else—the good you get out of 'em is all a question of how they're broke in."

"Rowena ain't like a horse or a hunting dog."

Link laughed, because this was something he'd heard a long time ago, when his brother Allen had married the little Hinkle girl. "Your Uncle Allen told me the same thing, and now look what's 'come of him. He don't draw a deep breath without he asks Edna Sue is it all right."

Link shook his head sadly. "You can't cross nature without it fights back at you, and ain't nothing so troublesome as a woman that's been lifted up outta her natural place."

The girl, outside of eating at the table with them, gave no trouble, and by the end of the first week Link had come to feel a great softness toward her.

"She's more a Hilton than a Thorne," he decided, and remembered Rowena's mother with a kindliness he'd put behind him twenty years ago when Naomi Hilton had walked out of the schoolhouse where she'd taught for two winters and married Knox Thorne, a drinker and a fighter who had, since the age of fourteen, been locked up every Election Day and most national holidays. Naomi, as Link remembered her in the years of her growing up, had been a solemn, big-eyed child who'd always seemed dwarfed and frightened by the world around her. It had been a marvel to everyone when she'd married Knox Thorne, like the mating of a rabbit and a mountain lion.

"The girl favors Naomi," Link told Gus Falk when he went for his mail that Saturday. "She's all Hilton."

Gus shrugged, and went on sorting mail. "Thorne blood's a tricky and powerful thing."

"She's all watered down with the Hilton strain," Link said, and went home humming to himself.

It was after dark when Slate and Rowena came back from town. Link, waiting for his supper, had finally gotten up and lighted the lamps himself, but since it was Saturday and the two of them were more than likely spending Slate's first wages on a good time, he didn't mind too much, although he did want to remind Rowena that after this she should fill all the lamps first thing Saturday morning and put them in place so he wouldn't have to go trudging around in the dark.

"Well, I reckon you've blowed all your money," Link said when they finally came home.

"Not all of it." Rowena motioned to Slate, who fidgeted a ten-dollar bill from his coat pocket and handed it to Link. "Thas for our next week's board and lodging," Rowena said.

Link shook his head. "It's no need to pay."

"We said we'd pay." Rowena, still in her town dress and her good shoes, sat down on the couch beside Slate. She began to play the phonograph.

"I'm hungry," Link said.

"We ate in town," Rowena said.

Link began to drum on the arms of his big chair. "*I* didn't eat in town."

"What she means is . . ." Slate shifted uneasily, the scraping of his shoes on the floor sounding unnaturally loud in the quiet room. "Well, we're paying now."

Link sprang up from his chair. "Damn it, I don't want your money! I want my supper."

"There's beans and bacon and cold corn bread in the kitchen," Rowena said.

"She means you can fix it yourself," Slate said, glancing quickly over everything within reach of Link's throwing hand.

Rowena yawned. "I'm going to bed."

"Me, too." Slate side-stepped the green ash tray, which shattered the framed portrait of Grandmother Morley.

Link, when the strip of light was gone from under their door and no sound came from their room, tiptoed out to the kitchen and quietly ate a cold supper. Afterward he lay awake wondering how a woman with Naomi Hilton's schooling could ever have lowered herself to marry Knox Thorne.

"She must of knowed she'd end up the mother of monsters."

Link was awakened next morning by the clatter of dishes, the sizzle of frying pork, and the smell of coffee. He lay in the bed, grinned up at the ceiling, not quite sure how he'd brought the girl to her senses, although it didn't matter just so long as she went on cooking and tending.

"Last night was just a li'l throwback to her Thorne blood," he decided as he headed for the kitchen, sniffing the Sunday breakfast. He took his regular place at the head of the table. "Them biscuits look good," he said, and found they were just beyond his reach.

"They ain't hard to make," Rowena said, not passing the plate.

"I can't seem to reach 'em."

"We haven't finished eating yet."

Slate, who seemed suddenly less hungry, explained, "She means you can have what's left over."

Link banged his clenched fist on the table, spilling sweet milk from Slate's glass. "I'm not a hound-dog begging scraps off'n the table," he said. "It's my house and I got certain rights."

Rowena went on eating. "Nobody's arguing your rights."

"I got a right to eat."

"You can eat what you help fix."

Link watched the girl knife the last of the meat and fried potatoes onto her plate. She upended the coffeepot, emptying it into her cup. She spread apple butter on the two remaining biscuits, handing one to Slate, taking the other for herself. She ate with a harvest hunger.

"We got no cause to quarrel," Link said, hoping to get through that stubborn Thorne shell to the sensible Hilton side of the girl. "I'll give you back the money."

"We don't want the money," Rowena said.

"She means she'd rather pay than work out her board," Slate said.

Rowena started clearing the table. "I'm married to Slate, not hired out to you."

"I won't listen to no such talk as that!" Link said, and Rowena looked down at him with that maddening Thorne smile which Link, in store arguments, had shouted into a thousand times, never with any effect.

"If you wanta help me round the house," Rowena said, "we can share out the work."

"I ain't gonna lower myself."

"Well, then, I'll do for Slate and me, but I won't lift a finger to cook nor clean for anybody else."

"There ain't anybody else, only me."

Slate coughed. "She means you."

Link began to throw things. He started with the saltcellar, then the sugar bowl, and because Slate and Rowena had cleared everything else from the table he got up and started throwing the dirty dishes on the sink.

"We'd best go dress for church," Rowena said, and walked out of the kitchen, Slate ducking out behind her.

Link threw the plain white dishes and the plates with the cluster of cherries painted on them. He threw all the cups and saucers, the iron skillets, the lamps, the glasses, the pots and pans, and even the drinking gourd. When there was nothing else to be thrown, he kicked over the kitchen table and stomped out of the kitchen. Rowena and Slate, in their church clothes, were crossing the parlor toward the front door.

"Don't come back," Link said. "Get out and stay out."

"We've paid for a week," Rowena said. "We'll come back."

Link roared and swung around, throwing parlor things until Slate and Rowena had walked down the path too far to hear the clatter of his rage. "I'd think it was maybe a judgment," he told himself, brushing crumbs of glass from the seat of his big chair, "only the Lord's got no cause to judge against me."

Link would have brewed a pot of coffee and fried some hen eggs while Slate and Rowena were gone, but he didn't want to give the girl the satisfaction of finding out he'd made his own breakfast. He was still sitting in his big chair when the two of them came back from church. They walked through the living room without a word to him, and he could hear them moving about in the kitchen. He eased over to the door and peered through the keyhole. Slate was setting the table with paper plates. Rowena was picking up knives and forks from the floor. There was no paper plate at the head of the table.

"It all started when he let her eat with us," he said, and limped back to his chair. He felt weak with hunger and helplessness. Slate opened the kitchen door part way and stood behind it, so it would shield him from any thrown thing. "She says you can eat if you work."

"I ain't concerned with what she says."

"She's making cream gravy with the chicken."

Link chewed his underlip. "What kinda work she have in mind?"

"Carry in the water."

"But I never done such a thing as that in my life."

"She says it's always a first time for everything."

Link sank back, groaning, shaking his head. "This is what comes of marrying too low."

He could hear the two of them eating together on the other side of the kitchen door, and when they came back to the parlor they had the shine of chicken grease on their mouths. Rowena stretched out on the couch and asked Slate to play the phonograph.

"Salvationists don't play music on Sunday," Link said.

"Foot Washers do," Rowena said.

Link left the house to which the girl had made him a stranger. He shuffled around back to the pump to draw himself a dipper of water, hoping it might soothe the gnawing ache of his empty stomach. His two beagle hounds were nuzzling a pan of chicken bones, and when they heard him coming, they filled their jaws and backed away into the shade of the giant honey locust.

"It's a merciful thing poor Emmy never lived to see me put second to the rabbit dogs," he said, and it suddenly seemed unreasonable and not like Emmy that she should have lain down one night and slept herself out of all this misery.

"She should of took better care of her health," he said, as though Emmy's death had been a thing of purpose and spite.

He was washing one of the larger bones when Rowena opened the kitchen door. He dropped the bone, shame burning in him like a fever. He sat down on the kitchen steps as Rowena moved past him, perfumed up like an apple orchard. "Well," he said, "you've finally did what you set out—brung me down level with the hunting dogs."

"You was asked to the table."

"On condition."

"No reason you can't help." She sat on a rock, facing him, the sun bathing her legs in a silken shine. "Slate helps me."

Link scooped a rock the size of an egg into the palm of his throwing hand. He took aim at the latticework around the springhouse.

"It's no use to throw things," Rowena said.

"It eases me."

The two dogs, when he scooped up the rock, took shelter beneath the porch steps. They peered out at Link, who still hadn't thrown the rock. Suddenly he let it drop from his hand. "You don't know what it is to raise up children and have 'em leave you, never give you another thought."

"Link, Jr., bought you your land."

"It ain't much 'count. It's rocky."

"The girls send you money."

"When they think about it. Sometimes."

"Mrs. Falk says they send it every month."

Link grabbed the rock and threw it. "You can't reason with a Thorne. No sense trying."

"I ain't a Thorne now. I'm a Morley."

"Boy! This *next* phase we go through is a *dilly!*"

"You just got the name, not the blood."

Rowena's laugh was like that Thorne smile set to organ music. "The babies'll all be Morleys."

Link slumped back against the porch steps, his mind a nightmare of unnatural grandchildren romping around the house like naked savages and probably growing up to preach atheism and free love.

"Slate might as well of married a Russian."

It was dark when he heard Slate and Rowena in the kitchen, starting supper. He pumped a pail of water and carried it in to them. "Just set it on the sink," Rowena said, without surprise, as though she'd expected it. Slate took a third paper plate from the shelf and put it at the head of the table. Rowena handed Link the broom and nodded at the floor. "I brung in water," Link said. "That oughta be enough."

"It's your mess," Rowena said, and Link started sweeping.

"Tomorrow I'm getting some new dishes," Rowena said.

"She means not to throw," Slate said.

Link drew himself up, a restless anger settling in his hands clenched on the broom handle. "When it comes over me to throw, I throw. I can't help myself. It's my nature."

"I don't want my dishes broke," Rowena said.

"You can't change human nature."

Rowena smiled that aggravating Thorne smile. "You can smoothen it out a little."

Link whirled around toward Slate with a roar. "Don't tell me what she means!"

Slate took shelter behind the stove. "I reckon you know what she means."

The three of them sat down at the table together, and it was Rowena's idea that Link should ask the blessing.

"It'll be Salvationist," Link said, because he had to hold on to something of what he'd been.

"It's your house," Rowena said, and bowed her head.

BACHELORS—TAXATION

(*From Godey's Lady's Book*, 1839)

We find it stated in some of the papers that a number of ladies lately petitioned the legislature to pass a bill laying a tax on Old Bachelors. One of the members, (a bachelor himself,) became the advocate of this measure, on the ground that *luxuries* ought to be taxed. He meant to say, peradventure, that *Old Bachelor-ship* is a luxury; certain we are that Old Bachelors themselves are no such matter.

As for taxing them, we doubt if that would be just; for it is not often their own fault that they are bachelors. It is generally an involuntary penance, and all the luxury that attends it is not to be envied. Where is the bachelor of thirty or upwards, who has not received at least half a dozen rejections, or *flats* as they are technically called! If an exception can be found, it is because the gentleman had not the *courage* to make proposals of matrimony. An Old Bachelor has usually been either too *sheepish* to woo a lady, or too little attractive to win one. And yet these oddities have the effrontery to insinuate that they *would* not get married, because they could not find a wife to their taste!

> "Ah ha! my noble fox will eat no grapes."

No; we are decidedly opposed to the taxation of bachelors. All com-

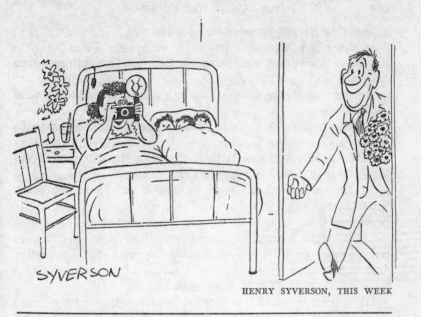

SYVERSON

modities taxed should have some specific value, else how shall the rate of duty be determined? If bachelors be taxed *ad valorem*, the tax will amount to little or nothing, and the advantages, public or private, will be nugatory and scarcely worth the trouble.

LIFE WITH SEARS, ROEBUCK

(From Flair Magazine)

On the very eve of the twentieth century, America received its first glimpse of a fabulous book. For decades to come it was to be the most familiar, most widely read and, in certain materialistic respects, the most civilizing publication in the country's rural history.

In 1899, replacing its semi-annual catalogs with an all-inclusive omnibus edition ("good for the entire year"), the mail order house of Sears, Roebuck issued its first big annual catalog. Merely as a publishing venture, Sears' catalog number 109 was, for its day, staggering. It was issued in an edition of 400,000 copies—one for almost every four ("show this catalog to your friends") of Sears' two million turn-of-the-century customers. Its 1286 pages were crammed with thousands of objects ("everything you need the year around"), almost all of them illustrated with black and white cuts . . . and even a few in full color. Best of all, the catalog was, except for "15 cents to help pay the 35 cents postage," absolutely free. There was no better reading value— or for that matter, paper value—in the country. In a word, number 109 was a beaut.

It covered the nation like road shows of *East Lynn*. Often it reposed in sitting room state on checkered tablecloths along with the Bible and the *Farmer's Almanac*. And it was read. By the light of oil lamps, to the creak of rocker and the slow tick of wall clock, it was read— particularly on long unsociable winter nights—for information, for entertainment, for escape. Furthermore, if number 109 was read in the farmhouse, it was also, as all America knew, perused again at leisure *out* of it, to the last and presumably most fascinating page. To the country's early scatological humorists, the shameful utilitarian destiny of its happily thin paper was inspiration for whole cycles of Chick Sale-ish wheezes that are far from obsolete in today's sticks.

The policies expressed in the catalog, its physical composition and, above all, its truly imperial prose style were largely the work of the company's founder, Richard Sears. Sears called his book a *Consumers Guide*, and wasting no time told his readers on the front cover, "This book tells just what your storekeeper at home pays for everything he buys, and will prevent him from overcharging you on anything you buy from him." The bitter obscenities which greeted this pious crack in many a crossroads general store are still ringing down the years. After delivering this body-blow to local enterprise, Sears went on to smooch up the distant individual customer. His early policy of "send no money" was followed by one of "satisfaction guaranteed." The switcheroo was that Sears meant it—not only meant it but, hell or high water, backed it up. To a gent who complained about breaking his Sears watch on a concrete sidewalk, Sears wrote that his watches were guaranteed not to fall on such and sent along a new watch. An Ohio boy who broke his leg riding a Sears bicycle was brought to Chicago at the company's expense to have his leg reset by a top surgeon. Even more to the point, Sears had a canny insight into certain shynesses of the unschooled back-country citizens who needed him almost as much as he needed them. "Don't be afraid that you will make a mistake in ordering," he reassured them, in his best crooning style. "Tell us what you want in your own way, written in any language, no matter whether good or poor writing, and the goods will promptly be sent to you."

They heard him, they wrote him, and the goods were certainly sent. Car after car after carload . . .

The early catalogs were largely prepared by Sears himself, whose long suit was a warm copiousness rather than fanatical precision. In readying his catalog, he managed to be at once dynamic and casual. His principal tools were a pencil and a pocketknife. If copy turned out short, he penciled in—obviously with no pain—more. When it was too long, he used the knife—not to cut the copy, Sears didn't believe in brevity—but to fit the type in somewhere. In the matter of indexing, his casualness reached the point of breezy indifference. The index was a wonderful place, after all, for inaccuracy, since it forced the prospective customer to thumb through the whole book to find what he wanted. After which, very possibly, he wanted much more than when he started . . .

One reason he wanted more was that Richard Sears' prose was little short of hypnotic. Once the reader got into it there was almost no chance of his getting out. This was no accident, for Sears' prose was in fact the perfection of a classic American style, as indigenous as baked squash and about as guileless as a bear trap. It was pure, knock-'em-cold medicine-show-ese, raised to a pitch of persuasive exaltation that leaves the ad-man at the starting post. Although Sears did not invent this style, he was without doubt one of its greatest masters. Writing for readers who had not forgotten spellbinder Daniel Webster and were already hearing from William Jennings Bryan, Sears put his concoction in print on a scale unequalled before or since, and with it he left an indelible mark, not only on the material values of America but on its esthetic evolution as well.

A good example of Sears' masterly control of his Muse is his paean for a 95-cent mantel clock—an object, as illustrated, of unrelieved hideousness. A well-nourished matron in an attitude of morose fortitude is planted beside a heap of floral junk which suggests that she is either dismantling or about to decorate a large convention hall, or possibly a float. The clockface artfully included in this teeming composition suggests that she has debated herself to an everlasting standstill. But listen to Sears: ". . . this beautiful bronze clock, solid metal through and through . . . weighing when boxed about 20 lbs., *at the unheard of price, 95¢ in bronze, $1.10 in full gilt* . . ." The weight for scrap alone is irresistible, but Sears is just warming up: ". . . fine lever escape movement, oil tempered steel parts and hand wrought brass parts, conical pivots, the hair spring agate drawn . . ." Pure poetry for the dawning machine age, especially the conical pivots, which are as rare in clocks as round wheels. But Sears never forgot his cultural mission, either: ". . . a masterpiece representing the emblems of Hope and Plenty, Hope being represented by a heroic figure of a woman with Greek drapery, resting her hand upon a cornucopia that represents Plenty." Like anything that fell under Sears' pencil, it certainly did—among other things, a revolutionary economic theory that absolutely defied inspection: "To sell this clock at this unheard of low price, a price that does not represent one-half its true value, we had to contract with the factory that makes them in such large quantities that the price of a single one is practically lost sight of." Poker-faced, graceful, and a strong smell of Houdini . . .

Sears knew what to begin his book with: Groceries. And with an eye on the country's climbing birthrate, what to end it with: Baby Carriages. The 1900 leader reproduced on page 166 has "a heavy antique frame, mitred, glued, screwed and plugged at joints," plus upholstery "in the highest style of the art." Meanwhile, groceries led appropriately to Drugs, for which Sears prepared a lurid encyclopaedia of misery and infallible cures which seemed to reflect, and might easily have produced, a nation of hypochondriacs. Laxatives galore, Liquor and Opium Cures, Obesity Powders, Female Pills for Weak Women, Blood Builders, Worm Cakes—not to forget Sears' 60-cent Nerve and Brain Pills, around which he drew a heartening picture of "the weak and timid young man made strong and bold again. BEWARE OF QUACK DOCTORS," warned Sears sternly at this point, "who advertise to scare men . . ." His Nerve and Brain Pills, as it happened, were just the thing for ". . . a sense of goneness, headache, blurring of eyesight, nervous irritability, poor memory, chilliness, hot flushes, palpitation of heart, short breath, cold feet, drowsiness after meals but nervous wakefulness at night, languor in the morning, and a constant feeling of dread, as if something awful was going to happen." As hangovers go, this evidently was an epic, and one rather wonders just who did the research for it. An even more galvanizing picker-upper, compensating for "overwork, long hours of study, dissipations and indiscretions in youth," was Dr. Owen's Electric Belt (reproduced at the left). With its batteries, switchboard and intimately planned wiring system, it turned the early Caspar Milquetoast into not only a business dynamo but a high-voltage Don Juan, and was doubtless a howl besides in the hands of the really conscientious practical joker.

There were, obviously, very few kinds of human assistance that Dick

Sears was not prepared to render his readers. And it would doubtless please him, in more ways than one, to know that today his mail order progeny uses faithfully some fifty million Sears catalogs annually.

A Selection from

THE BEHAVIOR BOOK, A MANUAL FOR LADIES

This charming essay on etiquette, written by Eliza Leslie in 1853, presents a picture of timidity and decorum unknown in our century. And a captivating picture it is, to say the least . . .

Few ladies that *are* ladies wear finery in rail cars and steam boats . . . above all do not travel in white kid gloves. Respectable women never do. . . . Few ladies go to the breakfast table [in a hotel] in any costume approaching to full dress. There must be no flowers or ribbons in the hair . . . a merino or cashmere wrapper—grey, brown, purple or olive—faced or trimmed with merino of an entirely different color . . . is a becoming morning dress. . . . The fashion of wearing black silk mittens at breakfast is now obsolete. . . . On arriving at a hotel ask immediately to see the proprietor . . . request him to see that you are provided with a good room . . . also to conduct you to the dining room at dinner time and allot you to a seat near his own . . . He will wait for you near the door. . . . If any gentleman asks you to take wine with him, politely refuse. . . . Avoid saying anything to women in showy attire, with painted faces and white kid gloves. . . . [On a steamboat] The captain will of course take charge of you during the voyage. . . . All trouble may be avoided on arriving by sending for the captain of the boat and requesting him to see you on shore. . . . Ladies no longer eat salt fish at a public table . . . the odor of it is considered extremely ungenteel. . . . The word "stomach" should never be uttered at any table or indeed anywhere else except to your physician or in private conversation with a female friend interested in your health. . . . The facilities of travelling are such that a lady evidently respectable, plainly dressed, and behaving properly, may travel very well without a gentleman. . . .

[At public entertainments] Most American ladies beyond the age of thirty-five, look better in caps than without them. A decidedly old lady persisting in going with her head uncovered is a pitiable object and scarcely looks respectable. . . .

[At an evening party in a private house] If any lady is without an escort, she should send for the master of the house to meet her near the door and give her his arm into the drawing room. He will lead her to the hostess and to a seat. Let her then bow as a sign that she releases him. . . .

[Toward literary women] When in company with literary women make no allusion to "Learned Ladies" or "Blue Stockings" or express surprise that they should have any knowledge of housewifery or needle work or dress, or that they are able to talk on "common things."

[In general] When you see a person slip down on the ice, do not laugh at them. . . . It is more feminine on witnessing such a sight, to utter an involuntary scream. . . .

THE GRAMMATICAL BOY

BILL NYE (1850–1896)

Sometimes a sad, homesick feeling comes over me, when I compare the prevailing style of anecdote and school literature with the old McGuffey brand, so well known thirty years ago. To-day our juvenile literature, it seems to me, is so transparent, so easy to understand, that I am not surprised to learn that the rising generation shows signs of lawlessness.

Boys to-day do not use the respectful language and large, luxuriant words that they did when Mr. McGuffey used to stand around and report their conversations for his justly celebrated school reader. It is disagreeable to think of, but it is none the less true, and for one I think we should face the facts.

I ask the careful student of school literature to compare the following selection, which I have written myself with great care, and arranged with special reference to the matter of choice and difficult words, with the flippant and commonplace terms used in the average school book of to-day.

One day as George Pillgarlic was going to his tasks, and while passing through the wood, he spied a tall man approaching in an opposite direction along the highway.

"Ah!" thought George, in a low, mellow tone of voice, "whom have we here?"

"Good morning, my fine fellow," exclaimed the stranger, pleasantly. "Do you reside in this locality?"

"Indeed I do," retorted George, cheerily, doffing his cap. "In yonder cottage, near the glen, my widowed mother and her thirteen children dwell with me."

"And is your father dead?" exclaimed the man, with a rising inflection.

"Extremely so," murmured the lad, "and, oh, sir, that is why my poor mother is a widow."

"And how did your papa die?" asked the man, as he thoughtfully stood on the other foot a while.

"Alas! sir," said George, as a large hot tear stole down his pale cheek and fell with a loud report on the warty surface of his bare foot, "he was lost at sea in a bitter gale. The good ship foundered two years ago last Christmastide, and father was foundered at the same time. No one knew of the loss of the ship and that the crew was drowned until the next spring, and it was then too late."

"And what is your age, my fine fellow?" quoth the stranger.

"If I live till next October," said the boy, in a declamatory tone of voice suitable for a Second Reader, "I will be seven years of age."

"And who provides for your mother and her large family of children?" queried the man.

"Indeed, I do, sir," replied George, in a shrill tone. "I toil, oh, so hard, sir, for we are very, very poor, and since my elder sister, Ann, was married and brought her husband home to live with us, I have to toil more assiduously than heretofore."

"And by what means do you obtain a livelihood?" exclaimed the man, in slowly measured and grammatical words.

"By digging wells, kind sir," replied George, picking up a tired ant as he spoke and stroking it on the back. "I have a good education, and so I am able to dig wells as well as a man. I do this day-times and take in washing at night. In this way I am enabled barely to maintain our family in a precarious manner; but, oh, sir, should my other sisters marry, I fear that some of my brothers-in-law would have to suffer."

"And do you not fear the deadly fire-damp?" asked the stranger in an earnest tone.

"Not by a damp sight," answered George, with a low gurgling laugh, for he was a great wag.

"You are indeed a brave lad," exclaimed the stranger, as he repressed a smile. "And do you not at times become very weary and wish for other ways of passing your time?"

"Indeed, I do, sir," said the lad. "I would fain run and romp and be gay like other boys, but I must engage in constant manual exercise, or we will have no bread to eat, and I have not seen a pie since papa perished in the moist and moaning sea."

"And what if I were to tell you that your papa did not perish at sea, but was saved from a humid grave?" asked the stranger in pleasing tones.

"Ah, sir," exclaimed George, in a genteel manner, again doffing his cap, "I am too polite to tell you what I would say, and besides, sir, you are much larger than I am."

"But, my brave lad," said the man in low musical tones, "do you not know me, Georgie? Oh, George!"

"I must say," replied George, "that you have the advantage of me. Whilst I may have met you before, I can not at this moment place you, sir."

"My son! oh, my son!" murmured the man, at the same time taking a large strawberry mark out of his valise and showing it to the lad. "Do you not recognize your parent on your father's side? When our good ship went to the bottom, all perished save me. I swam several miles through the billows, and at last, utterly exhausted, gave up all hope of life. Suddenly I stepped on something hard. It was the United States.

"And now, my brave boy," exclaimed the man with great glee, "see what I have brought for you." It was but the work of a moment to unclasp from a shawl-strap which he held in his hand and present to George's astonished gaze a large forty-cent watermelon, which until now had been concealed by the shawl-strap.

POPPING THE QUESTION

(From Godey's Lady's Book, 1839)

It must be admitted by every one who is practically or otherwise acquainted with the topic, that "popping the question," as it is familiarly called, is one of the most thrilling circumstances in the life of "a man of real sensibility." Imagine a youngster of two and twenty, or thereabouts, with a tallow-coloured face, an agitated deportment, and a heart throbbing with various emotions, seated by the side of a simpering damsel, who is labouring strenuously to make it appear that she has no suspicion concerning the subject about to be introduced. It is twenty to one, however, that she might relieve his embarrassment and abbreviate the period of palpitation by frankly telling him that she knows precisely what he intends to say. But etiquette and the usages of the sex will not sanction this piece of humanity. She cannot even be supposed to understand his hint, if he attempts to approach the affair by circumlocution. He wonders that such a divine creature can be so dull of comprehension.

Finding, at last, that he must either "speak or die," he nerves himself heroically for the task, his countenance becomes paler, if possible, one hand grasps his hat or cane convulsively, the other is usually laid on his heart, as if to still the tumultuous beatings of that troublesome little organ. Then from between his closed teeth and quivering lips, comes a scarcely articulate and almost inaudible sound, like the voice of a terrapin, when, in alarm, it closes the portals of its crustaceous habitation. Only two or three words can be distinguished, but they are sufficiently explicit to justify the lady in comprehending what is meant.

The answer depends entirely on circumstances. If it be unequivocally in the negative, the lover starts up, claps on his hat, and without the customary formalities of parting, leaves the house and hastens, it may be, towards the river, resolved on extinguishing his flames by a most infallible expedient. But, on his way, he usually finds some reasons to decline acting on this resolution, and sometimes compounds for the intended sacrifice to Cupid, by an extra libation to Bacchus.

If the lady should be more favourably disposed, she sometimes tortures the youth mischievously, remarking that she has never once thought on the subject of matrimony; when the probability is that she has thought of nothing else from her twelfth year upwards. This is a very naughty and unamiable piece of duplicity. Almost invariably, the nymph appears to be rather averse to the proposal, be it never so advantageous; or else so surprisingly careless about it, that it seems to be but the toss of a sixpence whether she shall be married or not.

Some young men are so chicken-hearted in affairs of this sort, that the least word which may be construed as a denial is sufficient to close the negotiation at once; and the inconsiderate belle is, perhaps, as much grieved at the result as the chap-fallen lover himself.

No doubt, the terrors attendant on "popping the question," are so numerous that the very *timidity* of some men causes them to remain in unblessed singleness for life. These poor fellows are objects of pity, and should not be included in those general anathemas which are promulgated against the fraternity of Old Bachelors.

LEARNING vs. HOUSEWIFERY

(*From Godey's Lady's Book, 1839*)

The opinions of modern schoolmen appear to be much divided on the question whether females should be taught the sciences, Natural Philosophy, Chemistry, Mathematics, Astronomy, &c., or merely the domestic arts, sewing, knitting, spinning, and all the other old-fashioned accomplishments, which were contemporary with hoops and whalebone jackets. They who contend for the latter course of study, should not lose sight of the fact that "the sciences" may be made auxiliary to almost every domestic operation.

Take *Chemistry* for example; what an advantage must it be for the lady who superintends the roasting of a leg of mutton to have a thorough knowledge of the nature and action of *free caloric!*—so that neither too much nor too little of that agent should be employed in the culinary process.

If dinners were always cooked philosophically, it may be that the *eating* of them could be managed with less philosophy than we sometimes find requisite. And again, by a perfect acquaintance with chemical affinities, how successful might the housewife be in the composition of *good coffee;*—a thing which is as rarely to be met with as pure carbon.

By some acquaintance with *Geometry*, a lady may be enabled to cut out a garment more skilfully than one who is ignorant of that science; and we find, as an illustration, that the most fashionable tailors of the present day require their apprentices to be tolerably familiar with Euclid, before they are suffered to try any experiments on the customers' cloth! This shows the march of improvement; and, in a short time, every lady who pretends to any skill in the construction of wearing apparel, will think a case of mathematical instruments quite as indispensable as her needle, scissors and thimble.

As for *Astronomy* and *Geology*, we do not see how *they* can be of much practical advantage to the sex; though the former may give some tolerable hints relative to the formation of a bed-quilt, in which a superior arrangement of calico constellations may be desirable. *Phrenology*, though a science of comparatively recent date, we take to be absolutely necessary. Every mother should be taught to make a scientific examination of her own children's craniums, whereby she may discover with precision the peculiar bent of their genius. For, it is not enough to know that the little treasures are uncommonly bright, but it is deeply interesting to ascertain in what brightness consists. And what an immense benefit would an acquaintance with this latter science be to a young woman in directing her choice of a husband!

With candour and seriousness, we must say that we cannot entertain a very favourable opinion of the intellect of those men who would restrict the acquirements of females to those branches of knowledge which were thought sufficient for them forty or fifty years ago. The change of public sentiment on this subject, we consider one evidence that the world is advancing to a perfect state of civilization.

FATHER WILLIAM

LEWIS CARROLL

(*After Southey*)

"You are old, Father William," the young man said,
  "And your hair has become very white;
And yet you incessantly stand on your head—
  Do you think, at your age, it is right?"

"In my youth," Father William replied to his son,
  "I feared it might injure the brain;
But, now that I'm perfectly sure I have none,
  Why, I do it again and again."

"You are old," said the youth, "as I mentioned before,
  And have grown most uncommonly fat;
Yet you turn a back-somersault in at the door—
  Pray, what is the reason of that?"

"In my youth," said the sage, as he shook his gray locks,
  "I kept all my limbs very supple
By the use of this ointment—one shilling the box—
  Allow me to sell you a couple?"

"You are old," said the youth, "and your jaws are too weak
  For anything tougher than suet;
Yet you finished the goose, with the bones and the beak—
  Pray, how did you manage to do it?"

"In my youth," said his father, "I took to the law,
  And argued each case with my wife;
And the muscular strength which it gave to my jaw
  Has lasted the rest of my life."

"You are old," said the youth, "one would hardly suppose
  That your eye was as steady as ever;
Yet you balanced an eel on the end of your nose—
  What made you so awfully clever?"

"I have answered three questions, and that is enough,"
  Said his father, "Don't give yourself airs!
Do you think I can listen all day to such stuff?
  Be off, or I'll kick you down-stairs!"

WHATEVER HAPPENED TO THE BAD BOY?

JOHN CROSBY

(November 19, 1948)

The closest thing we have around to Huck Finn and Tom Sawyer—
and it's pretty distant—is Henry Aldrich and Homer, which proves
how boyhood has degenerated since I was a boy. Boyhood—let's face
it squarely—has been going down hill for years, but it's come to a
pretty pass when its archetypes are Henry and Homer and Oogie
Pringle and Archie Andrews.

When I was young, roughly around the twelfth century, the blueprint of my deportment was drawn to scale by Huck and Tom and Penrod and the hero of "The Story of a Bad Boy," whose name I've forgotten. (I missed "Peck's Bad Boy" entirely. Different generation, I guess.) These three provided an outline of general hell-raising that any boy could be proud of.

Judging from the radio, the lads still get into mischief (a word we wouldn't be caught dead with), but they never get into it deliberately. The difference is one of intent, and that's where a boy's character is formed, which is why I think the education of our sons is in incapable hands. When Huck and Tom ran away from home, when the Bad Boy (what *was* that kid's name, anyway?) blew up the village cannon, they knew what they were doing.

In both cases there were unexpected consequences, but the sense of wrongdoing was present from the outset. They were active little fiends destined to be captains of industry when they grew up.

For Homer and Henry and Oogie and Archie, I see no hope whatever of future brilliance. Week after week, they get into one jam after another, always by accident, never by design. The trouble they see is a censored, respectable, passive trouble. They're the victims. In Huck's day somebody else was the victim.

Modern boys—and I'm judging by Oogie and company—are a bunch of namby-pambies. They never *try* to get into trouble. They try to stay out of it. But, with the best intentions in the world, they stick their elbows through windows, they fall flat on their faces in front of their best girls. Always they're crossed by circumstance or the idiosyncrasies of adults. What I object to is that they're trying so hard to be good. And they generally are foiled by their own stupidity.

What sort of example is that to hold up before a young boy? Penrod and Huck and Tom slipped once in a while in the mires of boyhood, but they were never stupid. They didn't put their feet in their mouths with such monotonous regularity. Their parents worried about them. Henry and Homer and Oogie and Archie worry about their parents. Also, the modern girl has got out of hand. There was a place in Penrod's life and in Tom Sawyer's life for girls, but there was also a place where girls weren't allowed. The modern boy seems to have girls on the brain all day long.

I dunno. These adenoidal infants they got on the air don't sound quite bright or quite virile. Of course, you might argue that all these

"Just one more question. How do you keep from going nuts?"

---

kids—Archie and Henry and Homer and Oogie—belong in the category of Tarkington's "Seventeen" rather than in the company of Huck Finn, but they're the nearest thing we have to Huck.

There aren't any Huck Finns in radio, the influence probably of mothers craving respectability. I'm against it. A couple of Huck Finns would be a lot better for the kids than Captain Midnight, Superman or Tom Mix.

There wasn't any real harm in Tom and Huck. They were just harum-scarum.

IS THERE A LIFE AFTER FORTY?

ROBERT M. YODER

For some reason or another, and all of them good, the age of forty is approached with dread and is a birthday in bold-face type. Men and women are glad to reach twenty-one, men at least like reaching thirty, nobody minds being thirty-eight and nobody minds being forty-two. But forty hangs in the mind like one of the big turning points, and not for good, either. Forty sounds like a turning point the way the fire was a turning point for Chicago or like a "Road Closed" sign on an auto trip. That is how you think of forty before you get there.

Well, the other day I reached that Jumping-Off-Place and am now in position to report how forty looks from the other side. I can report that it looks exactly as advertised. Before reaching forty you are likely to think of that birthday as one of life's major division points. Upon reaching forty you are convinced that forty not only is a division point on Life's Journey—why don't they fix that roadbed?—but probably is where the narrow gauge starts.

At forty you realize that it is no coincidence that entire books have been written to persuade people that this is not The End. You begin to understand why Prof. Walter Pitkin's famous *Life Begins at Forty* was a best seller; a book entitled *Drowning Can be Fun* would have the same sort of appeal, or one entitled *There's Money in Being Poor*. To reach forty not only gives you pause, but makes you wonder if you can start up again; it is a damned disturbing sensation. Because so many look upon this experience with fear and suspicion, I have kept notes on the experience. If you are one of the thousands to whom this will happen shortly, this report from The Great Beyond will not make you any happier about it. But if we can't grow old graciously, we can at least go down beefing.

To begin with, it is impossible to suppress the feeling that your Blue Book rating takes a bad tumble at forty. It is all too clearly the start of middle age, which is a raw deal to hand a broth of a boy like you and me. The actual event, however, is relatively quiet. (A quiet start for a long, quiet period, sonny.) One day you are thirty, and then, with little or nothing to account for the difference, you are forty. It does not bring general collapse; that idea is overdramatic. You don't wake up on your fortieth birthday with a film on the eyes and a gnarled cane by your bedside. You wake up feeling strange, but no stranger than you felt at thirty-nine. The main difference is emotional; the feeling is about what a race horse must feel when first he sees the dray wagon.

But as a matter of fact, people who are forty in the 1940's long since quit expecting to feel good. We were twenty in the '20's, and the '20's ended in a sensational collapse; we were thirty in the 1930's, which were years when the whole world went into a stall; and we are forty in a decade when a global war ended in a time of quiet frenzy. Fate's favorite patsies, that's us. God knows we've been in tune with our times. Here is the world going to pot, and look who's following suit. At forty you can look back a long way and see how you got here, although it's too late to do anything much about it. Still, if we have flopped, we're as appropriate to the twentieth century as a bride to a honeymoon.

One of the perquisites of being forty is a special note that creeps into doctors' voices, except that "creeps" isn't the word for it; it creeps into their voices like a yell creeps up on a cheerleader. All through your thirties they treat you with concern. You are pretty run down for thirty-five, they will say, or mighty decrepit for thirty-eight. But once you tell them you have passed the Great Boundary they grow kindly. The tone they use then, after examining the animate remains, is that of mechanics talking about a fine old 1920 Chalmers: the old wreck certainly sounds good, considering the model; though it must be hard to get acetylene for the lights. Their manner says clearly that all medical science can hope to do at this stage is to keep the battered old relic on the road; if you can walk to and from the doctor's office and play a little solitaire, they plainly regard it as a victory. No doctor will let you out of his office without volunteering the remark that, of course, at forty you can't do all the things you could do at twenty.

If you could, you could wrap the good doctor's stethoscope around his neck and throw him under the X-ray table, but you get this little truism in spite of all evidence of its truth. Most of the things they think you can't do are things you wouldn't have done at twenty-nine for three dollars an hour; the rest of the things you can't do at forty are things you didn't have money enough to do at twenty, anyway.

Forty is the real Awkward Age; you are old enough to realize that you would look silly doing things you are still young enough to wish you could do. One thing you realize is that you need no longer fear arousing mad emotions on the part of young girls; you may safely be as attractive as you like, kid. Forty is when young girls who are your natural playmates get to acting a little strange. They start calling you "mister" in very much the same tone they would use for Lionel Barrymore, and they treat you in a curious way which, it dawns on you, is disinterest in its purest form. They regard you as one with the trees, the hills, and the Gettysburg battlefield. Now you are an interesting example of the game in mother's day, and that's all. They ought to tremble when they see a roué like you, but instead they yawn. The way to look at this development is to say that it keeps you out of a lot of trouble that you'd sure like to be into. Look at it this way: forty is a kind of vaccination against a lot of things, most of which you'd like to catch a heavy case of.

They say you have to be a little more careful of your health, guarding against exertion, which I'll be glad to do. You can't stay out all night any more, even on nights when it would take a Federal subpoena to get you out of the house. You have to go easy on drinking, which is made easier by the fact that by this time you begin measuring the party against the probable hang-over, and you would rather not feel like that in the morning than get drunk on bonded bourbon with an all-star cast. People our age didn't survive prohibition gin and spiked beer just to get drunk with any casuals who are standing around a bar.

At forty you clearly aren't twice as smart as you were at twenty, and it is certainly more like two thirds of being sixty than it is like being four times ten. I avoid the possibility that forty is half of being eighty, which would suggest that forty is the adolescence of old age. That probably is true, but at forty you learn to skirt a lot of things that probably are true. There are clear-cut differences, however, between being forty and, say, twenty. They are differences largely of attitude.

At twenty you would climb a sixty-foot tree to get a leaf some girl said was pretty. At forty you'd mark her down as leaf-nutty and Nature-happy, and buy her a single ticket to the nearest arboretum.

At twenty, if a friend got thrown into jail for espousing some cause, you would organize mass meetings and demand to be thrown into jail with him. At thirty you would demand action by the Supreme Court. At forty you would telephone the precinct captain or the judge's sweetie and get action faster.

At twenty, if a girl gives you a long, direct look and smiles, you look into the next weighing-machine mirror to see why you are so attractive. At forty you look to see who's behind you.

At thirty you notice you are putting on a little weight, which is a public calamity, like having the Discus Thrower get flabby or Venus develop a double chin. So you play handball two nights a week, cut down desserts and alcohol, and sweat off four pounds by strenuous exertion. At forty you take another drink, order pie à la mode and make a note to get pleated trousers.

At twenty, if nine P.M. finds you at home, you are sore. At forty, if the phone rings after seven, you wish whoever is coming to drink up your last bottle could pick a night when you didn't want to listen to the radio.

At twenty you welcome a chance to dive off a bridge, rescue a drowning man and be a Page One hero. At forty, if you did not get drowned trying, you would clip the man twice—once to rescue him and once for ruining your good suit.

At twenty you would be indignant if somebody else got a mule trip into the Andes to do business with a wild tribe of white Indians. At forty you would locate their American branch in Rockefeller Center or the factory in Hohokus where they buy their quaint native handcraft; if you wanted to see their picturesque countryside, you would wait for a Technicolor travelogue at the neighborhood theater. You still have an occasional impulse to slap a mounted policeman on the horse or be the willing victim of a beautiful lady spy, but you are in no danger of running away to join the circus, and if the Foreign Legion wants you, they'll have to make striking changes in their program.

At twenty you will drive ninety miles an hour for 200 miles through a snowstorm to see one particular girl. At forty you would phone any girl who's home, invite her to come over by cab, and resent it if you miss the eleven-o'clock news broadcast.

At twenty you'd stand all night in line to ride in the first atomic-powered rocket plane. At forty you wouldn't stand in line to ride a magic carpet through Shangri-La on a pass; in fact, you wouldn't stand in line for anything except a place to sit down.

At twenty you'd work nights for a week to avoid missing a party. At forty you wouldn't stay out after midnight for anything up to and including one of the orgies of Imperial Rome, and even there you would have heard the stories. If the party is likely to involve dancing, you regard it with the same enthusiasm as if it involved an opportunity for ditch digging. On the dance floor you feel you ought to get taxi rates, say one dollar to pull your flag and fifty cents a yard anywhere in the city.

At twenty you will change ties six times to get one that looks smart with your new suit, and if the well-dressed man is wearing an ankle-length overcoat of green gunny sacking, you'll have one the minute you can raise the money. It would attract universal attention and cause serious distress if your studs were last year's model. At forty you would go to a White House reception in borrowed pants, wearing paper clips for cuff links, and any suit is in style that will still button.

At twenty you would sit in a hailstorm to see North Carolina Mining and Cowkeeping play Upper Nebraska for possession of the prized Wooden Turtle and the championship of the Soybean Belt. At forty you may get so fired with excitement as to say, "I'd like to see that game . . . in the newsreels," but you wouldn't go out into the traffic to see them play for the possession of North Carolina.

It seems to come down to this: Forty has its advantages, which you could put in your eye. It isn't the twilight of life, but it isn't youth's bright morning, either. There is a little gray in that handsome head of hair I was only yesterday soaking with pomade to get a smooth pompadour, and the dimples are longer now. A lot of my friends are looking pretty chunky and settled; they look like respectable citizens; they are pillars of the community who only yesterday were its chief worries. Once you thought that by this age you would be on top of the world and from forty or forty-five on you would be coasting. At forty you realize you are not coasting, but just skidding. Forty is the age by which you expected to be clipping coupons, and *at* which you find yourself trimming cuffs. About all I can say for it is that forty is no worse than thirty-nine, and probably not much better than forty-one. If anything begins at forty, I haven't noticed it.

THE FLEA POSITION

JOHN CROSBY

(*March 16, 1951*)

The mail packet is in with intelligence from overseas. I like to keep abreast of the more important news from Britain, and I'm sure you do, too. You want to know what's happening in England? I'll tell you what's happening in England. There's a shortage of fleas.

So severe a shortage—let's not mince words—that there probably won't be a flea circus at the Festival of Britain this year. Billy Rayner, who was to have staged the flea circus, reviewed the flea situation to "The Daily Telegraph," and, believe me, it's grim. Trained fleas, as any fool knows, have to come from human beings. Fleas from animals die when they are parted from the animal. Well, sir, no one seems to *have* fleas any more. Mr. Rayner has advertised for them without success. (He wants twelve.)

"Since the war the flea position has been getting steadily worse," explained Mr. Rayner. "I blame the vacuum cleaners and the newfangled disinfectants. The average flea lives only for about three months, and they do not breed in captivity. Toward the end of the three months they become stiff-jointed, just like humans in their old age. And then they cannot ride the cycles, pull chariots or do sword fighting. All the old fleas can manage is an occasional dance. The public won't pay to see that. It is just what they expect from fleas, anyway.

"We usually find that the more educated people are, the more interest they take in our fleas. At Oxford we bring the house down."

Horrifying situation, no doubt about it. Flea circuses are a much older and, in many ways, more respected form of show business than radio or television. We can't let it fall victim to vacuum cleaners and newfangled disinfectants. Seems to me, if we can ship a load of coal to Yorkshire, one of the leading coal-producing areas in the world (as we recently did), we ought to be able to rustle up twelve fleas for the British.

I've been looking around on my own. Inspected my four-year-old son from head to toe to see if he was harboring any talent. His fleas *used* to be able to do sword fighting with the authority of Errol Flynn. But not any more. Not any more. I blame it on the progressive school my son is attending. Nowadays, my son's fleas just lie around reading books. And the public won't pay to see that. It's just what they expect from fleas, anyway. They can't even muster up an occasional dance, these fleas.

It's all very well for Mr. Rayner to say that the more educated the people are, the greater their interest in fleas. But the more educated the *fleas* get, the more trouble they are. Our fleas are still young enough to ride the cycles, pull chariots or do sword fighting. They just won't. They've been educated to the point where they consider it beneath their dignity. And they don't think the money is right. These young American fleas all want to be Ed Sullivan; their aim is to *introduce* people and let *them* ride the cycles. The great ambition of one of our fleas is to introduce Ed Sullivan and make him pull the chariot for a change.

You can hardly blame them, the way the talent situation is these days. A girl can rehearse for three weeks, memorize sixty pages of dialogue and give a whale of a performance on, say, "Studio One." She'll make maybe $200, if she's lucky. It's much more rewarding to be Eva Gabor, tell the guests where to sit down and say "What's new?"—an easy line. If you ask me, these fleas just wised up a little quicker than the humans. There'll come a time—you mark my words —when the actors, the singers, the dancers are going to get darned tired of doing even an occasional dance for Mr. Sullivan. Let him do his own occasional dance.

WONDER FABRICS MAKE ME WONDER

C. S. JENNISON

I bought a petticoat today—uncreasable, unsquashable,
Immersible, reversible, unshrinkable and washable.

According to the ticket, if a spot should dare to show on it
I merely have to drag it through the faucet once and blow on it.

While laundry starches languish and the flatiron sits unheated,
The tucks will stay all smugly snug and permanently pleated.

Though I suppose this petticoat is pretty much a miracle,
I tend to grow more skeptical as labels grow more lyrical.

Besides the fact I lose the tags required for modern laundering,
The fickleness of underwear has kind of set me pondering.

With each new, sneaky fabric-name, my mind gets more uneasy.
I only want some honest cloth that's durable or sleazy.

I view as Counter-Irritants the garment clerks who smile on me
And scoff at silk and cotton as they super-Orlon-nylon me.

I miss the days when no one strove to make a girl or fella wear
The shifting wonder-underclothes they dream up down in Delaware.

GRANDFATHER'S NEW AUTOMOBILE

EMILY KIMBROUGH

Grandmother Kimbrough called our house one evening about six o'clock. I was washing my hands for supper and I heard Mother answer, because the telephone was in the back hall just across from the bathroom door. It hung so high on the wall that, stretching up to reach the mouthpiece, she always sounded a little breathless. Whenever I talked into it, I had to stand on a chair. All children did. There was a calendar hanging in our kitchen that showed a little girl with yellow curls, and wearing only a pair of panties. She was standing on a chair, and saying into the telephone, so the printing underneath read,

"Is 'oo there, Santa Claus?"

I listened to Mother's conversation, of course, and in a minute or two it was well evident to me that something was going on. I heard her say,

"We'll come right up; Hal's home. Don't worry, Mother."

And she hung up.

I whisked out the side door and hid behind the syringa bushes.

Grandfather's house was in the next block. I don't suppose in that flat Indiana landscape there was sufficient difference in elevation to be discernible to the naked eye, but it always seemed to me that Grandfather's house was on the top of a hill. Certainly it was higher than our house and bigger. In fact, it was known in the family as the big house. My Uncle Frank, Daddy's younger brother, and Aunt Helen lived a block beyond us and over one, on Main Street. Uncle Lloyd, Daddy's youngest brother, and Aunt Huda lived next door to Uncle Frank. We always talked about going to Uncle Frank's, or Uncle Lloyd's, but never to Grandfather's. We always said the big house. I thought it was necessarily bigger than ours, because grandparents lived in it. I thought when you were very little you lived in a little house, but when you got bigger your family moved. By the time you were grown up and had children, your parents, being grandparents, moved into a big house. My best friend, Betty Ball, lived in a big house herself. I explained that to myself, and to her, by the assurance that she must be adopted, and that her foster parents had real grandchildren somewhere. The people she called Mother and Father must actually be *grandparents*, with real grandchildren somewhere, or they wouldn't live in a big house. It haunted Betty, and annoyed her mother considerably. She was my mother's closest friend, and exactly her age. But it satisfied my sense of justice and the fitness of things.

Mother and Daddy came out the front door, and hurried up the street. I let them get a little ahead of me, and then scuttled after them. It was early Spring, but chilly. Mother had snatched her golf cape off the hat-rack in the vestibule, and was hooking it at the throat as they passed me. I had not stopped to put on any kind of a coat lest I be caught, but I was too excited to feel cold. I knew something was up, and I knew that if I *were* caught I would be given a sharp spank in the rear and sent home. This made the suspense almost unbearable. I passed the Ross's house safely—they were our next door neighbors—and then the Vatets'. After that there was a bad stretch, because there was a vacant field with no protecting shrubbery—nothing to hide behind until clear across Vine Street where Lydia Rich's house stood on the corner.

When Mother and Daddy reached the corner, they saw my two uncles and aunts hurrying along Vine Street, and waited for them. By the time they had all met and started off together, they were so busy talking that it was safe for me to pass the field and cross the street behind them. I was not allowed to cross the street alone, so that if I had been discovered then, I could expect the application of Daddy's bedroom slipper, but not one of them looked back. And by the time we had passed the Richs' and reached the big house itself, I was at their heels like a puppy. They stopped so abruptly in fact, that I very nearly walked up the back of Mother's legs before I could stop myself. She turned around, saw me, and all she said was,

"Out of the way, dear," and pushed me a little, nowhere in particular.

I knew then that whatever had stopped them must be awful, and I raced around in front of them with my heart pounding. I thought it must be something dead on the sidewalk, so I put my hands over my eyes and then looked down between them, but I couldn't see anything. I took my hands away and still I couldn't see anything. I looked back at the family, all of them, and they were staring into the street. There, against the curb, right at the carriage block, was a great, black *thing*. It had a top, with straps at the corners to tie it down. There was a front seat and a back seat. Far in front of the front seat were shining brass lamps. I could not imagine what the contraption was for, unless it was some kind of a couch to go in the Turkish corner of the library, except that it had big wheels.

Grandmother Kimbrough stood on the carriage block, with her back to the *thing*.

Barely five feet two, never weighing more than ninety-six pounds, she was as quick and sharp as a dragon-fly. Her dark eyes were flashing from one member of the family to another. She pushed up her hair off her forehead in a nervous gesture, that soft brown hair which was a constant exasperation to her.

"Why can't it turn gray, the pesky thing?" I heard her demand frequently. "Every respectable woman my age has gray hair. People will think I touch it up."

She folded her arms tight across her chest, a Napoleon on the carriage block I would remember her.

"Your father," she said grimly, "has bought an auto*mo*bile."

Grandfather was standing at the head of the *thing*. He looked very handsome, I thought, and not excited. I had *never* seen him look excited, nor even worried. Once I had heard him say to Uncle Frank, "If you're worrying about that, Frank, then I'll *stop* worrying. One is enough."

People frequently told me that my grandfather was a very distinguished looking man. He said, when I repeated it to him, that it meant he had a very large nose. He had brown eyes, too, very dark brown, a broad forehead, and more respectable hair than Grandmother's. It *had* turned gray, with white on top, like a blackboard that has recently been wiped over lightly with the chalk eraser. His mustache matched. He was not remarkably tall, but his shoulders were broad and straight, like a soldier's. That, I thought, was because he had been in the Civil War when he was eighteen and had been taught to march. When we walked down town, he spoke to everybody we saw.

"Hello, Mr. C. M.," or just "C. M.," people would call back, even from across the street.

He waved at that moment to me, and I waved back just a little, so as not to be noticed. He smiled at all of us and then looked at Grandmother, and then turned back and smiled at us again. I knew he was feeling exactly the way I was—pleased and scared.

Everybody started talking at once. Aunt Huda said you could get coats with bonnets and veils to match. They kept the dust off, and were the latest style. She was going to write to her sister Bertha in

"Your allergy tests suggest that you may have been intended for some other planet."

New York and ask her to send her an outfit. Aunt Helen was talking to Grandmother, telling her not to be upset, that it would be lovely. She had heard they were very safe, and she knew that Father Kimbrough would be careful. The boys—that is, my father and my two uncles, but I called them that because everyone else did—started over to the automobile itself. They were talking about machinery. Grandfather called out,

"Mr. Lockhart, I would like you to meet my sons, Hal and Frank and Lloyd."

I had not seen that there was somebody on the couch; but a man climbed down from it, and was introduced to us. He had driven the automobile from the factory and was going to stay for two weeks to teach Grandfather, and see that it was all right. He led the boys to the front and opened it up. They were all talking at once, and pretty soon they lay down on their backs and wiggled underneath. Grandmother was saying to the daughters-in-law—I always called them that, too, because everyone else did—

"It was that play we saw in Indianapolis, *The Man from Home*, that did it. Your father got it in his mind the moment he saw that same automobile on the stage."

Grandfather interrupted.

"A Haynes, made in Kokomo. A good *Indiana* product, and you are not to worry, Margaret."

And then, of course, it had to happen. Mother saw me again and recognized me. She didn't scold, which was astonishing, but she fussed. She took off her golf cape and wrapped it around me—I was always being enveloped in that plaid-lined, woolen garment, with the hood jerked down so that I couldn't see—and Daddy carried me home over his shoulder. He turned me over to Zoe for my supper and to go to bed, and that was the last of the excitement I saw. As I left, Grandfather was asking if anyone would like to take a drive, and Grandmother was the only one declining. I missed, too, what happened the next day, but both grandparents told it so many times during the later years of motoring, that I learned every word and gesture. A different version from each of them, of course.

Early in the morning my grandfather rode out to his factory in the machine, the trained expert, Mr. Lockhart, at the wheel. Some time later, about ten o'clock, he telephoned my grandmother and asked if she had been to market. She said that Noah, who was the hired man, was just bringing around Prince. Well, Grandfather told her, if she would care to drive down town in the new auto instead, he and Mr. Lockhart would come for her in about twenty minutes. A mental conflict must have rocked her. There was the danger of the infernal machine, the fact that the night before she had declared she would never set foot in it and Grandfather could go back with it to Kokomo, the knowledge that it was the first one in town, and the recollection of Aunt Huda saying that it was the most stylish thing you could have, everyone in the East was getting one, her sister Bertha had told her so.

When Grandfather arrived about half an hour later, Prince was back in the barn, and Grandmother was standing on the carriage block. At the sight of him, however, she jumped off and backed away,

"Well, here she is! Dead Man's Slide, we used to call it—hm-m-m—probably been graded down since I was a boy. . . ."

---

because *he* was at the wheel and the mechanic from Kokomo was sitting beside him.

"Charles," Grandmother said, "I will not put my foot in this carriage, with you driving. Why, you don't know anything about the crazy thing."

Grandfather told her that he had been driving that morning for two hours, and that Mr. Lockhart considered him extremely apt. Furthermore, he did, after all, build bridges and might therefore be supposed to know something about machinery. The steering contrivance was not unlike driving a horse, once you accustomed yourself to minor differences. But if Grandmother were nervous she had better have Prince brought around again.

Grandmother climbed into the back seat and sat down.

"I will die with you," she said with obscure menace, "and you will always be sorry."

She bounced herself down on the black leather cushion with all the vehemence of her ninety-six pounds and slammed the door, thwarting Mr. Lockhart, who had come round to perform that little courtesy.

Mr. Lockhart reported to Grandfather that she was safely aboard, and Grandfather recited aloud the steps toward putting the machine in motion. The left foot down, the right hand over and back, the right hand then on the steering wheel throttle. And with that a roar convulsed the machine so that it sprang into the air, and stopped dead. Mr. Lockhart got out, went around in front, released an iron bar from a leather loop, ground it a few times and the engine roared again. Grandmother was already out and on her way back to the house. But Mr. Lockhart coaxed her in again. Grandfather called out that he knew exactly the cause of the mishap. It was not the fault of the engine but of his own misjudgment of the allotment of gasoline. The machine moved ahead once more, in jumps, but it kept going. Grandmother grabbed the carriage strap nearest her. They turned the corner on Monroe Street, and she held on with both hands.

A great many people saw them go up Main Street, and witnessed the unusual behavior of Mr. Meeks, the butter and egg man. He was a sturdy man with a round face that was almost as red in the Winter as in the Summer. His hands were red, too, with cracks running up and down across them on both sides. He was a farmer and worked hard but he loved to tell jokes and to laugh, slapping his big red hand down as if he were spanking himself when he was especially tickled. Once a week he brought in butter and eggs to regular customers. When the automobile with Grandfather driving it passed him, he was just getting out of his buggy at the house next to Mr. Bernard's little store. The horse went up over the sidewalk into the yard and one of the shafts of the buggy got stuck between the fence palings. Grandfather called out that he was distressed but couldn't stop. People who didn't see it could scarcely believe what Mr. Meeks did. He turned around in the yard and shook his fist after Grandfather. Grandmother had her eyes closed in such angry determination that she didn't see it.

Of course Grandmother knew every inch of the way by heart. A railroad track ran along the first cross street beyond Mr. Bernard's little store. This was a branch line of the Pennsylvania Railroad and carried only freight but it did cut right across the town and people always drew in their horses to look up and down before they crossed the track. Grandfather didn't draw in the machine. He was concerned about Mr. Meeks' horse being stuck in the fence and not quite sure, furthermore, of the process of stopping, so he just bumped over the tracks without even slowing down. It jarred Grandmother but she kept her eyes closed. Fortunately there wasn't a freight train coming.

The stores began on the other side of the railroad track. They were low frame buildings, most of them, sometimes with a cement front and a big window to make the store look more stylish. The street was wide but from the railroad track on there were no trees. All the way into the center of town it was bare—dusty and hot in Summer, muddy at other seasons. There were hitching posts along the curb on either side and generally some horses and buggies or wagons waiting. Grandfather passed them safely. The Kirby House, a hotel, stood on the corner a few blocks beyond the railroad tracks. The building was higher than any near it. Mostly men hung around this hotel and in the Summer they sat in a row on wooden armchairs out in front on the sidewalk. There was a cuspidor between every two chairs and the men tilted their chairs back against the front wall of the hotel and watched the people go by. Grandfather passed the hotel and the men cheered. Even if Grandmother's eyes had been open she would have looked away. Walking down town, she would have taken the other side of the street.

There were saloons in that block, too. One of the saloons was made to look like a log cabin and had sawdust under the swinging door. I never could see far enough inside to know how it looked there, though I always squatted down and tried to. There were two drug stores on that side of the street also, and a boys' clothing store with life-sized wax figures in the window. Mr. Hummel's bakery was on that side, too. Walking along, you could get in one block a warm sugar and cinnamon smell from the bakery, a sharp tingling odor from the drug stores, and a sour, musty smell from the saloons. I considered it not only the preferable side of the street, but one of the most interesting stretches in the whole town. The other side of the street had the best market in town—the Sterling Cash Grocery. Above it was the best club in town, too—the Commercial Club. That was where the children's dancing classes were held and most of the grown-up dances, too. People gave parties there. If you were a member, you could watch parades from its front windows.

The next corner, at Main and Walnut Streets, was the busiest intersection in town. On Saturdays a policeman stood there all day. So many farmers came into town that the wagons and buggies were always getting snarled up. The policeman had to tell them when they could go. The buggy wheels were always getting caught, too, in the trolley track on Main Street, especially where it turned into Walnut. The policeman had to help pull them out. The dry-goods stores were on Walnut Street—Vatet's and McNaughton's. There were several buildings more than two stories high. It was the heart of what we called "down town," or "up street."

Grandfather came all the way up Main Street with no trouble; none of the horses along the curb shied; he didn't get caught in the trolley track nor have any difficulty about the trolley. The trolley wasn't even in sight. He was very pleased when he got to the corner of Main and Walnut. He even took one hand off the steering wheel to wave at the policeman, whose mouth dropped wide open at the sight of this vehicle. That pleased Grandfather, too. So he turned around and said loudly and cheerfully, "Where do you wish to go, Margaret?"

His voice was so loud and so close that it *made* her open her eyes, and when she saw that his face was turned toward *her*, and not out toward the *road*, she screamed at him,

"Mr. Topps's, Mr. Topps's!"

The shrillness of her tone and her agitation must, in turn, have startled him, for he jumped perceptibly as he turned his head back to the front again. And in the passage he caught sight of Mr. Topps's butcher shop. With a sweep that would have brought around the mighty *Oceanic*, "Greyhound of the Seas," he swung the wheel, and the machine responded. Up over the curb they went, across the sidewalk, and, cleaving a sharp, broad wake, straight through Mr. Topps's plate glass window to the very dot of their destination, the meat counter itself. There, shuddering, the carriage stopped.

Mr. Topps stood on the other side of the counter about two feet away from the front lamps, his cleaver upheld in his right hand, his eyes staring, his teeth bared in an unnatural grin. There *had* been two or three other people in the shop when the conveyance approached the window, but the sight of Mr. Topps's face had caused them to turn and see what was coming upon them. So they too were now on the far side of the counter with him.

When the clatter of falling glass stopped, Grandfather spoke out of the awesome silence.

"This, Margaret," he announced, "is where you said you wanted to come."

Place of Birth:

MIDDLE EAST CALLS MIDDLE WEST

ANNE SINCLAIR MEHDEVI

My husband hurried home one day with a telegram in his hand: he had been accepted as a member of the secretariat of the United Nations. We would have to leave Mazatlán, Mexico, where we'd been staying, and go to New York immediately.

Since my parents, who lived in Wichita, Kansas, had never met my Persian husband or our children, I suggested we make our return trip by way of Wichita. My husband agreed to the idea, and I wrote a letter announcing our arrival within two weeks.

While we were dismantling our household and arranging the trip, I found myself growing less and less confident about the prospective meeting between my husband and my parents. I began to remember fussy little habits and customs at home that were going to astonish Mohamed. And worse, I began to look at my husband through my parents' eyes. I found him wanting.

"You know," I said one day, "I think maybe you ought to get a crew cut." My husband wore his black hair long and brushed back, cavalier style. I was glad he didn't have a hairline moustache. He looked like the type of man who might.

"What for?" he said.

"Then you wouldn't look so—well, foreign."

He laughed. "Foreign where? I'm always being taken for a Mexican."

"That's what I mean!" I said triumphantly.

Mohamed shrugged.

I went on. "Now, please don't get mad. But you mustn't kiss my mother's hand. She'd faint with surprise. And when they ask you to chip in and help wash the dishes, don't be ironic."

Mohamed bridled. "I'll gladly wash *all* the dishes, but I refuse to chip in and pretend it's fun. What more?"

"And don't buy presents for everyone. They'll just suspect you're trying to make an impression. And if one of my brothers praises a tie or something you're wearing don't take it off and give it to him."

"Why not?"

"Well, they would all think you were showing off."

"O.K. What more?" he asked with simmering patience.

"And don't take taxis all the time. That's ostentatious. And don't look so spruced up except on Sunday. Let your shoes go dirty. They'll think you're putting on the dog if you look so shiny all the time."

"Good God!"

"And if we go out, don't tip more than 10 per cent. And don't get angry at going Dutch. They'll be insulted if you try to pay all the time. It's bad manners. And it's bad manners to let them pay all the time too."

"It's good manners to split?" Mohamed asked.

"Yes, and don't get mad if they call you Moe."

"Yes . . . ?"

"And try to tone down your accent. Don't keep saying 'isss' instead of 'is,' and 'hass' and 'wass.' And don't make any more of your silly words like 'hood-winkling' and 'electric lightening.' And don't call to-matoes 'to-mah-toes.' "

"Is that all?"

"Well, don't say 'lough,' say 'laff' . . . oh, I could go on and on about your accent."

"You always said you liked it. Complained that I was losing it, if I remember correctly."

"Well, this is different, and don't you dare buy an orchid for me or Mother or anything fancy like that. It will reflect on them because they don't buy orchids. See?"

"Enough! That's enough!" shouted Mohamed, waving me away.

I stopped and said: "Don't be mad now. And please remember all that I said."

He grinned. "I'll remember . . . it's been a revelation."

"And will you try to do as I say?"

"Lord, no. Wouldn't think of it."

After that Mohamed's original enthusiasm about meeting my family imperceptibly tapered off into a shy avoidance of the subject. When a telegram arrived, a few days before our scheduled departure, requesting that he report at once to Lake Success, I suspected that he arranged to have it sent to himself. It permitted him no time for a stopover in Wichita.

"You visit your parents anyway," said my husband gallantly. "Meanwhile I'll find an apartment."

"You mean I have to travel five thousand miles alone with two infants?" I said.

"Pish-posh. It's nothing. Give them both a sleeping pill. The plane will be there before they wake up."

"But I can't even carry them both at once. How can I get in and out of the plane?" I said.

"There are hostesses . . . those cuties that give you chewing gum. Let them carry one. Anyway, Rafael can walk."

"Walk! Two steps, that's all!"

"Where's your famous American pioneer spirit?" my husband asked, and that was the end of the matter. He left on the plane to Mexico City the next day, where he was to pick up the direct flight to New York. He seemed gay and carefree as he boarded the plane at the Mazatlán airport. All he carried was a little bag, and his overcoat pockets were full of rolled-up magazines. There was a relieved, almost bachelorish air about him I resented.

My parents fitted me into the household routine as if I had never been away; five years had passed since I had seen them and ten since I lived at home. But my mother, in spite of her earnest resolution to treat me as an adult, couldn't resist urging me to go to bed early and clean my plate. And I, tyrannized by ancient habit, stopped smoking except for occasional puffs in the bathroom with the windows open.

I wanted desperately to please. I felt I had to make up for my defection and insubordination in marrying a foreigner, and a Persian to boot. I tried anxiously to do what was expected of me.

The house ran upon a chronometric schedule: meals were served at the same time every day, the radio was turned on for certain programs and the newspapers read according to immemorial customs. Even baths were taken at foreordained hours.

After the haphazard makeshift of Mexico, this subjugation to routine cramped and harassed me, making me feel guilty whenever I forgot some time-honored detail. But after my mother had expanded the schedule to include children's feeding hours and children's nap hours, after she had organized the baby-food procurement and the diaper-washing, I was grateful. These problems I had been fighting for months now took care of themselves automatically. Mother even solved Alex's temperament by placing him on the dining room table whenever he was fretful. She would give the chandelier—a glittering globe of cut glass bangles hanging from a long silk cord—a little push. It kept moving for hours while Alex followed it with his eyes and forever tried to touch it with his hands. For the first time since my marriage I could wake up in the morning secure and safe in the knowledge that the day was already taken care of, that it would present no alarms, no surprises.

My parents and my younger brothers were disappointed that Mohamed had been unable to come, but they interpreted his default as devotion to duty and praised it. That he had denied himself the pleasures of the trip (my parents love traveling) was, to them, exemplary. Until this proof of his stability, my father had suspected that Mohamed might be one of those "café society youths." He told me this jovially, after he was sure it wasn't true.

I confess that I played up this unexpected evaluation of my husband's character for all it was worth. I had succeeded in picturing him as a model—conscientious, solid, earnest—when Mohamed himself dispelled the deception.

My parents, my three brothers and I were sitting as usual one morning over coffee in what we called the breakfast nook. The telephone, which stood on a telephone table in one corner of the room, began to ring. After my mother reached over and answered it, her face froze in alarm. She handed the phone to me with a whisper of fright: "It's New York calling."

The telephone, to my parents, was an instrument to be treated with respect and prudence. A long-distance call, like a telegram, was never to be indulged in flippantly. I can't recall our family ever receiving or making a long-distance call in all of my childhood. But I remember well that the ring of the Western Union boy at the door was enough to make my mother blanch. He was bringing news of death or disaster; good news or casual news was sent by letter. Only tragedy was urgent enough to warrant a telegram. And a long-distance call was even more alarming because it was more expensive and faster.

My husband, on the other hand, regarded the telephone as a gift to be made use of. Since most Persians are inveterate postponers, the telephone is a godsend to them. It precludes the necessity of making up their minds about anything beforehand. A call can settle anything in the manner of an impromptu conversation. You don't feel committed, you haven't signed anything, and if you should change your mind you can always ring back.

My mother, father and my three brothers sat rigid, solemn around the breakfast table while I answered the call. When my husband's voice came through, clear and calm, I was relieved. My family's attitude had infected me.

"Are you all right?" I couldn't help asking.

My husband didn't answer this question. Instead he said: "Madam, you're in for a letdown. One week in New York and I'm ready to go back to Mexico."

I glanced guiltily around the breakfast table. Five pair of eyes were fastened anxiously, sympathetically upon my face.

I couldn't bring myself to talk about the pleasantness or unpleasantness of New York within this circle of consternation. "Oh . . ." I said, trailing off.

"Are things going all right? If you want to stay longer, go ahead," my husband went on.

"No," I said.

"What's the matter? Anything wrong?"

How could I explain that my parents regarded the whimsical shifting of plans as a sign of instability? My plane reservation to New York was made. My father had arranged to leave his office to an assistant so he could drive me to the airport. My clothing was even then being pressed, mended and packed. Pleased as my parents would be at an extension of my visit, their pleasure would be negated by their distress at discovering that my husband was flighty. Any capricious tampering with serious plans was deplorable. Plans must be steadfastly kept to.

All I said was: "No, it's all fine."

"Well, call me up a day or two before you decide to come."

"I don't think I can," I said.

"What's the matter? You have a phone, don't you?"

"Yes, well . . ." I hedged.

"Wait a second, I'll give you my office number. Got a pencil?"

"Never mind. Anyway, I'll be coming as planned."

"Don't confine yourself. Stay on. You've got sun there. The weather is rotten here."

"Thanks, but . . ."

"Don't worry about me."

"I'm not!" I said emphatically.

My parents, having now understood that Mohamed had no tragic news to report, assumed that he had some vital personal or emotional information to convey. But it was taking an awfully long time. Father looked at his watch anxiously. Three minutes were already up.

"What the devil is the matter?" asked Mohamed, exasperated. "You sound as if you had a mouth full of mush."

"Yes . . ." I said vaguely.

"Are the children behaving?" my husband went on.

"Yes."

"Well, look, then it's decided. You stay on as long as you want to— a week, a month, more if you want to——"

"Oh, no!" I said hurriedly.

"Can't you give a straight answer?" said my husband. "Are you or aren't you getting along O.K.?"

"Yes."

"But you don't want to stay on? You've no idea when you'll see your family again."

"Yes, I know . . ." I glanced up to see my mother's face wrinkled in a worried frown. The second three minutes were half over. Father had placed his pocket watch, with the lid snapped open, on the table. All the family were watching its hair-fine gold minute hand sweep around, turn after turn. I knew they would ask me what drastic reason had made Mohamed call. I had to get some information from him to tell them later. I asked: "Did you find a house?"

"Well, yes and no," said Mohamed.

"What do you mean?"

"Well, I've been pretty busy. But I've got some pretty good leads."

"Oh," I said weakly.

At this moment my father held up the watch and pointed to its minute hand. He whispered "Six" loudly.

"Mohamed," I said, under pressure, "six minutes are up. I'll see you in three days. TWA, getting in about five."

"What's that?"

"Six minutes are up."

"That's all right. I'm in no hurry."

I said helplessly: "Will you remember the time of the plane?"

My husband sounded surprised. "Oh? You've decided not to stay on?"

"Yes, I've decided," I said firmly. "Well, good-by."

"Wait a minute! Did you get the roses I sent? Isn't it fantastic? I just went to a flower shop on Forty-second Street and *wired* flowers. Do they send them by rocket? It's amazing!"

I decided not to go into an explanation. The roses *had* arrived and had caused a flurry of disapproval. Mohamed had sent three dozen, and there were at least twenty dozen blooming in the garden of my parents' house.

"Yes, I got the flowers. Thanks," I said. . . . The six minutes were finished. My mother and father surreptitiously returned to their breakfast but their ears were attuned to my conversation. I could see a shadow of disapproval in my father's eyes. He was computing the cost of the phone call, and he fully realized, now, that it wasn't about anything important.

"Good-by," I said again, desperately.

"What's up? Is someone listening?" asked my husband.

"Yes," I said. "Good-by."

"Well, why didn't you tell me? Now, be sure to telephone when you finally decide to come to New York."

"Mohamed," I said, "I'm coming as planned."

"O.K., O.K.," he said. "But call me up if you change your mind. I'll give you my number."

"I don't *want* your number. Good-by." I hung up, just as the minute hand rushed toward the ninth minute.

Placing the phone in its cradle, I smiled bravely at the circle of faces around me. No one asked me anything, but there was expectation on every face. At last my father commented: "No bad news, I hope?" He hoped that there was, at least, important news; not because he would ever have wished me the slightest ill, but because, in this case, I suspect he did wish that I and my husband were cognizant of the importance of an instantaneous spanning of a thousand miles.

I dragnetted my mind for some answer, trying to think of something worthy of a long-distance call. At last I said: "He wanted to tell me he hasn't found an apartment yet."

My father chuckled. "That's nothing. I remember a good cabin camp up in the Bronx. I stayed there in 1927—a dollar a day, I think it

"Sometimes I think the kid'll never get the hang of it."

---

was, for five of us. Not high-class, of course, but at least a roof over your heads."

My mind quickly skipped over the vision of Mohamed in a Bronx cabin camp. Then hesitating, unsure, I went on: "He thought maybe I'd like to stay on here awhile—the sun, you know."

Both Mother and Father tried not to stare at me. Mother's coffee spoon paused in the air. Then she laid it down carefully on her saucer and said: "Yes, I suppose we'd all like to do the things we can't."

"Families should be together," said Father, firmly, suspiciously.

"Well," I said, "then I'd better send a telegram that I'm coming as planned."

My mother's eyebrows lifted gently. "But you've *written*, haven't you?"

"Yes, but Mohamed is so vague."

My mother laughed pleasantly. "*Surely* not about the arrival of his family," she said. There was no hint of doubt in her tone. She was stating a logical fact.

I let the conversation die, and just as we finished breakfast the telephone rang again. Quickly, I jumped for it first.

"Say," said Mohamed when I answered, "we must have been cut off. I didn't have a chance to say hello to your mother and father. Are they there?"

"IT MAKES ME NO DIFFERENCE"

RICHARD S. DAVIS

Without disrespect to either Cincinnati or St. Louis, it may be asserted that Milwaukee's speech has been colored more by the German influence than any other city's in America. Native Milwaukeeans, even after being exposed to the cultural refinements of Eastern schools, often cling to phrases and inflections that give them away on the instant. It may be nothing short of a calamity at Vassar or Princeton, but it is still amusing at home.

The German "*ja*" for "yes" is a habit quickly and all but incurably acquired. "*Ach!*" makes an exclamation far more serviceable than "Oh." "*Aina?*" is deemed less clumsy than "Isn't it so?" It is not true that the thicker phrases of German origin are employed by more than a small fraction of the population, but a stranger making a tour of the town is certain to be startled and perplexed by certain remarks. For example:

"He inquired *after* you."

"The *schnapps* is *all*, but the beer is *yet*," meaning that whisky has disappeared but that still, *Gott sei dank*, there is enough beer.

"Where can I *become* a glass of May wine?" does not seek a miracle, merely a well-stocked tavern.

"*By* Vliet Street, where the car *bends*," means, "on Vliet Street where the streetcar turns."

"*Bring* it in the paper," meaning to print it there.

"Do you want some *butter bread*?"—otherwise, bread and butter.

"Button up your *neck*," sage advice in a Milwaukee winter, counsels keeping the collar buttoned and the neck warm.

"Did you see all the bargains *ever*?"

"I *first* got up at eight this morning *already*."

"I had to laugh *from* her."

"I got a *invite* to the wedding."

"It *makes me* no difference."

"*Make* my apron shut," which means to tie it.

"Come *once*, just look at this *once*."

The untranslatable word, *gemütlichkeit*, which roughly means good will and good living, is generously employed in Milwaukee, more often than sometimes seems warranted. Politicos, also, are very fond of the phrase, "He won't get schneider," a term borrowed from the favorite card games, skat and *schafskopf* (sheep's head), which are played in the old taverns. Not to "get schneider" means to make a poor showing.

ON BEING TRANSLATED INTO ENGLISH

LESLEY CONGER

One Saturday morning the mailman tossed a magazine on the front porch, a magazine I'd never seen before. In fact, when I picked it up I couldn't quite make it out, neither the name of it nor the caption under the cover picture; so I turned it over, as one does any curious and unfamiliar object, and became immediately absorbed in a three-strip episode of *Tarzan*, entitled "Overrumplet af Guxa." When I had finished (leaving Tarzan engaged in furious hand-to-hand combat with a half-dozen pointed-toothed, bodyless heads which looked like nothing so much as rather malevolent Humpty-Dumpties) I turned back to the first inside pages and discovered the reason for the magazine's arrival at my door—an innocuous little short story of mine, beginning "Skrivemaskinens sejrberuste klapren forstummede . . ."

It was the first time I had ever been translated. My husband and I read it over aloud, rocking with laughter—not because Danish is any funnier than English, but because there is something innately ludicrous about one's own writing put into a language one can barely pick out. Of course, all translation, if the reader is familiar with the original, has something inevitably humorous about it; I remember some years ago being highly entertained by Sherlock Holmes *auf deutsch*, and I also possess a copy of some of Shaw's plays in (I confess) Russian—even Russian can, under such circumstances, amuse.

It might, no doubt, be even funnier to be translated into Tagalog or Bantu or Greenland Eskimo; but the kind of ephemeral reading-matter I produce has not yet reached those outposts of audience, Finland being as far as I have gone (and perhaps far enough). And yet

I suspect that of all translation, translation into English is actually the most intriguing.

Oh, of course I *write* in English—I mean translation into *English* English—British English, that is. I must say, first of all, that I have never been to England. My acquaintance with British life and manners is entirely derived from the printed page—and the most fascinating of such printed pages are the very pages on which my own stories are printed. I always skim my work when it appears, no matter where, just to ascertain the extent of editorial butchery. But things that arrive from England I read with scholarly attention, word by word, phrase by unfamiliar, metamorphosed, inexplicable phrase.

Some changes are expectable, a matter of mere vocabulary. A little boy who got into a cookie jar in America gets into a biscuit tin in England; his mother goes into the scullery, not the pantry. He eats porridge, not oatmeal, and listens to the wireless instead of the radio. The big downtown department store has, to American ears, a shrunken sound, having become merely the big shop in town. Other changes are more than a matter of substitute terms; they are concerned with actual differences, differences in reality. The front yard has become a garden, complete with garden-gate. Lunch-boxes have turned into satchels. The little boy puts on an overcoat and Wellington boots instead of a snowsuit, and instead of pulling off the hood of his snowsuit when he comes in, he takes off his scarf. He sits *in* the porch and not *on* it—I suppose that to make sense in terms of British architecture, though I'm not certain just how.

And then there is the mother who puts a wishbone to dry on top of the refrigerator. Refrigerators are, I suppose, understandable as refrigerators (leaving slang aside) in both countries. But this was a lower middle-class mother, or maybe upper-lower; by the time she had got to England, she had lost her refrigerator. She put the wishbone to dry on a windowsill. (Of course, it's possible I'm making too much of this. Perhaps it's that British housewives always keep the tops of their refrigerators neat and tidy, and tend to clutter up their window-sills; *I* pile my poor refrigerator to the ceiling and never put anything on a windowsill.) (Or could it be, perhaps, that the English house is so damp that no wishbone would ever dry unless placed in the direct blast of the English sun?)

You can readily see how complicated this can become, and how it can lead to endless speculation. I had a mother sitting at the living-room table across from her son, darning argyle socks while he did his home-work. But in England she is much more comfortable; she is set-tled cosily by the fire, mending school socks, this time. No table, per-haps? I thought, but I read on and found the poor boy still sitting at the table and working away—and shivering, I expect. Mom, by the way, or as they put it, Mum, was still using her darning-egg; I thought for certain that would be different, but it wasn't. In fact, I have seen flashlights remain flashlights and never turn into torches, and a run in a nylon stocking survive as a run, when I thoroughly expected it to become a ladder. On the other hand, in one story the Brooklyn Bridge turned into both Houses of Parliament. That *was* fun!

I have named two boys Tyler and Skip and have watched them ap-pear sedately as Keith and David. I have seen an eggnog with a table-spoonful of molasses in it become an egg-flip with a tablespoonful of golden syrup. I have seen a Bermuda onion pickling itself on the trans-atlantic crossing and forgetting where it came from. These things haven't upset me, actually, but there are some questions I want to ask. Why did my cream of asparagus soup turn into cream of tomato? Why couldn't a little boy sprinkle cinnamon on his toast? (His brother got him a dish of marmalade, instead.) And are there no high shelves in English kitchens to be reached by the short British housewife? I left a little boy sitting on a kitchen stepladder and found him sit-ting at the bottom of the kitchen stairs. Or if stairs = stepladder, then what = stairs?

But one of the more bewildering transformations perhaps a British housewife could explain to me. I had a heroine with short dark hair, wearing a Kelly green coat and her best brown pumps. I wasn't sur-prised that in England her coat was emerald green and her best brown pumps were her best brown court shoes. Her short dark hair, however, turned blonde; still, that may have been the translator's personal preference—we can leave it at that. To go on: my girl went home, put on her best suit, and went to see her rival, who turned out to be a dreadfully shabby little woman in an out-of-date blue print dress; but in England, besides bleaching her hair, she put on *her* blue print dress and went to see her rival, *who was wearing an out-of-date, shabby suit.* This alteration, I believe, can only be taken to imply that the two conceptions of suit vs. print dress, with all the words convey of shab-biness or of chic, must be completely opposite—otherwise why bother to switch them? Of course, I have not seen the British woman in the street; this quick costume change may be, all abstract conceptions and images aside, a mere reflection cast darkly upon the reality of British tailoring. I am left puzzling, and wait with renewed interest for my next view of British life—as seen through my own writings.

NEW YORKESE

FEDERAL WRITERS' PROJECT

Most New Yorkers speak English, but an understanding of the following expressions, while not essential to a pleasant visit to New York, will equip the visitor to deal with most of the ordinary situations encountered in the city. Ignorance of them may result in giving unnecessary offense, becoming involved with gendarmes, or even starving to death.

Fithavnya. An important thoroughfare running from Washington Square to 142nd Street in Manhattan.

Freshegginit? Wistful inquiry made by soda counterman when a milkshake is ordered. The expected answer is "No."

Gimmyaringforwensdy. "Call me by telephone before next Wednesday."

Giverair! Mass chant shouted over a woman who has fainted.

Howzigohinbud? "Good day, friend. Are your affairs progressing favorably?"

Juhearutased? Traditional second question policemen ask loiterers. Actions, not words, are indicated. See *Whyntchagoferawawk?*

Keepyurnozeouttathgutta. Advising temperance; "remember not to get too intoxicated."

Lawn Gyland. An insular appendix of New York State surrounding Amityville.

Lemawf! Lemawf! Subway guard's plea to allow passengers to leave the train.

Lezgehgohinbabe. "I suggest that we leave, Gwendolyn."

Maymineasame. Commonly spoken over a polished mahogany bar.

Phewkinfixzitlemmyknow. "In the event that you are able to make the desired arrangements, please inform me."

Sawlawf. "The suggested arrangement is not satisfactory" or "It is finished, over, done, ended."

Seeinya. Farewell, usually spoken in chorus; vaguely implies future meetings.

Sheeaingottafren, itzasista. What it costs a sailor two coins to learn in a telephone booth.

Slovlyonyamodom. Salesgirl's inevitable reaction to any gown on any customer.

Smatterthya? Expression of solicitude for the state of another's health, or implying misgivings concerning his mental capacity.

Smosamonryethlessenogrease. Drugstore counterman's verification of an order for a smoked salmon sandwich on rye bread with lettuce, but without butter or mayonnaise.

Taykadeezy, Taykadeezy. Redundant expression intended to calm the emotions.

Washastep! Subway guard's version of "Take care in alighting from the train, ladies and gentlemen."

Whyntchagoferawawk? Traditional first question policemen ask loiterers. No answer is required.

Yessirollaypape! Newspaper vendor's cry; means nothing, intended to draw the customer near enough to be asked—

Yessirwaddyaread? "Which paper do you wish to purchase?"

AMERICAN FOLK STORIES

MORITZ JAGENDORF

A folk story is not a petrified object, dull and unchanging, but a living, changing and growing entity. Each retelling adds new color, new wisdom, new variety from the enthusiasm and love of the new teller.

It has been Dr. Jagendorf's good fortune to travel slowly through many parts of our land and meet folks, old in experience and years, but young in mind and spirit. The stories set down here, for the first time, he heard as anecdotes to bring a smile. . . .

A TALE FOR TEXAS

There are no tall tales in all the world equal to those heard when Texan tall-tale tellers and New York tall-tale tellers get a-jawing. Brass-mounted lightning zooms around 'em like flies around a honey pot.

Brazobounders 'll cry, "Roy Bean," and Yorkers will bellow, "Big Mose," Texans 'll come back with "Big-Foot Wallace," and Yorkers will shout, "Johnny Darling." In the end the iron-nailed-Lone-Star-he-men 'll roar, "Pecos Bill, the greatest cowboy in the world," and then . . . Yorkers 'll be silent. Texans seeing they took the wind out of the Empire Staters 'd keep on jawing and snapping like all the alligators of the world busy with their supper.

"Ha! Never heard of Pecos Bill? You have bisons in your ears and mud in your eyes. He is the only living critter who is in a thousand places at one and the same time. He invented the cowboys and everything pertaining to them. He invented more things than all New England ever did. More adventures happened to him than sand in a sand storm. I'm not going to tell them to you because you wouldn't live long enough to hear 'em. I'm just going to tell you one and educate you so you can understand them properly. It's what happened to him with Slue-Foot Sue, his true love he never married because she was too strongheaded.

"Bill saw Sue for the first time riding a great catfish down the Rio Grande. In those days catfish were as big as yearling heifers and faster than wild mustangs. She was riding one of those great big catfish with whiskers long as a horse's mane, with only a surcingle as a guide and I tell you she was a sight to open moles' eyes. Bill he looked at that winsome beauty and Sue she looked at that handsome Texan and there was a great oil gush of love between them. They made up to go it together without waiting and a wedding day was set. Slue-Foot Sue was busy as a borer getting things ready.

"I'm going to tell you here that Pecos Bill had the finest mount in all the West. Bill called him 'Widow-Maker'—he had been raised on nitro-glycerine and dynamite and any cowboy who tried to ride that horse outside o' Bill left his wife a stranded, weeping widow. But Sue was a high-spirited Texan maiden who knew she could do what no man could do, and she was going to show Bill she could.

"'You say no man can ride Widow-Maker? Reckon you're right. But I ain't no man, I'm Slue-Foot Sue and I can ride any living critter and that goes for Widow-Maker too, and what's more, I'm going to ride that horse on my wedding day.'

"Bill begged with angel words, telling his beloved the danger that was awaiting her. But he might as well have argued with a tornado on a rampage, the more he begged her not to ride, the more Sue wanted to ride. And it's no use arguing with a woman or the wind. So Bill, he shook his head and prayed for the best.

"Came the wedding day leaping along like a calf in the spring and there was Slue-Foot Sue lovely as a daisy all dressed up in the finest steel spring bustle under her skirt, ready first to ride Widow-Maker and then to marry Pecos Bill.

"Bill looked at her, and loved her more than miles of cattle and was ready to weep with sorrow. He knew no good would come from Sue riding Widow-Maker.

"The horse marvel of the west stood a-prancing on its slender legs, eyes a-sparkling and neighing loud enough to be heard in the streets of New York. And there was Sue, eyes like stars, face like fresh apples, rarin' to show she could do what no man could do.

"Bill helped her mount, misgivings in his heart. No sooner did the horse feel the strange weight and steel bustle at the flanks than he shook himself like a California earthquake. But Sue she sat calm as the North Star. She was a great horsewoman. That made Widow-Maker mad, he began bouncing and rearing and throwing himself in all directions worse than a hooked mountain trout. But Sue, she sat, only her face got a little more pink.

"Then Widow-Maker put all he had into one leaping-pitching-twisting-rearing-hundred-foot jump and Slue-Foot Sue flew high in the air. Since everything that goes up comes down, Sue came down landing on the steel ribs of the bustle. The steel was so strong and springy it made her bounce even higher than before. So high she had to duck not to hit the moon. Down she came and up she went. Down she came and up she bounced.

"First, Pecos Bill and all the invited wedding guests thought bouncing Sue sailing high in the sky was a winsome sight, but after the second day of bouncing they got kind of worried. Bill tried to lasso her, but the force of the steel bustle tore his rope each time he tried. Sue wanted to tear off the skirt and pull the bustle down, but she was a modest maiden and she wouldn't do anything indiscreet before that crowd of cowhands and put Bill to shame, so she kept on bouncing from earth to sky. On the third day, Bill saw it was no use watching the sad spectacle so he put a merciful end to poor Sue, the bouncing bride."

OLDEN DAYS FISHING IN ARIZONA,
OR SOMETHING YOU CAN LEARN ABOUT FISH

This here our land is a great land, and I'm not boasting a bit if I call it the greatest land in all the world. And I can prove it sure as giant Sahuaras have thick arms. Just you listen.

There was a fellow called Skinny Beanshirt. It's the only name I ever heard folks call him. He was short, round and fat—kind o' chunky. I'd say sort o' full of flesh. Maybe that's why they called him Skinny. Folks always go contrary, like cows wandering off in the wrong pastures.

Now Skinny he was in the business of selling a fine patent medicine in New York around Utica. That medicine was so goldarn powerful it could grow hair on billiard balls, and on clean rocks the devil threw from up York State down to Connecticut.

One day a man came and told him 'bout the golden South West where folks paid no taxes. He, that man, said it was along the Colorado River way down to Arizona—a land just full o' free land, free cactus and free birds. He, the man, said there was plenty of bald men there 'd be only too glad to buy Skinny's hair medicine to grow long locks on their bald heads. It was the style out West in them days to grow long locks—that 'd fall down the shoulders to keep them warm on cold nights and make 'm long like Senators.

Skinny Beanshirt he listened and lit out thataway quicker than a cat's blink. In no time he came to that promised land and pretty soon he was shoveling in money selling his potent hair tonic. He was making more than if he'd been digging for gold, and—there was no taxes to pay to nobody.

"This is God's own country," Skinny said, "where folks need hair tonic and there ain't no bloomin' tax collectors."

He built himself a shack along the San Pedro River not far from Tombstone where he was manufacturing his fine hair tonic and selling it to miners in need of hair.

One fine day he made up three gallons of the potion figuring he'd take it acrost the river on his burro and sell it in town to a bunch of newcomers just blown in from the East.

That burro was a fine slick animal, sure of foot and mighty obedient. The two, that is Skinny and the burro, they was crossing the

river where it was pretty deep and the little fish they was tickling the
burro's legs.

After a time the burro lost its patience and decided to put an end to
the shenanigans of them fish. So when the next swarm of finny tor-
mentors slithered around its legs, it just lit out a hard kick against 'm.

Well, instead of kicking the little fish, it kicked one of them boulders you find in Arizona rivers. Maybe I'd better tell you that it was
the rock kicked the burro, not the burro the rock. For the rock didn't
seem to mind it a bit, but the burro did, mighty much. It shook its
head in anger and flung its haunches from side to side and . . . down
came the three jugs full of fine, strong hair tonic, breaking the jugs in
smithereens and pouring the wonder working elixir into the water,
right on the trout that were darting about all over.

Skinny was jumping mad, but pretty soon he figured there wasn't no
use crying over spilt hair tonic, so he went back to his shack to make
a new batch of the wonder-working liquid.

That's as far as Skinny was concerned, but it was another kind of
story with the fish. No sooner did the potent hair tonic touch the
fishes' scales and the good Arizona sun shone on 'm than they began
growing hair all over.

The very next day when some miners came down to fish, they saw
the fish floating around with beards on their chins, whiskers on their
snouts and hair all over like bears. It was a sight for sore eyes.

There was a fellow amongst them miners he was a tooth-doctor out
East—had a head slick as owl's grease. When he saw them bearded
fish, he ran back to his shack, painted a stick lying on the ground
red and white, put on a white coat, took a scissors in his left hand
and a net in his right and hoofed it back to the river. There he stuck
the pole in the sand, held the net up high and waved the scissors in
the air shouting: "Next, next, next!"

Jiminy jeepers! you should've seen them trout leaping in the air to
have their beards and whiskers trimmed. But instead of living up to
his promise, that dishonest, slick tooth-doctor from the East caught
the fish in his net. The rest of the miners seeing how much easier
that was than sitting with a hook in hand for hours, imitated the low
deception until the generation of hairy trout was all et up.

Since then they've not been seen around Arizona, because Skinny
carried his good hair tonic in wooden barrels instead of stone jugs.

THE SAINT OF KANSAS

I'm going to tell you a story about Kansas the great dry state of our land, where dead John Barleycorn has done so much good that ordinary men are called Saints. That's what foreign folk say, but it's just prevaricating. I'm going to tell you the real low-down Hancock about this business of Saints.

It began with the snakes of Kansas, just as Ireland with the snakes of Ireland. Snakes were mighty popular in Kansas. Fact is there were millions of them when folks first came there. Not glass hoop snakes, that was in another state. In Kansas it was rattlers and they did great harm to folks and cattle. The settlers just couldn't get rid of them, for every mile or so there was a snake's den with a couple of thousand snakes in it.

The settlers tried their level best to clear the land of the critters. Every Sunday and holiday, bands of men, women and children would make up snakebees. They'd go out together and club as many rattlers as they could. But the rattlers were slick gimpers. No sooner did a denful see a posse of settlers and their sticks than they'd set up a rattling which could be heard as far as Kalamazoo and this would warn rattlers in the next den. Then this denful would start rattling and so warn the next. These would start rattling warnings to the next and so pass the warning from one to another until all the rattlers of the state of Kansas would be warned and they'd hide. The settlers would clean out just one den. Now you know, cleaning out a single den a day wouldn't do much good when there were thousands and thousands of them all over the state. So things were pretty bad and the settlers were beginning to consider abandoning the place, just like an old house or an old mine, until Hog Trott came to Kansas and solved the whole problem in a very simple way. He was a short man, had shoulders wide as an ox and could drink Mike Fink under the table.

One day, Hog went out on a snake party, there were fourteen men and two boys in the party. A finer lot of men you never did see.

They had started early in the morning trying to locate a big rattler den where they hoped to finish five to ten thousand varmints. It didn't take 'em long when they found a fair-sized breeding place with about five thousand wiggling, slithering critters basking in the warm sunshine. The men went at 'em with a whoop and were laying about like hail on a summer day. Just as they were whooping and tearing around, one big poison buckaroo dug its fangs deep into Hog Trott's leg. He let out a great yell and the leg began swelling at once.

Now you know there is no better snake bite antidote than a couple of good snorters. Hog took a flask and drank down every drop of it. Then all his friends, they handed him their flasks made of tin, pewter and horn and Hog drank most of what was in them. He just mopped up the stuff like an Arizona desert good rain water.

When he was done, he had no pain and the swelling was going down and Hog went to work again. You should've seen that man Hog a-working. He went around faster with swinging arms and stick than a whirlwind in a hurricane. That was going on until another big fang-clapper dug his long ivories into Hog's arm that held the stick. Then something funny happened. The rattler sort of stopped for a split second, screwed up his rattling tail in a circle, near reaching its head, and then dropped down dumb dead!

All the men stopped their heavy work at the sight! Now you know Kansas men are bright as new dollars and it didn't take 'em long to understand the situation.

"Hoorah!" they shouted to a man. "That's a new way of destroying rattlesnakes. The likker that Hog drank done it. Come Hog, just stand there and let 'em bite you. The rattlers will suffer now and we'll give them no snorters either!"

Well, Hog, he just stood still and let the rattlers bite him. And the moment they bit, they dropped down dead until every one of the snakes in the den were lying around like fish out of water. It sure was a sight. Hog had killed more snakes by letting himself be bitten than the men had done with their clubs.

The story spread through the state and it gave Kansas folks an idea. A rattler might escape the club but he couldn't escape the strength of the likker bite. From then all a man had to do was just drink enough fine home brew and then go into the snakes' nest and let the reptiles bite. After each bite there were no reptiles left. From that time, every Kansas man for the good of the state and his cattle 'd drink enough to kill rattlers. Believe it or not soon there wasn't a single snake left in the state just as there is no snakes in Ireland.

That's how come men in Kansas call themselves Saint.

But like everything else the story has another side. When there were no more snakes to be destroyed Kansas lawmakers got to worrying what might happen to other critters if they bit a man full of Kansas juice and so it was decided for the best of the state to bring in prohibition and there it has been ever since. But, I'm sure certain that if any snakes 'd show their heads again, prohibition 'd get the gate quicker than a cat could wink an eye.

THE MARVELS O' THE WEST

Ever hear about Jim Bridger? Well, if you haven't you should. He was the world's greatest trapper and I ain't exajuratin'. Far from it. I'm just speakin' everyday language. He did more things than a busy rabbit on a Sunday mornin' and one of the things he did was discoverin' Yellowstone Park and all the thousand seventh wonders in it. It was there he found the Petrified Forest where even the sun and the moon shine with a petrified light. And 'twas he discovered that boilin'-water lake with fine cool water on the bottom.

One fine day he was hungrier than a bear awakenin' from his winter sleep so he went a-fishin' to the nearest lake he saw, never notin' that he was throwin' his line into a boilin'-hot-water lake. Soon he felt somethin' a-tuggin'. Somehow his line got entangled and he could draw it up only very slowly. When he got it near the top, it went even slower and when he got the fish out, Glory be! that fish was steamin' hot and cooked as good as any French chef could. He added a little salt and pepper and ate the finest lake trout he ever tasted. Jim was a generous kind and told all the world about that boilin'-hot-and-cold-water lake and from then on the miners all around came a fishin' to that lake when they wanted boiled fish without the trouble o' makin' a fire.

But even that wasn't the most important find o' that great discoverer. I'd say his greatest discovery was the glass mountain. That was as great a discovery as the discovery of America.

As the sayin' goes, it's best to begin at the beginnin'. Well Jim Bridger was out huntin' one day. He was lookin' for big game to lay up a supply for the comin' cold winter months. He was roamin' around and then, all of a sudden, he sighted a fine, big elk grazing along a little river. A big, fat elk that'd make fine venison. It wasn't no more 'n twenty or thirty yards away so he raised his trusty gun, aimed straight and true. Now you know Jim Bridger was the finest shot in all the West and when he aimed at a critter and the trigger went off, that critter was finished for good. He let go the trigger, there was a bang, louder 'n usual, but . . . the elk it kept on grazin' calmly not even lookin' up at the great bang! Well, you could've knocked Jimmy over with a blade o' grass. Nothin' like that had ever happened to him. It made him madder than a starved mountain lion.

He loaded his gun and raised it once again slowly-like and took sure, straight aim and—fired for the second time. There was a bang could be heard at the other end of the world. But the elk, it just kept on grazin' calmly as if nothing had happened. Well, that made Jimmy see red. He wasn't gonna waste shots any more. He turned the gun around, club to the front, and made a dash for the critter, aimin' to finish it with his own hands. He run about ten or fifteen yards when bang!! he hit somethin' that knocked him back clear ten paces makin' his head swim away from his body.

He got up like a man that's been drinkin' too much and walked slowly and wobbly forward and then—stubbed his toe and hit his head with a bang! And just what do you think he hit. A glass mountain! A mountain of solid glass clear as polished crystal and you could see clear through it to the other side where the elk was grazin' peacefully. And it wasn't just ordinary glass either but ground down by the wind and the sand to make a perfect telescope so that anything near thirty miles 'd look like twenty-five yards away.

And that's how the whole world came to know about the Glass Mountain o' the West considered one of the greatest—if not *the* greatest—marvel in the world.

OUR LEISURE CLASS

OLIVER HERFORD

Once—and not so terribly long ago at that—we used to be very fond of telling ourselves (and our visitors from Europe) that in America we have no Leisure Class.

That there were people of leisure in our midst, we could not deny, though we preferred to call them idle rich, but as for a special class whose whole business in life was to abstain from all useful activity—oh, no!

Even our idle rich, unblest as they are with the hereditary gift for idling, and untaught save by a brief generation or two of acquired experience, find the profession of Leisure a strenuous not to say noisy task, for while those to the leisure born know by the very feel of it that the habit of idleness is a perfect fit, the newly-idle must look for confirmation in the mirror of public admiration; hence Publicity, the blare of the Sunday Supplement.

But taken as a class our idle rich (though it is being rapidly licked or lick-spittled into shape) is at best an amateur aristocracy of leisure. For the real thing, for the genuine hunting, sporting, leisure-loving American aristocracy, we must go back to the aboriginal Red Man.

And how the busybody Puritan hated the Indian! With his air of well-bred taciturnity, his love of sport, of rest, of Nature, and his belief in a happy Hereafter, the noble Red Man was in every respect his hateful opposite, yet if any Pilgrim brother had dared even to hint that the Indian might have points of superiority it would have been the flaming woodpile for him, or something equally disagreeable in the purifying way.

How different it might have been!

If only the Puritan had been less stuck-up and self-righteous, the Red Man less reserved! If they could but have understood that Nature intended them for each other, these opposites, these complements of each other.

Why else had Nature brought them together from the ends of the earth?

But alas, Eugenics had not yet been invented and the Puritan and the Indian just naturally hated each other at first sight and so (like many another match-maker) Mother Nature slipped up in her calculations, and a wonderful flower of racial possibility was forever nipped in the bud.

If the Puritan, with his piety and thrift and domesticity and his doctrine of election and the Noble Red Man, with his love of paint and syncopated music and dancing and belief in a happy Hereafter, had overcome their mutual prejudices and instead of warring with flintlocks and tomahawks, had pursued each other with engagement rings and marriage licenses, what a grand and glorious race we might be today!

What a land of freedom might be ours!

Schools Attended:

THE CRUSTY PROFESSOR'S SONG

MORRIS BISHOP

Once in days of yore
   All the college scholars
Resolutely swore
   To give up stand-up collars.
Students never wore
   Stand-up collars, stand-up collars,
     Never any more.

They discarded cuff-links,
   And the cuffs likewise;
They abandoned tie-pins
   And dispensed with ties.
Students never wore
   Cuff-links, cuffs, tie-pins, ties,
   Stand-up collars, stand-up collars,
     Never any more.

They rejected headgear,
   Threw away their hats,
Eliminated garters,
   Extirpated spats.
Students never wore

Caps and hats, garters, spats,
    Cuff-links, cuffs, tie-pins, ties,
    Stand-up collars, stand-up collars,
      Never any more.

They renounced the jacket,
    They abjured the vest;
They undid the buttons
    To display the chest.
Students never wore
    Jackets, coats, waistcoats, vests,
    Caps and hats, garters, spats,
    Cuff-links, cuffs, tie-pins, ties,
    Stand-up collars, stand-up collars,
      Never any more.

Maybe time will banish
    Sweat-shirts, dirty jeans;
Maybe these will vanish
    From collegiate scenes.
Students will not wear
    Dirty sweat-shirts, dirty jeans,
    Jackets, coats, waistcoats, vests,
    Caps and hats, garters, spats,
    Cuff-links, cuffs, tie-pins, ties,
    Stand-up collars, stand-up collars—
      Then what *will* they wear?

CHARLES

SHIRLEY JACKSON

The day Laurie started kindergarten he renounced corduroy overalls with bibs and began wearing blue jeans with a belt; I watched him go off the first morning with the older girl next door, seeing clearly that an era of my life was ended, my sweet-voiced nursery-school tot replaced by a long-trousered, swaggering character who forgot to stop at the corner and wave goodbye to me.

He came home the same way, the front door slamming open, his cap on the floor, and the voice suddenly become raucous shouting, "Isn't anybody *here?*"

At lunch he spoke insolently to his father, spilled Jannie's milk, and remarked that his teacher said that we were not to take the name of the Lord in vain.

"How was school today?" I asked, elaborately casual.

"All right," he said.

"Did you learn anything?" his father asked.

Laurie regarded his father coldly. "I didn't learn nothing," he said.

"Anything," I said. "Didn't learn anything."

"The teacher spanked a boy, though," Laurie said, addressing his bread and butter. "For being fresh," he added with his mouth full.

"What did he do?" I asked. "Who was it?"

Laurie thought. "It was Charles," he said. "He was fresh. The teacher spanked him and made him stand in a corner. He was awfully fresh."

"What did he do?" I asked again, but Laurie slid off his chair, took a cookie, and left, while his father was still saying, "See here, young man."

The next day Laurie remarked at lunch, as soon as he sat down, "Well, Charles was bad again today." He grinned enormously and said, "Today Charles hit the teacher."

"Good heavens," I said, mindful of the Lord's name, "I suppose he got spanked again?"

"He sure did," Laurie said. "Look up," he said to his father.

"What?" his father said, looking up.

"Look down," Laurie said. "Look at my thumb. Gee, you're dumb." He began to laugh insanely.

"Why did Charles hit the teacher?" I asked quickly.

"Because she tried to make him color with red crayons," Laurie said. "Charles wanted to color with green crayons so he hit the teacher and she spanked him and said nobody play with Charles but everybody did."

The third day—it was Wednesday of the first week—Charles bounced a seesaw onto the head of a little girl and made her bleed and the teacher made him stay inside all during recess. Thursday Charles had to stand in a corner during storytime because he kept pounding his feet on the floor. Friday Charles was deprived of blackboard privileges because he threw chalk.

On Saturday I remarked to my husband, "Do you think kindergarten is too unsettling for Laurie? All this toughness and bad grammar, and this Charles boy sounds like such a bad influence."

"It'll be all right," my husband said reassuringly. "Bound to be people like Charles in the world. Might as well meet them now as later."

On Monday Laurie came home late, full of news. "Charles," he shouted as he came up the hill; I was waiting anxiously on the front steps. "Charles," Laurie yelled all the way up the hill, "Charles was bad again."

"Come right in," I said, as soon as he came close enough. "Lunch is waiting."

"You know what Charles did?" he demanded, following me through the door. "Charles yelled so in school they sent a boy in from first grade to tell the teacher she had to make Charles keep quiet, and so Charles had to stay after school. And so all the children stayed to watch him."

"What did he do?" I asked.

"He just sat there," Laurie said, climbing into his chair at the table. "Hi Pop, y'old dust mop."

"Charles had to stay after school today," I told my husband. "Everyone stayed with him."

"What does this Charles look like?" my husband asked Laurie. "What's his other name?"

"He's bigger than me," Laurie said. "And he doesn't have any rubbers and he doesn't ever wear a jacket."

Monday night was the first Parent-Teachers meeting, and only the fact that Jannie had a cold kept me from going; I wanted passionately to meet Charles' mother. On Tuesday Laurie remarked suddenly, "Our teacher had a friend come see her in school today."

"Charles' mother?" my husband and I asked simultaneously.

"Naaah," Laurie said scornfully. "It was a man who came and made us do exercises. Look." He climbed down from his chair and squatted down and touched his toes. "Like this," he said. He got solemnly back into his chair and said, picking up his fork, "Charles didn't even *do* exercises."

"That's fine," I said heartily. "Didn't Charles want to do exercises?"

"Naaah," Laurie said. "Charles was so fresh to the teacher's friend he wasn't *let* do exercises."

"Fresh again?" I said.

"He kicked the teacher's friend," Laurie said. "The teacher's friend told Charles to touch his toes like I just did and Charles kicked him."

"What are they going to do about Charles, do you suppose?" Laurie's father asked him.

Laurie shrugged elaborately. "Throw him out of school, I guess," he said.

Wednesday and Thursday were rousing; Charles yelled during story hour and hit a boy in the stomach and made him cry. On Friday Charles stayed after school again and so did all the other children.

With the third week of kindergarten Charles was an institution in our family; Jannie was being a Charles when she cried all afternoon; Laurie did a Charles when he filled his wagon full of mud and pulled it through the kitchen; even my husband, when he caught his elbow in the telephone cord and pulled telephone, ash tray, and a bowl of flowers off the table, said, after the first minute, "Looks like Charles."

During the third and fourth weeks there seemed to be a reformation in Charles; Laurie reported grimly at lunch on Thursday of the third week, "Charles was so good today the teacher gave him an apple."

"What?" I said, and my husband added warily, "You mean Charles?"

"Charles," Laurie said. "He gave the crayons around and he picked up the books afterward and the teacher said he was her helper."

"What happened?" I asked incredulously.

"He was her helper, that's all," Laurie said, and shrugged.

"Can this be true, about Charles?" I asked my husband that night. "Can something like this happen?"

"Wait and see," my husband said cynically. "When you've got a Charles to deal with, this may mean he's only plotting."

He seemed to be wrong. For over a week Charles was the teacher's helper; each day he handed things out and he picked things up; no one had to stay after school.

"The P.-T.A. meeting's next week again," I told my husband one evening. "I'm going to find Charles' mother there."

"Ask her what happened to Charles," my husband said. "I'd like to know."

"I'd like to know myself," I said.

On Friday of that week things were back to normal. "You know what Charles did today?" Laurie demanded at the lunch table, in a voice slightly awed. "He told a little girl to say a word and she said it and the teacher washed her mouth out with soap and Charles laughed."

"What word?" his father asked unwisely, and Laurie said, "I'll have to whisper it to you, it's so bad." He got down off his chair and went around to his father. His father bent his head down and Laurie whispered joyfully. His father's eyes widened.

"Did Charles tell the little girl to say *that*?" he asked respectfully.

"She said it twice," Laurie said. "Charles told her to say it *twice*."

"What happened to Charles?" my husband asked.

"Nothing," Laurie said. "He was passing out the crayons."

Monday morning Charles abandoned the little girl and said the evil word himself three or four times, getting his mouth washed out with soap each time. He also threw chalk.

My husband came to the door with me that evening as I set out for the P.-T.A. meeting. "Invite her over for a cup of tea after the meeting," he said. "I want to get a look at her."

"If only she's there," I said prayerfully.

"She'll be there," my husband said. "I don't see how they could hold a P.-T.A. meeting without Charles' mother."

At the meeting I sat restlessly, scanning each comfortable matronly face, trying to determine which one hid the secret of Charles. None of them looked to me haggard enough. No one stood up in the meeting and apologized for the way her son had been acting. No one mentioned Charles.

After the meeting I identified and sought out Laurie's kindergarten teacher. She had a plate with a cup of tea and a piece of chocolate cake; I had a plate with a cup of tea and a piece of marshmallow cake. We maneuvered up to one another cautiously and smiled.

"I've been so anxious to meet you," I said. "I'm Laurie's mother."

"We're all so interested in Laurie," she said.

"Well, he certainly likes kindergarten," I said. "He talks about it all the time."

"We had a little trouble adjusting, the first week or so," she said primly, "but now he's a fine little helper. With lapses, of course."

"Laurie usually adjusts very quickly," I said. "I suppose this time it's Charles' influence."

"Charles?"

"Yes," I said, laughing, "you must have your hands full in that kindergarten, with Charles."

"Charles?" she said. "We don't have any Charles in the kindergarten."

·

HELP! HELP! AU SECOURS!

RUTH McKENNEY

Every American knows that children acquire foreign languages by the painless, carefree process of osmosis. When Richard and I moved to Belgium, we cringed at the thought of learning French; but the children, of course, would not have any trouble—they would pick it up in no time. By ear. Especially Eileen.

We settled innocently into the rented purple-plush grandeur of our Brussels house. A month later, my mother-in-law wrote: "I can hardly imagine my own little Eileen, that chatterbox, chattering French."

Grandma's letter arrived the day after her own little Eileen flatly refused to return to the local Jardin des Enfants. Mommy and Daddy were flabbergasted. When we had left for Belgium, Miss Elouise, director of the Westport Pre-kindergarten Play Group, stated in her report on our daughter: "Eileen is the happiest, best adjusted, most co-operative, highest IQ in group." Under this scientific diagnosis, Miss Elouise had scrawled, in red ink: "Such a darling!"

Six weeks later, Darling declined to hustle-bustle right off to the Jardin des Enfants. Cross-questioned, Chatterbox admitted the attractions of the Jardin's seven communal turkeys, one communal guinea pig, and her very own rabbit; she conceded playing drum in the school band, plenty of finger paint, and weaving Daddy a lovely napkin ring. Nevertheless, she was never going back.

"But why?" Daddy demanded.

Eileen's large blue eyes filled with large silver tears. "They can't hear me, and I can't hear them."

Richard and I decided Eileen could stay home for a while and pick up French from Julia, the cook, and Phillipine, the chambermaid. Belgians adore children, but Julia and Phillipine positively worshiped at our angel's shrine. They clucked with excitement when she rode her miniature two-wheeler, and uttered passionate cries of admiration when they spotted her making mud pies in the sandbox. "Phillipine!" Julia bawled, from the terrace, "Look quickly! See the little princess!" Phillipine thrust her aging, work-weary, sad-horse face out of a fourth-story window. "But observe! Julia, observe! She carries water in her tiny pail! One is ravished!"

These ear-splitting tributes were fortunately in French (neither Julia nor Phillipine had a word of English); all the same, Richard and I feared we would have to "speak to" the good ladies. Eileen would be "rattling" French herself, in a day or two, and we really could not have her called gold-sugared-beauty, sweet-queen-blue-eyes, etc., etc., right to her small nose.

"But the first few days at home," I said comfortably, on our way back from the post office, "I guess it won't do her any harm. . . ."

Sauntering along in the April sunlight, we turned back into Rue François Stroobant. Phillipine stood in our fake-marble doorway, wildly flapping her apron, and keening: "Madame! Monsieur! Vite! Vite!"

We found Eileen huddled under her bed, wall on one side, rocking horse for barricade on the other. She was afraid of Julia; terrified by Phillipine. She could not "hear" them, they could not "hear" her.

This will indicate (dimly) how the well-adjusted, happy, co-operative American, aged four, acquires a foreign language by osmosis.

Eileen had taken up semipermanent residence under her bed, when one afternoon Mrs. McHenry, an American banker's wife, paid a formal call. "I don't know what's wrong with Eileen," I told Mrs. McHenry mournfully, "she seemed perfectly normal, in the United States, but now . . ."

Mrs. McHenry was reassuring. She scoffed at the osmosis theory. It seemed that no child, in the entire history of children, had ever *picked up* a language, and the only people mad enough to entertain such a notion were Americans domiciled in the U.S.A.

Mrs. McHenry knew the very teacher for Eileen. "The Lincolns—

he's Marshall Plan, you know—had her for their little Clara. The child was much worse than your Eileen—insisted on living entirely in a large armoire. They had to shove her food in through a crack in the door, I believe. Such a sweet child too. Mrs. Lincoln was utterly distracted."

I shuddered.

"Wouldn't even speak English, in the end," Mrs. McHenry reported, with relish. "Just made noises. Horrid noises. I called one afternoon, and really, it was trying, the most appalling sounds coming out of that armoire! Mrs. Lincoln was about to take the poor little thing back to the States, when she heard about this brilliant woman professor."

Madame Professor Nemour, *Diplômée* Child Psychology, University of Belgium, M. A. Cambridge, etc., etc., was brisk, over the telephone. She spoke fluent English-English, very birdy, with an accent half French and half Winston Churchill. She was so sorry, but she was occupied with her feeble-minded clinic; she never took private patients, unless the case presented unusual problems.

I said that while Eileen had not yet moved into an armoire, we feared the worst.

"Ah!" Madame Nemour cried, licking her scholarly chops, "language shock." I gathered she would be right over, next Monday. But first, a few questions: how old was the child? Health? Hearing?

". . . and what is the little girl's favorite fairy story?"

"Oh . . . *Red Riding Hood*," I replied, carelessly. Afterward, Richard blamed me very much, but how was I to know?

Madame Nemour's cure for language shock started with "the area of familiar interest."

"I have here," Madame Professor told us brightly, "what I call the screept. A small dram-uh I have prepared."

Richard and I (this was May 4th) were fascinated. The screept, neatly typed on facing pages in a heavy black-leather notebook, English on the left, French on the right, opened (Act I, Scene I) with little Red Riding Hood at home, scrubbing her teeth, and washing her neck; it built to a smash finish with the demise of the wolf. This small dram-uh was as precise as a sonnet, or a machine gun. The whole action developed in the 437 words Madame Nemour judged Eileen needed for the hurly-burly of daily life in Belgium; every prop was carefully noted, every gesture—Granny's, the wolf's, Red Riding Hood's.

"Please, if you find a word, in the Eeengleesh, not comfortable for the little girl. . . ."

I substituted "dress" for "frock" and changed "hotty dogs."

"Not hotty dogs?" Madame Nemour was surprised. "I weeshed to employ the colloquial; your American speech is so colorful, so vigorous, as in William Faulkner and *Tobacco Road*, do you not think?"

But we insisted Eileen did not frequent colorful American circles.

"All these seem trivial, perhaps, but eeet is not so. Each word match the gesture *naturel*, and each Eeengleesh word match in *français*. I will geeve example."

Madame Nemour was a small, pretty, serious professor, with grave black eyes, and an air of gentle dignity. Her linen suit came from Paris, her hair was softly waved, her gloves spotless. She handed Richard the notebook, took a fragile handkerchief from her purse, gave a well-bred cough, and remarked, "In the lah—st act, Red Rideeng Hud is seee—t—eeng beside the volfff. You see eeet?"

Richard found the lines.

"Hoh! Kay!" Madame Nemour twinkled shyly at the colorful Americans. "You be the volffff."

Richard wet his lip. "All-the-better-to-eat-you-with," he muttered sheepishly.

Madame Nemour leaped to her feet, threw out her arms, emitted a piercing shriek, and bawled: "Help! Help!"

I jumped almost as far as Madame Professor. Richard's jaw sagged.

Madame Nemour sat down, daintily. "Now. You have enough French? Read *le loup.* . . ."

"Yes, well, I think we get the idea. . . ."

But Madame Nemour insisted. She weeshed us to observe how the natural, instinctual, human gesture, repeated ah—gain, and ah—gain, became associated with the language seeeeem—bawls.

This time Richard and I braced ourselves for language symbols, but Madame Nemour's scream, "*Au secours! Au secours!*" brought Julia and Phillipine, on the double.

"*Madame!*" Julia advanced bravely. She was the stout-hearted daughter of a coal miner and equal to any emergency.

"Jul—ia!" Phillipine said faintly, from the hall. Phillipine's family made lace.

Madame Nemour turned graciously. "Ah! *La bonne Julia.* My excellent Phillipine, is it? Have no fears. I am only Red Riding Hood."

Afterward Madame Nemour explained that she always liked to put the servants at their ease. "I find the domestic staff so rarely comprehends mental therapy, do you not think?"

We had no opinion on this point until we found Phillipine in the upstairs hall, the next afternoon, clutching a mop handle. We were touched. Phillipine was timid and aging, but if Madame and Monsieur foolishly permitted a lunatic in the bedchamber of their innocent, helpless lamb, Phillipine knew her duty. She was prepared to defend Eileen's life with her own, if need be. The fearless Julia, meanwhile, prowled the kitchen, meat cleaver razor sharp, ready to advance in case of danger.

Phillipine became reconciled in June to Madame Professor, which is more than I can say for Madame and Monsieur.

Rehearsals began indoors, May 4th. Monday, Tuesday, and Wednesday afternoon Eileen indignantly hid under her bed, while Madame Nemour sat cross-legged on the floor, next to the rocking horse, and read *Little Red Riding Hood, A Play in Five Acts, Nineteen Scenes*, over and over again, in Eeengleesh.

Thursday, Madame Nemour reported what she called "splendid" progress: Eileen laughed when the wolf tickled Grandma.

"Tickled!" Richard said.

"Before the eating of her, I have put in the teeckleeng, for the joke. Children adore the humoristic."

Friday, Madame Nemour was greatly encouraged. Eileen had emerged from under the bed, and holding the rocking horse in front of her, had "peeeeeped out, to regard me!"

"You don't say." Richard was not able to share Madame Nemour's optimism.

"Yes. Monday, you will see. I think we begin the real enacting. She is now accustomed to my accent in Eeengleesh. A pity I do not speak American, it would have gone more queeeckly. I practice at home, talking through the nose, as on the American feelms, but I fear it did not help. No matter. The child hears me now."

Eileen heard, from Monday on. So did Ma and Pa.

"Hellllll—oh, Meeeeee—stair Volfffff!" Madame Nemour clarioned, falsetto.

"Helllll—oh, wolf," our daughter repeated, fascinated.

"Ah no, dar—leeng. We must say Meeeee—stair. Otherwise, our volfff, he will be hurt in his feeeeleeengs."

"Helllll—oh, Mister Wolf!"

"Good! Br—ravo! Now you say to heem, what beeeg ears . . ."

The weather was lovely. Madame Nemour, with Eileen trotting eagerly at her heels, shifted rehearsals to the garden. I heard my daughter's voice floating joyous on the warm May breeze, and leaned out my window. Madame Nemour, in a smart summer frock and Paris hat, lay growling on the grass below.

"Oh," I said vaguely and drew back.

Early in June, Richard abandoned his typewriter in the drawing room—off the garden terrace—and marched upstairs to my study. I was hanging out the window, hypnotized by Madame Nemour, who hobbled around on a cane, squealing, "Oooooh, don't eat me up, don't eat me up, I don't taste good!" Above this dismal bit of prose, Eileen's silver laughter floated, pure, ecstatic.

"How long will this go on?"

"Well, Madame Nemour thinks Eileen will have the English version by heart in another two or three weeks."

"Two or three weeks!"

Richard and I moved our typewriters to the street-front upper bedrooms; in vain. There was something curiously penetrating about Madame Nemour's wolf. Eileen was not so loud, but she was always forgetting stage directions, or going up on her lines. Madame Nemour's patience was inexhaustible; Papa's, I am sorry to say, was not.

Eileen said, in the garden: "Ooooh, don't eat me up, please, I'm . . ."

Madame Nemour: "No, no dar—leeeng, first Granny must say I don't . . ."

Richard, bawling out the third floor window: "*I don't taste good! I don't taste good!* For heaven's sake, Eileen, *I don't taste good!*"

Madame Nemour admonished Richard afterward: "The leetle one should not be startled, she does very well. I hope you have not set back the good progress."

Richard shuddered; he also hoped not.

French was introduced so gradually, word by word, a phrase one day, a short sentence the next, that Eileen (aged four) and Richard and I (aging faster every day) never noticed the change-over, until Phillipine startled the oldsters by shrieking one afternoon: "Ah! *Le Petit Chaperon Rouge! Mais oui! Ju-lia!*"

I have often wondered what Phillipine supposed Madame Nemour was doing, all those long afternoons, when she lay on her back in our garden, growling; probably Phillipine just figured oh well, Madame Nemour was a professor. And insane.

By the first of July, Madame Nemour and Phillipine—who by now had been pressed into the cast—were playing entirely in French; Eileen, apparently oblivious of the hated alien tongue, continued to read her lines in English.

"Isn't she ever going to speak a word of French?" Richard asked Madame Nemour bitterly.

"*La petite* Lincoln," Madame Nemour said, "required seven entire months."

Our talented child required but three months, one week and two days before (August 13th) her first French word. I almost missed it. Staring with savage glance at my typewriter keys, I heard the familiar Nemour growl. The wolf was showing his teeth, I figured. Two more lines, and Eileen would leap up, throw out her fat little arms and shriek for all of Rue François Stroobant to hear, "Help! Help!"

I braced myself and tried not to listen.

The howl came, on schedule. Then Eileen's four-year-old soprano: "*Au secours! Au secours!*"

Madame Nemour warned us. "Take no notice. She is not aware she has spoken the French."

When we heard that the dram-uh might be continued for perhaps another fortnight—until Eileen ran through all the roles, in French— Richard and I managed to contain our excitement.

But the Nemour play ran only another week. On August 16th, Eileen did Little Red all the way through, in *français*; on August 17th, she played the wolf; on the 18th, Granny. On the 19th, Madame Nemour gave Eileen her diploma—a day's outing in the park, a real peekneek *à deux*. The morning of the 20th, Papa inquired at breakfast, "Did you have a good time with Madame Nemour, darling?"

Eileen looked around uncertainly; her face crumpled up. "*Papa! Je ne peux pas t'entendre!*"

At first it was quite awkward—Eileen could not "hear" a word of English; but Richard and I worked grimly on our French lessons, and after a few months, we were able to communicate with our own daughter almost as easily as Julia, Phillipine, Mademoiselle Cemier, teacher at the Jardin des Enfants, and, of course, Madame Professor Nemour.

THE BLIND MEN AND THE ELEPHANT

JOHN G. SAXE (1816–1887)

It was six men of Indostan
To learning much inclined,
Who went to see the elephant
(Though all of them were blind).
That each by observation
Might satisfy his mind.

The first approached the elephant,
And, happening to fall
Against his broad and sturdy side,
At once began to bawl,
"God bless me! but the elephant
Is very like a wall!"

The second feeling of the tusk
Cried: "Ho! what have we here
So very round and smooth and sharp?
To me 'tis mighty clear
This wonder of an elephant
Is very like a spear!"

The third approached the animal,
And, happening to take
The squirming trunk within his hands,
Thus boldly up and spake:
"I see," quoth he, "the elephant
Is very like a snake!"

The fourth reached out his eager hand,
And felt about the knee;
"What most this wondrous beast is like
Is mighty plain," quoth he;
"'Tis clear enough the elephant
Is very like a tree."

The fifth, who chanced to touch the ear,
Said: "E'en the blindest man
Can tell what this resembles most.
Deny the fact who can.
This marvel of an elephant
Is very like a fan!"

The sixth no sooner had begun
About the beast to grope,
Than, seizing on the swinging tail
That fell within his scope,
"I see," quoth he, "the elephant
Is very like a rope!"

And so these men of Indostan
Disputed loud and long,
Each in his own opinion
Exceeding stiff and strong,
Though each was partly in the right,
And all were in the wrong!

So, oft in theologic wars
The disputants, I ween,
Rail on in utter ignorance
Of what each other mean,
And prate about an elephant
Not one of them has seen!

THE REAL FIRE LAWS OF MT. HOLYOKE FEMALE SEMINARY OF ABOUT 1857, AND THE BURLESQUE OF THEM BY STUDENTS OF MT. HOLYOKE COLLEGE IN THE 1870'S

(From photostat supplied by the library of Mt. Holyoke College)

Some of the Original Fire Laws

Leave no matches out of the safe.
Carry no lamps to the wood room.
Place the fender before the (wood) stove on leaving the room.
Leave no wood or kindling on the stove hearth or zinc.

Carry no fire from one room to another.

Do not leave the upper door (coal stove) closed.

Do not leave a lamp burning.

Avoid lighting matches on the walls.

Burlesque Fire Laws

If a fire breaks out in the seminary, the young lady who first discovers it may have permission to pour a pail of water on the fire, even if it is in silent study hours. If it is not then extinguished, she may go at once to Miss Ward, who will give her permission to go to the North Wing Parlor and inform Miss Edwards. Miss Edwards will give her permission to go to the room for her section teacher, who will send her to the bell-girl and cause a long bell to be rung. The young ladies will then assemble in the seminary hall, and Miss Ward will rise and say, "Good morning" or "Good afternoon, young ladies," as the case may be. "We have ascertained that a fire has broken out in our building, and it will be necessary for you to do some benevolent work. All who are willing to assist will arise." Their names will then be taken in alphabetical order. Then Miss Ward will say, "You may all arise. Those who have leaky pails may remain standing, while the rest may be seated." Their names will be taken, and then they may go to their rooms, take their pails, and carry them to the long drying room, and exchange them for whole ones. The bell will then ring again and all will meet in the seminary hall. Each section, with its section teacher at its head, will then march to the Connecticut River, fill their pails and return.

To avoid confusion, no two young ladies must empty their pails on the fire at the same time. No one must leave her place until the one immediately preceding her has returned.

If it becomes evident that the building will burn down, a long bell will ring again, and the young ladies will meet in the seminary hall. They will then be told to go to their rooms at the close of the exercise, put their rooms in order, being especially careful to dust the upper shelf in the closet and the top of the mirror. Each will then pack her trunk very neatly, remembering we put dresses on the top. Money must not be put in the trunks. Each will lock her trunk and place it in the hall. No one need call upon Cornelius for assistance, as he will be otherwise engaged, but when he has time he will take them downstairs.

HARRY MACE, THE SATURDAY EVENING POST

"It's very generous of you, Russell, but I don't believe your resignation would help our crowded school situation."

The seniors and the senior middles will then march promenade step out of the south door, the juniors and junior middles side-step out of the north door. Then, as the young ladies will be scattered through the town, a long bell will be rung through the streets, and they will all march to the graveyard, where a teacher will be found seated on a monument, ready to excuse all excusable exceptions made during the fire.

N.B. First-class exceptions will not be excused.

SOARING

BOOTH TARKINGTON

Half the members of the class passed out to a recitation-room, the empurpled Victorine among them, and Miss Spence started the remaining half through the ordeal of trial by mathematics. Several boys and girls were sent to the blackboard, and Penrod, spared for the moment, followed their operations a little while with his eyes, but not with his mind; then, sinking deeper in his seat, limply abandoned the effort. His eyes remained open, but saw nothing; the routine of the arithmetic lesson reached his ears in familiar, meaningless sounds, but he heard nothing; and yet, this time, he was profoundly occupied. He had drifted away from the painful land of facts, and floated now in a new sea of fancy which he had just discovered.

Maturity forgets the marvellous realness of a boy's day-dreams, how colourful they glow, rosy and living, and how opaque the curtain closing down between the dreamer and the actual world. That curtain is almost sound-proof, too, and causes more throat-trouble among parents than is suspected.

The nervous monotony of the schoolroom inspires a sometimes unbearable longing for something astonishing to happen, and as every boy's fundamental desire is to do something astonishing himself, so as to be the centre of all human interest and awe, it was natural that Penrod should discover in fancy the delightful secret of self-levitation. He found, in this curious series of imaginings, during the lesson in arithmetic, that the atmosphere may be navigated as by a swimmer under water, but with infinitely greater ease and with perfect comfort in breathing. In this mind he extended his arms gracefully, at a level with his shoulders, and delicately paddled the air with his hands, which at once caused him to be drawn up out of his seat and elevated gently to a position about midway between the floor and the ceiling, where he came to an equilibrium and floated; a sensation not the less exquisite because of the screams of his fellow pupils, appalled by the miracle. Miss Spence herself was amazed and frightened, but he only smiled down carelessly upon her when she commanded him to return to earth; and then, when she climbed upon a desk to pull him down, he quietly paddled himself a little higher, leaving his toes just out of her reach. Next, he swam through a few slow somersaults to show his mastery of the new art, and, with the shouting of the dumfounded scholars ringing in his ears, turned on his side and floated swiftly out of the window, immediately rising above the housetops, while people in the street below him shrieked, and a trolley car stopped dead in wonder.

With almost no exertion he paddled himself, many yards at a stroke, to the girls' private school where Marjorie Jones was a pupil—Marjorie Jones of the amber curls and the golden voice! Long before the "Pageant of the Table Round," she had offered Penrod a hundred proofs that she considered him wholly undesirable and ineligible. At the Friday Afternoon Dancing Class she consistently incited and led the laughter at him whenever Professor Bartet singled him out for admonition in matters of feet and decorum. And but yesterday she had chid him for his slavish lack of memory in daring to offer her a greeting on the way to Sunday-school. "Well! I expect you must forgot I told you never to speak to me again! If I was a boy, I'd be too proud to come hanging around people that don't speak to me, even if I *was* the Worst Boy in Town!" So she flouted him. But now, as he floated in through the window of her classroom and swam gently along the ceiling like an escaped toy balloon, she fell upon her knees beside her little desk, and, lifting up her arms toward him, cried with love and admiration:

"Oh, *Pen*rod!"

He negligently kicked a globe from the high chandelier, and, smiling coldly, floated out through the hall to the front steps of the school, while Marjorie followed, imploring him to grant her one kind look.

In the street an enormous crowd had gathered, headed by Miss Spence and a brass band; and a cheer from a hundred thousand throats shook the very ground as Penrod swam overhead. Marjorie knelt upon the steps and watched adoringly while Penrod took the drum-major's baton and, performing sinuous evolutions above the crowd, led the band. Then he threw the baton so high that it disappeared from sight; but he went swiftly after it, a double delight, for he had not only the delicious sensation of rocketing safely up and up into the blue sky, but also that of standing in the crowd below, watching and admiring himself as he dwindled to a speck, disappeared and then, emerging from a cloud, came speeding down, with the baton in his hand, to the level of the treetops, where he beat time for the band and the vast throng and Marjorie Jones, who all united in the "Star-spangled Banner" in honour of his aerial achievements. It was a great moment.

It was a great moment, but something seemed to threaten it. The face of Miss Spence looking up from the crowd grew too vivid—unpleasantly vivid. She was beckoning him and shouting, "Come down, Penrod Schofield! Penrod Schofield, come down here!" He could hear her above the band and the singing of the multitude; she seemed intent on spoiling everything. Marjorie Jones was weeping to show how sorry she was that she had formerly slighted him, and throwing kisses to prove that she loved him; but Miss Spence kept jumping between him and Marjorie, incessantly calling his name.

He grew more and more irritated with her; he was the most important person in the world and was engaged in proving it to Marjorie Jones and the whole city, and yet Miss Spence seemed to feel she still had the right to order him about as she did in the old days when he was an ordinary schoolboy. He was furious; he was sure she wanted him to do something disagreeable. It seemed to him that she had screamed "Penrod Schofield!" thousands of times.

From the beginning of his aerial experiments in his own schoolroom, he had not opened his lips, knowing somehow that one of the requirements for air floating is perfect silence on the part of the floater; but, finally, irritated beyond measure by Miss Spence's clamorous insistence, he was unable to restrain an indignant rebuke—and immediately came to earth with a frightful bump.

Miss Spence—in the flesh—had directed toward the physical body of the absent Penrod an inquiry as to the fractional consequences of dividing seventeen apples, fairly, among three boys, and she was surprised and displeased to receive no answer although to the best of her knowledge and belief, he was looking fixedly at her. She repeated her question crisply, without visible effect; then summoned him by name with increasing asperity. Twice she called him, while all his fellow pupils turned to stare at the gazing boy. She advanced a step from the platform.

"Penrod Schofield!"

"Oh, my goodness!" he shouted suddenly, "Can't you keep still a *minute?*"

Miss Spence gasped. So did the pupils. The whole room filled with a swelling conglomerate "O-o-o-o-h!"

As for Penrod himself, the walls reeled with the shock. He sat with his mouth open, a mere lump of stupefaction. For the appalling words that he had hurled at the teacher were as inexplicable to him as to any other who heard them.

Nothing is more treacherous than the human mind; nothing else so loves to play the Iscariot. Even when patiently bullied into a semblance of order and training, it may prove but a base and shifty servant. And Penrod's mind was not his servant; it was a master, with the April wind's whims; and it had just played him a diabolical trick. The very jolt with which he came back to the schoolroom in the midst of his fancied flight jarred his day-dream utterly out of him; and he sat, open-mouthed in horror at what he had said.

The unanimous gasp of awe was protracted. Miss Spence, however, finally recovered her breath, and, returning deliberately to the platform, faced the school. "And then, for a little while," as pathetic stories sometimes recount, "everything was very still." It was so still, in fact, that Penrod's new-born notoriety could almost be heard growing. This grisly silence was at last broken by the teacher.

"Penrod Schofield, stand up!"

The miserable child obeyed.

"What did you mean by speaking to me in that way?"

He hung his head, raked the floor with the side of his shoe, swayed, swallowed, looked suddenly at his hands with the air of never having seen them before, then clasped them behind him. The school shivered in ecstatic horror, every fascinated eye upon him; yet there was not a soul in the room but was profoundly grateful to him for the sensation—including the offended teacher herself. Unhappily, all this gratitude was unconscious and altogether different from the kind which results in testimonials and loving-cups. On the contrary!

"Penrod Schofield!"

He gulped.

"Answer me at once! Why did you speak to me like that?"

"I was——" He choked, unable to continue.

"Speak out!"

"I was just—thinking," he managed to stammer.

"That will not do," she returned sharply. "I wish to know immediately why you spoke as you did."

The stricken Penrod answered helplessly:

"Because I was just thinking."

Upon the very rack he could have offered no ampler truthful explanation. It was all he knew about it.

"Thinking what?"

"Just thinking."

Miss Spence's expression gave evidence that her power of self-restraint was undergoing a remarkable test. However, after taking counsel with herself, she commanded:

"Come here!"

He shuffled forward, and she placed a chair upon the platform near her own.

"Sit there!"

Then (but not at all as if nothing had happened), she continued the lesson in arithmetic. Spiritually the children may have learned a lesson in very small fractions indeed as they gazed at the fragment of sin before them on the stool of penitence. They all stared at him attentively with hard and passionately interested eyes, in which there was never one trace of pity. It cannot be said with precision that he writhed; his movement was more a slow, continuous squirm, effected with a ghastly assumption of languid indifference; while his gaze, in the effort to escape the marble-hearted glare of his schoolmates, affixed itself with apparent permanence to the waistcoat button of James Russell Lowell just above the "U" in "Russell."

Classes came and classes went, grilling him with eyes. Newcomers received the story of the crime in darkling whispers; and the outcast sat and sat and sat, and squirmed and squirmed and squirmed. (He did one or two things with his spine which a professional contortionist would have observed with real interest.) And all this while of freezing suspense was but the criminal's detention awaiting trial. A known punishment may be anticipated with some measure of equanimity; at least, the prisoner may prepare himself to undergo it; but the unknown looms more monstrous for every attempt to guess it. Penrod's crime was unique; there were no rules to aid him in estimating the vengeance to fall upon him for it. What seemed most probable was that he would be expelled from the school in the presence of his family, the mayor, and council, and afterward whipped by his father upon the State House steps, with the entire city as audience by invitation of the authorities.

Noon came. The rows of children filed out, every head turning for a last unpleasingly speculative look at the outlaw. Then Miss Spence closed the door into the cloakroom and that into the big hall, and came and sat at her desk, near Penrod. The tramping of feet outside, the shrill calls and shouting and the changing voices of the older boys ceased to be heard—and there was silence. Penrod, still affecting to be occupied with Lowell, was conscious that Miss Spence looked at him intently.

"Penrod," she said gravely, "what excuse have you to offer before I report your case to the principal?"

The word "principal" struck him to the vitals. Grand Inquisitor, Grand Khan, Sultan, Emperor, Tsar, Cæsar Augustus—these are comparable. He stopped squirming instantly, and sat rigid.

"I want an answer. Why did you shout those words at me?"

"Well," he murmured, "I was just—thinking."

"Thinking what?" she asked sharply.

"I don't know."

"That won't do!"

He took his left ankle in his right hand and regarded it helplessly.

"That won't do, Penrod Schofield," she repeated severely. "If that is all the excuse you have to offer I shall report your case this instant!"

And she rose with fatal intent.

But Penrod was one of those whom the precipice inspired. "Well, I *have* got an excuse."

"Well"—she paused impatiently—"what is it?"

He had not an idea, but he felt one coming, and replied automatically, in a plaintive tone:

"I guess anybody that had been through what I had to go through, last night, would think they had an excuse."

Miss Spence resumed her seat, though with the air of being ready to leap from it instantly.

"What has last night to do with your insolence to me this morning?"

"Well, I guess you'd see," he returned, emphasizing the plaintive note, "if you knew what I know."

"Now, Penrod," she said, in a kinder voice, "I have a high regard for your mother and father, and it would hurt me to distress them, but you must either tell me what was the matter with you or I'll have to take you to Mrs. Houston."

"Well, ain't I going to?" he cried, spurred by the dread name. "It's because I didn't sleep last night."

"Were you ill?" The question was put with some dryness.

He felt the dryness. "No'm; I wasn't."

"Then if someone in your family was so ill that even you were kept up all night, how does it happen they let you come to school this morning?"

"It wasn't illness," he returned, shaking his head mournfully. "It was lots worse'n anybody's being sick. It was—it was—well, it was jest awful."

"*What* was?" He remarked with anxiety the incredulity in her tone.

"It was about Aunt Clara," he said.

"Your Aunt Clara!" she repeated. "Do you mean your mother's sister who married Mr. Farry of Dayton, Illinois?"

"Yes—Uncle John," returned Penrod sorrowfully. "The trouble was about him."

Miss Spence frowned a frown which he rightly interpreted as one of continued suspicion. "She and I were in school together," she said. "I used to know her very well, and I've always heard her married life was entirely happy. I don't——"

"Yes, it was," he interrupted, "until last year when Uncle John took to running with travelling men——"

"What?"

"Yes'm." He nodded solemnly. "That was what started it. At first he was a good, kind husband, but these travelling men would coax him into a saloon on his way from work, and they got him to drinking beer and then ales, wines, liquors, and cigars——"

"Penrod!"

"Ma'am?"

"I'm not inquiring into your Aunt Clara's private affairs; I'm asking you if you have anything to say which would palliate——"

"That's what I'm tryin' to *tell* you about, Miss Spence," he pleaded, —"if you'd jest only let me. When Aunt Clara and her little baby daughter got to our house last night——"

"You say Mrs. Farry is visiting your mother?"

"Yes'm—not just visiting—you see, she *had* to come. Well of course, little baby Clara, she was so bruised up and mauled, where he'd been hittin' her with his cane——"

"You mean that your uncle had done such a thing as *that!*" exclaimed Miss Spence, suddenly disarmed by this scandal.

"Yes'm, and mamma and Margaret had to sit up all night nursin' little Clara—and *Aunt* Clara was in such a state *somebody* had to keep talkin' to *her*, and there wasn't anybody but me to do it, so I——"

"But where was your father?" she cried.

"Ma'am?"

"Where was your father while——"

"Oh—papa?" Penrod paused, reflected; then brightened. "Why, he was down at the train, waitin' to see if Uncle John would try to follow 'em and make 'em come home so's he could persecute 'em some more. I wanted to do that, but they said if he did come I mightn't be strong enough to hold him, and——" The brave lad paused again, modestly. Miss Spence's expression was encouraging. Her eyes were wide with astonishment, and there may have been in them, also, the mingled beginnings of admiration and self-reproach. Penrod, warming to his work, felt safer every moment.

"And so," he continued, "I had to sit up with Aunt Clara. She had some pretty big bruises, too, and I had to——"

"But why didn't they send for a doctor?" However, this question was only a flicker of dying incredulity.

"Oh, they didn't want any *doctor*," exclaimed the inspired realist promptly. "They don't want anybody to *hear* about it because Uncle John might reform—and then where'd he be if everybody knew he'd been a drunkard and whipped his wife and baby daughter?"

"Oh!" said Miss Spence.

"You see, he used to be upright as anybody," he went on explanatively. "It all begun——"

"Began, Penrod."

"Yes'm. It all commenced from the first day he let those travelling men coax him into the saloon." Penrod narrated the downfall of his Uncle John at length. In detail he was nothing short of plethoric; and incident followed incident, sketched with such vividness, such abundance of colour, and such verisimilitude to a drunkard's life as a drunkard's life should be, that had Miss Spence possessed the rather chilling attributes of William J. Burns himself, the last trace of skepticism must have vanished from her mind. Besides, there are two things that will be believed of any man whatsoever, and one of them is that he has taken to drink. And in every sense it was a moving picture which, with simple but eloquent words, the virtuous Penrod set before his teacher.

His eloquence increased with what it fed on; and as with the eloquence so with self-reproach in the gentle bosom of the teacher. She cleared her throat with difficulty once or twice, during his description of his ministering night with Aunt Clara. "And I said to her, 'Why, Aunt Clara, what's the use of takin' on so about it?' And I said, 'Now, Aunt Clara, all the crying in the world can't make things any better.' And then she'd just keep catchin' hold of me, and sob and kind of holler, and I'd say, '*Don't* cry, Aunt Clara—*please* don't cry.' "

Then, under the influence of some fragmentary survivals of the respectable portion of his Sunday adventures, his theme became more exalted; and, only partially misquoting a phrase from a psalm, he related how he had made it of comfort to Aunt Clara, and how he had besought her to seek Higher guidance in her trouble.

The surprising thing about a structure such as Penrod was erecting is that the taller it becomes the more ornamentation it will stand. Gifted boys have this faculty of building magnificence upon cobwebs

—and Penrod was gifted. Under the spell of his really great perform-ance, Miss Spence gazed more and more sweetly upon the prodigy of spiritual beauty and goodness before her, until at last, when Penrod came to the explanation of his "just thinking," she was forced to turn her head away.

"You mean, dear," she said gently, "that you were all worn out and hardly knew what you were saying?"

"Yes'm."

"And you were thinking about all those dreadful things so hard that you forgot where you were?"

"I was thinking," he said simply, "how to save Uncle John."

And the end of it for this mighty boy was that the teacher kissed him!

WHY THE CLEVER OXFORD SCHOLAR
LOST HIS SUPPER

ANONYMOUS

(1526)

A rich franklin in the country, having by his wife but one child and no more, for the great affection that he had to his said child found him at Oxford to school by the space of two or three year. This young scholar, in a vacation time for his disport, came home to his father.

It fortuned afterward in a night, the father, the mother, and the said young scholar sitting at supper, having before them no more meat but only a couple of chickens, the father said this wise: Son, so it is that I have spent much money upon thee to find thee to school, where-fore I have great desire to know what hast learned. To whom the son answered, and said: Father I have studied sophistry, and by that science I can prove that these two chickens in the dish be three chick-ens. Marry, said the father; that would I fain see. The scholar took one of the chickens in his hand, and said: Lo here is one chicken; and incontinent he took both the chickens in his hand jointly and said, here is two chickens: and one and two maketh three. Ergo here is three chickens. Then the father took one of the chickens to himself, and gave another to his wife, and said thus: Lo I will have one of the

SID GORDON, COLLIER'S

"Can you do anything besides graduate?"

---

chickens to my part; and thy mother shall have another; and because
of thy good argument thou shalt have the third to thy supper, for thou
gettest no more meat here at this time—which promise the father kept,
and so the scholar went without his supper.

By this tale men may see that it is great folly to put one to school
to learn any subtle science which hath no natural wit.

B. SC.

EMILY HAHN

My career as a mining engineer has this much in common with many
success stories—it was founded on an accident. Otherwise, there is no
comparison, because mine is not a success story. As an engineer, I
have been a flop, but there were a few glorious weeks, back in 1926,
when it might have been otherwise. Flushed with the glory and the
triumph of my B. Sc., excited by the publicity which I received as the

First Woman Graduate in Mining Engineering from the University of Wisconsin, and generally on top of the world, I completely forgot the reason for my acquiring that extraordinary diploma and actually took a job with a mining company. Yet the facts are simple and stark. I never meant to be a mining engineer at all. The whole thing was a complete misapprehension.

At the age of seventeen, I was an earnest, plump young woman, much annoyed by my parents' insistence on my going to college, because I felt that I was destined for Art. Once installed at the University of Wisconsin, though, I had to study something. At first I enrolled myself in the College of Letters and Science, where by temperament I belonged; it offered that potpourri of language, literature, history, and science that made, I thought, for Culture. It was the required science course which led me astray. A half-year term of freshman geology stirred me up to try chemistry. I had heard that among the chemistry professors at Wisconsin there was a really good teacher, Kahlenberg, but when I tried to get into his class, I ran into a trifling technical difficulty. Kahlenberg's course, the dean explained, though it exactly paralleled that of the Letters and Science brand of chemistry, was usually taken only by engineering students.

"Well, that's all right," I said. "I'm sure I can persuade Professor Kahlenberg to give me special permission to go to his lectures. Since they cover the same ground, what's the difference? May I do it that way?" Now, the dean may have fought with his wife that morning, or maybe he was worried about his bank account, or perhaps it was necessary that he say no once in a while, just to prove he was a dean. I'm sure that he never intended thus carelessly to mold my future life with one hasty word, but that is what he did. "No," said the dean rudely, and turned back to his desk.

His manners hurt my feelings, but that alone wouldn't have done the mischief. Like many young people in my day, I was bristling with principles, eager to find abuses in the world and burning to do away with them. In five seconds I had condemned the dean's decision as an abuse. He was wrong in saying no—wrong on technical grounds, because Professor Kahlenberg's consent would have been enough for any dean in a reasonable mood, and wrong in principle, because a student should be allowed to select his own teachers. Anyway, those were my sentiments.

I was mad. Boy, was I mad! I couldn't have remained in the same college with that dean for one single day more. Before the registrar's office closed that afternoon, I had transferred myself to the College of Engineering, enrolled for the chemistry course I wanted, and sent off a confused letter of explanation to my parents. There, if only anybody in the Engineering College had had a grain of sense, the great revolt would have ended. I would have listened to Kahlenberg's chemistry lectures, shaken hands with him, and transferred myself right back to Culture and a chastened dean at the end of term. The engineers, however, were not wise.

They were stunned when they discovered me, a seventeen-year-old female freshman, enrolled in the Engineering College. The university had a long-standing tradition, as well as a charter, for being a coeducational institution. Women studied medicine at Wisconsin, and the "pure science" courses were full of girls; the Agricultural College, too, had them. Nobody argued about that. But nobody had yet heard of a coed engineer. The engineers' immunity through the years had bred in their ranks a happy confidence that it could never happen there, and I was a horrid surprise. They lost their heads and went into a panic and, in the ensuing weeks, actually appealed to the state legislature to heave me out. After due consideration, the legislature regretfully refused. It couldn't heave me out, it explained, much as it would like to as a group of red-blooded he-men, because the university was a coeducational, tax-supported institution, and if a woman wanted to study any course it offered, and if she fulfilled the requirements and behaved herself, you couldn't turn her down.

Even then, if the engineers had only known, all was not lost. They couldn't keep their mouths shut, though. They were the engineers—hearty, simple folk. All of them, faculty members and students, tried to live up to the college pattern—the awkward guy, the diamond in the rough. To a man, they wore stiff corduroy trousers, smoked pipes or chewed tobacco, and looked down haughtily on the other colleges, which they condemned as highbrow. It was not in them to be diplomatic, and I maintain that they brought upon themselves what followed.

The custom in college is to allocate each student to a professor, who acts as his adviser. In the College of Letters and Science, my adviser had been a fragile lady who taught French literature, but my new adviser in the Engineering College was a mining engineer. I had elected mining engineering as my particular course. Professor Shorey was no pedant, nor was he tactful. My first advisory hour with him was given over to a violent argument.

"But why?" he demanded. "Why should a woman want to be an engineer? I never heard of such nonsense!"

"Why did *you* want to be an engineer?" I retorted. I was still talking in a more or less academic spirit, of course. I meant to leave engineering in peace, and before long. Sooner or later I intended to break down and explain the circumstances to Professor Shorey and reassure him, but in the meantime his attitude interested me. I wanted to hear more about it.

"It's not at all the same thing," he said. "In the first place, you'll never get a job, even if you should take your degree, which is very doubtful. If I were running a mine, I'd never hire a woman in any technical capacity. You wouldn't have the practical experience, and you'd be a nuisance around the office."

"Why wouldn't I have the experience, Mr. Shorey?"

"How would you get it? Who's going to let *you* go down a mine? Why, the miners would go on strike. They'd call it bad luck and expect a cave-in. It's too foolish to discuss. It's all a waste of time, anyhow— your time and mine—because you won't get your degree."

I moved closer to the desk, all alert. "Why won't I get my degree?" I said.

Shorey sighed. "The female mind," he explained carefully and kindly, "is incapable of grasping mechanics or higher mathematics or any of the fundamentals of mining taught in this course."

That remark, *tout simple*, is why I am a Bachelor of Science in Mining Engineering. From that moment until graduation, I completely forgot that I had not always, from my earliest youth, intended to become a mining engineer. Every day offered fresh reason for forgetting. I was awfully busy for the next three years, up to my neck in mechanics and drafting and calculus. It was enough to make any girl forget a little thing like Art.

One afternoon soon after my argument with Shorey, I attended my first class in surveying. We met indoors to get our instructions. I sat on a separate bench a little way off from the men, and none of them looked at me. The instructor, too, avoided my eye in a sulky manner. He explained, with chalk on a blackboard, the simple rules for running a line with a hand level. Then he announced, "We will now go to the instrument room and take out our equipment. You people choose your partners for the term—surveyors always work in pairs. Go ahead and divide yourselves up."

He leaned back in his chair behind the desk. There were fourteen men in the class, and in two minutes there were seven couples. While the other students got up and scrambled to make their arrangements, I just sat still, wondering where I went from there.

"Well," said the instructor, "let's go and get our instruments."

We straggled after him and waited as he unlocked the storeroom. The levels we were to use, the type called "dumpy" levels, are heavy, metallic objects on tripods. Seven men stepped up and took one apiece, and then, as the instructor hesitated, I walked over defiantly and picked up an eighth. The instructor rubbed his chin and looked at me furtively. I looked at my feet.

"I was sure we had an even number in the class," he said. "I guess Bemis has dropped out."

Fourteen men and I stood there tongue-tied, impatient to bring all this to an end. Then I noticed a tall, lanky boy, who had not been in the lecture room, leaning against the door looking on, a good-natured sneer on his freckled face. He now gathered his bones together and shambled over.

"Aw," he said gruffly, "I'll take her."

"Oh, there you are, Bemis. O.K.," said the instructor, loud in his relief.

Bemis picked up my level and tripod and, with his free hand, waved me toward the long rod which one man of a surveying pair always carries. "Come along," he said. "I know these things. I've already run a few, working in the summer." He turned and started to walk out, and after a second, during which I stared at him, registering eternal devotion, I scampered after him. Behind me there was a loud general exhalation of relief and wonder.

Reginald Bemis—for Reginald was his name—found out all too soon that his responsibility was not temporary. Whatever whimsical impulse of kindliness had pushed him into his offer vanished when he realized that he was stuck with me for the term, but once he learned this bitter fact, he decided at least to bring me up the way I should go. He had worked in open-pit mines before coming to the university, and it was typical of his scornful attitude, that of a veteran miner, that he hadn't deigned to come to the explanatory lecture. He was one of those gangling, undernourished boys who work their way through college; he waited on table at a hash house when he wasn't in class, and got good marks and had a future. As a surveyor, he knew his business as well as our instructor did. By the time we graduated from the dumpy level to the transit, Reginald and I had the best record of any pair of engineers for our reports and drawings. None of this excellence, obviously, was due to my talents.

Not that I didn't do my share of the heavy work. I did. We took turns carrying the cumbersome instruments. Sometimes our trail led us to a very public spot, and when passersby suddenly noticed that I was a female—that took a moment or two, for I wore khaki coveralls most of the time—Reginald became very touchy. The minute a stranger paused to take another look at me holding up the rod or squinting laboriously into the transit, Reginald would make such ferocious noises and wiggle his fingers at his nose so insultingly that the passersby would soon move on. His attitude was brutal but right, and I tried to show him that I appreciated it.

One evening, near the end of the surveying course, as we plodded along through snowdrifts toward the instrument room to turn in our equipment, I said to Reginald, "Excuse me for saying so, but you've been awfully nice. I don't know what I would have done that day if you hadn't said you would take me along for a partner."

"You was all there was left," said Reginald gruffly.

"Yes, but you didn't have to go on with me after that day. It must have been very hard sometimes."

"You ain't kiddin'," said Reginald, with deep feeling. "You know what they was calling me all year? Her Choice—that was it. Once I hadda fight a guy."

"It's a shame," I said. "But anyway, I've learned how to survey."

"Oh, you ain't so dumb," he admitted. "Only trouble with you is, sometimes you don't think straight. It's like you was dreamin'. Like today, when we couldn't find that bench mark. You just stood there with your mouth open while I went around kicking snow up, trying to find it. Lazy, that's your trouble."

"I'll try to do better," I said.

"Anyway," remarked Reginald cheerfully as we entered the door, "the worst is over. I got only one more week with you."

"You've been *awfully* nice," I repeated.

I knew one of the geology professors socially, as it happened, and though I never crossed his orbit in an official way, I did drop in on him once in a while to unburden my soul. He gave me a piece of advice early in the game. "These boys are just afraid you'll interfere with their daily routine," he said. "As soon as they realize you don't, it will be all right. They've got some idea, for instance, that they'll have to be careful of their talk when you're around."

"You mean," I asked, brightening, "that there are words I don't know?"

The professor ignored this and said warningly, "Don't pay any attention, no matter what they say. Don't expect special privileges just because you're a woman. Try to let them forget you're a woman. Pretty soon everything will be all right."

As a result, I trained myself to keep very quiet and to maintain a poker face wherever I was in the college. The mining-engineering course was a stiff one, and we were all too busy to indulge in any feud, anyway. Now and then, however, some complication cropped up. I was excused permanently from one lab course because there was no ladies' room in that building. I was also formally excused from the gymnasium classes the other coeds had to take, on the ground that I got enough exercise just learning to be an engineer. The khaki coverall garment I wore for surveying and ore dressing had to do for more orthodox classes as well, and I could see that my French teacher didn't like it, but she never complained.

It was at this time that I acquired the name Mickey as a permanent label. It was a nursery nickname of mine which had been more or less forgotten by everyone but Mother. The engineers heard it and adopted it as a more acceptable, masculine-sounding name than my real one, which was hopelessly ladylike. Of course, there were brief flareups and resentments now and again. Some of the boys were unfair, I felt. At the beginning of a math course, one of them yelled at me, "You'll never be able to get through this! You're a girl!" Yet at the end of term, when he asked me what grade I had and I replied exultingly that I was in the first five on the list, he said, "Huh, that's just because you're a girl you got that mark." It was irritating, but after all I *had* stuck my neck out. I continued to keep mousy quiet, and our mechanics instructor finally said to a friend, "You know, I've been dreading the day that girl would have to come to my lectures. But now that she's here, she's—why," he said in astonishment, "she's quite a lady."

As I look back on it now, I am amazed that I passed any of those examinations. Half the time and energy I should have given to my work was used up in the effort to prove that I could hold my own without being in the way. I was painfully self-conscious. My professor friend's words had sunk in so deep that I couldn't get them out of my head or my behavior. I took it as an insult when some absent-minded engineering student so far forgot himself as to hold open a door for me or stood up and offered me a chair. In time, though, most of these little frictions wore away. The one serious problem was the matter of field trips.

Field trips are study journeys into the country. Students, both of mining engineering and geology, go out with instructors and wander about looking at rock formations, geographical features, mines, or whatever they are interested in at the time. Of course, I went out on the small trips that were over in one day, but from the longer trips, including one expedition to mines in the West, which took up a whole summer and taught the boys how to work in the tunnels, I was barred. It was simply impossible to surmount that obstacle. The Wisconsin state legislature couldn't help me this time, because the State of Montana would have kept me out of its mines. How, then, was I to qualify for my degree?

I figured something out at last as a substitute for the mining experience. I went up that summer and stayed with relatives who had a farm in Michigan. Every morning I went out with a hand level and a Brunton compass and ran lines back and forth at half-mile intervals, straight across the township, until I had made a respectable contour map of the region to take back to the college. The authorities studied the map, smoked a few pipes over it, and unanimously voted to give it the status of the summer's field work the boys had put in. Perhaps this really definite triumph went to my head a little. Perhaps the summer of walking alone under the Michigan sun had sweated out of me my hard-won humility. Anyway, that autumn, the beginning of my final year, I was in a mood to fight my great, all-out battle with the Geology Club.

Again, it wasn't my fault. I didn't start it; the men did. They should have known that the sign they put up on the bulletin board in Science Hall would be enough to knock me off balance. A stranger would not have understood. All the sign said, in formal lettering, was that the Geology Club was holding an extra-special meeting that night for two purposes—first, to introduce the semi-yearly crop of newcomers to the group, and, second, to hear the highly respected visitor, Professor Such-and-So, world-renowned expert on volcanoes or coral reefs or something, deliver the first of his series of lectures. But someone had added a significant line in red pencil: "Women not invited."

I recognized this as an insult aimed directly at me. No other woman would have been crazy enough to want to go to a Geology Club meeting. The sign was the worse for being unnecessary. I knew perfectly well I wasn't invited; I had not been invited, repeatedly, for three years. They had thrashed the matter out many times. I always pretended not to know, but it was an old grievance, because all members of the mining-engineering courses had heretofore automatically been invited to become members of the Geology Club. Once I showed up, though, the Geology Club members maintained that they were not a formal institution of the college but a social organization, and, as such, didn't have to abide by the cruel law of coeducation, which forced open their lecture halls to the female sex. True, I did belong to the Mining Engineers' Club—we held our meetings in the ore-dressing laboratory and cooked hamburgers in the blast furnace—but that club, said the geologists, was different, somehow—more entangled in the web of the educational setup. The geologists claimed that their taking mining engineers into their club was a voluntary courtesy, and they said that they preferred not to extend it to me. Inviting me would, they said darkly, establish a precedent.

For three years I had silently accepted this argument, because I was, thank God, a lady, and besides there didn't seem to be any way around it. This red-pencilled message, though, affected me strongly. I was as angry as I had been that long-ago day in the dean's office, back in those prehistoric times when, for some reason, I wasn't yet studying engineering.

It wasn't fear. I hadn't been bothering their old Geology Club. Yet there the men were, jeering and making faces at me in this bulletin-board announcement. Rub it in, would they? I'd show them!

My eyes narrowed as I read the sign through for the fourth time. Somebody had slipped up. Professor Such-and-So had been invited by the college faculty to give that series of lectures, and, as one of the college students, I was, of course, entitled to hear the entire series. Entitled? Why, I was probably *required* to hear them. Not that I had ever felt any particular emotional yearning for information about volcanoes or coral reefs or whatever it was. That was not the point. The point was a matter of principle. The point was that the Geology Club, in thus selfishly arrogating one of the visiting professors' lectures to their own session, sacrificed their standing as an amateur social organization. They had made themselves, at least for the time being, one of the college classes, and that class I was entitled by law to attend. I was a perfect lady, all right, but just the same I decided to visit the Geology Club that night.

The most painfully uncertain people are the ones who seem poised and self-assured. I walked into the club meeting as bold as brass, but the slightest push would have upset me, and my old pal, the friendly professor, quite unwittingly almost administered it. As I made my way past the rows of dismayed, silent, flummoxed men, he shouted in a whisper, "Bravo!" It took a gigantic effort to finish the walk, to sit down demurely in an empty chair, to pretend that nothing at all extraordinary was happening. This was my first overt rebellion. Just when I had almost captured the good will of the college, too, and was so near to graduation and release. Just when they were about to confer on me the ultimate honor, the priceless boon of indifference.

The visiting lecturer saved my face, though he couldn't have known that, by climbing to the platform and breaking the tension. The ensuing hour must have gratified him, for the whole roomful of young people sat in a dead hush while he told us about volcanoes—or was it coral? If some of the graduate students hadn't been polite enough to ask a few perfunctory questions at the close of his talk, he would have noticed a strain in the atmosphere, but the amenities were properly observed, and after a vote of thanks he said good night and left us alone to wash our dirty linen.

The club president, a kindly soul named Clyde, took the floor and went through a few formalities—minutes of the last meeting and a brief résumé of the club's aims, for the benefit of the new members. Then he said, "It's our custom, just to make things less formal, to ask the men who are new to the club to introduce themselves. I'll call on them in order of seating. Mr. Blake?"

"Class of twenty-eight," mumbled a scarlet Mr. Blake. "No other clubs. Transferred this year from Michigan College of Mines. Majoring in petrology."

Everyone grew quieter and quieter as the introductions proceeded. I wasn't just quiet; I was rigid. Were they going to pretend that I wasn't there? If Clyde skipped me, I would have to make a demonstration of some sort. I would *have* to. I held my breath until I nearly strangled. Clyde's eyes fell on me and he cleared his throat.

"Since our friend Miss Hahn has taken the bull by the horns," he said, "I will call on her to introduce herself to our new friends."

Everybody let out his breath a little; the crisis was postponed. I stumbled to my feet and duly made my recital. The meeting proceeded without interruption. Clyde finished up the official business of the meeting by announcing that it was the evening for collection of dues. If the members would kindly pay their dues—a dollar a head—

to the treasurer, he said, we would be able to proceed with refreshments —the customary coffee and vanilla wafers.

We stood in line, with our dollars in our hands, and that was when the trouble started. When I reached the collection table, the treasurer shook his head. "Can't take it," he said.

"Why not?"

"Well, uh . . ." The unhappy boy swallowed hard, and then in desperation raised his voice. "Clyde! Come over here, will you?"

It had all been arranged in advance, evidently. Clyde came over and took my arm with a sort of reluctant affection, and said, "Come on out in the hall, Mickey. I want to talk to you."

I pushed his hand away. "Talk to me here," I said.

"Come on, Mickey. Do me this favor, won't you?"

We marched out between serried ranks of embarrassed young geologists.

"It's this way," said Clyde miserably. "A bunch of us tried to—I mean, this thing came up again, the way it always does, last week, and though I personally, and some of your other friends, tried to persuade the fellows, the thing is—"

"All right," I said abruptly. "Here's my dollar, anyway. Take it for wear and tear on the bench. Nobody wants to—" To my horror, it suddenly became urgently necessary to be alone. My unhappy nature had played me false. Whenever I am keyed up to violent anger, tears begin to flow. I ran down the hall, completely routed. This was disaster. I had committed the one unforgivable sin: I had been feminine. I wanted to kick myself for shame. I wanted to die.

What happened after that is public knowledge. Clyde walked slowly back into the clubroom and shook his head in misery when the boys asked him what had happened. "Was she awfully sore?" they asked. "Did she make a scene? Did she say—"

"Oh, gosh," said the president, "don't talk about it. She—she *cried*."

"Cried?" Appalled, they stared at each other. Cried! They lowered their eyes, unable to meet each other's gaze.

Somebody proposed a vote. There and then they voted.

A half hour later I was sitting in the study room at Science Hall, huddled in my chair, despair clutched round me like a blanket. There Clyde found me and brought the news. Practically unanimously, I had been elected a member of the Geology Club. One lone man who still stood out against me, admitting that his attitude spoiled the record, was yet unable to give up his convictions, and so he had left the room while the vote was taken. Public opinion had demanded that he do this.

"And in conclusion," Clyde said to me, "permit me to say that I'm sure all the fellows are *awfully* sorry it all happened."

Though stunned, I managed to say a few gracious words of accept- ance, so that Clyde would leave me the sooner. I needed solitude; I had a lot of reorienting to do. I sat a long time at my desk, looking backward at a three-year program of mistaken strategy. It was the friendly professor, I realized, who had started me off on the wrong foot. Well, it was all right now. I knew better now. Just in time, too.

I blew my nose and started to search my briefcase, diving far down, trying to find a long-forgotten pocket mirror.

PRIVATE SCHOOL

HARRY DUBIN

". . . so remember: don't say *yeah* or *yah*, say *yes*. Don't interrupt. Don't sit while the principal stands, and say *yes, sir* and *no, sir*."

"And I shouldn't suck my thumb!" added Addison Beech.

"Don't be funny, Addy," his father snapped back with a jerk of the arm, "this school is small and they probably have more applicants than desks. You've got to make a favorable impression and appear to be well-bred. They don't like smart alecks and loud mouths in a place like this."

"And what do I want to be, dad?"

"Again? We've been through all of that. You can't stand the sight of blood. Lawyers are a dime a dozen. You yourself said you want to be a business man. Tell him so. Tell him you are going to enter the business world—you want to do *creative* manufacturing. We're not signing a contract here as to your future, you know. Just remember it's important to impress this guy Smythington. *Impress* him. Just a stroke of his pen can let you in or keep you out."

They entered the center hall. The thick, wood panelling, the grand- father clock, and several pieces of elaborately carved oak furniture in Georgian design exuded an odor and created the atmosphere usually associated with time-honored institutions of learning or chambers of state. To the right was a slightly more modern Library-Study Hall and, to the left, two offices: one bearing the legend "Headmaster" on the door, the other "Secretary's Office," the occupant of which, coming into the lobby, noticed the two strangers and inquired if she might be of assistance.

"Good afternoon, I am Mr. Beech; this is Addison. We have an appointment."

"Oh yes, I recall the name. Step into the headmaster's office, won't you? Mr. Smythington will be free in a moment." She pointed to the adjoining office and involuntarily ran her eyes down Mr. Beech's new summer suit. Mr. Beech, because of the presence of his son or through preoccupation with other thoughts, did not return the compliment of the pleasant and comely though middle-aging Miss Treaker, secretary. He ushered Addison into the Sanctum Smythington.

Addison had just finished wiping his right shoe clean on the back of his left trouser leg and had just taken a wriggling perch on the leather couch when Mr. Smythington, whom nature had admirably cast for his role, entered his office. He had aplomb and dignity that bordered on but did not quite range into pomposity. He bade his callers welcome and took his seat behind his desk as Addison, recalling instructions, leaped gazelle-like to his feet. In view of the awkwardness of the timing Addison thought it best to follow through. So he remained standing.

"Want to say something, lad?" asked the headmaster.

"No, sir."

"Well then, do sit down and be at ease. We like having a chat with our boys before admission. Ours is an intimate group and, since we shall be spending four years together, I should like to have you or your father ask any questions that may come to mind." The question uppermost in Addison's mind that moment was the direction of the lavatory but he discreetly chose silence.

"Well now," continued Mr. Smythington with an eye on Addison, the budget for the fiscal year beginning and the condition of the classrooms in the lower middle school, "you *are* a fine looking youngster and the transcript of your elementary school record reads very well indeed. Tell me, Addison, are you interested in sports?"

"Yes . . . sir, I like baseball, and football and bike riding and skating," recounted Addison and then added, "I like swimming, too."

"And horseback riding," interposed Mr. Beech, regarding this activity as a social grace worthy of mention and wishing to capitalize on a twenty-five-dollar investment in Addison's riding lessons at summer camp.

The headmaster entered a few notes on the application form before him. "Have you any hobbies?"

Addison looked at his father for reassurance.

"I like to draw, sir," he replied modestly, "and take pictures."

"He does a little stamp collecting as well," contributed Mr. Beech, recalling the many hours he had devoted to Addison's stamp albums, long after Addison was asleep, thumbing through catalogues, checking water marks, policing Addison's almost prescient acts of philatelic imperialism by pulling India from the Mongolian spaces, Japan from the Chinese, Poland from the Russians. "Tell him, Addy, tell him everything. They want to know *all* about you."

"Oh fine, fine; I was a bit of a philatelist myself in my undergraduate days—specialized in British Colonials—an interesting and educational hobby. Do you do much outside reading, Addison?"

Mr. Beech visualized the stack of comics, Superman, and fictional science in Addy's room and mentally crossed his fingers. Though he had never given credence to tales of psychic phenomena, he tried generating a telepathic quickie to his son.

"Yes, sir," Addison answered.

Mr. Smythington laid down his pen, obviously pleased with the course of the interview thus far and fairly convinced that he was dealing with potential Fairfield material.

"Now then, Addison, have you thought much of your future? Have you any idea of the profession or occupation you wish to pursue? Have you or your parents or teachers discovered any particular inclination or aptitude on your part?"

Not too many years back, Addison would have responded to that question with great conviction and resolution. He *knew* that he would be a fireman, a policeman or a cowboy. Now, as he became more aware of the refinements of the social structure, the question had become academic.

He was prepared however. "I don't think I want to be a doctor or a lawyer or anything like that. I might change my mind later but I think I would like to be a business man. I might like to. . . ."

"Quite right, gentlemen," interrupted the headmaster. "I have always maintained that the average student, occupationally speaking, does not seriously begin to consider his life's work until the senior year and, most often, not until he is well into his college program. I believe that statistics will bear me out on this.

"However, in instances where we find a definite predisposition toward a specific vocation, we like to conform the electives in the curriculum to it. What phase of business are you interested in, Addison, do you know?"

"I would like to do *creative manufacturing*," Addison replied with an inspired air.

Mr. Smythington took up his pen again. He faltered a moment before making the entry. "How's that?" he asked, sensing a new one for the books.

"I wanta be a creative *manufacturer*," Addison repeated, this time slurring the adjective and looking to Mr. Beech for reassurance. Mr. Beech nodded a defiant approval.

At the conclusion of several more routine questions and some observations on matters irrelevant to the purpose of the interview, Mr. Smythington advised Mr. Beech that he would be notified shortly of the school's disposition of the application. Meanwhile the secretary would be glad to accept his check for fifty dollars as a deposit. Which transaction the headmaster observed through a knothole connecting both offices.

Done, the amiable Miss Treaker conducted a tour of the remainder of the plant which proved to be most unpretentious but neat and charming withal.

As they drove from the school grounds Addison regained his volubility.

"How did I do, dad?"

"A little timid but I'm pretty sure you'll make it. Otherwise why ask me for a deposit? Say did you notice how small those classrooms were? Individualized instruction practically."

"Yah, and did you see those snazzy purple sweaters with the big 'F' on it?" Addison said, volunteering an item of equal significance. "Boy, I feel good—high school and everything—you'll have to increase my allowance, you know, dad. I'll need carfare and extra stuff. . . ."

"Let's not discuss that now. All I hope is that you will get something worthwhile from Fairfield; that you will appreciate the fact that it costs me not a little money to send you through private school; that you come through with *results*."

Private school! To himself, Mr. Beech multiplied the cost of tuition by four years and added the price of hot lunches for the period. Even if Addy carried a lunch box to school, the food would cost something and the savings were not too great.

Private school! He had long since convinced himself and Sue that it wasn't only because of a desire to elevate the social position of his son and delight in the prestige of saying, "My son attends private school," that the decision had been made. Addy's temperament, inherited from the distaff side, Mr. Beech avowed, was a bit nervous and high strung. It had manifested itself from infancy and for many years thereafter when Addy could not fall asleep without banging his face on the pillow and making a steady smothered hum punctuated by the rhythmic banging so that he sounded like a little motor laboring in its cycle.

Hadn't Sue, as early as the third grade, been summoned to school on account of Addison's walking up and down the aisle during class? Not as an act of insubordination or mischievousness but just through sheer boredom and an urge to be doing something. "This child should be in private school," the teacher had even then suggested to Sue. "We cannot progress his studies beyond the ability of the slowest children in his class (of 40) to master them."

And then the time Addy had frightened Sue into near hysteria by disappearing from the apartment only to be found at the controls of the elevator, feeding the operator peanuts and tootsie-rolls and riding up and down for the sheer sense of movement. Then there was the quiet tiptoeing through his parents' bedroom early each Sunday morning and the accidental sneeze or tripping over a shoe and then the question, "What are we doing today, daddy?"

He required recognition and encouragement, the Beeches rationalized, to bring his mental faculties into full play; he required personal direction and supervision to keep from being bored. He *needed* private school.

They made a semicircle into the parkway leading back to the city. Addison picked up the conversation.

"Dad."

"Yes, Addy."

"What is *creative* manufacturing?"

Beech was slow to answer. "Well, er . . . it means making something original, unusual . . . uh, something *useful* to man."

They sat silent for a few moments, Addison to pretend he understood, Beech to figure out what he had meant.

Two miles along they recognized the orange dome of a Howard

"There you have the rest of them. -T-U-V-W-X-Y-Z."

Johnson and stopped for sodas. Three clerks and dozens of customers meant a long wait. The sign over an archway said LOUNGE and pointed to downstairs. They went, Addison taking the steps three at a time. When Mr. Beech reached the lower level a door to the right snapped open and Addison, red as a full-blown hothouse tomato, shot out, tugging at a zipper. The door slapped back angrily, clipping off a crescendo of screams, then opened again wide enough for a silver-haired, white-gowned attendant to thrust out a menacing head and splatter them with: "Degenerates! They need a policeman here, not a matron!"

Addison, befuddled and agape, pointed a wavering finger at the sign on the door. "It says LADDIES ROOM, for Pete's sake, don't it?"

In a sense Addison wasn't too much to blame, Mr. Beech thought. The public places all over were modernizing their washrooms with: STALLIONS——MARES; HE——SHE; LADDIES——LASSIES; etc. But this one still clung to convention.

He pushed, almost kicked, Addison to the door marked GENTLE-MEN at the other end of the lounge. "High school boy! Laddies is with *two* D's, you dope!"

RING OUT, WILD BELLS

WOLCOTT GIBBS

When I finally got around to seeing Max Reinhardt's cinema version of "A Midsummer-Night's Dream," and saw a child called Mickey Rooney playing Puck, I remembered suddenly that long ago I had taken the same part.

Our production was given on the open-air stage at the Riverdale Country School, shortly before the war. The scenery was only the natural scenery of that suburban dell, and the cast was exclusively male, ranging in age from eleven to perhaps seventeen. While we had thus preserved the pure, Elizabethan note of the original, it must be admitted that our version had its drawbacks. The costumes were probably the worst things we had to bear, and even Penrod, tragically arrayed as Launcelot in his sister's stockings and his father's drawers, might have been embarrassed for us. Like Penrod, we were costumed by our parents, and like the Schofields, they seemed on the whole a little weak historically. Half of the ladies were inclined to favor the Elizabethan, and they had constructed rather bunchy ruffs and farthingales for their offspring; others, who had read as far as the stage directions and learned that the action took place in an Athenian wood, had produced something vaguely Athenian, usually beginning with a sheet. Only the fairies had a certain uniformity. For some reason their parents had all decided on cheesecloth, with here and there a little ill-advised trimming with tinsel.

My own costume was mysterious, but spectacular. As nearly as I have ever been able to figure things out, my mother found her inspiration for it in a Maxfield Parrish picture of a court jester. Beginning at the top, there was a cap with three stuffed horns; then, for the main part, a pair of tights that covered me to my wrists and ankles; and finally slippers with stuffed toes that curled up at the ends. The whole thing was made out of silk in alternate green and red stripes, and (unquestionably my poor mother's most demented stroke) it was covered from head to foot with a thousand tiny bells. Because all our costumes were obviously perishable, we never wore them in rehearsal, and naturally nobody knew that I was invested with these peculiar sound effects until I made my entrance at the beginning of the second act.

Our director was a man who had strong opinions about how Shakespeare should be played, and Puck was one of his favorite characters. It was his theory that Puck, being "the incarnation of mischief," never ought to be still a minute, so I had been coached to bound onto the stage, and once there to dance up and down, cocking my head and waving my arms.

"I want you to be a little whirlwind," this man said.

Even as I prepared to bound onto the stage, I had my own misgivings about those dangerously abundant gestures, and their probable effect on my bells. It was too late, however, to invent another technique for playing Puck, even if there had been room for anything but horror in my mind. I bounded onto the stage.

The effect, in its way, must have been superb. With every leap I rang like a thousand children's sleighs, my melodies foretelling God knows what worlds of merriment to the enchanted spectators. It was even worse when I came to the middle of the stage and went into my gestures. The other ringing had been loud but sporadic. This was persistent, varying only slightly in volume and pitch with the vehemence of my gestures. To a blind man, it must have sounded as though I had recklessly decided to accompany myself on a xylophone. A maturer actor would probably have made up his mind that an emergency existed, and abandoned his gestures as impracticable under the circumstances. I was thirteen, and incapable of innovations. I had been told by responsible authorities that gestures went with this part, and I continued to make them. I also continued to ring—a silvery music, festive and horrible.

If the bells were hard on my nerves, they were even worse for the rest of the cast, who were totally unprepared for my new interpretation. Puck's first remark is addressed to one of the fairies, and it is mercifully brief.

I said, "How now, spirit! Whither wander you?"

This unhappy child, already embarrassed by a public appearance in cheesecloth and tinsel, was also burdened with an opening speech of sixteen lines in verse. He began bravely:

> "Over hill, over dale,
>> Thorough bush, thorough brier,
> Over park, over pale,
>> Through flood, through fire . . ."

At the word "fire," my instructions were to bring my hands up from the ground in a long, wavery sweep, intended to represent fire. The bells pealed. To my startled ears, it sounded more as if they exploded. The fairy stopped in his lines and looked at me sharply. The jingling, however, had diminished; it was no more than as if a faint wind stirred my bells, and he went on:

> "I do wander every where,
>> Swifter than the moone's sphere . . ."

Here again I had another cue, for a sort of swoop and dip indicating the swiftness of the moone's sphere. Again the bells rang out, and again the performance stopped in its tracks. The fairy was clearly troubled by these interruptions. He had, however, a child's strange acceptance of the inscrutable, and was even able to regard my bells as a last-minute adult addition to the program, nerve-racking but not to be questioned. I'm sure it was only this that got him through that first speech.

My turn, when it came, was even worse. By this time the audience had succumbed to a helpless gaiety. Every time my bells rang, laughter swept the spectators, and this mounted and mingled with the bells until everything else was practically inaudible. I began my speech, another long one, and full of incomprehensible references to Titania's changeling.

"Louder!" said somebody in the wings. "You'll have to talk louder."

It was the director, and he seemed to be in a dangerous state.

"And for heaven's sake, stop that jingling!" he said.

I talked louder, and I tried to stop the jingling, but it was no use. By the time I got to the end of my speech, I was shouting and so was the audience. It appeared that I had very little control over the bells, which continued to jingle in spite of my passionate efforts to keep them quiet.

All this had a very bad effect on the fairy, who by this time had many symptoms of a complete nervous collapse. However, he began his next speech:

> "Either I mistake your shape and making quite,
> Or else you are that shrewd and knavish sprite
> Call'd Robin Goodfellow: are you not he
> That . . ."

At this point I forgot that the rules had been changed and I was supposed to leave out the gestures. There was a furious jingling, and the fairy gulped.

"Are you not he that, that . . ."

He looked miserably at the wings, and the director supplied the next line, but the tumult was too much for him. The unhappy child simply shook his head.

"Say anything!" shouted the director desperately. "Anything at all!"

The fairy only shut his eyes and shuddered.

"All right!" shouted the director. "All right, Puck. *You* begin *your* next speech."

By some miracle, I actually did remember my next lines, and had opened my mouth to begin on them when suddenly the fairy spoke. His voice was a high, thin monotone, and there seemed to be madness in it, but it was perfectly clear.

"Fourscore and seven years ago," he began, "our fathers brought forth on this continent a new nation, conceived . . ."

He said it right through to the end, and it was certainly the most successful speech ever made on that stage, and probably one of the most successful speeches ever made on any stage. I don't remember, if I ever knew, how the rest of us ever picked up the dull, normal thread of the play after that extraordinary performance, but we must have, because I know it went on. I only remember that in the next intermission the director cut off my bells with his penknife, and after that things quieted down and got dull.

Special Aptitudes:

HOW TO SLAY THEM WITH SMALL TALK

ROBERT THOMAS ALLEN

For a number of years now I've found that instead of speaking in epigrams as writers are supposed to do, I keep getting into a peculiar tongue-tied conversation with a man in a dark topcoat who just flew in from Regina. I don't know whether this man has any hobbies or any particular interests. In fact I don't know who he is. He is always introduced to me hurriedly just before lunch by an editor who says: "This is Mr. Withers. He just flew in from Regina. I'll be back in a minute," and goes wherever editors go just as you start out to lunch with them. I'm left with Withers in a hallway, or standing beside someone's desk. We both stare at the same spot in the centre of the room. As I haven't been to Regina, and neither of us knows anything about airplanes, we just look at one another, then look back at the same spot.

At last I say: "Did you bring this rain with you?"

Withers laughs, wipes the tears from his eyes, shakes his head, and goes back to tapping his knee with his briefcase.

A minute or so later he shakes his head and says: "It certainly is raining. Two inches, I'd say. Or one and a half. One newspaper said one and a half. The other said two."

"Probably about one and three-quarters," I say. "Still, we can use it."

"Yes," says Withers. "It was pretty dry—before it got so wet."

"Well, we can't do much about it anyway," I say. We both burst out laughing, and glance around to see if there's any sign of the editor.

If it isn't Withers I have this conversation with it's with seven strangers in a small crowded living room where someone has left me while he writes out a receipt for a lawn mower he had advertised in the evening paper. There is a second uncle, the woman from the house next door and her sister and an old friend from Toledo, and a six-foot youth who just keeps looking at me and sneering, and a half-brother who is going back to Montreal tomorrow, and somebody's grandmother. We all sit there with the identical smile on our faces, looking at the same spot in the living-room floor. I try to think of something to say, but the only thing that occurs to me is an article I just read about sexual perversion among the Fiji Islanders. Nobody else seems to be trying.

I say, "Nice weather we're having."

Everybody shouts, "Yes, isn't it," in unison and smiles politely at the chandelier. About this time a dog walks into the room and everybody starts to pat it at once. There are so many of us that half of us are patting one another's hands.

I've made several tries at learning how to cope with these profound silences, including reading a book I saw on sale one day on the art of conversation, but for the most part the book dealt with conversations carried on with people like grand dukes, about whether that affair had been patched up with the countess, while sipping five-hundred-year-old brandy. I could handle this type of conversation easily enough if I knew a countess and the brandy held out. But the kind of conversation I'd like to be able to handle is the kind you encounter from day to day with ordinary people. For instance, I vaguely know a proof-reader with horn-rimmed glasses whom I've been meeting on and off for five years in halls, washrooms and on stairways; we both say something like: "Ho, Mister h-m-m-m," "How's everything?" and "Fine." There should be something I can say to this man, but I haven't thought of it yet.

And I'm always getting into the most idiotic conversations with some casual acquaintance on the street, ten minutes before the banks start marking my cheques NSF, when I'm carrying three pairs of children's slippers and trying to remember whether my wife wanted me to exchange them for the same size in pink or the same color in a size smaller. On these occasions I try to go on thinking of the bank and the slippers, and to talk at the same time.

I say, "How are you?"

"Okay."

"Still at the same place?"

"Sure. Thirty-five years now. I get six weeks holidays and a watch next year."

"Nice going. Have a good time?"

"How do you mean?"

"On your holidays."

"*Next* year I get them. Haven't had them this year yet."

"Nice going," I say, circling him. "Welp—" I edge along, "How's your wife?"

"Milly? She passed away."

"*Did* she?" I say, walking backward. "I'm certainly glad to hear that. How is she?"

"She's dead."

"I thought you said she'd passed away." I back into a guy with hair sticking out of his T-shirt.

"That's what I meant."

"Well," I say. "We all have to die sometime."

This half-conscious, hair-brained type of conversation is the kind I find myself in sometimes when I don't really want to have a conversation at all, but just want to renew my contact with the human race after I've been at my desk too long. I'll go over to watch a neighbor building a cottage.

"Getting along pretty well, eh?" I say.

"Not bad." The neighbor stops and stands there swinging his hammer and looking at the roof. "The only thing, I was just wondering whether I should take that strip of sheeting off over the breakfast-nook window and build up the stripper underneath to two and three-quarter inches or leave the eave the way it is and just brace it with a ferrule bracket."

"Well, you're certainly getting along fine," I say.

"But if I do that I'll have to mortise the transom cribbing."

He watches me sharply and I realize that he actually wants an answer. I say, studying the roof, "I don't think it matters much one way or another."

"What do you mean?" He looks at me sideways as if he just smelled something burning.

"Well, I mean you can either take the sheeting off and—uh—follow your original plan, or just go ahead with the ferrule bracket."

"What am I going to do with the bracket over the sheeting?" he asks a bit testily.

"I'm sure it will all work out all right," I say. "Everything always does."

I edge away while the guy watches me as if he's thinking, "—knew writers were impractical; I didn't know they were complete morons."

I find that in some cases what I need is not so much a technique of handling a conversation but some way of not starting conversations at all. A few weeks ago a farmer near our cottage told me to drop in to his farm any time I wanted eggs. When I did, a woman answered the door. I put on my best manners and said, "You're Mr. Wyatt's mother, I suppose."

She said coolly, "I'm Mr. Wyatt's wife."

"His *wife?*" I squeaked, then shook my head in elaborate amazement. "Well, he certainly is the youngest-looking man I've ever seen. But I've noticed the country air always makes people seem younger. Husbands, that is."

She was looking as if she'd like to turn me under with last year's turnips, but I couldn't seem to stop. "Of course, I knew you were a young-looking woman for a mother."

"But I'm not his mother."

"Oh, I know. What I mean is if you were a mother you'd look younger than my mother, for instance. Of course she's worked hard all her life."

"Well, I don't know; I think most farmers work as hard as anyone else."

"Oh yes, *most* farmers. But I thought your farm looked as if nobody had to work very hard on it."

"How many eggs was it?" the woman said, backing away from the door.

I also frequently get into a conversational mess at 1.30 in the morning after I've eaten and drunk myself into an uncomfortable, yawning pulp, tightly bound in brown sharkskin and suspenders. Instead of going home I carelessly drop some old dull dog-eared thought of mine, such as: "No government has ever survived that hasn't constitutionally provided for the average man's personal frame of values," and sink back into a coma.

But some wide-awake extrovert pounces on it and says, "What do you mean?"

I start to figure out just what I *do* mean, and wish this wise guy wouldn't crowd me.

"Well, a perfect illustration of it is in our attitude toward Scandinavia."

"I thought our foreign policy there was pretty sound. Just what's wrong with it?"

I realize that I haven't a clue what our foreign policy is—the last time I came out with this remark was back in 1932. In fact, right at the moment I'd have a tough time remembering what our national anthem is.

I yawn and grope blindly for an olive. "It's too high-handed," I say. "But I'd better get along. My car is hard to start when there's a heavy dew."

I don't always have to be half asleep to say the wrong thing. I remember one time at a dinner party I started talking to a vivacious brunette about how delicious the celery was.

"Wonderful," the girl said.

"Would you care for some more?" I asked, feeling pretty suave.

"Yes, thank you. I wonder how they grow it so tender."

Thinking of an uncle of mine who used to grow the best celery in the block, I said in a clear confident voice, just as everyone else at the table stopped talking, "It's simply a matter of covering it up with plenty of horse manure."

The woman put down the celery and turned to a bearded gentleman on her other hand. The rest of the evening I spent out on the hostess' veranda exchanging grunting sounds with a carpenter who was repairing the steps.

One thing I continually have trouble with is thinking up polished bits of repartee when I need them, like when a streetcar motorman slams on the brakes, sends sand flying all over the tracks and says, "I CALLED OUT YOUR STREET FIVE TIMES."

I've always been able to think up an answer to this guy just before I go to bed, when I'm wandering around the kitchen in my pyjama tops eating bread and peanut butter. In fact this is the time when I've come out with some of the most annihilating remarks known to man. In this particular case I always say, "Why don't you try it with your teeth in, my good man."

But actually I never have a chance to use this, as the next time the motorman says: "I DIDN'T SAY THIS CAR TURNED ALONG BLOOR STREET," and to tell him to try it with his teeth in just doesn't make sense. I find myself standing under a sign that says where the car is going, shrieking in an unnatural voice that he should put a sign up somewhere, trying to get out the wrong way, and kicking some old woman's basket of flowers out of her hands.

Just recently, however, I've prepared a couple of stock comebacks that fit any situation. For instance, I just bend down and talk to the motorman in a low voice about how much do children under four feet have to pay on Sunday, then straighten up and yell: "OH, SO YOU THINK PEOPLE WHO RIDE IN STREETCARS SHOULDN'T HAVE A VOTE?"

Another type I work this on is the man who uses a discussion like a sledge hammer and, no matter if we're talking about petunias, sounds as if he's just about to pin a murder rap on me. He does it by backing me into a corner and forcing me to answer questions.

He'll say: "You wouldn't plant a petunia in the snow, would you?"

"Why—no—but—" (All I said was, "Will petunias grow anywhere?")

"Okay then," he glares at me. "Well. I'm telling you that petunias will only grow if they have sun and water." He pokes me on the chest. "Am I right or wrong?"

"Well, I guess you're right, but—"

"You *guess* I'm right," he snarls. "Do you admit that you can't expect flowers to live if you spray them with nitric acid?"

"Sure, but—"

The treatment I've doped out for this guy is to wait till his wife is nearby, then say, "Well, it's all in the way you look at it, BUT IN MY OPINION YOUR WIFE WORKS JUST AS HARD AS YOU DO."

One type I haven't been able to figure out yet though is the one who can survive in silence indefinitely, raising his eyebrows in it, tapping his knees with his gloves in it, or slowly rotating a gold-headed cane in it. Bank managers use this on me when I go in for a loan, knowing instinctively that I'll do practically everything if they wait long enough, including going away.

One time I decided that when he asked how much I made in a year, instead of saying "Urgh—seven—fifty-five—lessee, sixty-five—was it?" while he sat there playing with an ivory paper knife, I'd fill the silence with clear-cut facts and figures. I put the information in a black folder I carry around with me, took a seat near the open window for plenty of light, and when the question came I snapped, "YESSIR! ONE MOMENT, PLEASE."

I whipped open my folder and just then a gust of wind blew everything in it all over the manager's office. There were little sketches of Indian teepees, a half-finished manuscript, an overdue notice from a loan company, the music for the first ten bars of I Wish I Could Shimmy Like My Sister Kate, a cartoon and a dirty photograph a printer had given me and which I didn't know what to do with.

The next moment I was down on my hands and knees under his desk, giving timid little tugs to his pant leg, asking him if he'd mind raising his foot, crawling around the room knocking my head against chairs and losing my glasses. As far as I can remember the only things I said from then on were "Oops!" "Aha!" "I got them!" "Goldarn it!" and "Jes' a sec."

But apart from a few gimmicks I've worked out for my own preservation the art of conversation seems as far as I'm concerned to be pretty well lost for good. In fact I've found that to start monkeying with an overly-conscious use of words sometimes leads me into speech difficulties that would have worried my parents back in the days when I was asking for more Pablum. I start off in a clear, commanding voice: "As a matter of fact I think it's largely a matter of—" and find that I've been listening so closely to my own voice that I've forgotten what I was going to say. I try to ad lib the rest of the statement and usually end up still doing it fifteen minutes later when people begin to wander into the hall, pick up their coats and murmur it was a lovely evening.

The only thing I got out of my book on the art of speech was a thing the writer called a "donkey exercise" for loosening the jaw muscles, which is done by intoning "ee, aw; ee, aw; ee, aw," several times. I still fascinate myself by doing this in the bathroom mirror, and occasionally it comes in handy for limbering up my face after a rough shave. But as far as I can see it has nothing to do with the art of conversation and will never do me much good unless I can find someone who doesn't mind standing there while I make sounds like a donkey, which is pretty much what I often find myself doing anyway.

WEASELS IN THE CORN MEAL

JOSEPH HENRY JACKSON

When Marta came to us, complete with impeccable letters, we knew we had a treasure. Her graying hair was neat; it framed a pink, plump, confident face. Her china-blue eyes, wide like a doll's, were clear evidence of physical health. One child in the house, she said comfortably, was nothing; she took to our cat instantly, and it took to her.

There remained one small worry. My mother-in-law, who had said,

"I'll never be found with my feet under a son-in-law's table!" and meant it, lived down the block in her own bungalow. It would be part of Marta's duty to clean for her once a week, my wife taking over in our own house on that day. And on Tuesdays and Fridays Marta was to see that good, really nourishing dinners were cooked there. The old lady liked to do for herself, she insisted, but far too often she ate out of cans.

Marta was easygoing and she seemed the soul of tact. But, well, my mother-in-law had her ideas, one of them being that she didn't like people she didn't like. It was never wholly certain what governed her in the views she took, dim or otherwise, but there was never any doubt what those views were.

For a day or two the problem did not arise. It was evident at once that Marta could cook, though she liked to go her own way. The aspect of the kitchen was immediately changed, spices and staples rearranged according to a mysterious pattern that suited her. My wife began to adjust herself to Marta's conversation, too, and was not as startled as she might have been when Marta told her that she had found weasels in the corn meal. It was good to know they had been discovered and promptly dealt with. "I got rid of 'em," Marta said briskly, "every single sanitary one!"

Then the first Tuesday arrived, and the first dinner Marta would cook for my mother-in-law. My wife took her to the bungalow, introduced her, and left. It would work out or it wouldn't. Next night after dinner, she told me how it had gone.

Marta had come back smiling. She was frank about the little shingled bungalow: it was a kind of old ramble-shack, she said. But the old lady was sweet; she put Marta in mind of that famous painting of Hitler's Mother. It was nice to do things for people who didn't mind lending a hand; my mother-in-law had helped Marta wrench out the cups after the coffee, which showed she had her heart in the right end.

They had talked a good deal, too, Marta reported, and it was a pleasure to discuss things with her; she never went off on a tandem the way so many ladies did. It was plain that they had much in common, for Marta had mentioned my mother-in-law's science trouble. It was the fog, Marta explained; some people were just septic to it. They shared another idiosyncrasy, too: strawberries gave them both whelps all over their arms.

One thing had bothered Marta. The old lady ought to eat more.

They had talked this over, and although Marta's chubbiness made their agreement fantastic, they had concluded that both had the same difficulty: neither of them assumed their food properly.

After that first day, Marta took to carrying special dishes over to the bungalow. The second week she slipped out for ten minutes at dinnertime on the Friday. When she came back we learned why. She had taken over to my mother-in-law the dessert in which she took the greatest pride—her Baked Elastic. She never claimed to be a better cook than the old lady, however. The two had exchanged secrets from their store of kitchen tricks, and Marta admitted they had come out nick and tuck.

As it worked out, it turned into a close friendship; but while this was pleasant in its way, we found that we were getting less and less of Marta's time. She was always just stepping over to see how things were; she said firmly that the old lady had told her to drop in for a snag whenever she felt like it. In the end, it all added up: we lost our treasure.

It began when my mother-in-law gave Marta an old evening dress. Marta was enormously pleased with its style—black velvet, covered with Seagram's. And the gift led directly to evening dances at Oakland's most popular Social Ballroom. There, properly introduced by the lady-manager, Marta met a man, and from that moment romance had the upper hand. She hadn't known him from Adams, she told us, but he had met her once before in Southern California. They agreed that they really liked Los Angeles better, and he was returning to his old job there. He said The Right Things, and he wanted Marta to go with him as his wife when he left. She would have liked to stay with us, particularly with my mother-in-law. But anybody knew that it was silly to cut off your nose in spite of your face.

Perhaps it was just as well; for, as Marta told my wife with a self-conscious giggle, he was a man who liked to step out; he was a great one for burning the camel at both ends.

It may have been this propensity of his that eventually parted them. Marta had admitted that he was the kind that carried things to the inch degree. Whatever the reason, she was her own woman again in six short months. She sent us a postcard telling us she had gone back to work for her old employers, a family named Trott. She thought of us often, though, especially my mother-in-law, who had been a garden angel to her.

We passed on the message, and it was only then that we realized

ALFRED W. ISLER, COLLIER'S

"There goes the left rear!"

how really close the two women had been. For my mother-in-law made it quite clear that we had been a pair of simpletons to let Marta go. She was the best cook we'd ever had or were likely to have, the old lady said, and for a simple reason: Marta had been taught right; she knew the principles of homey comics.

VICTORY

TOM MASSON

(*About 1900*)

I turned to the dictionary
   For a word I couldn't spell,
And closed the book when I found it
   And dipped my pen in the well.

Then I thought to myself, "How was it?"
   With a sense of inward pain,

And still 'twas a little doubtful,
  So I turned to the book again.

This time I remarked, "How easy!"
  As I muttered each letter o'er,
But when I got to the inkwell
  'Twas gone, as it went before.

Then I grabbed that dictionary
  And I sped its pages through,
And under my nose I put it
  With that doubtful word in view.

I held it down with my body
  While I gripped that pen quite fast,
And I howled, as I traced each letter:
  "I've got you now, *at last!*"

THE HIGH DIVERS

JACK CONROY

From Charlie DeMelo, a superannuated circus clown and strong man:

You ask me why I'm all bunged up this way, going on crutches, both arms busted and what may still be a fractured skull. The doctor ain't sure about that yet. I'll live, I guess, but I don't know what for. I can't never be a high diver any more. I'll go to selling razor blades, like as not, and there's plenty doing that already.

Eddie La Breen is to blame for it all. High diving was an easy and high-paying profession before he tried to root me and every other out of it. I would go traveling in the summer with a carnival company, and my high dive would be a free feature attraction. The local merchants would kick in for signs to put on my ladder and advertise their goods. Sometimes I'd make a little spiel from the top of the ladder just before I dived off into the tank.

Eddie La Breen called himself "The Human Seal." He bragged that he could dive higher into shallower water than any man alive. I was pretty good myself, being billed as Billie the Dolphin, spectacular and death-defying high diver extraordinary.

I'm doing all right with Miller's Great Exposition Shows, using a twenty-five-foot ladder and diving into a ten-foot tank. Big crowds of people would come from miles around to see me, and not a soul ever seemed dissatisfied until we happen to be playing Omaha on a lot over ten blocks away from where Eddie La Breen is playing with Barker's World's Fair Shows.

Just when I come up out of the tank and start to take a bow one night I hear somebody say: "That ain't *nothing*. You ought to see Eddie La Breen over on Farnum Street diving twice as high into water half as deep."

I found out it's so. Eddie has been diving into five feet of water from a fifty-foot ladder, and Mr. Miller threatens to let me go if I can't do as well.

It sure looked high when I got up there and I could feel my nose scraping on the bottom of the tank just as I made the upturn. But I'm no slouch at the high dive myself, and Eddie La Breen ain't going to outdo me if I can help it.

I added the fire act to my dive, too, and most of the time I could hardly see where to dive. For the fire act you have a little bit of gasoline pouring into the tank. It stays right on top of the water and when you fire it it makes a fearful sight, splashing fire in every direction when you hit the water.

Eddie sends me word that I might as well give up. "I'm going to dive next from a thousand feet into a tank of solid concrete," he says, "and I'll do it while playing the ukulele, eating raw liver, and keeping perfect time. Why, when I was a kid of ten or so I could dive off a silo onto the dew in the grass, bellybuster, and never even grunt when I lit."

He didn't do quite that, but he did enough. He raised his ladder to a hundred feet, and kept only two and a half feet of water in the tank.

I practised and practised and got a few bruises, but I cut that depth to two feet and I raised my ladder to a hundred and fifty feet.

By this time Eddie sent word he was good mad, and he's going to call himself the Minnow. "You know how a minnow just skitters along on top of a pond," he says. "Well, that's the way I'll light on that tank. From two hundred feet I'll dive into six inches of water and just skim off without hardly making a bubble."

If ever a man practised hard to make a shallow dive, that was me. I did that minnow dive in four inches of water from a height of 250 feet, lit right on my feet after barely touching the water, and didn't even muss my hair.

When Eddie makes it from 300 feet into three inches, I'm a little put out but I don't give up. I tell Miller to get me a good heavy bath mat and soak it good all day. First time I hit that bath mat it sort of knocked me dizzy. You know how it is when you have the breath knocked out of you and all you can do is croak like a frog. But I got better and better at it until I hardly puffed at all.

I beat Eddie La Breen fair and square, but he wasn't man enough to admit it or take it like a man. He showed that he was rotten to the core and treacherous from the word go.

We were playing Sheboygan, Wisconsin, and I had no idea that Eddie was anywhere within miles. I had heard that Barker had told him to pack his keister and get out when I bested him.

When I hit that bath mat that night I thought my time had come. That was six months ago, and look at me now. Still on crutches, and lucky if I ever get off of them.

Well, sir, I don't know anybody but Eddie who wanted to have done me that dirt. They had soaked my heavy bath mat in water, all day, the same as usual, but they must have let it get out of their sight some time or other, because some one had wrung it out practically dry.

That's the way I had it done to me. I hears somebody say later that a man answering to the description of Eddie La Breen had been seen lurking around the show grounds that evening.

And if he didn't do it, who did?

THE MAN ON THE FLYING TRAPEZE

ANONYMOUS

Once I was happy, but now I'm forlorn,
Like an old coat, all tattered and torn,
Left in this wide world to fret and to mourn,
Betrayed by a maid in her teens.
Oh, the girl that I loved she was handsome,
I tried all I knew her to please,
But I could not please one quarter as well
As the man on the flying trapeze.

Chorus

He would fly through the air
With the greatest of ease,
This daring young man
On the flying trapeze;
His movements were graceful,
All girls he could please,
And my love he purloined away.

Her father and mother were both on my side,
And very hard tried to make her my bride.
Her father he sighed, and her mother she cried
To see her throw herself away.
'Twas all no avail, she'd go there every night
And throw him bouquets on the stage,
Which caused him to meet her; how he ran me down
To tell you would take a whole page.

One night I as usual called at her dear home,
Found there her father and mother alone.
I asked for my love, and soon they made known
To my horror that she'd run away.
She packed up her goods and eloped in the night
With him with the greatest of ease;
From three stories high he had lowered her down
To the ground on his flying trapeze.

Some months after this, I chanced in a hall,
Was greatly surprised to see on the wall
A bill in red letters that did my heart gall,
That she was appearing with him.
He taught her gymnastics and dressed her in tights
To help him to live at his ease,
And made her assume a masculine name,
And now she goes on the trapeze.

Chorus

She floats through the air
With the greatest of ease,
You'd think her a man
On the flying trapeze.

She does all the work
While he takes his ease,
And that's what became of my love.

GRASSHOPPERS A LA MODE

JEAN CONDIT

In case anyone wonders what happened to the college boys who ate live goldfish back in the forties, the answer may be right at hand. It's possible—allowing for the refinement of the palate that comes with maturity—that they have gone on to become conspicuous consumers of fried grasshoppers.

According to T. G. Koryn, a local importer, more than 150,000 cans of these crispy cocktail accompaniments have been sold in this country in the last seven months—most of them to men. Delicacy shop proprietors, an impassive lot, agree that the Japanese *inago*, or grasshopper, has been steadily climbing in popularity since it was first introduced in 1953. Cans of grasshoppers are stacked up like peanuts or any other staple in one Los Angeles store; a Chicago dealer had thirty crates of them flown in last December to supply an unusually brisk Christmas demand; and in New York, Bloomingdale's, Vendôme and the stately house of Charles & Co. all indicate grasshoppers are moving nicely.

One reason for the phenomenon is that grasshoppers are accessibly priced: less than half a dollar for a five-and-a-half-ounce tin—a size, by the way, that will slip neatly into a conservative gray flannel coat pocket. The gag, of course, is to serve your *inagos* incognito, along with more conventional tidbits such as fried bacon rind, which they resemble somewhat in taste. And how guests do laugh when they learn what they've eaten!

But a leading Chicago distributor argues that the grasshopper customer is after more than a gastronomical leg-pull. "You'd think it was a one-shot," he asserts, "but no—these people come back and back."

Other experts agree there's a real demand these days for party foods that are new, exotic, "different." And once initiated, many Americans are surprised to find themselves quite won over by foods they wouldn't —wittingly—have eaten on a bet.

After all, the experts point out, there's nothing funny about fried grasshoppers to the Japanese. After all, some well-traveled *bons viveurs* already look on them with favor. And after all, fried *agave* worms, a popular Mexican between-meal snack, have enjoyed a steady sale in the luxury shops for years.

As quick to spot a trend as any other merchants, live-wire food importers are now negotiating for French fried bees from the Orient. Fried ants (possibly from Africa) and chocolate-covered ants from South America are also in the blueprint stage.

Meantime, there's an ample supply of exotica available for the cocktail party shelf. Tidbits of octopus in his own ink, from Japan. Pickled cockles from England. Lamprey in Bordelaise sauce from France. Quail eggs from Japan. Cod livers (with a taste like that of *pâté*) from Canada. Snails from Morocco. Stuffed vine leaves from Turkey. Pickled cactus from Mexico. *Epis de maïs* from France: tiny ears of corn not more than an inch and a half long, pickled in vinegar.

But it would be wrong to give the impression that such fanciful foods travel a one-way route. A European prince, of a house which has long doted on macabre humor, recently sailed home from the United States with a family-size crate of canned muskrat and diamondback rattlesnake meat. This canned rattlesnake, first put out by a Floridian as a stunt to publicize his reptile farm, has done so well that he has followed it up with canned alligator soup.

And there are other home-grown treats that can hold their own with any in the world. Canned bear steak. Canned buffalo and elk meat, put up, it so happens, by a Viennese chef in Brooklyn. Canned venison, put out under the lofty imprimatur of "21." Barbecued buffalo. And the latest wrinkle—barbecued nutria.

Although such solid provender can be eked out with canned caribou, whale steak and wild boar meat from foreign parts, this suggests it might be worth while for venturesome gourmets to stand firm until American ingenuity produces the climactic canned triumph. Say, a ragoût of ranch mink. Or perhaps something truly and significantly international: a bouillabaisse of Asiatic bumblebees and native goldfish in a saffron-spiced alligator broth.

WHEN FATHER CARVES THE DUCK

E. V. WRIGHT

We all look on with anxious eyes
    When father carves the duck,
And mother almost always sighs
    When father carves the duck;
Then all of us prepare to rise,
And hold our bibs before our eyes,
And be prepared for some surprise,
    When father carves the duck.

He braces up and grabs a fork
    Whene'er he carves a duck,
And won't allow a soul to talk
    Until he's carved the duck.
The fork is jabbed into the sides,
Across the breast the knife he slides,
While every careful person hides
    From flying chips of duck.

The platter's always sure to slip
    When father carves a duck,
And how it makes the dishes skip!
    Potatoes fly amuck!
The squash and cabbage leap in space,
We get some gravy in our face,
And father mutters Hindoo grace
    Whene'er he carves a duck.

We then have learned to walk around
    The dining-room and pluck
From off the window-sills and walls
    Our share of father's duck.
While father growls and blows and jaws
And swears the knife was full of flaws,
And mother laughs at him because
    He couldn't carve a duck.

SLURVIAN SELF-TAUGHT

JOHN DAVENPORT

Listening to a well-known Hollywood radio commentator some time back, I heard her say that she had just returned from a Yerpeen trip, and had had a lovely time nittly. I at once recognized her as an accomplished Slurvian linguist and, being a student of Slurvian, readily understood that she had just returned from a European trip, and while there (in Yerp) had had a lovely time in Italy.

Slurvian is coming into common use in the United States, but I am, so far as I know, the only scholar to have made a start toward recording it. There is no official written Slurvian language, but it is possible, by means of phonetic spelling, for me to offer a brief course of instruction in it. In a short time, the student can learn enough to add immeasurably to his understanding and enjoyment of conversation wherever he travels in the country.

I first heard pure Slurvian fluently spoken by a co-worker of mine who told me that his closest friend was a man named Hard (Howard). Hard was once in an automobile accident, his car, unfortunately, cliding with another, causing Hard's wife Dorthy, who was with him, to claps. Dorthy didn't have much stamina but was a sweet woman— sweet as surp.

I soon discovered I had an ear for Slurvian, and since I began to recognize the language, I have encountered many Slurvians. At ballparks, they keep track of hits, runs, and airs. On farms, they plow furs. In florist shops, they buy flars. When hard up, they bar money from banks, and spend it for everything from fewl for the furnace to grum crackers for the children.

When Slurvians travel abroad, they go to visit farn (or forn) countries to see what the farners do that's different from the way we Murcans do things. While in farn countries, they refer to themselves as Murcan tersts, and usually say they will be mighty glad to get back to Murca. A Slurvian I once met on a train told me he had just returned from a visit to Mexico. He deplored the lack of automobiles down there, and said that the natives ride around on little burrs.

A linguistic authority of my acquaintance, much interested in my work in Slurvian, has suggested to me the possibility that the language may be related to, or a variation of, the one still spoken in England of which such a contraction as "Chumley," for "Cholmondeley," is a familiar example. However, I think the evidence insufficient for drawing such a conclusion. Surnames cannot be considered subject to the ordinary rules of pronunciation. In fact, the only one I have positively identified in Slurvian is Faggot, the name of the American admiral who won the Battle of Mobile Bay.

The name Faggot brings me to a discussion of what I designate as "pure" Slurvian. This includes those Slurvian words that, when spelled exactly as pronounced, also make good English words (such as "Faggot," "burr," and "claps"). The day I can add to the lexicon such a word, hitherto unrecorded, is a happy day for me. Here are some examples of pure Slurvian, alphabetically listed:

bean, n. A living creature, as in *human bean*.

cactus, n. pl. The people in a play or story.

course, n. A group of singers.

fiscal, adj. Pertaining to the body, as opposed to the spurt.

form, n. Gathering place of the ancient Romans.

gnome, n. Contraction for *no, ma'am*. Colloq.

line, n. The king of beasts.

lore, n. The more desirable of the two berths in a Pullman section.

myrrh, n. A looking glass.

par, n. An attribute of strength, as in *the par and the glory*.

plight, adj. Courteous.

sears, adj. Grave, intent.

sport, v.t. To hold up, to bear the weight of.

wreckers, n. pl. Discs on which music is recorded for phonographs.

I am presently engaged in compiling a dictionary of Slurvian words, which I hope will prove to be the definitive work on the subject. The help of any interested students is welcomed, but I must caution such students to be certain the words are genuine Slurvian, and not merely regional speech, such as that of Alabama, Texas, or New England.

Let me close with a final example, to make my meaning clear. Wherever you may be in the United States, if you hear the word "tare," the speaker probably is not referring to a Biblical weed growing in the wheat. More likely, he is describing the sensation of extreme fear experienced by a movie fan watching Borse Karloff in a harr picture.

HOW TO KNOW THE WILD ANIMALS

CAROLYN WELLS

If ever you should go by chance
    To jungles in the East,
And if there should to you advance
    A large and tawny beast—
If he roars at you as you're dyin',
    You'll know it is the Asian Lion.

If, when in India loafing round,
    A noble wild beast meets you,
With dark stripes on a yellow ground,
    Just notice if he eats you.
This simple rule may help you learn
    The Bengal Tiger to discern.

When strolling forth, a beast you view
    Whose hide with spots is peppered;
As soon as it has leapt on you,
    You'll know it is the Leopard.
'Twill do no good to roar with pain,
    He'll only lep and lep again.

If you are sauntering round your yard,
    And meet a creature there
Who hugs you very, very hard,
    You'll know it is the Bear.
If you have any doubt, I guess
    He'll give you just one more caress.

Whene'er a quadruped you view
    Attached to any tree,
It may be 'tis the Wanderoo,
    Or yet the Chimpanzee.
If right side up it may be both,
    If upside down it is the Sloth.

Though to distinguish beasts of prey
    A novice might nonplus;

Yet from the Crocodile you may
    Tell the Hyena, thus:
'Tis the Hyena if it smile;
    If weeping, 'tis the Crocodile.

The true Chameleon is small—
    A lizard sort of thing;
He hasn't any ears at all
    And not a single wing.
If there is nothing on the tree
    'Tis the Chameleon you see.

JEFF PETERS AS A PERSONAL MAGNET

O. HENRY

Jeff Peters has been engaged in as many schemes for making money as there are recipes for cooking rice in Charleston, S.C.

Best of all I like to hear him tell of his earlier days when he sold liniments and cough cures on street corners, living hand to mouth, heart to heart with the people, throwing heads or tails with fortune for his last coin.

"I struck Fisher Hill, Arkansas," said he, "in buckskin suit, moccasins, long hair and a thirty-carat diamond ring that I got from an actor in Texarkana. I don't know what he ever did with the pocket knife I swapped him for it.

"I was Dr. Waugh-hoo, the celebrated Indian medicine man. I carried only one best bet just then, and that was Resurrection Bitters. It was made of life-giving plants and herbs accidentally discovered by Ta-qua-la, the beautiful wife of the chief of the Choctaw Nation, while gathering truck to garnish a platter of boiled dog for the annual corn dance.

"Business hadn't been good at the last town, so I only had five dollars. I went to the Fisher Hill druggist and he credited me for a half gross of eight-ounce bottles and corks. I had the labels and ingredients in my valise, left over from the last town. Life began to look rosy again after I got in my hotel room with the water running from the tap, and the Resurrection Bitters lining up on the table by the dozen.

"Fake? No, sir. There was two dollars' worth of fluid extract of cinchona and a dime's worth of aniline in that half-gross of bitters. I've gone through towns years afterwards and had folks ask for 'em again.

"I hired a wagon that night and commenced selling the bitters on Main Street. Fisher Hill was a low, malarial town; and a compound hypothetical pneumo-cardiac anti-scorbutic tonic was just what I diagnosed the crowd as needing. The bitters started off like sweetbreads-on-toast at a vegetarian dinner. I had sold two dozen at fifty cents apiece when I felt somebody pull my coat tail. I knew what that meant; so I climbed down and sneaked a five-dollar bill into the hand of a man with a German silver star on his lapel.

" 'Constable,' says I, 'it's a fine night.'

" 'Have you got a city license,' he asks, 'to sell this illegitimate essence of spooju that you flatter by the name of medicine?'

" 'I have not,' says I. 'I didn't know you had a city. If I can find it tomorrow I'll take one out if it's necessary.'

" 'I'll have to close you up till you do,' says the constable.

"I quit selling and went back to the hotel. I was talking to the landlord about it.

" 'Oh, you won't stand no show in Fisher Hill,' says he. 'Dr. Hoskins, the only doctor here, is a brother-in-law of the Mayor, and they won't allow no fake doctors to practice in town.'

" 'I don't practice medicine,' says I, 'I've got a State peddler's license, and I take out a city one wherever they demand it.'

"I went to the Mayor's office the next morning and they told me he hadn't showed up yet. They didn't know when he'd be down. So Doc Waugh-hoo hunches down again in a hotel chair and lights a jimpsonweed regalia, and waits.

"By and by a young man in a blue necktie slips into the chair next to me and asks the time.

" 'Half-past ten,' says I, 'and you are Andy Tucker. I've seen you work. Wasn't it you that put up the Great Cupid Combination package on the Southern States? Let's see, it was a Chilian diamond engagement ring, a wedding ring, a potato masher, a bottle of soothing syrup and Dorothy Vernon—all for fifty cents.'

"Andy was pleased to hear that I remembered him. He was a good street man; and he was more than that—he respected his profession, and he was satisfied with 300 per cent. profit. He had plenty of offers to go into the illegitimate drug and garden seed business; but he was never to be tempted off of the straight path.

"I wanted a partner, so Andy and me agreed to go out together. I told him about the situation on Fisher Hill and how finances was low on account of the local mixture of politics and jalap. Andy had just got in on the train that morning. He was pretty low himself, and was going to canvass the town for a few dollars to build a new battle-ship by popular subscription at Eureka Springs. So we went out and sat on the porch and talked it over.

"The next morning at eleven o'clock when I was sitting there alone, an Uncle Tom shuffles into the hotel and asked for the doctor to come and see Judge Banks, who, it seems, was the mayor and a mighty sick man.

"'I'm no doctor,' says I. 'Why don't you go and get the doctor?'

"'Boss,' says he. 'Doc Hoskin am done gone twenty miles in the country to see some sick persons. He's de only doctor in de town, and Massa Banks am powerful bad off. He sent me to ax you to please, suh, come.'

"'As man to man,' says I, 'I'll go and look him over.' So I put a bottle of Resurrection Bitters in my pocket and goes up on the hill to the Mayor's mansion, the finest house in town, with a mansard roof and two cast-iron dogs on the lawn.

"This Mayor Banks was in bed all but his whiskers and feet. He was making internal noises that would have had everybody in San Francisco hiking for the parks. A young man was standing by the bed holding a cup of water.

"'Doc,' says the Mayor, 'I'm awful sick. I'm about to die. Can't you do nothing for me?'

"'Mr. Mayor,' says I, 'I'm not a regular preordained disciple of S. Q. Lapius, I never took a course in a medical college,' says I. 'I've just come as a fellow-man to see if I could be of any assistance.'

"'I'm deeply obliged,' says he. 'Doc Waugh-hoo, this is my nephew, Mr. Biddle. He has tried to alleviate my distress, but without success. Oh, Lordy! Oh-ow-ow!!' he sings out.

"I nods at Mr. Biddle and sets down by the bed and feels the May-or's pulse. 'Let me see your liver—your tongue, I mean,' says I. Then I turns up the lids of his eyes and looks close at the pupils of 'em.

"'How long have you been sick?' I asked.

"'I was taken down—ow-ouch—last night,' says the Mayor. 'Gimme something for it, Doc, won't you?'

" 'Mr. Fiddle,' says I, 'raise the window shade a bit, will you?'

" 'Biddle,' says the young man. 'Do you feel like you could eat some ham and eggs, Uncle James?'

" 'Mr. Mayor,' says I, after laying my ear to his right shoulder blade and listening, 'you've got a bad attack of super-inflammation of the right clavicle of the harpsichord!'

" 'Good Lord!' says he, with a groan. 'Can't you rub something on it, or set it or anything?'

"I picks up my hat and starts for the door.

" 'You ain't going, Doc?' says the Mayor with a howl. 'You ain't going away and leave me to die with this—superfluity of the clap-boards, are you?'

" 'Common humanity, Dr. Whoa-ha,' says Mr. Biddle, 'ought to prevent your deserting a fellow-human in distress.'

" 'Dr. Waugh-hoo, when you get through plowing,' says I. And then I walks back to the bed and throws back my long hair.

" 'Mr. Mayor,' says I, 'there is only one hope for you. Drugs will do you no good. But there is another power higher yet, although drugs are high enough,' says I.

" 'And what is that?' says he.

" 'Scientific demonstrations,' says I. 'The triumph of mind over sarsaparilla. The belief that there is no pain and sickness except what is produced when we ain't feeling well. Declare yourself in arrears. Demonstrate.'

" 'What is this paraphernalia you speak of, Doc?' says the Mayor. 'You ain't a Socialist, are you?'

" 'I am speaking,' says I, 'of the great doctrine of psychic financier-ing—of the enlightened school of long-distance, sub-conscientious treatment of fallacies and meningitis—of that wonderful indoor sport known as personal magnetism.'

" 'Can you work it, Doc?" asks the Mayor.

" 'I'm one of the Sole Sanhedrims and Ostensible Hooplas of the Inner Pulpit,' says I. 'The lame talk and the blind rubber whenever I make a pass at 'em. I am a medium, a coloratura hypnotist and a spirituous control. It was only through me at the recent seances at Ann Arbor that the late president of the Vinegar Bitters Company could revisit the earth to communicate with his sister Jane. You see me peddling medicine on the streets,' says I, 'to the poor. I don't prac-tice personal magnetism on them. I do not drag it in the dust,' says I, 'because they haven't got the dust.'

" 'Will you treat my case?' asks the Mayor.

" 'Listen,' says I. 'I've had a good deal of trouble with medical societies everywhere I've been. I don't practice medicine. But, to save your life, I'll give you the psychic treatment if you'll agree as mayor not to push the license question.'

" 'Of course I will,' says he. 'And now get to work, Doc, for them pains are coming on again.'

" 'My fee will be $250.00 cure guaranteed in two treatments,' says I.

" 'All right,' says the Mayor. 'I'll pay it. I guess my life's worth that much.'

"I sat down by the bed and looked him straight in the eye.

" 'Now,' says I, 'get your mind off the disease. You ain't sick. You haven't got a heart or a clavicle or a funnybone or brains or anything. You haven't got any pain. Declare error. Now you feel the pain that you didn't have leaving, don't you?'

" 'I do feel some little better, Doc,' says the Mayor, 'darned if I don't. Now state a few lies about my not having this swelling in my left side, and I think I could be propped up and have some sausage and buckwheat cakes.'

"I made a few passes with my hands.

" 'Now,' says I, 'the inflammation's gone. The right lobe of the perihelion has subsided. You're getting sleepy. You can't hold your eyes open any longer. For the present the disease is checked. Now, you are asleep.'

"The Mayor shut his eyes slowly and began to snore.

" 'You observe, Mr. Tiddle,' says I, 'the wonders of modern science.'

" 'Biddle,' says he. 'When will you give uncle the rest of the treatment, Dr. Pooh-pooh?'

" 'Waugh-hoo,' says I. 'I'll come back at eleven tomorrow. When he wakes up give him eight drops of turpentine and three pounds of steak. Good morning.'

"The next morning I went back on time. 'Well, Mr. Riddle,' says I, when he opened the bedroom door, 'and how is uncle this morning?'

" 'He seems much better,' says the young man.

"The Mayor's color and pulse was fine. I gave him another treatment, and he said the last of the pain left him.

" 'Now,' says I, 'you'd better stay in bed for a day or two, and you'll be all right. It's a good thing I happened to be in Fisher Hill, Mr. Mayor,' says I, 'for all the remedies in the cornucopia that the regular schools of medicine use couldn't have saved you. And now that error has flew and pain proved a perjurer, let's allude to a cheerfuler subject —say the fee of $250. No checks, please. I hate to write my name on the back of a check almost as bad as I do on the front.'

" 'I've got the cash here,' says the Mayor, pulling a pocketbook from under his pillow.

"He counts out five fifty-dollar notes and holds 'em in his hand.

" 'Bring the receipt,' he says to Biddle.

"I signed the receipt and the Mayor handed me the money. I put it in my inside pocket careful.

" 'Now do your duty, officer,' says the Mayor, grinning much unlike a sick man.

"Mr. Biddle lays his hand on my arm.

" 'You're under arrest, Dr. Waugh-hoo, alias Peters,' says he, 'for practicing medicine without authority under the State law.'

" 'Who are you?' I asks.

" 'I'll tell you who he is,' says the Mayor, sitting up in bed. 'He's a detective employed by the State Medical Society. He's been following you over five counties. He came to me yesterday and we fixed up this scheme to catch you. I guess you won't do any more doctoring around these parts, Mr. Fakir. What was it you said I had, Doc?' the Mayor laughs, 'compound—well it wasn't softening of the brain, I guess, anyway.'

" 'A detective,' says I.

" 'Correct,' says Biddle. 'I'll have to turn you over to the sheriff.'

" 'Let's see you do it,' says I, and I grabs Biddle by the throat and half throws him out the window, but he pulls a gun and sticks it under my chin, and I stand still. Then he puts handcuffs on me, and takes the money out of my pocket.

" 'I witness,' says he, 'that they're the same bills that you and I marked, Judge Banks. I'll turn them over to the sheriff when we get to his office, and he'll send you a receipt. They'll have to be used as evidence in the case.'

" 'All right, Mr. Biddle,' says the Mayor. 'And now, Doc Waugh-hoo,' he goes on, 'why don't you demonstrate? Can't you pull the cork out of your magnetism with your teeth and hocus-pocus them handcuffs off?'

" 'Come on, officer,' says I, dignified. 'I may as well make the best of it.' And then I turns to old Banks and rattles my chains.

" 'Mr. Mayor,' says I, 'the time will come soon when you'll believe

"Well, maybe I *don't* know what I'm talking about, but if
I *did* know what I'm talking about, I'd be right!"

---

that personal magnetism is a success. And you'll be sure that it succeeded in this case, too.'

"And I guess it did.

"When we got nearly to the gate, I says: 'We might meet somebody
now, Andy. I reckon you better take 'em off, and—' Hey? Why, of
course it was Andy Tucker. That was his scheme; and that's how we
got the capital to go into business together."

THE TWO PEDESTRIANS

CAROLYN WELLS

Once on a time there were two Men, one of whom was a Good Man
and the other a Rogue.

The Good Man one day saw a Wretched Drunkard endeavoring
to find his way Home.

Being most kind-hearted, the Good Man assisted the Wretched Drunkard to his feet and accompanied him along the Highway toward his Home.

The Good Man held fast the arm of the Wretched Drunkard, and the result of this was that when the Wretched Drunkard lurched giddily the Good Man perforce lurched too.

Whereupon, as the Passing Populace saw the pair, they said: "Aha! Another good man gone wrong," and they Wisely Wagged their Heads.

Now the Bad Man of this tale, being withal of a shrewd and canny Nature, stood often on a street corner, and engaged in grave conversation with the Magnates of the town.

To be sure, the Magnates shook him as soon as possible but in no wise discouraged he cheerfully sauntered up to another Magnate. Thus did he gain a Reputation of being a friend of the Great.

Morals:

This Fable teaches us that A Man is known by the Company he Keeps, and that We Must not Judge by Appearances.

CENTER SHOT

ANONYMOUS

Cowan and Hoffman, Western hunters, were dead shots and each hotly jealous of the other's prowess. Setting out together one day after deer, they separated in the woods, taking opposite sides of a ridge.

Almost immediately, Hoffman heard Cowan's rifle fired off. He ran over to the spot, expecting to be obliged to help hang a deer. He found Cowan reloading but no deer carcass in sight. However, a startled calf was crashing off through the hazelnut bushes.

"Oh Lord!" Hoffman whooped with delight. "You didn't shoot at that calf, did you, hoss?"

"Suppose I did?" growled Cowan.

"Why'd you do a thing like that?"

"Took it for a deer."

"Don't look like you hit it."

"No—missed."

"How in the nation did that happen?"

"Wasn't just sure that it wasn't a calf."

"That," crowed Hoffman, "is what I call a pretty sorry hunter—to shoot at a calf for a deer, and miss it at that!"

"Don't be a fool," drawled Cowan, ramming home the charge in his rifle. "I shot at it just so as to hit it if it was a deer, and miss it if it was a calf."

TOIDY DAYS

STANLEY AND JANICE BERENSTAIN

The realization of the ideal of dry pants may completely exhaust your reserves of perseverance and grit, but, like Boulder Dam, it's worth all the effort. For it's a sunny, sunny day when your child achieves complete mastery of his recalcitrant plumbing and you are able to tell the diaper-service man he need never darken your door again.

Your own attitude toward the bathroom and its function is the key to your success. Throw all modesty out the window. Pocket the key to the bathroom door and keep the door open. Have a warm light glowing within, and toss a cozy mat upon the floor with the word WELCOME imprinted thereon. As soon as Baby is steeped in the jolly atmosphere of the place, and familiar with the role of the toilet in particular, it is time to set up his own little throne.

A low affair with a detachable training seat is recommended. This seat may later be used on the big toilet. It should be equipped with a deflector—seat and deflector being, preferably, all of a piece. This type of seat is the most desirable for boys and girls alike, the point being that, like a Western saddle, it makes dismounting difficult; also, a girl's seat would greatly inconvenience small male guests.

You may have quite a time finding a really workable potty chair such as we have described. Some of the more impractical items currently being pushed by Baby Department managers are: a ten-inch lifesaver with a Disney Duck quacking at the helm; a spidery affair of blue plastic which collapses into pocket size for convenience when traveling but is not so convenient when it comes to a hurried reconstruction; and the hard-to-resist super-deluxe upholstered leatherette number which plays "Please to put a penny in the old man's hat" when it is sat upon.

You may begin bowel training any time after baby is able to sit up strongly. On the day you decide to take the plunge, wait until the time he usually soils his diaper, then strap him on his new potty. Never refer to the strap as such, but by all means use it. Don't fasten it on the sly. After placing baby in his seat, say simply, "I'll buckle your nice blue belt for you." Before his steely fingers begin testing it, stuff them with a banana, a piece of orange, or some other intriguing food he's allowed to have but is seldom allowed to feed himself (for obvious reasons).

As he sits there kneading a banana or massacring an orange, you must convey to him what he's expected to do. He is too young to comprehend a long verbal briefing, but is apt to astound you by his ability to grasp the meaning behind a grimace or a grunt. If you are a particularly adept mime, your efforts may be rewarded the very first day. Don't be disappointed, though, if they are not. Actually, you have done well if all you have engendered in your trainee is a grimacing and grunting acceptance of the potty. Eventually, say in about two weeks, baby may accidentally use the potty for its intended purpose. Congratulate him. Show him you are impressed. If your enthusiasm is sufficiently contagious, he may have another accident in another couple of weeks. After this, he may hit the jackpotty three or four days in a row. When he has caught on to the extent that he has only one miscalculation in his diaper every two weeks, he is ready to take up Bladder Control.

Bladder Control consists of putting him on the pot every hour on the hour. It also entails sponging up a puddle every hour on the hour, roughly two minutes after you take him off the pot. Stated in its simplest terms, your objective is to get the puddle in the pot. The solution is largely a matter of sticking rigidly to a schedule and constantly keeping a weather eye squinted for signs of precipitation.

The time to dispense with the low chair and use the training seat on the big toilet comes when your toddler's legs grow long and sturdy enough to carry him, seat and all, into the next room to let you know he is "froo." You may try to strong-arm the underneath clamps into holding the seat to the chair more securely, but Billy-boy will be delighted by the challenge and drag the whole clanking business down the hall to help you see who's at the front door.

When Junior graduates to the big toilet, appeal to his pride by mak-

ing it clear to him that he is being accorded a signal honor. He's in
the big league now, and unless he proves able to handle himself in
fast company he'll have to be sent back to the minors for further
seasoning.

TAKE MY WORD FOR IT

BENNETT CERF

(From The Cerfboard)

Your name does not have to be Webster to qualify you as a definer
of words. The list below, for example, was composed by a variety of
otherwise sane citizens, not one of whom was related to the great
lexicographer.

The list *has* won the *tacit* approval of a direct descendant of Noah
Webster. At least, he didn't disapprove. He was standing unabridge
when I showed it to him, and promptly fell off. Rescued, he began
reciting:

Accumulate: A convenient way of asking, "Why are you tardy?"

Acoustic: What you use when you shoot pool.

Autobiography: The life story of an automobile.

Bachelor: An average male over 21 whom no average female ever
has made a serious attempt to marry. (*H. L. Mencken*)

Choosy: The day that follows Monday.

Coincide: What you do when it starts raining.

Coronation: A lady who smashed bars with her little hatchet.

Co-signer: A dope with a fountain pen.

Egotist: A man who's always me-deep in conversation.

Fad: Something that goes in one era and out the other.

Father: A man whose daughter marries a man vastly her inferior
mentally but then gives birth to unbelievably brilliant grandchildren.

Fireproof: The boss's relatives.

Forger: A man who goes out and makes a name for himself.

Gladiator: What the cannibal said after he dined on the lady ex-
plorer.

Gulch: Birds who follow ocean vessels.

Highbrow: A person who enjoys a thing until it becomes popular.

Hobo: A roads scholar.

Janitor: A floor flusher.

Loafer: A fellow who is trying to make both week ends meet.

Love: One darn thing after another.

Oboe: An ill wind that nobody blows good.

Psychologist: A man who pulls habits out of rats.

Sentry: A hundred years.

Spartan: A person who can eat just one salted peanut.

Tips: Wages we pay other people's help.

Tree: An object that stands in one place for ages, then leaps in front of a wife who is driving.

Zythum: The last possible word for a column like this.

THE CHAMELEON

JAMES MERRICK

(Poet and divine, born at Reading, Berkshire, 1720; died, 1769)

Oft has it been my lot to mark
A proud, conceited, talking spark,
With eyes that hardly served at most
To guard their master 'gainst a post;
Yet round the world the blade has been,
To see whatever could be seen.
Returning from his finished tour,
Grown ten times perter than before;
Whatever word you chance to drop,
The travelled fool your mouth will stop:
"Sir, if my judgment you'll allow—
I've seen—and sure I ought to know."—
So begs you'd pay a due submission,
And acquiesce in his decision.

Two travellers of such a cast,
As o'er Arabia's wilds they passed,
And on their way, in friendly chat,
Now talked of this, and then of that;
Discoursed awhile, 'mongst other matter,
Of the Chameleon's form and nature.
"A STRANGER ANIMAL," cries one,
"Sure never lived beneath the sun:
A lizard's body lean and long,
A fish's head, a serpent's tongue,
Its foot with triple claw disjoined;
And what a length of tail behind!
How slow its pace! and then, its hue—
Whoever saw so fine a blue!"

"Hold there," the other quick replies,
"'Tis green, I saw it with these eyes,
As late with open mouth it lay,
And warmed it in the sunny ray;
Stretched at its ease the beast I viewed,
And saw it eat the air for food."

"I've seen it, sir, as well as you,
And must again affirm it blue;
At leisure I the beast surveyed
Extended in the cooling shade."

"'Tis green, 'tis green, sir, I assure ye."
"Green!" cries the other in a fury;
"Why, sir, d'ye think I've lost my eyes?"
"'Twere no great loss," the friend replies;
"For if they always serve you thus,
You'll find them but of little use."

So high at last the contest rose,
From words they almost came to blows
When luckily came by a third;
To him the question they referred:
And begged he'd tell them, if he knew,
Whether the thing was green or blue.

"Sirs," cries the umpire, "cease your pother,
The creature's neither one nor t'other.
I caught the animal last night,
And viewed it o'er by candle-light:
I marked it well, 'twas black as jet—
You stare—but, sirs, I've got it yet,
And can produce it."—"Pray, sir, do;
I'll lay my life the thing is blue."
"And I'll be sworn, that when you've seen
The reptile, you'll pronounce him green."

"Well, then, at once to ease the doubt,"
Replies the man, "I'll turn him out:
And when before your eyes I've set him,
If you don't find him black, I'll eat him."

He said; and full before their sight
Produced the beast, and lo!—'twas white.
Both stared, the man looked wondrous wise—
"My children," the Chameleon cries
(Then first the creature found a tongue),
"You all are right, and all are wrong:
When next you talk of what you view,
Think others see as well as you:
Nor wonder if you find that none
Prefers your eyesight to his own."

FATHER SEWS ON A BUTTON

CLARENCE DAY, JR.

It must have been hard work to keep up with the mending in our house. Four boys had to be kept in repair besides Father, and there was no special person to do it. The baby's nurse did some sewing, and Cousin Julie turned to and did a lot when she was around, but the rest of it kept Mother busy and her work basket was always piled high.

Looking back, I wonder now how she managed it. I remember her regularly going off to her room and sewing on something right after dinner or at other idle moments, when she might have sat around with the rest of us. My impression as a boy was that this was like going off to do puzzles—it was a form of amusement, or a woman's way of passing the time.

There was more talk about Father's socks and shirts than anything else. Most of this talk was by Father, who didn't like things to disappear for long periods, and who wanted them brought promptly back and put in his bureau drawer where they belonged. This was particularly true of his favorite socks. Not the plain white ones which he wore in the evening, because they were all alike, but the colored socks that were supplied to him by an English haberdasher in Paris.

These colored socks were the one outlet of something in Father which ran contrary to that religion of propriety to which he adhered. In that day of somber hues for men's suits and quiet tones for men's neckties, most socks were as dark and severe as the rest of one's garments; but Father's, hidden from the public eye by his trousers and his high buttoned shoes, had a really astonishing range both of color and fancy. They were mostly in excellent taste, but in a distinctly French way, and Wilhelmine used to tease him about them. She called them his "secret joys."

Father got holes in his socks even oftener than we boys did in our stockings. He had long athletic toes, and when he lay stretched out on his sofa reading and smoking, or absorbed in talking to anyone, these toes would begin stretching and wiggling in a curious way by themselves, as though they were seizing on this chance to live a life of their own. I often stared in fascination at their leisurely twistings and turnings, when I should have been listening to Father's instructions about far different matters. Soon one and then the other slipper would fall off, always to Father's surprise, but without interrupting his talk, and a little later his busy great toe would peer out at me through a new hole in his sock.

Mother felt that it was a woman's duty to mend things and sew, but she hated it. She rather liked to embroider silk lambrequins, as a feat of womanly prowess, but her darning of Father's socks was an impatient and not-too-skillful performance. She said there were so many of them that they made the back of her neck ache.

Father's heavily starched shirts, too, were a problem. When he put one on, he pulled it down over his head, and thrust his arms blindly out right and left in a hunt for the sleeves. A new shirt was strong enough to survive these strains without splitting, but life with Father rapidly weakened it, and the first thing he knew he would hear it beginning to tear. That disgusted him. He hated any evidence of weakness, either in people or things. In his wrath he would strike out harder than ever as he felt around for the sleeve. Then would come a sharp crackling noise as the shirt ripped open, and a loud wail from Mother.

Buttons were Father's worst trial, however, from his point of view. Ripped shirts and socks with holes in them could still be worn, but drawers with their buttons off couldn't. The speed with which he dressed seemed to discourage his buttons and make them desert Father's service. Furthermore, they always gave out suddenly and at the wrong moment.

He wanted help and he wanted it promptly at such times, of course. He would appear at Mother's door with a waistcoat in one hand and a disloyal button in the other, demanding that it be sewn on at once. If she said she couldn't just then, Father would get as indignant as though he had been drowning and a life-guard had informed him he would save him tomorrow.

When his indignation mounted high enough to sweep aside his good judgment, he would say in a stern voice, "Very well, I'll sew it on myself," and demand a needle and thread. This announcement always caused consternation. Mother knew only too well what it meant. She would beg him to leave his waistcoat in her work basket and let her do it next day. Father was inflexible. Moreover, his decision would be strengthened if he happened to glance at her basket and see how many of his socks were dismally waiting there in that crowded exile.

"I've been looking for those blue polka-dotted socks for a month," he said angrily one night before dinner. "Not a thing is done for a man in this house. I even have to sew on my own buttons. Where is your needle and thread?"

Mother reluctantly gave these implements to him. He marched off, sat on the edge of his sofa in the middle of his bedroom, and got ready to work. The gaslight was better by his bureau, but he couldn't sit on a chair when he sewed. It had no extra room on it. He laid his scissors, the spool of thread, and his waistcoat down on the sofa beside him, wet his fingers, held the needle high up and well out in front, and began poking the thread at the eye.

Like every commander, Father expected instant obedience, and he wished to deal with trained troops. The contrariness of the needle and the limp obstinacy of the thread made him swear. He stuck the needle in the sofa while he wet his fingers and stiffened the thread again. When he came to take up his needle, it had disappeared. He felt around everywhere for it. He got up, holding fast to his thread, and turned around, facing the sofa to see where it was hiding. This jerked the spool off onto the floor, where it rolled away and unwound.

The husbands of two of Mother's friends had had fits of apoplexy and died. It frightened her horribly when this seemed about to happen to Father. At the sound of his roars, she rushed in. There he was on the floor, as she had feared. He was trying to get his head under the sofa and he was yelling at something, and his face was such a dark red and his eyes so bloodshot that Mother was terrified. Pleading with him to stop only made him more apoplectic. He said he'd be damned if he'd stop. He stood up presently, tousled but triumphant, the spool in his hand. Mother ran to get a new needle. She threaded it for him and he at last started sewing.

Father sewed on the button in a violent manner, with vicious haulings and jabs. Mother said she couldn't bear to see him—but she couldn't bear to leave the room, either. She stood watching him, hypnotized and appalled, itching to sew it herself, and they talked at each other with vehemence. Then the inevitable accident happened: the needle came forcibly up through the waistcoat, it struck on the button, Father pushed at it harder, and it burst through the hole and stuck Father's finger.

He sprang up with a howl. To be impaled in this way was not only exasperating, it was an affront. He turned to me, as he strode about on the rug, holding onto his finger, and said wrathfully, "It was your mother."

"Why, Clare!" Mother cried.

"Talking every minute," Father shouted at her, "and distracting a man! How the devil can I sew on a button with this gibbering and buzz in my ears? Now see what you made me do!" he added suddenly. "Blood on my good waistcoat! Here! Take the damned thing. Give me a handkerchief to tie up my finger with. Where's the witch-hazel?"

TO A FROG . . . AND A MAN

ELEANOR HOLLISTER

I've a wee dead frog
  In alcohol.
But he really isn't
  A frog at all.

He's a prince, enchanted,
  Who can not tell
The proper word
  To break the spell.

Perhaps he earned
  The wrath of witches
By lying drunken
  In the ditches.

Perhaps he punched
  His princely brother
Or loved one girl
  And wed another.

Perhaps he lied
  Or broke a vow
But anyway
  He's sorry now.

And so I carry
  Him about
In case the right word
  Should slip out.

I SAY IT'S FALSE!

PARKE CUMMINGS

Almost all of the newspapers I read, and a good many of the magazines, contain information tests, and I am never the one to pass these

up. And I take pride in reporting that on those questions of the true-or-false variety I am nothing short of a bearcat. I practically never miss.

It isn't that I'm well-informed or smart; it's simply that, from study, I've evolved an almost foolproof system, one that is simplicity itself.

If I am asked to determine the truth or the falsity of any commonly accepted generality, any statement that seems reasonable and sensible, I simply say "False!" and I'm invariably right.

I never bother to study the question on its merits. That's a waste of time, and it may prompt me to go wrong. These fellows who make up the questions seem to have a knack of picking holes in all the established beliefs of humanity. "Blondes are more emotional than brunettes." False, of course. "Cats can see in the dark." We've all been brought up to believe that they can, so the statement is obviously wrong. "Women are worse drivers than men." You'd think they are, so obviously they aren't. See how simple it is?

I have taken so many of these tests that I do them in my sleep now. In my mind I see the questions, the answers (always "false," remember), and the detailed explanations of how mankind happened to become seized with the particular delusion that is now being exploded before my eyes. A sample true-or-false test, as my impressions form it, runs about like this:

Q: Horses have four legs. True or false?

A: False! Horses have three legs. Scientific tests have determined that the so-called left fore-"leg" of a horse is not a leg at all. Study of its cellular structure shows that it is in reality merely an extension of the equine breastbone, and hence cannot qualify technically as being a leg. The popular belief that horses have four legs accordingly has no basis in scientific fact.

Q: Washington was the first president of the United States. True or false?

A: False! There have never been any presidents of the United States. In the Federal Convention of 1783, a man named Scopesby was assigned to incorporate provisions for the election of a president into the Constitution, but he was suddenly stricken with appendicitis, and, without the consent of the assembly, turned the task over to a compatriot, John Wade. It was Wade who unconstitutionally worked up the provisions which thereby have no legal standing whatsoever. The error still persists to this day, and the American populace still believes that the men it elects to office are presidents in good constitutional standing.

Q: *Blind people cannot see. True or false?*

A: False! Blind people *can* see. Careful study of the derivation of the word "see" reveals that it springs from the old Anglo-Saxon word *se* (Dutch: *ze*) which means, as nearly as it can be translated: "to get a general hazy idea of things." It is obvious that the impressions that blind people get of their surroundings either by touch and smell or from the information relayed to them by people with normal eyesight, qualify under this definition.

Q: *You can sleep better in a comfortable bed than on a hard floor. True or false?*

A: False as usual! Recent tests at the University of Chicago revealed the opposite. Ten subjects slept in comfortable beds for seven nights after which they were assigned various tasks. They were then ordered to sleep on hardwood floors for another period of seven nights. There were complaints for the first two nights, but after that, every subject slept like a baby. Moreover, the subjects accomplished nothing unusual after sleeping on beds, but after the floor tests, here is what the group did: Wrote two symphonies. Placed in the semi-finals of the intercollegiate boxing tournament. Discovered a cure for whooping cough. Painted a picture which compared favorably with the *Mona Lisa*. Cornered U. S. Steel. Received a total of 742 proposals of marriage. The explanation lies in the fact that the fabular muscles (the ones that make people accomplish unusual things) are given beneficial stimulation by contact with hard materials where lying in soft beds simply tends to atrophy them.

Q: *Fat people weigh more than thin people. How about it?*

A: Not on your life! All wrong as usual. Fat people have greater volume than thin people, and this extra volume causes more air resistance to their susceptibility to gravity. In other words, fat people only *appear* to weigh more than thin people because our present-day scales are not correctly graduated to deduct properly for this additional air-resistance. If they were, it would be found that all people weigh exactly the same.

Q: *Dogs cannot climb trees. True or false?*

A: False! All dogs are perfectly capable of climbing trees. The reason they do not do so is because of an element in the bark of trees (scennic acid) which is injurious to their feet. If it were not for that, as tests with trees from which that acid has been removed prove, dogs would climb trees just as eagerly as cats.

Q: *It is colder in winter than in summer. True or false?*

A: Not on your tintype! The common custom of wearing heavy clothing in wintertime has caused this popular misconception. Heavy clothing impedes the circulation and hence leads to the erroneous belief that one is "cold." The so-called "evidence" of the thermometer also adds to the misconception. Actually the mercury in thermometers does not sink lower on account of the colder weather but because there is a different chemical make-up in the air during the winter season. The proof of this whole matter lies in the fact that certain animals, that do not wear binding clothes and never look at thermometers, get along all right.

Q: *Skunks smell terrible. True or false?*

A: False! It is not the skunk that smells terrible, but the air surrounding him. Therefore skunks do *not* smell terrible.

Q: *Fish suffocate if they are removed from water. How about it?*

A: No sir! This delusion belongs strictly in the realm of folklore and superstition. Fish, it is true, die when taken out of their native element, but they only *appear* to suffocate. Actually the reason for their demise is due to the fact that fish cannot stand the intense light that pervades the atmosphere. Their eyes suffer so severely from it, that they die for this reason.

Q: *Wellington defeated Napoleon at the Battle of Waterloo. True or false?*

A: False! Neither of them was at the scene of battle, recently-disclosed records prove. Napoleon was killed in the retreat from Moscow, and a French sergeant named Duprois, who resembled him closely, was chosen to take command of the armies so that the enemy should never become aware of the truth. As for Wellington, documentary evidence proves that he was on leave of absence in England at the time.

Q: *Two and two are four. Yes or no?*

A: No! Careful study of history shows that prior to 1363, the word "four" was used to connote the number currently known as "five." A monk, named Groschius, in adding a simple sum, inadvertently put down "five" as the total of three added to two, and future scholars who got hold of his work moved the number "four" back a notch. The error was not discovered until recently.

Q: *New York is north of Miami. True or false?*

A: False. Medieval map makers, unaware that the world is round, started drawing their maps upside down, and all subsequent map makers followed them. The terms "North" and "South" were first invented by Askaran, an Egyptian philosopher, and careful reading of his treatise, *Boundaries of the Earth,* will convince anybody that he intended North to be what we now consider South, and vice versa. Hence, in the only true sense, New York is *south* of Miami.

Q: It is better to be healthy than sick. Is that right?

A: It *is* not. On the contrary, it is better to be sick than healthy. "Healthy," correctly defined, means to be without any ailments whatsoever. This would even mean being devoid of such common physiological symptoms as aging through the process of time, running low on energy due to exercise, suffering brain-fatigue or sleepiness from being awake, etc., etc. Thus, no living mechanism can exist without suffering ailments of one sort or another, and the only truly "healthy" person is a dead one. What we *really* mean is that it is better to be sick than to be *very* sick.

Q: It is lighter in the daytime than at night. True or false?

A: False. A moment's thought should convince us that all the light we get on this planet comes from the sun. The sun gives just as much light all the time—at night just as much as in the daytime. It is really just as light at night, accordingly, but we just don't see it.

Q: Ducks like the water. How about it?

A: Not a bit of it. This is another example of the common habit of arriving at foolish beliefs through improper observation and faulty inferences. The fact that ducks are frequently seen in water has led to this delusion. Laboratory experiments have disclosed the fact that ducks don't like *anything,* and that they go in the water purely to get away from land which they dislike even more intensely than water. This disclosure has led some scientists to believe the duck's lack of sympathy with his surroundings (*her* surroundings, to be accurate) will lead to her extinction in another century or two. And the drake's also.

Q: Vienna is the capital of Austria. True or false?

A: Oh, let's not go into *that* again.

CLYDE LAMB, THIS WEEK

"Yessir—thirty-seven per cent less nicotine."

MAXIMS

BENJAMIN FRANKLIN

Never spare the parson's wine, nor the baker's pudding.

A house without woman or firelight is like a body without soul or spirit.

Kings and bears often worry their keepers.

Light purse, heavy heart.

He's a fool that makes his doctor his heir.

Ne'er take a wife till thou hast a house (and a fire) to put her in.

To lengthen thy life, lessen thy meals.

He that drinks fast pays slow.

He is ill-clothed who is bare of virtue.

Beware of meat twice boil'd, and an old foe reconcil'd.

The heart of a fool is in his mouth, but the mouth of a wise man is in his heart.

He that is rich need not live sparingly, and he that can live sparingly need not be rich.

He that waits upon fortune is never sure of a dinner.

COWARD IN THE CONGO

ART BUCHWALD

Deep down in every writer lies the horn of the hunter. To most people it may sound like gas on the stomach, but when a writer hears it, he knows Africa is calling. There was a time, many years ago, when to be a writer all you had to do was write. Today if you want to be a writer you have to shoot a big-game animal. You've got to go to the Dark Continent and prove you're a lion among men, a killer of kudu, a butcher in the bush and a fearless fellow in the forest.

While covering the European scene for the New York *Herald Tribune* in the last year I have been insulted by friends and strangers. "Hemingway has killed his leopard," they say, "Ruark has killed his lion. Pray, what have you killed?"

Last summer I began to feel the pressure even at home. My wife would never come out and say anything, but I could tell by the little things that all was not going well. Finally, after an unexpected outburst of tears, she told me what was bothering her. "We've been married for more than two years," she said, "and you don't have a trophy to your name. Everyone is laughing at me. They ask me what you do and when I tell them they say, 'If he's a writer, what's the name of his white hunter?' "

I tried to comfort her, but I knew I had failed her. I knew if I wanted our marriage to last I could no longer keep the killer instinct down inside me, next to my ulcer. I could no longer ignore the horn of the hunter.

I picked up the phone and called Sabena Airlines.

"Let me have two tickets to the Congo."

"Why two tickets?" my wife asked.

"You have to come with me to take pictures of my trophies. All the wives do it."

"I'm not going," she said. "I can't stand the sight of your blood.

Take Joe Covello. He's a photographer and he can give you moral support. Besides he'll make a wonderful gin bearer."

"Gin?"

"You heard me."

It's funny she should have mentioned Covello. The last I had heard from him, he was in Rome photographing Italian movie stars on leopard skins. He probably knew a great deal about animals by now, and I was sure he would welcome a change. Besides, this safari would give him an opportunity to photograph animals in the flesh, instead of vice versa.

Covello seemed reluctant to leave his work, but he did admit he was running out of leopard skins, and Africa seemed like a good place to replenish his supply.

We flew directly to Stanleyville, our yellow fever shots tingling in our arms, our eyes glassy from typhoid serum, our hands shaking from the effects of quinine pills. Even before we landed I could hear the native tom-toms beating out a message. "White hunter . . . no guts . . . white hunter . . . no guts."

In Stanleyville we took a taxi to the office of José Ingels & Son, who operate a company called Congo Safari. Ingels is no stranger to the safari business. He took John Huston out in search of wild boar, he took Katharine Hepburn out in search of wild crocodiles and he took Humphrey Bogart out in search of a drink. During the shooting of the movie The African Queen, he saw that Lauren Bacall had 45 bottles of soda water a day for her bath, and he killed hundreds of mosquitoes on producer Sam Spiegel's back. Ingels is a good man for a tough job.

I stuck out my trigger finger and we shook hands.

"Do you have any safaris for cowards?" I asked Ingels.

"Not at the moment," he replied. "I've got a group of 35 Americans, the oldest eighty-seven, who are going to the Albert National Park to take some movies. I could put you on that."

I was about to sign up when Covello reminded me I had to kill an animal.

"Oh, you want to *kill* something," Ingels said, putting on his pith helmet. "Well, you've come to the right place. The Belgian Congo is full of wild game. We can offer anything you want. What about a lion?"

"Is it dangerous?"

"Heavens, no. Except of course if the creature is hiding in the bush, or if you wound him or have to follow him into the dense undergrowth. Or if the female is trying to protect her cubs, or if the lion thinks he's cornered and wants to make a fight of it, or if you attack the male and the female tries to sink her claws in you. But on the whole lion hunting isn't dangerous."

"What else do you have?"

"How about a nice pachyderm? Elephants are great fun, particularly if they know they're being hunted and decide to hunt the hunter. You have to get right up to an elephant to get in a good shot and naturally he'll charge if he sees you. He'll put up his flappy ears and head straight at the man with the gun. If you don't kill him on the first shot it may be your last.

"When he gets on top of you he'll grab you with his trunk and smash you against a tree or the ground. Then he'll either trample on you or gut you with his tusks. Once he thinks you're dead he'll cover you up with leaves or grass. Elephants always give their victims a proper funeral. I must warn you of one thing. It will cost you $200 for a license if you want an elephant."

"Two hundred dollars," I said thoughtfully. "That's not too bad, considering you get a burial and everything. But don't you have something a little more my size?"

Ingels measured me around the waist.

"You can try for rhino if you wish, but rhinos usually attack without provocation and there is not much to shoot at, once one is coming toward you. You'll be a big man if you shoot a rhino.

"Then there's always leopard. I'll bet you'd like to bring your wife back a nice leopard coat. Shooting leopards in the Congo is a praiseworthy business and the natives will be grateful if you do it. But leopards are not easy to find. They've been known to hide in trees and jump on you as you walk under them. They'll rip you to bits with their claws. Even if they just scratch you, some people say, the poison in their talons can kill you. But they do make wonderful coats."

Ingels ran down the list of other game. He mentioned hartebeest, waterbuck, sassabies, red and black lechwes, Vardon cob, Thomas cob, impala buck, bushbuck, oribis, klipspringer, wart hogs, Livingstone eland, bongos, topis, Neuman cob and scaly anteaters.

"You are not permitted to hunt gorillas," he said. "They're protected by law."

It was the first good news I had heard all day.

Finally it was decided by Ingels and Covello that I would shoot a buffalo. The buffalo is the meanest, most thieving, card-cheating, wife-stealing animal in the Congo. But Covello tried to be encouraging. "The buffalo isn't as dangerous as everyone makes him out to be. Statistics prove that in the United States more Americans are killed in automobile accidents than are killed by buffalo."

Ingels arranged to send us out with his son, a strapping twenty-five-year-old lad who would be in charge of our porters, buy our food, take care of our transportation, guns and camping equipment, and tell us true stories of other hunting safaris.

Before we left Stanleyville, Ingels and his son took me to be outfitted. They bought me regulation shorts, a bush jacket, a slouch hat, a toothbrush and a bottle of gin. There was no doubt about it, I was dressed to kill.

We loaded the car with mosquito netting and first-aid equipment and—as is the custom with anyone who is going out hunting for the first time—I was asked to pay Ingels in advance. "The executors of the estate are sometimes reluctant to pay," Ingels explained apologetically.

It is 250 miles as the crow flies from Stanleyville to Irumu. No crow would make it if he went by car. The road twists and turns through the rain-soaked Ituri forest, and the elephants, which have a habit of sitting in the middle of the road, are neither frightened nor impressed by an automobile horn. The law of the jungle reads that under all conditions an elephant has the right of the way, and in the few recorded cases where the driver and the elephant have both lost their tempers, the elephant has always come out on top.

As an added attraction on the safari, we stopped off at a Pygmy camp to take pictures. It cost us only twenty dollars each, but the Pygmies warned us if we made any post cards from the photos they wanted royalties on the sales.

In Irumu we found the white hunter. His name was Alex Pierrard and in six years he had bagged more than 100 elephant, lion, leopard, rhino and pythons. His walls were jammed with trophies and you couldn't walk on the floor without slipping on an antelope or leopard skin. He had rhino horns for ash trays and elephant tusks for coat racks, and wild boar heads for doorstops. Pierrard was a white hunter to give any yellow hunter confidence.

Young Ingels explained to Pierrard that I was after buffalo, and the white hunter, who noticed that the left side of my face was twitching, looked surprised.

"I can find you all the buffalo you want," Pierrard said. "But are you sure you want to do it? It's pretty risky business, particularly if you've never hunted them before."

"See here, sir," said Covello. "We know it's risky business and that's why we're out here. If you don't want to take us we'll find another white hunter."

I tried to shut Covello up, but he was very indignant. "It just so happens my friend here is one of the best shots in Paris. Just because his face is twitching and he's cowering behind your couch is no reason for you to become insulting. My friend wants a buffalo in the worst way and he's determined to pay for it."

Pierrard apologized and said he would arrange porters and would borrow a *tipoye*—a carrying chair for rough travel—as we had a great deal of country to cover. "If it's buffalo you want," he said, "it's buffalo you're going to get."

The next morning we started out bright and early to find a camp. We hired 25 porters at 20 cents per head. They were in the truck with the supplies and we followed in a station wagon. Our first inkling that all would not go well on the safari came when the truck, which was being towed on a raft across a fast-moving river, sank to the muddy bottom. We saved the porters and the supplies, but it took us two days to get the truck out of the river. It was heartbreaking work, particularly when I thought about the porters costing me 20 cents a day.

We finally made camp and I was given a tent to myself and my own Gideon Bible. These modern safaris think of everything.

The best part of hunting in Africa is camping out. There—underneath an autumn moon, with a large roaring fire and the companionship of good fellows, large safari ants and malaria-ridden mosquitoes feeding on what little there is left after the scorpions get finished with you—a man is at peace with the world.

Over warm beer and pickled elephant ears, we talked the talk of men—the animals we had shot, the women we had known, the Marilyn Monroe pictures we had seen.

Pierrard cleaned and oiled the guns, Covello and Ingels practiced making tourniquets and splints in case anything went wrong, and the natives argued amongst themselves who was going to draw my bath the next morning.

It was a pleasant evening, and I thought to myself, perhaps for the last time, that it was good to be alive.

The next morning Pierrard and I went out to find my buffalo. The porters carried me for three miles in the *tipoye* and my gunbearer walked by my side. I had intended to shoot my buffalo from the seat, but Pierrard wouldn't permit it. Besides, if the buffalo charged and the porters ran, I would be caught with my *tipoye* down.

So the white hunter, the beaters, my gunbearer and I went into the savanna on foot. About seven o'clock we sighted a herd. We dropped down on our bellies and Pierrard indicated it was time to crawl forward. I kept thrashing with my arms and legs but I wasn't going anywhere and finally Pierrard made the beaters pull me along. We got within 60 yards and then Pierrard whispered:

"That's your boy."

He pointed to the largest bull in the herd, the meanest, cruelest hunk of fauna in the entire green hills of Africa. He had horns the size of two curved Eiffel Towers, and a face that could stop Big Ben. His hump was slightly smaller than Mount Everest and each shoulder looked like the front of the Super Chief. To top it off he had Native Dancer's legs.

I tried to crawl away but Pierrard held me by the belt.

"Let's forget the whole idea," I whispered. "Live and let live, I always say."

"It's too late now. You better take him. Bust him between the neck and the chest."

I got up on one knee and sighted. I squeezed the trigger slowly.

You think a lot of things when you're about to kill your first buffalo. You remember a lot of people who have been close to you.

As I squeezed the trigger I thought about the boys at Toots Shor's and how we used to sit around together with Leo Durocher, Joe DiMaggio, Bill O'Dwyer, Bob Considine and Tallulah Bankhead.

I thought about my good friends Leonard Lyons, Earl Wilson and Ed Sullivan and how we used to hunt items together in much darker places than Africa.

I thought about Sherman Billingsley. Good old Sherm. I knew I was going to miss him, even though he used to throw me out of the Stork Club every night. Well, that's not exactly true. He never let me in.

I thought of Elsa Maxwell and what a fine buffalo hunter she would make if only she took it seriously. I thought of Walter Winchell and the many Sunday nights we used to stay up together, he in his radio studio and I in my home in Forest Hills. I fervently wished he and Lenny Lyons would stop feuding.

I kept squeezing the trigger.

I thought of Hedda Hopper and Louella Parsons, who had gone

after much bigger game than I had, and had Hollywood's finest collections of shrunken heads of movie stars and producers.

I thought of Aly Khan and Rubi Rubirosa and the wonderful trophies they had collected during the years.

There was so much to think about and I kept squeezing and squeezing.

All of a sudden, just before I got to Jane Russell, the gun went off. For a second I was blinded but when I looked up the buffalo was gone.

"I got him, I got him!" I shouted.

"The hell you did," said Pierrard. "You missed him by a mile."

"But I hit something. I could hear the thud."

"You hit a Thomas cob antelope which was standing two hundred yards to the right of the buffalo. Let's have a look."

We crawled up to the animal and found him dead. I had shot him true and straight and he had died brave and strong. I fainted.

The gunbearers and porters whooped for joy.

They threw the antelope on the carrying chair and then they threw me over the antelope and carried the whole mess into camp.

Covello was waiting for us at the camp.

"Where's the buffalo?" he asked.

"I was about to shoot one," I explained, "when I saw this Thomas cob. They're very rare and Pierrard insisted I shoot it instead. What could I do? Buffalo are a dime a dozen, but have you ever seen a Thomas cob like that? He charged me and I had time for only one shot. Fortunately I got him in the chest, right smack in the heart."

Pierrard nodded his head, and the gunbearers didn't speak any English.

The porters gave me the tail of the cob as well as the horns and carried me on their shoulders to the airport in Irumu. It took only a half day, so I was in my rights when I paid them only 10 cents each.

I'm back in Europe now and I can already tell the difference. People are now saying, "Hemingway killed his leopard, Ruark killed his lion and Buchwald killed his Thomas cob."

Now that I'm a full-fledged writer I'm even thinking of writing a book. I've got a great idea for one, about an old man who goes fishing off the coast of Cuba by himself, and catches the biggest fish in the sea only to have the sharks eat it before the old man can get it back to shore. I haven't got a title for it yet, but it should make a whale of a story.

THE DEACON'S MASTERPIECE,
OR THE WONDERFUL "ONE-HOSS SHAY"

OLIVER WENDELL HOLMES

Have you heard of the wonderful one-hoss shay,
That was built in such a logical way
It ran a hundred years to a day,
And then, of a sudden, it—ah, but stay,
I'll tell you what happened without delay,
Scaring the parson into fits,
Frightening people out of their wits,—
Have you ever heard of that, I say?

Seventeen hundred and fifty-five.
Georgius Secundus was then alive,—
Snuffy old drone from the German hive.
That was the year when Lisbon-town
Saw the earth open and gulp her down,
And Braddock's army was done so brown,
Left without a scalp to its crown.
It was on the terrible Earthquake-day
That the Deacon finished the one-hoss shay.

Now in building of chaises, I tell you what,
There is always *somewhere* a weakest spot,—
In hub, tire, felloe, in spring or thill,
In panel, or crossbar, or floor, or sill,
In screw, bolt, thoroughbrace,—lurking still,
Find it somewhere you must and will,—
Above or below, or within or without,—
And that's the reason, beyond a doubt,
That a chaise *breaks down*, but doesn't *wear out*.

But the Deacon swore (as Deacons do,
With an "I dew vum," or an "I tell *yeou*,")
He would build one shay to beat the taown
'N' the keounty 'n' all the kentry raoun';
It should be so built that it *couldn't* break daown:

—"Fur," said the Deacon, "'t's mighty plain
Thut the weakes' place mus' stan' the strain;
'N' the way t' fix it, uz I maintain,
Is only jest
T' make that place uz strong uz the rest."

So the Deacon inquired of the village folk
Where he could find the strongest oak,
That couldn't be split nor bent nor broke,—
That was for spokes and floor and sills;
He sent for lancewood to make the thills;
The crossbars were ash, from the straightest trees,
The panels of white-wood, that cuts like cheese,
But lasts like iron for things like these;
The hubs of logs from the "Settler's Ellum,"—
Last of its timber,—they couldn't sell 'em,
Never an axe had seen their chips,
And the wedges flew from between their lips,
Their blunt ends frizzled like celery-tips;
Step and prop-iron, bolt and screw,
Spring, tire, axle, and linchpin, too,
Steel of the finest, bright and blue;
Thoroughbrace bison-skin, thick and wide.
Boot, top, dasher, from tough old hide
Found in the pit when the tanner died.
That was the way he "put her through."—
"There!" said the Deacon, "naow she'll dew!"

Do! I tell you, I rather guess
She was a wonder, and nothing less!
Colts grew horses, beards turned gray,
Deacon and Deaconess dropped away,
Children and grandchildren—where were they?
But there stood the stout old one-hoss shay
As fresh as on Lisbon Earthquake-day!
Eighteen hundred;—it came and found
The Deacon's masterpiece strong and sound.
Eighteen hundred increased by ten;—
"Hahnsum kerridge" they called it then.
Eighteen hundred and twenty came;—
Running as usual; much the same.

Thirty and forty at last arrive,
And then come fifty, and fifty-five.

Little of all we value here
Wakes on the morn of its hundredth year
Without both feeling and looking queer.
In fact, there's nothing that keeps its youth,
So far as I know, but a tree and truth.
(This is a moral that runs at large;
Take it.—You're welcome.—No extra charge.)
First of November,—the Earthquake-day—
There are traces of age in the one-hoss shay,
A general flavor of mild decay,
But nothing local, as one may say,
There couldn't be,—for the Deacon's art
Had made it so like in every part
That there wasn't a chance for one to start.
For the wheels were just as strong as the thills,
And the floor was just as strong as the sills,
And the panels just as strong as the floor,
And the whiffle-tree neither less nor more,
And the back crossbar as strong as the fore,
And spring and axle and hub *encore*.
And yet, *as a whole*, it is past a doubt
In another hour it will be *worn out!*

LOOK NOW

H. L. GOLD

Some months back, I heard of the unsettling experience of a writer who found himself trudging up the subway steps behind two men. The first exclaimed that the sun had been out when they got aboard . . . and here it was pouring downtown! "Well," said the other, "it's better than nothing."

I speculated on the possibility that the second speaker was an alien from a world without weather, or perhaps from an unknown part of Earth where weather was optional. Then I had to drop the subject, having run out of data.

That's not so any longer and I can't say I'm happy it isn't. All of it adds up to the conclusion that there are indeed Aliens Among Us.

No, it's not a matter of looking for slight scars where antennae have been neatly lopped off, signs of third eyes, fingers grafted onto tentacles, legs that bend backward at the knee, or where the knee should be, or watching for "people" to emerge from burrows in Central Park.

Even we, with our necessarily less advanced science, would be cleverer than that. The giveaways, as you can see, can't be that easily detected.

Then must we remain dupes? Not at all!

One thing that can't be shucked very readily is conditioning. You've had one example. Did the "man" who betrayed himself get flustered and fear exposure? I doubt it; we're accustomed to laugh off such flubs as unthinking answers or slips of the tongue and any well-trained scout would exploit that human trait.

But no longer! Regard this blooper: A letter to a newspaper blamed subway accidents on the "fact" that, for the past few years, transport workers have had *no working conditions at all!*

Somebody (or something), I'll wager, is going to get recalled and made an example of. Besides shooting off his mouth, if that is what it is, he falsified *in our terms*, which are the ones that count, for if there's anything the transport workers have, it's working conditions.

I admit that I was bothered by both these instances being associated with the subway. Now, considering the others at hand, I think it's only coincidence.

In my first editorial job, I was jolted by this astonishing sentence: "Gibbering idiotically, his bare feet padded across the floor." Naturally, I thought it was merely a dangling participle—but gibbering feet aren't so impossible when you remember that crickets communicate, or whatever they do, by rubbing their hind legs together.

Then there's the now defunct (or recalled) Broadway character who enthused over a movie: "Don't miss it if you can!"

Translating that is as frustrating as staring at the optical-illusion blocks—just when you think you have it, the whole meaning turns upside down. I *think* it may indicate a desperate lack of free will. But it may be exactly the opposite . . . or something else entirely that we can't even imagine.

Sam Goldwyn's famous—well Goldwynisms could stand deciphering— For example: "I'll believe in color TV when I see it in black and white." Anybody who sees color in black and white *could* be seeing black and white in color!

He is also reported to have said: "These guys who are working on the atom bomb must be crazy. Don't they know they're playing with dynamite?" I sense contempt here, a hint of alien weapons so powerful that even our most horrible are like blasting powder by comparison.

He denies authorship of these and other—well, Goldwynisms. I believe him, if only because no scout would be allowed to goof so often.

Or is that more of the same contempt? After a recent TV commercial, I can understand such superiority: Super Anahist, the announcer said, gets rid of sniffles *and red, swollen eyes.* If we had detachable eyes, I guess we'd be feeling pretty superior, too, eh?

I think I'm on the right track in decoding these weird glimpses of outworld conditioning, but there are at least two complications:

—It sounds as if we're playing unwitting host to more than one alien species.

—Some human beings *do* have tangled tongues, like the Rev. Spooner's "Pardon me, madam; you're occupewing the wrong pie. I'll sew you to another sheet." That doesn't make detection a bit easier.

But what I'm really worried about is a quote from The Pocket Book of Boners, an omnibus of (supposedly) schoolboy howlers:

Name a noted foreigner assisting the colonists in the Revolutionary War.

God.

Now what in the name of Heaven does *that* mean?

I've talked about this considerably. I felt I should be issuing intelligence reports that allow only one conclusion: There Are Aliens Among Us.

My intent was to inform without alarming; I'm not sure that I succeeded, for I've since received two letters, both anonymous, and only one of them intelligible and, therefore, clearly from a human reader.

"It is strange how one may brood for years over a problem and then suddenly have it brought into focus by hearing another's views on the subject. The similarity between your conclusions and mine is, if you'll pardon the expression, astounding.

"The subject is my wife. It happens that she has been a very good wife and I have no desire to alter our relationship, even if she is an alien. Good wives are not easy to find and represent a substantial investment. Therefore, I am signing this with a pseudonym and mailing it from a false address—and request that *both* be kept confidential

"Many of her statements are perfectly ordinary spoonerisms. Her reference to a 'platation from Quoto' is an example of this. As you suggest, perhaps it is a deliberately cultivated type of protective coloration designed to draw attention away from those slips even the best of agents, human or otherwise, inevitably make.

"Some of these verbal prat-falls are quite humorous, which supports your theory, for humans are notoriously uncritical when laughing. For instance, she doesn't care for a neighbor's home because she says she doesn't like 'overwrought iron.'

"Yet a certain chilling alien viewpoint occasionally reveals itself. Ever since my wife told me that the 'washee-pot needs coughing,' I have become uncomfortable in the presence of all pots. I keep wondering if this or that pot is a washee-pot and if it intends to cough.

"I will give you three more examples and ask you to think about them. I have tried to reason them out, but I always somehow get the feeling that my mind is going cross-eyed. Here they are: 'It's half of one and six-a-dozen of the other.' Close questioning has ascertained that this is meant to indicate two equal quantities, but I challenge any human mathematician to prove this or even understand it.

"'Did you know that Chinese is spoken by more people than anybody else?' This implies that beings other than people speak Chinese. The only comfort I can find in the remark is that we outnumber them.

"'While you're out in the kitchen, dear, the uncoffee should be plugged.' I don't feel that this statement requires comment. Anyone can see that the washee-pots need coughing because they are full of uncoffee that hasn't been plugged.

"I don't know whether or not this is relevant, but we have a ten-month-old daughter who wakes up every night and chuckles delightedly in the dark at something we can't see or hear. At any rate, my wife claims she can't see or hear it. I know I can't."

There may be more here than meets the eye, but what meets the eye is certainly disturbing enough. That overwrought iron, for example,—if metal can get fatigued and X-rays can detect it, what makes you think your wife can't sense nervousness in at least iron? If she is able to, *what else can she sense?*

"Just last night, my wife said to me in a very stern voice, 'If you don't know how to behave nicely, *don't be at all!*' With a deadly line like that to toe, the odds are that you may not hear from me any longer, in which case you will know that my behavior was somehow unsatisfactory and I am no more. I'd like to sign this sincerely, but I think I had better say good-bye while I have the chance. Or—there's an understandable need to cling to some straw, any straw—do you think I am overestimating the power of this woman?"

Now maybe you see why I don't share your comfort in the fact that we outnumber the beings who speak Chinese. One machine gun, remember, could have won any war before 1863 or so. And have you noticed that she has not mentioned any other language?

However, you're safe. Whatever happens, your wife can probably protect you. If not, your daughter can—she seems on the best of terms with the thing or things in the dark, and half her loyalty presumably is, if not to humanity, then to her dad.

But what of the rest of us? Those "platations from Quoto" sound formidable enough to upset anyone who knows military organization. This uneasiness is not lulled by the baffling communication from my alien respondent:

"Of time some courses I can't see my face in front of my hand and some people don't think I think like a people.

"But I do. I just go bored from without and say things brightly through a mirror dark-wards. It is only a profound disassociation of intent and meaning. Any human can do."

Very homy-sounding . . . but at the bottom of the letter is a pink blur, 2.1508 inches across, that looks like a vast fingerprint. It isn't, though. I checked with a friend who knows fingerprinting.

It's the mark of a bare heel.

NIRVANA

ANONYMOUS

I am
  A Clam!
Come learn of me
Unclouded peace and calm content,
  Serene, supreme tranquillity,
Where thoughtless dreams and dreamless thoughts are blent.

When the salt tide is rising to the flood,
  In billows blue my placid pulp I lave;
And when it ebbs I slumber in the mud,
  Content alike with ooze or crystal wave.

I do not shudder when in chowder stewed,
  Nor when the Coney Islander engulfs me raw,
When in the church soup's dreary solitude
  Alone I wander, do I shudder? Naw!

If jarring tempests beat upon my bed,
  Or summer peace there be,
I do not care: as I have said,
  All's one to me;
    A Clam
    I am.

Single . . . :

HOW THE DAUGHTERS COME DOWN AT DUNOON

H. CHOLMONDELEY PENNELL

How do the daughters
Come down at Dunoon?
    Daintily,
    Tenderly,
    Fairily,
    Gingerly,
    Glidingly,
    Slidingly,
    Slippingly,
    Skippingly,
    Trippingly,
    Clippingly,
    Bumpingly,
    Thumpingly,
    Stumpingly,
    Clumpingly,
Starting and bolting,
And darting and jolting,
And tottering and staggering,
And lumbering and slithering,
And hurrying and scurrying,
And worrying and flurrying,
And rushing and leaping and crushing and creeping;
Feathers a-flying all—bonnets untying all—
Petticoats rapping and flapping and slapping all,
Crinolines flowing and blowing and showing all
Balmorals, dancing and glancing, entrancing all;

Feats of activity—
Nymphs on declivity—
Mothers in extacies—
Fathers in vextacies—
Lady-loves whisking and frisking and clinging on
True-lovers puffing and blowing and springing on,
Dashing and clashing and shying and flying on,
Blushing and flushing and wriggling and giggling on,
Teasing and pleasing and squeezing and wheezing on,
Everlastingly falling and bawling and sprawling on,
Tumbling and rumbling and grumbling and stumbling on,
Any fine afternoon,
About July or June—
That's just how the Daughters
Come down at Dunoon!

BY COURIER

O. HENRY

It was neither the season nor the hour when the park had frequenters; and it is likely that the young lady, who was seated on one of the benches at the side of the walk, had merely obeyed a sudden impulse to sit for a while and enjoy a foretaste of coming Spring.

She rested there, pensive and still. A certain melancholy that touched her countenance must have been of recent birth, for it had not yet altered the fine and youthful contours of her cheek, nor subdued the arch though resolute curve of her lips.

A tall young man came striding through the park along the path near which she sat. Behind him tagged a boy carrying a suit-case. At sight of the young lady, the man's face changed to red and back to pale again. He watched her countenance as he drew nearer, with hope and anxiety mingled on his own. He passed within a few yards of her, but he saw no evidence that she was aware of his presence or existence.

Some fifty yards further on he suddenly stopped and sat on a bench at one side. The boy dropped the suit-case and stared at him with wondering, shrewd eyes. The young man took out his handkerchief and wiped his brow. It was a good handkerchief, a good brow, and the young man was good to look at. He said to the boy:

"I want you to take a message to that young lady on that bench. Tell her I am on my way to the station, to leave for San Francisco, where I shall join that Alaska moose-hunting expedition. Tell her that, since she has commanded me neither to speak nor to write to her, I take this means of making one last appeal to her sense of justice, for the sake of what has been. Tell her that to condemn and discard one who has not deserved such treatment, without giving him her reasons or a chance to explain is contrary to her nature as I believe it to be. Tell her that I have thus, to a certain degree, disobeyed her injunctions, in the hope that she may yet be inclined to see justice done. Go, and tell her that."

The young man dropped a half-dollar into the boy's hand. The boy looked at him for a moment with bright, canny eyes out of a dirty, intelligent face, and then set off at a run. He approached the lady on the bench a little doubtfully, but unembarrassed. He touched the brim of an old plaid bicycle cap perched on the back of his head. The lady looked at him coolly, without prejudice or favor.

"Lady," he said, "dat gent on de oder bench sent yer a song and dance by me. If yer don't know de guy, and he's tryin' to do de Johnny act, say de word, and I'll call a cop in t'ree minutes. If yer does know him, and he's on de square, w'y I'll spiel yer de bunch of hot air he sent yer."

The young lady betrayed a faint interest.

"A song and dance!" she said, in a deliberate, sweet voice that seemed to clothe her words in a diaphanous garment of impalpable irony. "A new idea—in the troubadour line, I suppose. I—used to know the gentleman who sent you so I think it will hardly be necessary to call the police. You may execute your song and dance, but do not sing too loudly. It is a little early yet for open-air vaudeville, and we might attract attention."

"Awe," said the boy, with a shrug down the length of him, "yer know what I mean, lady. 'Tain't a turn, it's wind. He told me to tell yer he's got his collars and cuffs in dat grip for a scoot clean out to Frisco. Den he's goin' to shoot snow-birds in de Klondike. He says yer told him not to send 'round no more pink notes nor come hangin' over de garden gate, and he takes dis means of puttin' yer wise. He says yer refereed him out like a has-been, and never give him no chance to kick at de decision. He says yer swiped him, and never said why."

The slightly awakened interest in the young lady's eyes did not abate. Perhaps it was caused by either the originality or the audacity of the snow-bird hunter, in thus circumventing her express commands against the ordinary modes of communication. She fixed her eye on a statue standing disconsolate in the disheveled park, and spoke into the transmitter:

"Tell the gentleman that I need not repeat to him a description of my ideals. He knows what they have been and what they still are. So far as they touch on this case, absolute loyalty and truth are the ones paramount. Tell him that I have studied my own heart as well as one can, and I know its weakness as well as I do its needs. That is why I decline to hear his pleas, whatever they may be. I did not condemn him through hearsay or doubtful evidence, and that is why I made no charge. But, since he persists in hearing what he already well knows, you may convey the matter.

"Tell him that I entered the conservatory that evening from the rear, to cut a rose for my mother. Tell him I saw him and Miss Ashburton beneath the pink oleander. The tableau was pretty, but the pose and juxtaposition were too eloquent and evident to require explanation. I left the conservatory, and at the same time, the rose and my ideal. You may carry that song and dance to your impresario."

"I'm shy on one word, lady. Jux—jux—put me wise on that, will yer?"

"Juxtaposition—or you may call it propinquity—or, if you like, being rather too near for one maintaining the position of an ideal."

The gravel spun from beneath the boy's feet. He stood by the other bench. The man's eyes interrogated him, hungrily. The boy's were shining with the impersonal zeal of the translator.

"De lady says dat she's on to de fact dat gals is dead easy when a feller come spielin' ghost stories and tryin' to make up, and dat's why she won't listen to no soft-soap. She says she caught yer dead to rights, huggin' a bunch o' calico in de hot-house. She side-stepped in to pull some posies and yer was squeezin' der oder gal to beat de band. She says it looked cute, all right all right, but it made her sick. She says yer better git busy, and make a sneak for de train."

The young man gave a low whistle and his eyes flashed with a sudden thought. His hand flew to the inside pocket of his coat, and drew out a handful of letters. Selecting one, he handed it to the boy, following it with a silver dollar from his vest-pocket.

"Give that letter to the lady," he said, "and ask her to read it. Tell her that it should explain the situation. Tell her that, if she had mingled a little trust with her conception of the ideal, much heartache might have been avoided. Tell her that loyalty she prizes so much has never wavered. Tell her I am waiting for an answer."

The messenger stood before the lady.

"De gent says he's had de ski-bunk put on him widout no cause. He says he's no bum guy; and, lady, yer read dat letter, and I'll bet yer he's a white sport, all right."

The young lady unfolded the letter, somewhat doubtfully, and read it.

Dear Dr. Arnold:

I want to thank you for your most kind and opportune aid to my daughter last Friday evening, when she was overcome by an attack of her old heart-trouble in the conservatory at Mrs. Waldron's reception. Had you not been near to catch her as she fell and to render proper attention, we might have lost her. I would be glad if you would call and undertake the treatment of her case.

Gratefully yours,
Robert Ashburton.

The young lady refolded the letter, and handed it to the boy.

"De gent wants an answer," said the messenger. "What's de word?"

The lady's eyes suddenly flashed on him, bright, smiling and wet.

"Tell that guy on the other bench," she said, with a happy, tremulous laugh, "that his girl wants him."

THE TALL GENTLEMAN TO HIS LADY LOVE

ANONYMOUS

Upbraid me not! I never swore
  Eternal love to thee;
For thou art only four feet high,
  And I am six feet three:
I wonder, dear, how you supposed
  That I could look so low;
There's many a one can tie a knot,
  Who cannot tie a beau!

Besides, you must confess, my love,
    The bargain's scarcely fair:
For never could we make a match,
    Although we made a pair;
Marriage, I know, makes one of two,
    But there's the horrid bore,
My friends declare if you are *one*,
    That I at least am *four!*

'Tis true, the moralists have said,
    That Love has got no eyes;
But why should all my sighs be heaved
    For one who has no size?
And on our wedding-day, I'm sure
    I'd leave you in the lurch,
For you never saw a steeple, dear,
    In the inside of a church!

'Tis usual for a wife to take
    Her husband by the arm—
But pray excuse me, if I hint
    A sort of fond alarm,
That when I offered *you* my arm,
    That happiness to beg,
Your highest efforts, dear, would be,
    To take me by the leg!

I do admit I wear a glass,
    Because my sight's not good,
But were I always quizzing you,
    It might be counted rude.
And though I use a convex lens,
    I still cannot but hope
My wife will e'er "look up to me"
    Through Herschel's telescope!

Then fare thee well, my gentle one,
    I ask no parting kiss;
I must not break my back, to gain
    So exquisite a bliss:
Nor will I weep, lest I should hurt
    So delicate a flower:

The tears that fall from such a height
  Would be a thunder shower!

Farewell! and pray don't throw yourself
  In a basin or a tub;
For that would be a sore disgrace
  To all the Six-Feet Club!
But if you ever love again,
  Love on a smaller plan,
For why extend to six feet three
  The life that's but a span?

A PAIR OF SEXES

FRANKLIN P. ADAMS

I. A Man Telephones

"Ed? . . . Lunch at one. Whyte's. Right."

II. A Woman Telephones

"Hello, operator. Operator? I want Caledonia five eight six seven, please. Oh, this *is* Caledonia five eight six seven? Oh, I beg your pardon, I'm terribly sorry. I thought it was the operator. I've had so much trouble with the telephone lately. May I speak to Miss Lucille Webster, please? Oh, *speaking*? Oh, I'm terribly sorry. Is this Miss Webster? Is this you, Lucille? I didn't recognize your voice at first. First I thought it was the operator, and then I thought it was somebody answering for you, Lucille. I didn't recognize your voice at first. Got a cold or something? Oh, you sound as though you had. There's so much of it around this wretched weather. I never saw anything like it in my whole life. Well, I'm glad you haven't got a cold, though at first you certainly sounded like it. . . . I was just talking to Ethel for a second, and she had such a cold she could hardly talk. That's the reason I asked you. There's an *awful* lot of it around this wretched weather. . . . Oh, nothing particular. . . . Oh, yes, there is too. How silly of me! I was so interested in what you were saying, I almost forgot. Lucille, what are you doing tomorrow? . . . No, about lunch time. Or a little earlier. Or a little later. It doesn't matter. Because I expect to be in your part of town about that time, around lunch time, oh, maybe one or one-thirty or so, I have an appointment at twelve-thirty, and it oughtn't to take me more than half an hour, or at the most three quarters, surely not over an hour, I'm almost certain, and probably I'll be through in half an hour, but, anyway, I ought to be all through by one-thirty, and I could meet you anywhere you say. . . . Oh, I know, but Maillard's is pretty crowded about that time, and isn't there some place nearer? My appointment is on Forty-seventh Street near Madison—no, it's near Fifth, I guess. But that doesn't matter. I'll take a cab. If I can get one. Did you ever see anything like how hard it is to get a cab nowadays? My dear, last night I was twenty-five minutes trying to get one, and it got me late for dinner, and I *know* they didn't believe me. But if I can't get one I'll walk. It's only a block. And I guess a little exercise wouldn't do me any harm . . . Maillard's. . . . How about the Ritz? No, there's such a jam there. And it's hard to meet. Well, any place *you* say. . . . Oh, Lucille, that's a dreadful place. The food's so—oh, I don't know. You know. So—bad; if you know what I mean. Well, let's take a chance on Maillard's. Only it's so crowded. . . . Oh, no, I never heard that. . . . No, I haven't. I haven't read a thing in months, absolutely months. Where the time goes to I don't know. *I* simply do not know where the time goes to. Lucille, you're sure you've got tomorrow at lunch free? Because if you haven't, or there's something you'd rather do, just say so and we'll try again. Well, suppose we say at Maillard's at—oh, do you know that little tea shop on Forty-seventh? I think it's between Park and Madison on the—let's see—on the downtown, that's the south side of the street. I'll be there by one, or anyway one-thirty, and if I'm there first I'll get a table, and you do the same if you are. But I ought to be there by one. My appointment is for half-past twelve, and it may take me only a few minutes. I might be there before one. But surely by quarter past, and certainly by one-thirty. . . . All right, then. Suppose we say about one, at Maillard's. . . . Oh, no, what am I thinking of? We decided that would be too crowded, didn't we? Unless you'd rather go there. That little tea shop is very nice. . . . Well, yes, I'd just as soon go to Maillard's. It doesn't matter much. It's seeing you I care about. There's a *lot* I want to talk to you about. These little snatches at the telephone are so, well, so sort of unsatisfactory, if you know what I mean. . . . All right, suppose we say Maillard's, then. And then if we don't like the looks of things we can go somewhere else. . . . All right, then, at . . . oh, let's go to the tea room. It's quieter. . . . All right then. I'm longing to see you, Lucille. . . . Tomorrow, then. At the tea shop, that's on Forty-seventh between Park and Madison, on the downtown, that's the south side of the street. Tomorrow, then, about one. That's Wednesday. . . . What? Is it Tuesday? . . . Well, I'm *all* turned around. I thought it was Wednesday. I'm terribly sorry, Lucille. I can't *possibly* meet you tomorrow if it's Tuesday. I've got a luncheon appointment I've had for ages, simply for weeks, and I've postponed it so often I don't dare do it again. . . . You can't Wednesday? I'm terribly sorry. . . . Well, I'll try again. Ring me up. I'll be in all afternoon until five twenty-five, and then I have to go uptown. . . . Yes. . . . Well, I'm glad we had a nice little talk, anyway. . . . And I'll see you soon. . . . What? No, *soon*—S for Sam. . . . Yes, soon. . . . Good-bye, Lucille. . . . Good-bye. Good-bye. Good-bye."

LOVE IN A COTTAGE

NATHANIEL PARKER WILLIS (1807–1867)

They may talk of love in a cottage,
   And bowers of trellised vine—
Of nature bewitchingly simple,
   And milkmaids half divine;
They may talk of the pleasure of sleeping
   In the shade of a spreading tree,
And a walk in the fields at morning,
   By the side of a footstep free.

But give me a sly flirtation
   By the light of a chandelier—
With music to play in the pauses,
   And nobody very near;
Or a seat on a silken sofa,
   With a glass of pure old wine
And mama too blind to discover
   The small white hand in mine.

Your love in a cottage is hungry,
   Your vine is a nest of flies—

Your milkmaid shocks the Graces,
  And simplicity talks of pies!
You lie down to your shady slumber
  And wake with a bug in your ear.
And your damsel that walks in the morning
  Is shod like a mountaineer.

True love is at home on a carpet,
  And mightily likes his ease—
And true love has an eye for a dinner,
  And starves beneath shady trees.
His wing is the fan of a lady,
  His foot's an invisible thing,
And his arrow is tipped with a jewel,
  And shot from a silver string.

THE TIME I'VE LOST IN WOOING

THOMAS MOORE (1779–1852)

The time I've lost in wooing,
In watching and pursuing
    The light that lies
    In woman's eyes,
Has been my heart's undoing.
Tho' Wisdom oft has sought me,
I scorn'd the lore she brought me,
    My only books
    Were women's looks,
And folly's all they taught me.

Her smile when Beauty granted,
I hung with gaze enchanted,
    Like him the Sprite
    Whom maids by night
Oft meet in glen that's haunted.
Like him, too, Beauty won me;
But when the spell was on me,
    If once their ray

Was turn'd away,
O! winds could not outrun me.

And are those follies going?
And is my proud heart growing
　　Too cold or wise
　　For brilliant eyes
Again to set it glowing?
No—vain, alas! th' endeavour
From bonds so sweet to sever;—
　　Poor Wisdom's chance
　　Against a glance
Is now as weak as ever.

THE TRANSFERRED GHOST

FRANK R. STOCKTON

The country residence of Mr. John Hinckman was a delightful place to me, for many reasons. It was the abode of a genial, though somewhat impulsive, hospitality. It had broad, smooth-shaven lawns and towering oaks and elms; there were bosky shades at several points, and not far from the house there was a little rill spanned by a rustic bridge with the bark on; there were fruits and flowers, pleasant people, chess, billiards, rides, walks, and fishing. These were great attractions, but none of them, nor all of them together, would have been sufficient to hold me to the place very long. I had been invited for the trout season, but should probably have finished my visit early in the summer had it not been that upon fair days, when the grass was dry, and the sun was not too hot, and there was but little wind, there strolled beneath the lofty elms, or passed lightly through the bosky shades, the form of my Madeline.

This lady was not, in very truth, my Madeline. She had never given herself to me, nor had I, in any way, acquired possession of her. But, as I considered her possession the only sufficient reason for the continuance of my existence, I called her, in my reveries, mine. It may have been that I would not have been obliged to confine the use of this possessive pronoun to my reveries had I confessed the state of my feelings to the lady.

But this was an unusually difficult thing to do. Not only did I dread, as almost all lovers dread, taking the step which would in an instant put an end to that delightful season which may be termed the ante-interrogatory period of love, and which might at the same time terminate all intercourse or connection with the object of my passion, but I was also dreadfully afraid of John Hinckman. This gentleman was a good friend of mine, but it would have required a bolder man than I was at that time to ask him for the gift of his niece, who was the head of his household, and, according to his own frequent statement, the main prop of his declining years. Had Madeline acquiesced in my general views on the subject, I might have felt encouraged to open the matter to Mr. Hinckman; but, as I said before, I had never asked her whether or not she would be mine. I thought of these things at all hours of the day and night, particularly the latter.

I was lying awake one night, in the great bed in my spacious chamber, when, by the dim light of the new moon, which partially filled the room, I saw John Hinckman standing by a large chair near the door. I was very much surprised at this, for two reasons: in the first place, my host had never before come into my room; and, in the second place, he had gone from home that morning, and had not expected to return for several days. Therefore it was that I had been able that evening to sit much later than usual with Madeline on the moonlit porch. The figure was certainly that of John Hinckman in his ordinary dress, but there was a vagueness and indistinctness about it which presently assured me that it was a ghost. Had the good old man been murdered, and had his spirit come to tell me of the deed, and to confide to me the protection of his dear—? My heart fluttered, but I felt that I must speak. "Sir," said I.

"Do you know," interrupted the figure, with a countenance that indicated anxiety, "whether or not Mr. Hinckman will return to-night?"

I thought it well to maintain a calm exterior, and I answered:

"We do not expect him."

"I am glad of that," said he, sinking into the chair by which he stood. "During the two years and a half that I have inhabited this house, that man has never before been away for a single night. You can't imagine the relief it gives me."

As he spoke he stretched out his legs and leaned back in the chair. His form became less vague, and the colors of his garments more distinct and evident, while an expression of gratified relief succeeded to the anxiety of his countenance.

"Two years and a half!" I exclaimed. "I don't understand you."

"It is fully that length of time," said the ghost, "since I first came here. Mine is not an ordinary case. But before I say anything more about it, let me ask you again if you are sure Mr. Hinckman will not return to-night."

"I am as sure of it as I can be of anything," I answered. "He left to-day for Bristol, two hundred miles away."

"Then I will go on," said the ghost, "for I am glad to have the opportunity of talking to some one who will listen to me. But if John Hinckman should come in and catch me here, I should be frightened out of my wits."

"This is all very strange," I said, greatly puzzled by what I had heard. "Are you the ghost of Mr. Hinckman?"

This was a bold question, but my mind was so full of other emotions that there seemed to be no room for that of fear.

"Yes, I am his ghost," my companion replied, "and yet I have no right to be. And this is what makes me so uneasy and so much afraid of him. It is a strange story, and, I truly believe, without precedent. Two years and a half ago, John Hinckman was dangerously ill in this very room. At one time he was so far gone that he was really believed to be dead. It was in consequence of too precipitate a report in regard to this matter that I was, at that time, appointed to be his ghost. Imagine my surprise and horror, sir, when, after I had accepted the position and assumed its responsibilities, that old man revived, became convalescent, and eventually regained his usual health. My situation was now one of extreme delicacy and embarrassment. I had no power to return to my original unembodiment, and I had no right to be the ghost of a man who was not dead. I was advised by my friends to quietly maintain my position, and was assured, that, as John Hinckman was an elderly man, it could not be long before I could rightfully assume the position for which I had been selected. But I tell you, sir," he continued with animation, "the old fellow seems as vigorous as ever, and I have no idea how much longer this annoying state of things will continue. I spend my time trying to get out of that old man's way. I must not leave this house, and he seems to follow me everywhere. I tell you, sir, he haunts me."

"That is truly a queer state of things," I remarked. "But why are you afraid of him? He couldn't hurt you."

"Of course he couldn't," said the ghost. "But his very presence is a shock and terror to me. Imagine, sir, how you would feel if my case were yours."

I could not imagine such a thing at all. I simply shuddered.

"And if one must be a wrongful ghost at all," the apparition continued, "it would be much pleasanter to be the ghost of some man other than John Hinckman. There is in him an irascibility of temper, accompanied by a facility of invective, which is seldom met with; and what would happen if he were to see me, and find out, as I am sure he would, how long and why I had inhabited his house, I can scarcely conceive. I have seen him in his bursts of passion, and although he did not hurt the people he stormed at any more than he would hurt me, they seemed to shrink before him."

All this I knew to be very true. Had it not been for this peculiarity of Mr. Hinckman, I might have been more willing to talk to him about his niece.

"I feel sorry for you," I said, for I really began to have a sympathetic feeling toward this unfortunate apparition. "Your case is indeed a hard one. It reminds me of those persons who have had doubles; and I suppose a man would often be very angry indeed when he found that there was another being who was personating himself."

"Oh, the cases are not similar at all," said the ghost. "A double, or doppelganger, lives on the earth with a man, and being exactly like him, he makes all sorts of trouble, of course. It is very different with me. I am not here to live with Mr. Hinckman. I am here to take his place. Now, it would make John Hinckman very angry if he knew that. Don't you know it would?"

I assented promptly.

"Now that he is away, I can be easy for a little while," continued the ghost, "and I am so glad to have an opportunity of talking to you. I have frequently come into your room and watched you while you slept, but did not dare to speak to you for fear that if you talked with me Mr. Hinckman would hear you, and come into the room to know why you were talking to yourself."

"But would he not hear you?" I asked.

"Oh, no!" said the other. "There are times when any one may see me, but no one hears me except the person to whom I address myself."

"But why did you wish to speak to me?" I asked.

"Because," replied the ghost, "I like occasionally to talk to people, and especially to some one like yourself, whose mind is so troubled and perturbed that you are not likely to be frightened by a visit from one of us. But I particularly want to ask you to do me a favor. There is every probability, so far as I can see, that John Hinckman will live a long time, and my situation is becoming insupportable. My great object at present is to get myself transferred, and I think that you may, perhaps, be of use to me."

"Transferred!" I exclaimed. "What do you mean by that?"

"What I mean," said the other, "is this: now that I have started on my career, I have got to be the ghost of somebody, and I want to be the ghost of a man who is really dead."

"I should think that would be easy enough," I said. "Opportunities must continually occur."

"Not at all! Not at all!" said my companion, quickly. "You have no idea what a rush and pressure there is for situations of this kind. Whenever a vacancy occurs, if I may express myself in that way, there are crowds of applications for the ghostship."

"I had no idea that such a state of things existed," I said, becoming quite interested in the matter. "There ought to be some regular system, or order of precedence, by which you could all take your turns, like customers in a barber's shop."

"Oh, dear, that would never do at all!" said the other. "Some of us would have to wait forever. There is always a great rush whenever a good ghostship offers itself—while, as you know, there are some positions that no one would care for. It was in consequence of my being in too great a hurry on an occasion of the kind that I got myself into my present disagreeable predicament, and I have thought that it might be possible that you would help me out of it. You might know of a case where an opportunity for a ghostship was not generally expected, but which might present itself at any moment. If you would give me a short notice, I know I could arrange for a transfer."

"What do you mean?" I exclaimed. "Do you want me to commit suicide or to undertake a murder for your benefit?"

"Oh, no, no, no!" said the other, with a vapory smile. "I mean nothing of that kind. To be sure, there are lovers who are watched with considerable interest, such persons having been known, in moments of depression, to offer very desirable ghostships, but I did not think of anything of that kind in connection with you. You were the only person I cared to speak to, and I hoped that you might give me some information that would be of use; and, in return, I shall be very glad to help you in your love affair."

"You seem to know that I have such an affair," I said.

"Oh, yes!" replied the other, with a little yawn. "I could not be here so much as I have been without knowing all about that."

There was something horrible in the idea of Madeline and myself having been watched by a ghost, even, perhaps, when we wandered together in the most delightful and bosky places. But then, this was quite an exceptional ghost, and I could not have the objections to him which would ordinarily arise in regard to beings of his class.

"I must go now," said the ghost, rising, "but I will see you some-where to-morrow night; and remember—you help me, and I'll help you."

I had doubts the next morning as to the propriety of telling Made-line anything about this interview, and soon convinced myself that I must keep silent on the subject. If she knew there was a ghost about the house, she would probably leave the place instantly. I did not mention the matter, and so regulated my demeanor that I am quite sure Madeline never suspected what had taken place.

For some time I had wished that Mr. Hinckman would absent him-self, for a day at least, from the premises. In such case I thought I might more easily nerve myself up to the point of speaking to Made-line on the subject of our future collateral existence. But now that the opportunity for such speech had really occurred, I did not feel ready to avail myself of it. What would become of me if she refused me?

I had an idea, however, that the lady thought that if I were going to speak at all, this was the time. She must have known that certain sentiments were afloat within me, and she was not unreasonable in her wish to see the matter settled one way or the other. But I did not feel like taking a bold step in the dark. If she wished me to ask her to give herself to me, she ought to offer me some reason to suppose that she would make the gift. If I saw no probability of such generosity, I would prefer that things should remain as they were.

That evening I was sitting with Madeline on the moonlit porch. It was nearly ten o'clock, and ever since supper-time I had been working myself up to the point of making an avowal of my sentiments. I had not positively determined to do this, but wished gradually to reach the proper point when, if the prospect looked bright, I might speak. My companion appeared to understand the situation—at least, I imag-ined that the nearer I came to a proposal the more she seemed to ex-pect it. It was certainly a very critical and important epoch in my life. If I spoke, I should make myself happy or miserable forever; and if I did not speak, I had every reason to believe that the lady would not give me another chance to do so.

Sitting thus with Madeline, talking a little, and thinking very hard over these momentous matters, I looked up and saw the ghost, not a dozen feet away from us. He was sitting on the railing of the porch, one leg thrown up before him, the other dangling down as he leaned against a post. He was behind Madeline, but almost in front of me, as I sat facing the lady. It was fortunate that Madeline was looking out over the landscape, for I must have appeared very much startled. The ghost had told me that he would see me some time this night, but I did not think he would make his appearance when I was in the company of Madeline. If she should see the spirit of her uncle, I could not answer for the consequences. I made no exclamation, but the ghost evidently saw that I was troubled.

"Don't be afraid," he said; "I shall not let her see me, and she cannot hear me speak unless I address myself to her, which I do not intend to do."

I suppose I looked grateful.

"So you need not trouble yourself about that," the ghost continued. "But it seems to me that you are not getting along very well with your affair. If I were you, I should speak out without waiting any longer. You will never have a better chance. You are not likely to be interrupted, and, so far as I can judge, the lady seems disposed to listen to you favorably—that is, if she ever intends to do so. There is no knowing when John Hinckman will go away again; certainly not this summer. If I were in your place, I should never dare to make love to Hinckman's niece if he were anywhere about the place. If he should catch any one offering himself to Miss Madeline, he would then be a terrible man to encounter."

I agreed perfectly to all this.

"I cannot bear to think of him!" I ejaculated aloud.

"Think of whom?" asked Madeline, turning quickly toward me.

Here was an awkward situation. The long speech of the ghost, to which Madeline paid no attention, but which I heard with perfect distinctness, had made me forget myself.

It was necessary to explain quickly. Of course, it would not do to admit that it was of her dear uncle that I was speaking, and so I mentioned hastily the first name I thought of.

"Mr. Vilars," I said.

This statement was entirely correct, for I never could bear to think of Mr. Vilars, who was a gentleman who had, at various times, paid much attention to Madeline.

"It is wrong for you to speak in that way of Mr. Vilars," she said. "He is a remarkably well educated and sensible young man, and has very pleasant manners. He expects to be elected to the legislature this fall, and I should not be surprised if he made his mark. He will do well in a legislative body, for whenever Mr. Vilars has anything to say he knows just how and when to say it."

This was spoken very quietly, and without any show of resentment, which was all very natural, for if Madeline thought at all favorably of me she could not feel displeased that I should have disagreeable emotions in regard to a possible rival. The concluding words contained a hint which I was not slow to understand. I felt very sure that if Mr. Vilars were in my present position he would speak quickly enough.

"I know it is wrong to have such ideas about a person," I said, "but I cannot help it."

The lady did not chide me, and after this she seemed even in a softer mood. As for me, I felt considerably annoyed, for I had not wished to admit that any thought of Mr. Vilars had ever occupied my mind.

"You should not speak aloud that way." said the ghost, "or you may get yourself into trouble. I want to see everything go well with you, because then you may be disposed to help me, especially if I should chance to be of any assistance to you, which I hope I shall be."

I longed to tell him that there was no way in which he could help me so much as by taking his instant departure. To make love to a young lady with a ghost sitting on the railing near by, and that ghost the apparition of a much-dreaded uncle, the very idea of whom in such a position and at such a time made me tremble, was a difficult, if not an impossible, thing to do. But I forbore to speak, although I may have looked my mind.

"I suppose," continued the ghost, "that you have not heard anything that might be of advantage to me. Of course, I am very anxious to hear, but if you have anything to tell me, I can wait until you are alone. I will come to you to-night in your room, or I will stay here until the lady goes away."

"You need not wait here," I said; "I have nothing at all to say to you."

Madeline sprang to her feet, her face flushed and her eyes ablaze.

"Wait here!" she cried. "What do you suppose I am waiting for? Nothing to say to me, indeed! I should think so! What should you have to say to me?"

"Madeline," I exclaimed, stepping toward her, "let me explain." But she had gone.

Here was the end of the world for me! I turned fiercely to the ghost.

"Wretched existence!" I cried, "you have ruined everything. You have blackened my whole life! Had it not been for you—"

But here my voice faltered. I could say no more.

"You wrong me," said the ghost. "I have not injured you. I have tried only to encourage and assist you, and it is your own folly that has done this mischief. But do not despair. Such mistakes as these can be explained. Keep up a brave heart. Good-by."

And he vanished from the railing like a bursting soap-bubble.

I went gloomily to bed, but I saw no apparitions that night except those of despair and misery which my wretched thoughts called up. The words I had uttered had sounded to Madeline like the basest insult. Of course, there was only one interpretation she could put upon them.

As to explaining my ejaculations, that was impossible. I thought the matter over and over again as I lay awake that night, and I determined that I would never tell Madeline the facts of the case. It would be better for me to suffer all my life than for her to know that the ghost of her uncle haunted the house. Mr. Hinckman was away, and if she knew of his ghost she could not be made to believe that he was not dead. She might not survive the shock! No, my heart might bleed, but I would never tell her.

The next day was fine, neither too cool nor too warm. The breezes were gentle, and nature smiled. But there were no walks or rides with Madeline. She seemed to be much engaged during the day, and I saw but little of her. When we met at meals she was polite, but very quiet and reserved. She had evidently determined on a course of conduct, and had resolved to assume that, although I had been very rude to her, she did not understand the import of my words. It would be quite proper, of course, for her not to know what I meant by my expressions of the night before.

I was downcast and wretched, and said but little, and the only bright streak across the black horizon of my woe was the fact that she did not appear to be happy, although she affected an air of unconcern. The moonlit porch was deserted that evening, but wandering about the house, I found Madeline in the library alone. She was reading, but I went in and sat down near her. I felt that, although I could not do so fully, I must in a measure explain my conduct of the night before. She listened quietly to a somewhat labored apology I made for the words I had used.

"I have not the slightest idea what you meant," she said, "but you were very rude."

I earnestly disclaimed any intention of rudeness, and assured her, with a warmth of speech that must have made some impression upon her, that rudeness to her would be an action impossible to me. I said a great deal upon the subject, and implored her to believe that if it were not for a certain obstacle I could speak to her so plainly that she would understand everything.

She was silent for a time, and then she said, rather more kindly, I thought, than she had spoken before:

"Is that obstacle in any way connected with my uncle?"

"Yes," I answered, after a little hesitation, "it is, in a measure, connected with him."

She made no answer to this, and sat looking at her book, but not reading. From the expression of her face, I thought she was somewhat softened toward me. She knew her uncle as well as I did, and she may have been thinking that if he were the obstacle that prevented my speaking (and there were many ways in which he might be that obstacle), my position would be such a hard one that it would excuse some wildness of speech and eccentricity of manner. I saw, too, that the warmth of my partial explanations had had some effect on her, and I began to believe that it might be a good thing for me to speak my mind without delay. No matter how she should receive my proposition, my relations with her could not be worse than they had been the previous night and day, and there was something in her face which encouraged me to hope that she might forget my foolish exclamations of the evening before if I began to tell her my tale of love.

I drew my chair a little nearer to her, and as I did so the ghost burst into the room from the doorway behind her. I say burst, although no door flew open and he made no noise. He was wildly excited, and waved his arms above his head. The moment I saw him, my heart fell within me. With the entrance of that impertinent apparition, every hope fled from me. I could not speak while he was in the room.

I must have turned pale, and I gazed steadfastly at the ghost, almost without seeing Madeline, who sat between us.

"Do you know," he cried, "that John Hinckman is coming up the hill? He will be here in fifteen minutes, and if you are doing anything in the way of love-making, you had better hurry it up. But this is not what I came to tell you. I have glorious news! At last I am transferred! Not forty minutes ago a Russian nobleman was murdered by the Nihilists. Nobody ever thought of him in connection with an immediate ghostship. My friends instantly applied for the situation for me, and obtained my transfer. I am off before that horrid Hinckman comes up the hill. The moment I reach my new position, I shall put off this hated semblance. Good-by! You can't imagine how glad I am to be, at last, the real ghost of somebody."

"Oh!" I cried, rising to my feet and stretching out my arms in utter wretchedness, "I would to Heaven you were mine!"

"I *am* yours," said Madeline, raising to me her tearful eyes.

ASK AND HAVE

SAMUEL LOVER (1797–1868)

"Oh, 'tis time I should talk to your mother,
  Sweet Mary," says I;
"Oh, don't talk to my mother," says Mary,
  Beginning to cry:
"For my mother says men are deceivers,
  And never, I know, will consent;
She says girls in a hurry who marry,
  At leisure repent."

"Then, suppose I would talk to your father,
  Sweet Mary," says I;
"Oh, don't talk to my father," says Mary,
  Beginning to cry:
"For my father, he loves me so dearly,
  He'll never consent I should go—
If you talk to my father," says Mary,
  "He'll surely say, 'No.'"

"Then how shall I get you, my jewel?
  Sweet Mary," says I;
"If your father and mother's so cruel,
  Most surely I'll die!"
"Oh, never say die, dear," says Mary;
  "A way now to save you I see;
Since my parents are both so contrary—
  You'd better ask *me!*"

. . . or Married:

MY WIFE NEVER LOOKS AT GAUGES

PHILIP MINOFF

Remember the news item predicting a day when one tablespoon of atomic energy would send a huge ocean liner back and forth across the Atlantic (even if it didn't want to go)?

Well, I watched my wife's expression as she was reading that story, and she didn't even bat an eyelash. What's more, I didn't bat an eyelash at her failure to bat an eyelash, for I know the way her mind works. The plain truth is that she never thought of ocean liners as requiring any fuel at all.

I know that's so, because she thinks exactly the same thing about the car she drives. She is, in short, a creature who never for a moment stops to ponder the force that moves her vehicle from the warm security of our garage to the swift completion of her appointed rounds.

To say that she's indifferent to the gadgets on the dashboard would be the rawest kind of understatement. She's convinced that thingama-bobs like fuel indicators, oil-pressure gauges, ammeters and thermom-eters were installed as optional (and wholly irrelevant) equipment— for the sole benefit of the curly-haired salesman who sold us the car.

No man can fully appreciate this wifely quirk unless he has, on some hurried morning, jumped behind the wheel of his chariot; turned on the ignition; pressed the starter, and listened in vain for the engine to come to life. A quick, fearful look at the gasoline gauge (ignored by his spouse during the past three days she'd monopolized the vehicle) confirms his worst suspicions. As he runs to catch the bus that may possibly get him to the 7:58 in time, his mind is alive with lovely thoughts of justifiable uxoricide.

There was one occasion, a couple of years ago, when a service station man drained all the old oil out of our engine but inadvertently failed to replace it with new oil. This was a human slip anyone could make (as his lawyer later told our lawyer) but it would not have had such deadly results if my wife had looked at the oil-pressure gauge before picking the car up at the service station. As it was, she drove it some seven miles in that condition, and stopped only because the vehicle itself refused to go an inch further.

"But didn't you hear any funny noises during all those seven miles?" I asked her, after calling the local junkyard.

"I was with Ursula Simmons," was her answer. "When you're with Ursula, you don't hear anything but Ursula."

Then, one torrid day last summer, I returned home from the office to hear another tale of woe about another of our cars—a more recent acquisition. "She behaved terribly today," complained the wife. "The radiator was smoking all the way from Valley Stream to Oceanside. I thought she'd explode."

"Didn't you look at the temperature gauge?" I asked.

"Oh," she replied. "I thought that was important only in the winter."

That last rejoinder might make a little sense if she did, indeed, make a practice of glancing at the thermometer on the dashboard during the winter-time, but she's never done anything of the kind. You know she hasn't.

For a while, I'm proud to say, I did manage to persuade her to take a peek at the ammeter from time to time, but that was pretty fruitless, too, because she never knew what it meant. The concepts of "charge" and "discharge" confused her no end, and when the needle was *exactly* in the center of the dial, she'd go to pieces completely.

"Well, if you're so smart," she'd challenge, "what *is* the battery doing when it's neither charging nor discharging?" A good question, I suppose, and she had a perfect right to get an answer. I'm just not the guy to give it to her, that's all.

In a way, of course, I think I'm being too harsh on the old gal. Things could be much worse. Suppose, for example, our kitchen walls at home were lined with gauges telling her when to replenish our food supply. Why, within four weeks the whole family would be looking like schoolboys out of a Dickens novel, and we'd find ourselves being interviewed by a steady stream of sob-sisters from the *New York Post*.

It goes without saying that my wife loudly denies this groundless charge. She insists she's just as vigilant as the next woman, which can cost me an automobile every three months. "I've changed," she assured me a while ago. "I really pay attention to all those clocks on the dashboard now."

I have no way of checking on her when she's driving alone (or even when she's with Ursula Simmons), so I devised a scheme. I cut out a long piece of cardboard and, after providing slits for the ignition switch and the headlight knobs, taped the whole thing to the dashboard, covering every gauge in sight.

Then, across the full expanse of this cardboard shield, I wrote in bold, black crayon, "Unless you ask me about this sometime before March 1, I'm leaving the house forever." Well, that was three weeks ago, and nary a word about it from her. The thought that she hasn't noticed the cardboard in all this time simply horrifies me. There's only one possibility that's more frightening. Maybe she has.

THE CO-OPERATIVE HOUSEKEEPERS

ELLIOTT FLOWER

Ten thoughtful women, ever wise,
A wondrous scheme did once devise
For ease, and to economize.

"Co-operation!" was their cry,
And not a husband dared deny
'Twould life and labor simplify.

One gardener, the ten decreed,
Was all the neighborhood would need
To plant and trim and rake and weed.

The money saved they could invest
As vagrant fancy might suggest,
And each could then be better dressed.

So well this worked that, on the whole,
It seemed to them extremely droll
To pay so much for handling coal.

One man all work then undertook,
And former methods they forsook,
Deciding even on one cook.

One dining-room was next in line,
Where, free from care, they all could dine
At less expense, as you'll divine.

"Two maids," they said, "could quickly flit
From home to home, so why permit
Expense that brings no benefit?"

Economy of cash and care
Became a hobby of the fair,
Until their husbands sought a share.

"Although," the latter said, "all goes
For luxuries and costly clothes,
The method still advantage shows.

"While we've not gained, we apprehend
Good Fortune will on us attend,
If we continue to the end.

"If you've succeeded, why should we
From constant toil be never free?
One income should sufficient be;

"And, taking turns in earning that,
We'll have the leisure to wax fat
And spend much time in idle chat.

"So let us see the matter through,
And, in this line, it must be true
One house for all will surely do.

"And if one house means less of strife,
To gain the comforts of this life,
Why, further progress means one wife."

. . . . . .

Ten women now, their acts attest,
Prefer ten homes, and deem it best
To let co-operation rest.

FRITZ WILKINSON, LOOK

"This is my big surprise—I'm going to make all our furniture."

TAKE TWO CANS OF TUNA . . .

BYRON FISH

Wives who fuss about the high cost of groceries must not read the food sections of women's magazines. For years, the home economists have been telling how to prepare a tasty, low-cost meal with the most inexpensive cuts of meat, or with a can of tuna.

The recipes work, too. I tried one myself, and saved so much money we just don't know what to do with it.

Ordinarily I'm not the cook, but on Thursday evenings my wife throws pots. She goes to a ceramics class and pats her hands in the mud as a sort of therapy for having to cope with three small sons and a husband.

Last Thursday she had to go to town in the afternoon and was worried over how she'd return to prepare dinner and still get to class on time. I said never mind, I'd fix the meal. She agreed I'd fix it good.

She wanted to coach me about the menu, but I waved her away.

"You've got several cookbooks and a whole file of recipes," I said. "Anybody who can read can cook."

She gave a last, sad look around the kitchen, murmured something about wanting to remember it the way it was, and left.

Her attitude was inspired by seeing too many cartoons about husbands messing up the kitchen. Actually, I'm quite adept at cooking with no fuss or pans, having at times prepared a whole meal with one old coffee can and a forked stick.

This time, though, I decided to add more of an epicurean touch, so I pawed through the recipes my wife always is snipping and storing in a drawer. I doubt if women who do this ever read the clippings again, and I ascribe their scissors work to a hangover from the days when they cut out paper dolls.

Most of the suggestions I found seemed to come under the heading of low-budget meals, or what to do with leftovers. The home economists must be kept busy cooking leftovers so they can use them up in recipes.

We didn't seem to have enough leftovers for a real gourmet dish, so I resolved to start from the foundation. The clipping that caught my eye was entitled "Take a Can of Tuna . . ." and it went on to describe a budget-saver called Tuna Molto Vivace.

Although it could be "thrown together quickly, any evening," its name showed it was no ordinary fish dish, but something worthy of a chef. Besides, the color illustration looked good enough to eat.

Although it was only midafternoon, I had the foresight to glance through the ingredients and check them against what we had on hand.

Sure enough, the recipe called for things we didn't have, such as half a pint of whipping cream, champagne, imported cheese, and shrimp crisps. My wife is not too careful about keeping up her inventory of stock items.

I rounded up the boys and drove to the store. It took a little longer than I had figured, because we learned that ordinary grocery stores didn't carry all the ingredients and we had to find a specialty delicatessen.

After this loss of time, I thought it best to begin preparations immediately upon return to the house. I took the first step, opening a can of tuna and putting it in a dish.

The boys were curious about my action. "Why are you doing that, Daddy?" they chorused.

"I'm going to get dinner," I told them, smiling confidently.

At this revelation, the oldest, a first-grader, giggled skeptically. "Aw, you're kidding," he said.

The three-year-old asked in alarm, "When's Mama coming back?"

"She's staying in town for school," I said. "The four of us will have a stag dinner. Won't that be fun?"

He showed how much fun he thought it would be. He bawled, "I want dinner! When's Mama going to get dinner?"

"*Daddy* is going to get dinner," I snarled. "Now, stand back."

I got out eight eggs and put them on to hard-boil. The recipe said they should be marinated in the champagne before they were stuffed.

"If the eggs are packed in a small container," the directions read, "so they can be covered with a minimum of wine, the remainder of the champagne may be served with the meal."

It was a good example, I thought, of how planning ahead can result in worthwhile economies.

As long as there'd be champagne left over, I sipped some and turned to mixing the whipped cream, chopped olives, dry mustard, and Roquefort for stuffing the eggs.

"If you have more stuffing than you need," I read, "don't throw it away. The thrifty housewife makes use of leftovers. Placed on shrimp crisps, the mixture provides a delicious hors d'oeuvre."

I reached for the crisps, but they had disappeared. Now that I noticed it, so had the boys. A trail of shrimp crumbs led to a closet and a muffled thumping inside. I shrugged and returned to look up the next step.

"Meanwhile," it said, "you have boiled two cups of wild rice."

Meanwhile, I'd done no such thing. Cooking the rice delayed dinner for a while, but the boys were full of shrimp crisps and I drank some more champagne to keep it from going flat.

When the rice was almost done, I added the half pound of butter, for flavor, that the recipe called for.

"For sauce," it went on, "melt the other half pound butter in a hot pan, add mushrooms, a dash of sweet basil, white wine vinegar, cubed green peppers, and a handful of fine herbs. Pour the sauce on the rice."

Having bought these items earlier, I was able to complete the simple casserole dish shortly after nightfall. I might have done it faster, but the boys kept distracting me with their raids on the breadbox and the milk.

"When is Mama coming home?" they wailed. "We're hungry."

"Wash your hands and sit down," I ordered. "Dinner is ready." I showed them a casserole almost as pretty as the illustration.

"Can I have some peanut butter?" the five-year-old asked.

I shoved him into his place and was about to dish up when I remembered one more step. I'd forgotten the tuna.

After all, the tuna was what made it an economical meal. I whisked the dish away and put in two cans of tuna. That way, I saved twice as much money.

I finished what champagne was left, to keep it from going to waste, and ate three portions of Tuna Molto Vivace. It tasted fine, something like a tuna casserole.

The boys ate a little of it. "Now can we have a peanut butter sandwich?" they pleaded. I made them the sandwiches. They're a little young, anyway, to have developed the refined palate of an epicure.

When my wife got home, she peered into the casserole with a puzzled expression. Quite a bit of the entree remained. "What am I going to do with this . . . this whatever it is?" she asked.

"Why," I said, "you have lots of clippings on how to use leftovers."

But her question made me think. It's no wonder women complain about the food bill when they don't take the advice they're offered on the economical planning of meals.

TWO HUSBANDS

CAROLYN WELLS

Once on a Time there were Two Men, each of whom married the Woman of his Choice. One Man devoted all his Energies to Getting Rich.

He was so absorbed in Acquiring Wealth that he Worked Night and Day to Accomplish his End.

By this Means he lost his Health, he became a Nervous Wreck, and was so Irritable and Irascible that his Wife Ceased to live with him and Returned to her Parents' House.

The Other Man made no Efforts to Earn Money, and after he had spent his own and his Wife's Fortunes, Poverty Stared Them in the Face.

Although his Wife had loved him Fondly, she could not Continue her affection toward One who could not Support her, so she left him and Returned to her Childhood's Home.

Morals:

This Fable teaches that the Love of Money is the Root of All Evil, and that When Poverty Comes In At the Door, Love Flies Out Of the Window.

JUST LEAVE A NOTE, HONEY

DICK ASHBAUGH

Whenever I come in at night to be greeted by a pear-shaped silence, I know that somewhere around the house there will be a note. These little documents are remarkable for their brevity and whimsey.

One beauty I've picked at random reads: I'M AT MOTHER'S. WATCH FOR EGG MAN. FEED DOG. WHEN EGG MAN COMES PUT HIM IN THE BASEMENT. HEARD FUNNY NOISE IN CHIMNEY TODAY. DO YOU SUPPOSE A BIRD IS IN THERE? BAKED BEANS IN THE OVEN.

It was obvious from this communiqué that I was in for a ticklish evening. A bird in the chimney, baked beans in the oven and either the egg man or the dog, or both, locked in the basement and snarling at each other. As I remember, I put the dog in the attic, locked the egg man in the garage, put my hair up in curlers and went to bed with a good book.

One item of last summer that was worked into a tea towel with colored thread said: IF YOU GET HOME EARLY, WE'VE GONE SWIMMING. IF YOU GET HOME LATE, WE'LL BE BACK BY THEN AND I'LL HAVE DINNER READY. I spent several days trying to forget that one.

Sometimes the notes will come in series. They start at the front door and cancel each other out as they go through the house. One set that I've had mounted read like this: GONE TO CLUB. MAN CALLED ABOUT NOON. VERY URGENT. HE WAS BREATHING HARD, BUT WOULDN'T LEAVE NUMBER. DO YOU OWE SOMEONE MONEY? This little jewel was on the hall table just inside the door. A second note lying on the desk in the living room said: MAY NOT GO TO CLUB TODAY. BREATHING MAN CALLED AGAIN AT TWO. THINK BABY SWALLOWED ONE OF MY EARRINGS.

Prowling on through the house in a slight daze, I came into the kitchen. My wife was standing at the sink, peeling onions.

"Hello," she said. "It wasn't an earring after all. It was a button. I called the doctor and he said not to worry."

"That's nice," I said. "What about the breathing man?"

"Oh, him," she said. "Didn't you read my note? It's on the telephone stand."

I went back in and read the note.

This one said: FORGET ABOUT BREATHING MAN. HE HAD YOU MIXED UP WITH SOMEONE WHO WANTED TO RENT A HOUSE. DECIDED NOT TO GO TO THE CLUB TODAY.

With measured tread I walked back through the kitchen.

"Don't go away," said my wife. "Dinner will be ready in a few minutes."

"I'll be out in the back yard," I said.

"Okay," she answered. "I'll call you when we're ready."

"Send me a note," I said.

HEZEKIAH BEDOTT'S OPINION

FRANCES M. WHICHER

He was a wonderful hand to moralize, husband was, 'specially after he begun to enjoy poor health. He made an observation once when he was in one of his poor turns, that I never shall forget the longest day I live. He says to me one winter evenin' as we was a settin' by the fire,—I was a knittin' (I was always a wonderful great knitter) and he was a smokin' (he was a master hand to smoke, though the doctor used to tell him he'd be better off to let tobacker alone; when he was well he used to take his pipe and smoke a spell after he'd got the chores done up, and when he wa'n't well, used to smoke the biggest part of the time). Well, he took his pipe out of his mouth and turned toward me, and I knowed something was comin', for he had a pertikkeler way of lookin' round when he was gwine to say anything oncommon. Well, he says to me, says he, "Silly" (my name was Prissilly naterally but he ginerally called me "Silly," cause 'twas handier, you know). Well, he says to me, says he, "Silly," and he looked pretty sollem, I tell you—he had a sollem countenance naterally—and after he got to be deacon 'twas more so, but since he'd lost his health he looked sollemer than ever, and certainly you wouldent wonder at it if you knowed how much he underwent. He was troubled with a wonderful pain in his chest, and amazin' weakness in the spine of his back, besides the pleurissy in the side, and having the ager a considerable part of the time, and bein' broke of his rest o' nights 'cause he was so put to't for breath when he laid down. Why it's an onaccountable fact that when that man died he hadent seen a well day in fifteen year, though when he was married and for five or six years after I shouldent desire to see a ruggeder man than he was. But the time I'm speakin' of he'd been out o' health nigh upon ten year, and O dear sakes! how he had altered since the first time I ever see him! That was to a quiltin' to Squire Smith's a spell afore Sally was married. I'd no idee then that Sal Smith was a gwine to be married to Sam Pendergrass. She'd ben keepin' company with Mose Hewlitt, for better'n a year, and everybody said *that* was a settled thing, and lo and behold! all of a sudding she up and took Sam Pendergrass. Well, that was the first time I ever see my husband, and if anybody'd a told me then that I should ever marry him, I should a said—but lawful sakes! I most forgot, I was gwine to tell you what he said to me that evenin', and when a body begins to tell a thing I believe in finishin' on't some time or other. Some folks have a way of talkin' round and round and round forevermore, and never come to the pint. Now there's Miss Jinkins, she that was Poll Bingham afore she was married, she is the tejusest individooal to tell a story that ever I see in all my born days. But I was a gwine to tell you what husband said. He says to me, says he, "Silly"; says I, "What?" I dident say, "What, Hezekier?" for I dident like his name. The first time I ever heard it I near killed myself a laffin. "Hezekier Bedott," says I, "well, I would give up if I had sich a name," but then you know I had no more idee o' marryin' the feller than you had this minnit o' marryin' the governor. I s'pose you think it's curus we should a named our oldest son Hezekiah. Well, we done it to please father and mother Bedott; it's father Bedott's name, and he and mother Bedott both used to think that names had ought to go down from gineration to gineration. But we always called him Kier, you know. Speakin' o' Kier, he is a blessin', ain't he? and I ain't the only one that thinks so, I guess. Now don't you never tell nobody that I said so, but between you and me I rather guess that if Kezier Winkle thinks she is a gwine to ketch Kier Bedott she is a *leetle* out of her reckonin'. But I was going to tell what husband said. He says to me,

says he, "Silly"; I says, says I, "What?" If I dident say "what" when he
said "Silly" he'd a kept on saying "Silly," from time to eternity. He
always did, because you know, he wanted me to pay pertikkeler attention, and I ginerally did; no woman was ever more attentive to her
husband than what I was. Well, he says to me, says he, "Silly." Says
I, "What?" tho I'd no idee what he was gwine to say, dident know
but what 'twas something about his sufferings, though he wa'n't apt
to complain, but he frequently used to remark that he wouldent wish
his worst enemy to suffer one minnit as he did all the time: but that
can't be called grumblin'—think it can? Why I've seen him in
sitivations when you'd a thought no mortal could a helped grumblin';
but *he* dident. He and me went once in the dead of winter in a one-
hoss shay out to Boonville to see a sister o' hisen. You know the snow
is amazin' deep in that section o' the kentry. Well, the hoss got stuck
in one o' them are flambergasted snow-banks, and there we sot, onable
to stir, and to cap all, while we was a sittin' there, husband was took
with a dretful crik in his back. Now *that* was what I call a perdicker-
ment, don't you? Most men would a swore, but husband dident. He
only said, says he, "Consarn it." How did we get out, did you ask?
Why we might a been sittin' there to this day fur as I know, if there
hadent a happened to come along a mess o' men in a double team,
and they hysted us out. But I was gwine to tell you that observation of
hisen. Says he to me, says he, "Silly" (I could see by the light o' the
fire, there dident happen to be no candle burnin', if I don't disre-
member, though my memory is sometimes ruther forgitful, but I know
we wa'n't apt to burn candles exceptin' when we had company)—I
could see by the light of the fire that his mind was oncommon sol-
emnized. Says he to me, says he, "Silly." I says to him, says I, "What?"
He says to me, "*We're all poor critters!*"

A BRIDE'S DREAM

ANONYMOUS

Brundy has been married two weeks, and has left his wife. Brundy
is a little man, and his wife weighs two hundred and forty pounds,
and was the relict of the late Peter Potts. About ten days after mar-

riage Brundy was surprised, on awakening in the morning, to find his better half sitting up in bed, crying as if her heart would break.

Astonished, he asked the cause of her sorrow, but receiving no reply he began to surmise that there must be some secret on her mind that she withheld from him, that was the cause of her anguish; so he remarked to Mrs. B. that as they were married she should tell him the cause of her grief, so, if possible, he could avert it, and after considerable coaxing he elicited the following from her:

"Last night I dreamed I was single, and as I walked through a well-lighted street I came to a store where a sign in front advertised husbands for sale. Thinking it curious I entered, and ranged along the wall on either side were men with prices affixed to them. Such beautiful men; some for $1,000, some for $500, and so on to $150. And as I had not that amount I could not purchase."

Thinking to console her, Brundy placed his arm lovingly around her, and asked: "And did you see any men like me there?"

"Oh, yes," she replied, drawing away from him, "lots like you; they were tied up in bunches like asparagus and sold for ten cents per bunch."

Brundy got up, and went to ask his lawyer if he had sufficient grounds for divorce.

LOVE'S MOODS AND SENSES

ANONYMOUS

Sally Salter, she was a young lady who taught,
And her friend Charley Church was a preacher who praught!
Though his enemies called him a screecher who scraught.

His heart when he saw her kept sinking and sunk,
And his eye, meeting hers, began winking and wunk;
While she in her turn fell to thinking, and thunk.

He hastened to woo her, and sweetly he wooed,
For his love grew until to a mountain it grewed,
And what he was longing to do then he doed.

In secret he wanted to speak, and he spoke,
To seek with his lips what his heart long had soke;
So he managed to let the truth leak, and it loke.

He asked her to ride to the church, and they rode,
They so sweetly did glide, that they both thought they glode,
And they came to the place to be tied, and were tode.

Then, "Homeward" he said, "let us drive" and they drove,
And soon as they wished to arrive, they arrove;
For whatever he couldn't contrive she controve.

The kiss he was dying to steal, then he stole:
At the feet where he wanted to kneel, then he knole,
And said, "I feel better than ever I fole."

So they to each other kept clinging, and clung;
While time his swift circuit was winging, and wung;
And this was the thing he was bringing, and brung:

The man Sally wanted to catch, and had caught—
That she wanted from others to snatch, and had snaught—
Was the one that she now liked to scratch and she scraught.

And Charley's warm love began freezing, and froze,
While he took to teasing, and cruelly toze
The girl he had wished to be squeezing and squoze.

"Wretch!" he cried, when she threatened to leave him, and left,
"How could you deceive me, as you have deceft?"
And she answered, "I promised to cleave, and I've cleft!"

YOU CAN'T CURE AN EPICURE

SCOTT CORBETT

Well, I came home after a hard day to find the table set with real cloth napkins and my wife polishing the silver candlesticks.

"Who's coming?"

"Nobody. Just you and I," she said sweetly. "We're going to have a real gourmet's dinner."

"A what?"

"I've been cleaning out the icebox and checking what's in the freezer and I found all sorts of interesting things you've insisted on buying from time to time. I decided we'd simply let ourselves go tonight and have a real spread."

There were even little nut dishes at each place, but the stuff in them did not look like nuts.

"What's this?"

"Oh, that's pieces of raw coconut from the dried-up half of the one you said you were so fond of. But don't get into that yet—we're going to start off with *hors d'oeuvres*. We're having stale goat cheese on Swedish hardtack, or whatever you call that stuff, plus pickled mussels and the five imported Mexican cherry peppers we still have left from the half-dozen you decided it would be fun to try."

"That's a very happy thought," I said heartily, not wanting her to think she was bothering me any. None of it sounded very good, somehow, but I figured that would be that and then we would sit down to a good dinner. Thursdays we generally had pork chops, cream gravy, and mashed potatoes, or something of the sort.

"I'm glad you're happy, because I've worked hard on this," said my wife. "Next we're going to sit down to a steaming bowl of Czechoslovakian cucumber soup. Fortunately I was going through our canned goods today, too, and came across the can you bought last year. It was 89¢ a can then, but I'll bet it's even more now, so it's a good thing you looked ahead. Then we're having melted cheese on toast made out of all the hunks of cheese you never finish up before you buy more cheese, and with it a nice tossed salad drenched with that bottle of dill dressing that intrigued you so, before you tasted it."

"Okay, so I made a mistake," I said. "So it tasted like plain dill pickle juice. A fellow can make mistakes once in a while, can't he?"

"Yes—and he can eat them, too. Guess what else we're having? That imported fresh frozen genuine Hawaiian poi I've been pushing around the freezer for two years. And with dinner you get a choice of two desserts. Candied cumquats, or the rest of that jar of Indian pudding you hadn't had since you were a boy. So now just go make yourself comfy in the living-room while I put the appetizers on a tray and fix the drinks—I found a recipe that was the perfect way to use up that papaya juice you got curious about."

"Well, all right, but there's just one think I'd like to add to the bill of fare," I said tentatively.

"Well?"

"Well, coming home tonight I happened to pass that new delicatessen on French Street, and they had just got in a shipment of imported Papuan breadfruit—"

"IF IT WAS A SNAKE——"

RALF KIRCHER

One of the little difficulties that often make matrimony a source of pained surprise is a wife's talent for hiding even large bulky objects in such a way that no husband alive could ever find them.

My wife, for instance, could place a football in a bucket so cunningly that I could browse through that bucket all afternoon and never find it. Not that we keep footballs in buckets, ha-ha! Actually, we keep them in daddy's new hat when Junior has his way about it. But let's suppose we kept them in buckets.

"Dear," my wife would say, using her this-is-going-to-hurt-a-little tone, "will you go to the basement and bring up the football that I put in the bucket by the foot of the stairs? There's a lamb!"

There is no use telling her that I won't be able to find it, so I go down and sit looking into the bucket for several minutes before I call, "I don't find any football in this bucket."

"It is right in the bucket, dear," she calls down the stairs to me. "Just keep on looking. There's a lamb!"

It is nice to know that I am still a lamb, but the fact remains that I still can't find the football. However, I wait five minutes to show that my heart is in it, and then I yell that definitely, positively there is no football in the bucket. At this, she comes patiently down the stairs, removes a large football from the bucket, and says, "Here it is, dear. If it was a snake, it would have bitten you."

This goes on all the time. When I can't find my black tie, she picks it off the rack with her eyes shut. If it was a snake, it would have bitten me. When I can't find the seltzer bottle when company calls, she excuses herself with a wry laugh and finds it behind the salt shaker. If it was a snake, it would have bitten me. When I can't locate the rake, or the wardrobe trunk, or the paper, or my brief case, she finds these at once. Needless to say, if they were snakes, they would have bitten me.

Maybe I'm bothered more by the snake angle than anything else. In any case, that's the direction my plans are taking. As it happens, I have an old college chum who owes me fifteen dollars and who is, on top of that, a keeper at the zoo. Next time my wife sends me up-

JOHN GALLAGHER, THE SATURDAY EVENING POST

"Did you see what the moths did to my overcoat?"

---

stairs to find the sun lamp, or the vacuum cleaner, or some other un-findable thing, she is in for a surprise. I am going to leap down the stairs shouting, "It WAS a snake! And it bit me! Run out in the kitchen and see if you can find some whisky. There's a lamb!"

RED HAIR

W. L. ALDEN (1837–1908)

The name of the lady who a few weeks since dropped her back hair on the sidewalk of a street in Clinton, Illinois, has never been ascertained. The hair in question was of a bright red color, and few persons imagined that it was dangerous when unconnected with its owner. Nevertheless, that seemingly innocent back hair led to a tragedy that nearly ruined the peace of two happy and respectable families.

Messrs. Smith and Brown are two leading citizens engaged in the grocery business in Clinton. They are men of great worth of character, and have reached middle age without incurring the breath of slander. One evening Mr. Smith returned from the store and sitting down at the tea-table, produced a Chicago paper from his pocket and remarked with much indignation, "That revolting Beecher scandal has been revived, and its loathsome details are again polluting the press and corrupting the minds of the public."

Mrs. Smith replied that "it was a shameful outrage that the papers were allowed to publish such things," and asked her husband "which paper had the fullest account of the matter." That excellent man said that he believed the *Gazette* contained more about it than any other paper, and that after tea he would send one of the boys to get a copy of it. His wife thanked him, and was in the act of remarking that he was always thoughtful and considerate, when the oldest boy exclaimed, "Pa, you've got a long red hair on your coat-collar!"

A prompt investigation made by Mrs. Smith confirmed the boy's accusation. There was an unmistakably female hair on the collar of Mr. Smith's coat, and it was obtrusively red. Mr. Smith said that it was a very extraordinary thing, and Mrs. Smith also remarking "very extraordinary indeed," in a dry, sarcastic voice, expressed deep disgust at red hair, and a profound contempt for the "nasty creatures" who wore it.

About the same hour Mr. Brown was also seated at his tea-table, and was endeavoring to excuse himself to Mrs. Brown for having forgotten to bring home a paper. That lady, after having expressed the utmost indignation at the revival of the Beecher scandal, had asked for the paper in order to see who was dead and married, and was, of course, indignant because her husband had not brought it home. In the heat of the discussion she noticed a long red hair on Mr. Brown's coat-collar, and, holding it up before him, she demanded an explanation. In vain did Mr. Brown allege that he had not the least idea how the hair became attached to his collar. His wife replied that what he said was simply ridiculous. "Red hair don't blow round like thistledown, and at your time of life, Mr. Brown, you ought to be ashamed of yourself. The less you say the better, but I can tell you that you can't deceive me. I'm not a member of Plymouth Church, and you can't make me believe that black is white."

Now, both Mr. Brown and Mr. Smith were perfectly innocent. Of course, they were annoyed by the remarks of their respective wives, but like sensible men, they avoided any unnecessary discussion of the painful topic. The next day they each brought home all the Chicago papers that contained any reference to the Beecher matter, and, as the papers were received by Mrs. Brown and Mrs. Smith with many protestations of the disgust which they felt at hearing any mention of the scandal, they naturally supposed that they had made peace.

But marital suspicion once awakened is not easily put to sleep. While Mr. Brown was handing his wife the bundle of newspapers, she was closely scrutinizing his coat-collar, and, after she had laid the papers on her plate and told the children not to touch them, she quietly took two long red hairs from her unfortunate husband's coat, and held them solemnly before his face.

"Mary, I give you my solemn word," began the alarmed Mr. Brown; but he was not permitted to finish his sentence. "Don't say one word," exclaimed Mrs. Brown. "Falsehoods won't help you. I am a faithful and loving wife, and I'll have you exposed and punished if there is any law in Illinois." Thus saying she gathered up her newspapers and rushing to her room, locked herself in.

It was not until later in the evening that Mrs. Smith, as she was about to turn down her husband's lamp, which was smoking, perceived that two red hairs were attached to his shoulder. She said nothing, but after laying them on the table before him, burst into tears and refused to be comforted until Mr. Smith solemnly swore that he had not seen a red-haired girl for months and years, and offered to buy her a new parlor carpet the very next day.

Of the two ladies, Mrs. Brown was much the stronger and the more determined. The next evening when Mr. Brown brought back from the store no less than five red hairs on his coat-collar, she broke a pie-plate over his head, and leaving him weltering in dried apples, put on her bonnet and left the house.

Mrs. Smith on the same evening, found four of the mysterious red hairs on her husband's coat, but she refrained from violence, and merely telling him that she would not believe in his innocence if he was to swear till he was black in the face, called loudly for her sainted mother, and was about to faint when Mrs. Brown burst into the room. Mr. Smith, like a wise man, fled from the scene, and the two ladies soon confided their wrongs to one another.

When Mr. Brown and Mr. Smith met the next day, the former confessed to the latter that he was in a terrible scrape. Confidence begat confidence, and they soon became convinced that they were the victims of a frightful conspiracy to which some unknown wearer of red back hair was a party. Their distress was increased early in the afternoon by the appearance of their respective wives, who walked up and down the opposite side of the street for hours, each carrying a conspicuous rawhide, and evidently lying in wait for the imaginary red-haired woman. Messrs. Smith and Brown felt that they were ruined men, and that a tremendous scandal was about to overwhelm them. They even wished they were dead.

About 4 o'clock P.M. Mrs. Smith clutched her companion's arm and bade her listen to a small boy who was relating one of his recent crimes to a youthful companion. "I just picked up that there hair," remarked the wicked youth, "and put some of it on old Smith's and old Brown's coats; I kep' a puttin' some of it on every day, and you just bet they ketched it from their old women when they went home; Smith, he's as solemns a nowl, and old Brown looks as if he was goin' to be hung."

The remains of the boy were removed by the constable, and the Smith and Brown families are once more united and happy.

A MAN'S TELEVISION SET IS HIS CASTLE

GOODMAN ACE

(April 1953)

The crisis came on a Sunday evening—March 22, to be exact. At exactly 7:50 Eastern Standard Time, to be scrupulously exact.

She was looking over the night's TV listings.

"Whom do you think is on Ed Sullivan's show in ten minutes!" she exclaimed.

"I don't know. Whom is?" I asked.

"Rita Hayworth, Shirley Booth, Debbie Reynolds, Lilli Palmer, and Roberta Peters," she announced.

I knew the names only too well. I had known all day. I also knew that on the opposition channel at exactly the same time was the "Colgate Comedy Hour" with Bob Hope, Eddie Cantor, Abbott and Costello, Martin and Lewis, and Donald O'Connor. And I knew that she knew I knew they were on.

She also knew that I knew they were on. Her problem was to have us agree before the next ten minutes to watch Rita Hayworth, Shirley Booth, Debbie Reynolds, Lilli Palmer, and Roberta Peters. Mine, to wangle us into watching Hope, Cantor, Abbot and Costello, Martin and Lewis, and O'Connor.

The big television networks, fighting as they do for the elusive high rating, are little concerned with the crumbling of a man's home. Programs are indiscriminately placed in direct opposition one to the other, regardless of domestic consequence.

That she likes Ann Sothern and I much prefer Wally Cox opposite Miss Sothern is of little import to the executive vice-presidents in charge of programming. Perry Como sings for our supper while I wonder where John Cameron Swayze is hopscotching for headlines on the competitive network. The same goes for Dinah Shore and Doug Edwards with the news. When I should be at ringside for a Wednesday night fight, I'm watching "This Is Your Life." The "Studio One" and Robert Montgomery presentations play simultaneously across the street from each other. As do Walter Winchell and Ed Murrow; the "All Star Revue" and Jackie Gleason; "State of the Nation" and "Kukla, Fran, and Ollie"; "Mama" and "Ozzie and Harriet"; Milton Berle and Fulton J. Sheen. Although, due to personal contractual obligations, I am permitted to watch Berle. That I have to recite Psalm XXIII before the show comes on is beside the point.

I don't believe it's asking too much of the networks to spread their shows around to give us all a chance. I imagine my problem is the problem of all television viewers, although five or six years ago when we first got our TV set the problem was not too critical. Then she was content just to watch the box light up. That was the year she became a television director.

"Make it lighter," she directed. "Make it softer. Make it darker. Make it louder. Make it clearer." And once when it was getting near bedtime, "Make it faster."

Then selectivity set in.

In the olden days of radio there was little or no problem about selecting programs. Living in an apartment with three rooms and a bath I soon discovered that four radio sets pretty well covered every contingency. And even when television brought baseball into her life and she became a Yankee fan, I watched her Yankees play on our TV screen while I held a portable radio close to my ear and rooted for the Giants.

While I was going through this flashback, the minutes were ticking away. It was nearly eight o'clock. Realizing the futility of logic, and

MARVIN TOWNSEND, V.F.W. MAGAZINE

"It helps keep the married men from getting homesick."

---

remembering that I had always fought for the show I wanted to see and lost, I suddenly improvised a diabolical scheme.

"Well!" I exclaimed. "Rita Hayworth, you say? And Shirley Booth and Debbie Reynolds and Lilli Palmer and Roberta Peters all on one show? Let's watch them instead of Bob Hope and Eddie Cantor and Abbott and Costello and Martin and Lewis and Donald O'Connor who are on at the same time on the other network."

So we did.

But I don't believe I was the only loser that night. Even if one program grabbed off the highest rating ever, what is a network profited if it shall gain a whole listening audience but continue to break up homes? Who will be left to buy the large economy family size?

If the networks won't co-operate in smoothing out this critical domestic issue it's up to the viewers, especially those who are about to buy their first sets. Don't be misled by advertisements announcing the large 24-inch screens. Buy two 12-inch screens. And don't think of it as losing your eyesight but rather as gaining a wife.

WOMEN HAVE NO SENSE OF HUMOR

ROBERT THOMAS ALLEN

When I was six I said to a little girl who lived next door, "I bet I can stand two inches away from you and you can't touch me."

"How?" she asked.

"By standing behind a door." I laughed so hard that marbles and chestnuts rolled out of my pants pockets.

The little girl looked at me as if I were a frog. "What's so funny about that? *Nobody* could touch you if you were silly enough to stand behind a door."

I gave up fooling around with women then until I was seventeen. Then one night when I called on a girl named Lorna Gulch to take her to a movie I rolled up my pant legs, creased my hat into a shape like a canoe, pulled my coat down off my shoulders, brought my front teeth out over my bottom lip, and rang the bell.

When Lorna opened the door Mr. and Mrs. Gulch were standing beside her. The old man took one look at me, let out a great wheezing roar, bent over and whacked his knee, went into a coughing fit and finally said through his tears, "By golly, son, that's the funniest thing I ever seen. Come in. Come in. You old enough to take a nip of dandelion wine?"

Lorna, in the meantime, looked at my rolled-up pants, then at my hat, then right past me at the autumn night and said, "Do you think I'll need a topcoat?"

Her mother looked at me: "Something has dinted your hat, Mr. Allen?"

Later on I got married. I found out a lot of things about women, but one thing always threw me, and still does: I haven't yet been able to figure out a woman's sense of humor.

Women either laugh at the wrong time or at the wrong joke or they don't laugh at all while I'm slapping my forehead and howling. I know one quaint little elderly woman who says: "Hmmmm—then what?" after the joke is over; and another who laughs all the way through the joke until the punch line, then sobers up and asks me where I'm living now.

I've found that women either don't laugh at any dirty joke or they laugh at all dirty jokes, whether they're funny or not. I've seen my best jokes go as flat as if I'd read the instructions from a box of cereal; yet more than once I've snaked in the back way during a bridal shower or afternoon bridge and sat on the cellar steps listening to hysterical feminine laughter from upstairs, burning with curiosity about what they were laughing at, and concluding that the women were all making faces at one another or reading out their husbands' old love letters.

The whole thing, of course, is that the humor in a joke doesn't come from the joke itself, but from a lot of mental pictures, ideas, feelings and associations that the joke suggests. A person whose interior atmosphere is made up of mental pictures of new living-room drapes, wall paints, cute little spring suits, permanents, Gregory Peck and half-inch bias tape is sure to see things differently from a person whose psyche evolves around main bearings, lake trout, eager-eyed little stenographers, prize fights and the income-tax department.

One thing, for instance, that makes a woman an entirely different audience is the fact that she is essentially more practical. She carries around with her a solid ballast of down-to-earth realism that won't let her bounce very high. This is one reason for the dismal way they react to shaggy-dog stories, which derive their humor from being directly contrary to all normal channels of reasoning.

The first week after our honeymoon I came home fresh from a couple of quick ones with the boys at the office, and as soon as I got in the door I said: "You want to hear a really funny joke, honey? Well, there was a guy, see, and every day he sat in a restaurant with a piece of celery behind his ear. Then one day he put an onion behind his ear, and another guy who had been watching him every day couldn't stand it any longer so he went over and said, 'Say, Mac, why you got an onion behind your ear?' and the guy says, 'They didn't have any celery.'" The last words I just got out before I collapsed on our only easy chair, wheezing and gasping in helpless mirth.

My wife said, "Why didn't they have any celery?"

I broke off in the middle of a guffaw. "Well, I mean, the thing is, see this guy always put a piece of celery behind his ear—"

"That reminds me," my wife said absently. "We're having Bill and Grace over tonight. We need some cheese."

For the rest of the evening until our company arrived I didn't try anything funnier than asking whether my blue suit needed pressing. That night I told the joke to Bill and Grace.

Bill put his head back and let out a great belly laugh. Grace smiled amiably and said, "Celery is so expensive, too," then turned to my wife and said, "I said to myself just today that if food prices keep going up I'll have to get a husband that makes more money."

At this my wife let out a shriek and the two girls went into gales of laughter while Bill and I sat there solemnly sucking olives.

From that time on I tried to figure out a woman's sense of humor. I tried different kinds of jokes. I kept it up after our two daughters had arrived. It got worse.

A woman doesn't give herself over to pure play as readily as a man, which is the reason most women can take a drink or leave it alone, whereas most men just take it. A man will hold up a business conference, sales talk, speech or introduction to tell a joke. A woman will listen to one when the dishes are done and the kids are safe with a sitter and she's out for the evening. In between she gives only a fraction of her mind to it, which isn't enough.

I remember one time I told my wife the one about the Englishman whose wife had died. "You want to hear a really funny joke, dear?" I said. "Well, there were two old guys sitting in an English club, see, and one says: 'Sorry to hear you buried your wife this morning, old boy,' and the other—here I added a toothy effect that I thought was a pretty good imitation of a Colonel Blimp—the other Englishman said, 'Yes. Had to. Dead, you know.' "

My wife looked at me with the same expression she'd started with. We both looked at one another. My smile felt as if it were falling off my face in chunks.

"What did she die of?" my wife asked.

"Look," I said, flushing. "One guy says, 'Sorry to hear you buried your wife—' "

"I got that part," my wife said. "And don't start shouting. How can I understand a joke when you won't explain it to me?"

"Well, for—look—the OTHER guy says——"

"Just a minute." My wife reached across the table and fed Mary a couple of spoonfuls of spinach. "Now, what were you saying? Is this the same story?"

I gritted my teeth. "There was a guy—"

"Can I have some more milk?" Jane asked.

"You're old enough to get it for yourself," my wife said. Then, turning to me, "That reminds me, you forgot to put the milk bottles out last night."

"I'M TELLING A JOKE," I hollered, pounding the table. "THERE WERE TWO GUYS—"

"If you're going to act that way," my wife said, "I don't want to hear it."

On the occasions when a woman does give herself over completely to a joke she does it the way she drives a car—all enthusiasm for the objective but little interest in how she gets there. Sometimes my wife laughs as hard as I do at the end, then says something that makes me wonder just what she's been laughing at.

I remember one time I told her a joke about a connoisseur of rare foods who had tasted every kind of food but *poi*, and who had taken four months to reach a remote Pacific island by ship, launch, dug-out canoe and pack mule, just to taste a very special kind that was prepared by one of the islanders. When he finally reached the tiny eating place, the proprietor beamed and said: "Sure a-mister. We gotta apple a-poi, a strawberry poi, a-cherry poi, a-peacha-poi."

My wife laughed as hard as I did. When she'd stopped she wiped the tears from her eyes and said, "What did the other man do with it?"

"What did the other man do with what?"

"What did the man do with the mule?"

There's another reason why things often go flat when a man tries to make a woman laugh. It's not the joke that's wrong, but the fact that a man is telling it. A woman thinks a man is funny most of the time, although she rarely lets him know. I've seen women go into hysterics telling one another how their husbands shop, or the way they pamper their cars, or behave with blondes. But to have a *man* start thinking he's funny spoils the joke. It's like children being shown how to act cute, or dogs dressed up like professors. One thing cancels out the other.

After seeing some of my best jokes torn to shreds I made the mistake of thinking that something of a more visual, slapstick nature might go over better. I had a party-act at the time that used to have the boys hollering encores. It was an imitation of a certain type of girl playing the piano. It was very funny. At least, it had been while I was single.

The first time I tried it at a party after I was married my wife just sat there looking at me as if she wished there had been marriage schools in her day. She didn't say anything about it but, from then on, whenever she referred back to the party she always said, "You know, that night you made such an ass of yourself."

Practical jokes once got me into an awful mess. I lived next door to a chap who told me of a trick he'd pulled on his wife. One night he'd gone to bed a few minutes ahead of her, left the light out and crawled under the sheets with his head at the foot of the bed and his feet on the pillow. The idea fascinated me. I tried it the night after he'd told me about it, and lay there waiting for a startled shriek followed by a burst of appreciative laughter.

My wife didn't notice that my head wasn't on the pillow for about five minutes. Then she said: "WHAT on EARTH! . . ."

I sat up at the foot of the bed, grinning from ear to ear, waiting for the full humor of the situation to strike my wife.

She looked at me with a puzzled expression. "Why are you sleeping that way?"

"It was just for fun." I was beginning to feel silly already.

She looked at me with a worried little frown. The next night she told my mother about it. My mother said that even when I was a boy I hadn't liked a hard pillow. The following day my wife told her girl friend who was visiting her from Waterloo about it, as an illustration of how *different* writers are; and she was still telling people about it a week later when Grace and Bill were over for the evening. Grace looked at me with a quizzical yet friendly smile.

"With his feet on the *pillow?*" she said. "I could never sleep that way. My head always has to be higher than my feet."

I found that it wasn't just *my* wife's sense of humor I couldn't figure out. I ran into the same trouble with other guys' wives. Occasionally at a party when things got rolling and one or two of the girls would tell a couple of jokes of a biological type, I'd dig up a juicy one of my own. The girls, including my wife, would all stop laughing. They'd look at their shoes, then turn to one another and say brightly, "Your hair looks lovely since you let the ends grow." The whole thing would leave me feeling the way I do in one of those dreams where I suddenly find myself Christmas shopping in my pajama tops.

I've gradually learned to tread lightly when it comes to mixing humor with women. Now I save my jokes till the boys are out in the kitchen watching me measure the drinks, and let the women go on talking about the little summer dress they picked up for next to nothing. Then dropping their voice to a whisper and bursting out into gales of laughter.

Someday, somehow, I'll find out what's so funny.

Number of Dependents:

DRESSING THE BABY

JOHN D. SHERIDAN

It may happen some fine day that you will be asked to dress the baby, so you might as well learn how it is done.

First you must catch your baby. Having located him in the wardrobe or under the bed you lure him into the open by promising bic-bics. Then you place him, face downwards, across your knees and clutch him firmly with both hands. With your other two hands you draw his nightdress up as far as his head: since you haven't opened the buttons it won't go any further. Next you open the buttons and draw the nightdress up again. This time it will go right over his head and stifle his howls. Be careful, of course, not to stifle the baby.

When the nightdress comes off you will find that you have lost control of the baby for the time being, so you must catch him again. This should be done, if possible, before he reaches the floor.

Now we are ready to make a start. Take the first of the foundation garments and slip it twice over the baby's head; once before you remember to open the buttons and once for keeps. He will do his best to keep you from slipping his arms through the arm-holes, and will try to make new arm-holes where only small tears exist at the moment, so you must be brusque, brisk, and brutal. Next you re-fasten the buttons, a job which is about as easy as putting in dress studs when you have boxing gloves on, but if you stick at it you'll manage it after a while. The only real danger is that while you are occupied with the buttons the baby may fall from your knees. If he does you simply replace him and sing at the top of your voice. If you can't sing keep your hand over his mouth.

Practically the same technique is used with the five other woolly vests, the six bodices, and the three jerseys which protect the infant from the icy blast, except that the further you get from his skin the less scrupulous you get about the buttons.

The trickiest part of the whole business is the adjusting of the one garment which does not go on over the baby's head. This essential and serviette-like covering, suitably folded, is attached to four of the woolly vests with two enormous safety-pins. At the first attempt you will probably attach it to the baby, but if you don't draw blood the slip may never be noticed—except, of course, by the baby. You must be careful, however, not to attach it to your own person, as adults are much more sensitive to pain.

When you have got on the baby's clothes you proceed, if you are still capable of muscular co-ordination, to put on his socks. Some authorities recommend you to put the baby on his back during this operation, but if you do you should be careful, for though a baby is only a baby a kick in the mouth is always a kick in the mouth. A better way is to grip the child, still in your lap, with your elbows and stomach, and lodge one of his ankles between your tensed knees. This renders him comparatively helpless and leaves you free to give all your attention to the sock.

There is not much bother in putting one sock on, or even in putting the two socks on: the whole bother is keeping them on. Whilst you are drawing the second sock into position the owner is pulling off the first, and by the time you get the first on again you will find him chewing the second.

This clash of wills might go on interminably, but after a decent interval you tether the baby to the leg of the bed with your neck-tie and make a short speech from the landing. Does anyone in the house realize that you have a job to go to? Will someone *please* come upstairs and finish off the baby? (Of course this isn't what you mean: you only want someone to finish his dressing.)

Then you go into the bathroom and cut yourself shaving.

EVENSONG; OR, BE THERE, SANDMAN, YOU BUM

ROBERT M. YODER

What Romeo felt for the Capulet gal,
    What Johnny felt for Frankie,
What Damon felt for his life-long pal,
    And Chase for the National Bankie;

A mother's love for an only child,
  The love of Saroyan for Willie,
Rolled all into one they are meager and mild,
  They are dally, denatured and dilly,
Compared to the love as strong as the rock,
  The love all-embracing and deep,
That a father knows around eight o'clock,
  For his infant son, who
  (after finding the sharpest pair of scissors in
  the house, and a bottle of nail polish; after
  climbing the dining-room table and two
  window sills; after chewing tentatively on
  an electric-light cord; after taking a little
  flier into literature with blue crayon on the
  kitchen door, and seeing if it is true that we
  don't pull dishes off the kitchen table; after
  being told no, don't rub the end table with
  the poker, no, we don't pat the cat with the
  golf stick, get away from that hot coffee,
  keep your mitts out of that ash tray, don't
  go into the fireplace; after having run for
  an hour from one dangerous object to another and been rescued from perhaps forty
  disasters, has reluctantly been lashed safely
  into his bed and at long, long last)
                              is finally asleep.

DADDY WON'T LISTEN TO REASON

ROBERT THOMAS ALLEN

I used to feel that children were little empty vessels to be filled with pure reason. But events of my later, or paternal, years have taught me what a precarious hold we have on logic, and how sometimes we find ourselves hanging onto words by our fingernails, like an early movie hero hanging onto a boxcar, while beneath us is a vast pit of human misunderstanding.

After a few minutes' talk with my youngest daughter I sometimes sit staring at the wallpaper and reflecting that if my dear old professor of logic tried that "Man is immortal: Socrates is a man" routine on my Mary, in no time at all she would have him admitting that Socrates was running somewhere, and trying to prove that tigers wouldn't like the way he tasted, if tigers weren't birds.

I'll say to her, for instance, when my wife has left me to mind her for a while, "Now look, I'm just going around the corner for some cigarettes. I don't want you to leave this house till I get back. I'll only be gone a minute. Do you understand?"

"Yes, Daddy." This very innocently, as she gets ready to break me down.

I eye her suspiciously and add, "No matter what happens, or which one of your friends comes around and asks you to come and play. Understand?"

"Yes, Daddy."

I start off, feeling the way I do when I'm passing a little boy with a water gun. I think, with gestures, "That's clear enough. Leave the house . . . no matter which friends . . ."

"Daddy."

I duck my head.

"No matter *who* tells me to leave the house?"

I whip around. "Nobody's going to tell you to leave the house. You just see that you stay here."

"I know nobody will tell me to leave the house," Mary says.

"Fine." I start off.

"But if somebody does tell me to leave the house. I'm not to leave, am I?"

"NO!" I say, wishing she'd stop playing with me like a cat with a mouse.

"Not even if a policeman came along and said I had to leave the house?" Mary asks.

"What would a policeman be doing coming around and telling you to leave the house?" I yelp. "Policemen are all busy—being policemen."

"Yes," Mary agrees with a sweet smile and a sigh.

I start off again.

"Do I have to leave if Grandma comes along and says, 'You leave this house, Mary'?"

"No—yes—OKAY! If Mummy, Grandma or a policeman tell you

to leave—BUT THASS ALL! Why you gotta drag your grandmother into it?" (You'll notice that here, along with not being very logical, I'm not even speaking English any more.)

"And if a fireman came along and told me that the house is on fire, I'd have to leave, wouldn't I? Or if a lot of soldiers told me to leave, or a skunk got in, or my Sunday-school teacher told me to leave, or if I looked out the window and saw a lion coming in the front door, should I leave then, Daddy?"

I start to take a swat at her with a magazine, just as my wife comes home, looks at me acidly and says, "Can't you stand your own children just for TWO hours a week?"

My kids can take little bricks of pure logic and make reasonable constructions out of them that I know are stuck together with bubble gum and puffed wheat but I can't prove anything.

My youngest daughter will briskly sharpen a pencil about six in the morning and say, "Well, this morning I'm going to win a horse. Can I make a stable?"

"How are you going to win a horse?" I ask her.

She brings me an ad off a cereal-box top. "It says here, if you write a poem about Hopalong Cassidy, they'll send you a horse."

"It says if you write the *best* poem on Hopalong Cassidy."

"Well, I'm going to write the best," she says. "Can I have some nails, the hammer, a saw, some wood about ten feet long and some tarpaper?"

"*You're not going to win a horse.*" I raise my voice over the sound of my electric razor.

"How do you know?"

"BECAUSE I KNOW, THAT'S WHY."

Her little pigtails bristle. "*The Tasty-Toasty Company doesn't tell fibs,*" she wails, "and they say I can win a horse."

"Sure you *can* win a horse, but—"

"That's what I said. What am I going to do with him if I haven't got a stable?"

This sort of thing goes on until she makes *me* drop all semblance of reason and yell, "If you don't shut up I won't give you any allowance next week," which, of course, is no way of proving that someone won't win a horse.

The kids can somehow get me going along so fast sometimes, pulling little planks of words out from under me all the way, that I run right into a brick wall.

I'll come out of my bedroom in the morning, blink at one of the kids going out the door for the day, and say, "Have you washed your neck this morning?"

She'll look at me in surprise. "No." I sit wearily on the arm of a chair.

"Well, why haven't you?"

"You didn't tell me to."

"For the love of—Don't you remember the row we had just yesterday morning about you not washing your ears?"

"You said my neck."

"Do I have to tell you every morning to wash your neck, ears, hands, fingers, eyes, cheeks and knees?"

"I don't have to wash my knees. Mummy said I didn't, once when I had a cut on my knee."

"Look, you wash everything every morning. Everybody does."

"You didn't wash this morning."

"I *know* I didn't. I haven't had time yet. I got up, walked out of the bedroom and I'm standing here talking to you."

"You're sitting down."

I lunge at her.

All in all, there's something about a child's logic that can't be equated to the adult mind. It's the same with those, What-do-they-do? questions. I've been trying to figure out for years what my youngest means when she asks what flowers do. A flower sits. Or sort of sticks. A flower is. Flowers stick around. A wheel rounds. Giraffes go around with a long neck. One time Mary asked me what makes a knock in a motor. I said, well, it might be a main bearing or it might be a connecting rod. She said, if there was a knock in your motor, which would it be?

I still wonder what the answer is sometimes as I go up to bed, dragging the shredded evening paper after me.

MAY WE SEE YOU A MOMENT, OUTSIDE?

CASKIE STINNETT

Man has figured out a lot of ways of making himself miserable, but the soundest idea he has hit on in a long while is to take a small child into a public restaurant. As nearly as we can figure it, this reduces everybody to the level of Pleistocene primates: the parents abandon hope of the child developing normally, the waiter starts working out the proportion of chloral hydrate required for a junior-grade mickey finn; the owner considers selling the restaurant and going to live with his son, and as for the other guests, three out of five will stop by the neighborhood library tomorrow morning and pick up *Malthus on Population.*

A child psychologist, whose name we will not reveal because of a genuine concern for his safety, now comes forward with the suggestion that the child should be given what's known as an object lesson. This involves taking a child to a restaurant and doing all the things the child does. We can understand how this would be gratifying to the child, but we shudder to think of the effect on the other customers. For example:

1. Knock the milk over, yourself. To beat the child to it you will have to strike with the speed of a cobra. Try to hit the glass in such a way that the milk flows across the table and into the lap of an adult. You will probably never achieve the casual, sure touch that the child displays, but you can do a good workmanlike job if you apply yourself spiritedly.

2. Kick the table so as to spill coffee into the saucers. A well-placed kick during the soup course can get the entire party moved to another table.

3. Twist around in your chair until, as nearly as possible, you have your back to the table. This permits you to see the coming and going of waiters, the seating of customers, and makes it possible to ignore the food completely.

4. Most of the food, of course, goes on the floor where it belongs, but a certain amount should be saved for the tablecloth. Spear the lamb chop violently and let the fork strike the plate a glancing blow. This *propels* the peas across the table, which is better theatre than having them dribble over the sides of the plate.

5. As part of the squirming process, it is interesting to tip the chair over backwards. While this contains some excellent possibilities for upsetting the entire restaurant, there is always the possibility of getting hurt and can be recommended only when other efforts to make the occasion memorable have failed.

6. It's good social custom to get down from the chair and wander

"Please don't . . .

slam . . .

ROY L. FOX,
THE SATURDAY EVENING POST

the door."

around other tables, staring at strangers and even inquiring what they are eating. This adds immeasurably to the sociability of the meal.

These are the main points to remember in teaching the child a lesson, but there's one other thing. Keep your eye on the manager and be ready to leave as soon as you see him make a furtive telephone call from the cashier's desk. If there's a side door, take it.

FIRST BOOKS

STANLEY AND JANICE BERENSTAIN

The importance of exercising extreme care in choosing the books which your child will read and reread cannot be overemphasized. Lack of intelligent discrimination in this matter can discourage a child to such a degree that he may never come to know the wonderful World of Books. Here are some questions to ask yourself about any book you are considering for your child:

1. If he hits you with it, will it hurt?
2. What will be the effect on the book if the child takes it into the bath with him and gives it a good scrubbing with Daddy's toothbrush? What will be the effect on Daddy's toothbrush? Finally (and of least importance), what will be the effect on Daddy?
3. If half the pages are ripped out and torn to shreds, will it affect the story line?
4. In the event that the child demands it be read over and over again for as much as an hour, will it produce nausea?
5. Is the volume small enough to be quickly and easily hidden in the event that you *have* been forced to read it over and over again for as much as an hour and it *has* produced nausea?
6. Is the type bold enough to be read through a thin layer of strained squash?
7. Will it fill a specific need? Is it exciting enough to distract him while you spoon him full of cereal, or is it sufficiently soporific to lull him to sleep after a wild day at the sandbox?

If the answers to these questions seem to be in the book's favor and the cost isn't much more than four or five dollars, it won't do much harm to buy it.

Once you've bought the book, catchily entitled *Cocky-Locky Bakes*

Some Cookie-Lookies, and taken it home, what then? Should you just hand it to him and say, "Here's a quarter book I brung ya"? Definitely not! Hold on to it. It's money in the bank. Keep it under wraps until, in the normal course of events, a crisis arises. Then say, in your most casual manner, "If you don't stop eating the leaves off Mommy's nice philodendron, I won't give you the pretty new book I bought you." If you manage just the proper tone, he'll stop. He might even spit out what he has in his mouth. You then have him—and philodendron pulp—in the palm of your hand.

He sits down beside you on the sofa, and you begin to read. "*One bright sunshiny day, Cocky-Locky got up and said, 'Isn't this a bright sunshiny day! I think I'll bake some cookie-lookies!'*" As you struggle through to the end of the tale, your docile little lamb leaps from the sofa and heads for his playroom. He's back in a flash with a tall stack of all the books he's ever owned. He nestles down beside you, his face lit with a happy, anticipatory smile. There's nothing for it but to take the top book off the pile and begin to read: "*One bright sunshiny day, Bunny-No-Good was hopping down the path. As he hopped, he passed seven naughty dandelions. 'Naughty Dandelions,' he said. . . .*"

Later—much later—you go numb and it isn't so bad.

CHIVALRY IS BORN

HEYWOOD BROUN

Every now and then we hear parents commenting on the fearful things which motion pictures may do to the minds of children. They seem to think that a little child is full of sweetness and of light. We had the same notion until we had a chance to listen intently to the prattle of a three-year-old. Now we know that no picture can possibly outdo him in his own fictionized frightfulness.

Of course, we had heard testimony to this effect from Freudians, but we had supposed that all these horrible blood lusts and such like were suppressed. Unfortunately, our own son is without reticence. We have a notion that each individual goes through approximately the same stages of progress as the race. Heywood Broun, 3d, seemed not yet quite as high as the cavemen in his concepts. For the last few months he has been harping continuously, and chiefly during meal times, about cutting off people's noses and gouging out eyes. In his range of speculative depredations he has invariably seemed liberal.

There seemed to us, then, no reason to fear that new notions of horror would come to Heywood Broun, 3d, from any of the pictures being licensed at present in this State. As a matter of fact, he has received from the films his first notions of chivalry. Of course, we are not at all sure that this is beneficial. We like his sentimentalism a little worse than his sadism.

After seeing "Tol'able David," for instance, we had a long argument. Since our experience with motion pictures is longer than his we often feel reasonably certain that our interpretation of the happenings is correct and we do not hesitate to contradict H. 3d, although he is so positive that sometimes our confidence is shaken. We knew that he was all wrong about "Tol'able David" because it was quite evident that he had become mixed in his mind concerning the hero and the villain. He kept insisting that David was a bad man because he fought. Pacifism has always seemed to us an appealing philosophy, but it came with bad grace from such a swashbuckling disciple of frightfulness as H. 3d.

However, we did not develop that line of reasoning but contended that David had to fight in order to protect himself. Woodie considered this for a while and then answered triumphantly, "David hit a woman."

Our disgust was unbounded. Film life had seared the child after all. Actually, it was not David who hit the woman but the villainous Luke Hatburn, the terrible mountaineer. That error in observation was not the cause of our worry. The thing that bothered us was that here was a young individual, not yet four years of age, who was already beginning to talk in terms of "the weaker vessel" and all the other phrases of a romantic school we believed to be dying. It could not have shocked us more if he had said, "Woman's place is in the home."

"David hit a woman," he piped again, seeming to sense our consternation. "What of it?" we cried, but there was no bullying him out of his point of view. The fault belongs entirely to the motion pictures. H. 3d cannot truthfully say that he has had the slightest hint from us as to any sex inferiority of women. By word and deed we have tried to set him quite the opposite example. We have never allowed him to detect us for an instant in any chivalrous act or piece of partial sex politeness. Toasts such as "The ladies, God bless 'em" are not drunk in our house, nor has Woodie ever heard "Shall we join the ladies," "the fair sex," "the weaker sex," or any other piece of patronizing masculine poppycock. Susan B. Anthony's picture hangs in his bedroom side by side with Abraham Lincoln and the big elephant. He has led a sheltered life and has never been allowed to play with nice children.

But, somehow or other, chivalry and romanticism creep into each life even through barred windows. We have no intention of being too hard upon the motion pictures. Something else would have introduced it. These phases belong in the development of the race. H. 3d must serve his time as gentle knight just as he did his stint in the rôle of sadistic caveman. Presently, we fear, he will get to the crusades and we shall suffer during a period in which he will try to improve our manners. History will then be our only consolation. We shall try to bear up secure in the knowledge that the dark ages are still ahead of him.

McEVOY IN NURSERYLAND—I

J. P. McEVOY

When I was young and charming I had a small son who refused to practice the piano, so I told him sternly: "No practice, no lessons," which seemed eminently fair, logical and satisfactory to him. So he grew up without piano and has lived to regret it. Me, too.

Now I have a little daughter age seven who also refuses to practice her piano lessons. But this time I know better than to give her the choice—and the out. For I had read a zillion books and articles on child psychology, and I was particularly sold on one expert who held that children always learn by example, not precept. "Expose the darlings to outstanding exponents of success and you'll be surprised what those sensitive little photographic plates will develop." It says here.

Well, my friend Yehudi Menuhin was coming to give a concert in Havana where we live and I said to my wife, "Let's ask him to come out to stay with us and bring his fiddle. It may be the turning point in the life of our little Pat. Peggy, too, for that matter, because she doesn't practice, either." I asked Menuhin and he said sure and he hoped I wouldn't mind if he practiced before the concert instead of having dinner, and I told him fire away, trying to make it sound casual, although I was all of a flutter. So we moved him into the guest room next to the nursery where we herded the children and mounted guard on them so they couldn't get away and Yehudi shut himself in, and sawed away on a Brahms concerto all through dinner hour. I looked up to see the children standing outside his door on the patio balcony listening with their four little ears sticking out like clam shells.

All puffed up with pride over the success of my strategy I went up to clinch matters. "How do you like it?" I asked them.

Seven-year-old Pat looked at me gravely and asked, "Who's that in there?" I told her that was Yehudi Menuhin, one of the world's greatest violinists, who was giving a concert that evening in the biggest theater in Havana. "What's he doing in there?" asked Peggy, age six.

"He is practicing the pieces he is going to play tonight," I said, not too smugly I hoped. Pat was incredulous. "You mean he doesn't know them yet?"

"Of course he knows them." I was a trifle irritated. "But a great artist believes one should never be satisfied with less than perfection. That is why he is still practicing."

"I see," said Pat thoughtfully. The next day I waited with superb confidence. No practice. Slightly shaken I said nothing, but waited until the following day. No practice. "It's developing slowly," I said hopefully. "Their little brains are just like photographic plates. That's what the man said. Tomorrow she'll start practicing."

After a week I confronted her. "Pat," I said grimly, "I haven't heard the piano around here for days. Why?"

"Maybe because I haven't practiced," said Pat.

"Exactly, and why haven't you practiced? Why? Why?" I'm afraid I sounded a bit shrill but there are limits to a father's patience. "Well, Daddy," she said, "I've been thinking about Mister Meenooning and I said to myself that if Mister Meenooning has to practice after all these years what's the use. So I've quit."

What do I do now?

Any suggestions?

McEvoy in Nurseryland—II

My wife claims all little children dawdle over their food, and all parents have trouble getting children to eat, and this is the nature of children, and our children are no different—and nothing can be done about it. And I claim this is all nonsense and pure defeatism. The children claim nothing. They just do as they please. Some days they are still eating breakfast when it's naptime. Other days they gulp everything down like a couple of small boa constrictors.

Recently I decided that the well-meaning but ineffectual fumbling which women call their intuition was getting nowhere, and it was time for me to step in with my calm, dispassionate and logical mind. "Children are just little animals," I said, "and all animals eat when they're hungry."

"Animals also eat the wrong things," said my wife, "and they over-eat and get sick. Did you ever hear of a horse foundering?" And I said, "Did you ever hear of a child foundering?" My wife replied triumphantly, "That's different. Or are you trying to say Pat and Peggy are not as bright as an old horse?"

"Let's go out and come in again," I said. "Children are just little animals, and if I had my way I'd put their food on the table and yell: 'Come and get it!' And if they came, all right; and if they didn't, I'd just leave it there until they did. But, of course, you wouldn't subscribe to anything so logical as that."

"Logical!" sniffed my wife. "What kind of children do you think we would have? They'd eat like animals."

"Exactly," I said, "and their eyes would glow, their hair would glisten, their teeth would gleam, and they'd grow up as healthy as bear cubs and sleek as pussycats."

"Perhaps you'd like to go out and come in again," said my wife.

"Very well," I replied stiffly. "For your information, I have been reading up on parental authority and filial obedience, and the experts say children are little primitives. They can be trained, like savages, to accept authority when it is transferred to an inanimate object like a totem pole, or a fetish, or a stone idol. In this case you merely transfer your authority to something which the children cannot argue with."

"Like what?" said my wife.

And then I came up with my great idea: "The alarm clock! It rings. So does the school bell—and the school bell spells authority. Set the alarm to ring at the time you want the children to finish their breakfast. Tell them the clock will warn them when breakfast is over, and when the bell rings the plates will be whisked away to the kitchen."

"It won't work," said my wife.

"You'll see," I told her.

Next morning I set the alarm clock. The two little girls sat fascinated over their breakfast, watching the minute hand creep around to the fatal spot. On previous mornings they ate something, at least. But this morning they were so hypnotized, watching the clock and waiting for the bell to ring, they wouldn't eat anything. When the alarm sounded I was ruthless. I whisked the plates away. The children whisked right after me with howls of rage. I was calm but firm. Result: the children had such hysterics they couldn't go to school.

Naturally, my wife was inordinately pleased with the collapse of my theory, but I pointed out to her that this was not a fair, scientific test. After all, the electric light, telephone and radio were not all perfected with just one experiment. "We'll try again tomorrow."

And we did. And just as I predicted, the result was different. Again the children were fascinated, watching the hand go round, but also they remembered that when the bell rang their food disappeared. So just as the bell started to ring they began gulping everything down as fast as they could. I tried to take the plates away from them, but I wasn't strong enough. They wolfed everything down in one minute flat. Result: they had such violent indigestion they couldn't go to school that day, either.

"I hope you're satisfied now," said my wife, and her triumph was something majestic. "For the innocent habit of dawdling over their food you have substituted two vicious habits which will probably stay with the poor little dears all their lives, blasting their health, happiness, and careers as wives and mothers: (a) you have turned them into clockwatchers; (b) you've started them down the road to dyspepsia and stomach ulcers."

I still think there's a place in this cockeyed world of intuitive mothers and unpredictable children for the calm, logical, masculine mind.

But I can't find it.

THERE WAS A LITTLE GIRL

ANONYMOUS

There was a little girl,
And she had a little curl
   Right in the middle of her forehead.
When she was good
She was very, very good,
   And when she was bad she was horrid.

One day she went upstairs,
When her parents, unawares,
   In the kitchen were occupied with meals
And she stood upon her head
In her little trundle-bed,
   And then began hooraying with her heels.

Her mother heard the noise,
And she thought it was the boys
   A-playing at a combat in the attic;
But when she climbed the stair,
And found Jemima there,
   She took and she did spank her most emphatic.

THE BALD-HEADED MAN

ANONYMOUS

The other day a lady, accompanied by her son, a very small boy, boarded a train at Little Rock. The woman had a careworn expression, and many of the rapid questions asked by the boy were answered by unconscious sighs.

"Ma," said the boy, "that man's like a baby, ain't he?" pointing to a bald-headed man sitting just in front of them.

"Hush!"

"Why must I hush?"

After a few moments' silence: "Ma, what's the matter with that man's head?"

"Hush, I tell you. He's bald."

"What's bald?"

"His head hasn't got any hair on it."

"Did it come off?"

"I guess so."

"Will mine come off?"

"Some time, maybe."

"Then I'll be bald, won't I?"

"Yes."

"Will you care?"

"Earth, please."

AL BOIME, COLLIER'S

"Don't ask so many questions."

After another silence, the boy exclaimed: "Ma, look at that fly on that man's head."

"If you don't hush, I'll whip you when we get home."

"Look! There's another fly. Look at 'em fight; look at 'em!"

"Madam," said the man, putting aside a newspaper and looking around, "what's the matter with that young hyena?"

The woman blushed, stammered out something, and attempted to smooth back the boy's hair.

"One fly, two flies, three flies," said the boy, innocently, following with his eyes a basket of oranges carried by a newsboy.

"Here, you young hedgehog," said the bald-headed man, "if you don't hush, I'll have the conductor put you off the train."

The poor woman, not knowing what else to do, boxed the boy's ears, and then gave him an orange to keep him from crying.

"Ma, have I got red marks on my head?"

"I'll whip you again, if you don't hush."

"Mister," said the boy, after a short silence, "does it hurt to be bald-headed?"

"Youngster," said the man, "if you'll keep quiet, I'll give you a quarter."

The boy promised, and the money was paid over.

The man took up his paper, and resumed his reading.

"This is my bald-headed money," said the boy. "When I get bald-headed, I'm goin' to give boys money. Mister, have all bald-headed men got money?"

The annoyed man threw down his paper, arose, and exclaimed: "Madam, hereafter when you travel, leave that young gorilla at home. Hitherto, I always thought that the old prophet was very cruel for calling the bears to kill the children for making fun of his head, but now I am forced to believe he did a Christian act. If your boy had been in the crowd, he would have died first. If I can't find another seat on this train, I'll ride on the cow-catcher rather than remain here."

"The bald-headed man is gone," said the boy; and as the woman leaned back a tired sigh escaped from her lips.

WHAT MAKES CHILDREN LAUGH?

ROBERT THOMAS ALLEN

Child psychology has recently turned its attention to children's humor, not only as an important element of character, but as an emotion that has a function in child management. I would like to contribute anything I can to this new field of research but first, it seems to me, we have to establish just what a child's sense of humor is.

For instance, I'd like to know what goes on inside my youngest daughter when she decides to get funny in a letter. She'll spend half an hour absorbed in writing to a great-aunt in Elmira. When she's finished, she brings the letter in to us and reads:

"Dear Aunt Florence: Last night Daddy fell over a duck."

My wife and I look at one another with puzzled frowns. Her great-aunt already thinks writers drink too much, among other things, and is capable of thinking they always keep ducks.

My wife says, "What on earth do you want to say a thing like that for?"

"To make my letter funny," Mary says.

"Well, it's silly," my wife says. "I think you should change it."

Mary studies it thoughtfully. She suddenly puts her head on her arm, disappears behind her hair, wraps her legs around the chair, rubs about half an ounce of paper off the page, and starts over, as if carving her initials in the table.

She looks up and says, "I wrote something else."

"Well, that's better," my wife says. "What did you write?"

"Last night Daddy fell over a kangaroo," Mary reads.

She'll keep this up until somebody stops her and makes her write, "I am saving stamps." But the point is, she's not the least bit embarrassed by the fact that her jokes are flopping like cool Yorkshire puddings. She's completely cold-blooded about the whole thing.

In fact, I often wonder if children have a sense of humor in the sense that we think of it. Comic books, for example, never make children laugh. You can't tell whether they're reading the funny ones or the ones about setting fire to a gangster's feet, by the expression on their faces. My youngsters often bring friends home after school and hand them all comic books as solemnly as if they are handing out instructions for applying for citizenship papers. They sit in a row on the chesterfield, twitching, sniffing and shaking their pony tails in complete dead-pan silence. When they've finished a stack, they turn on TV with the same joyless attention. They sit watching men in space helmets who laugh, scream, sell chocolate drinks, chuckle, giggle and shriek until my wife and I are in a daze and wondering whether we'll go down and sit in the garage until it's over. The kids evidently love it but they must think it's Medic or Kraft Theatre or something because their expressions never change. Occasionally one of them will reach down, catch hold of her foot and slowly bring it up until I'm wondering if her leg's going to snap, or one of them will reach up behind herself stealthily, catch herself by the hair and try to pick herself up off the chesterfield. But nobody even comes close to laughing.

One little girl about a foot and a half high comes in from next door. She won't talk to my wife or me, won't answer us, won't look at us, won't even say good-by. She just appears at four-thirty, taps softly on the door, walks under my arm, says, "I have to be home by five o'clock," and comes in and watches presumably the funniest stuff designed by man for children, then gets up and goes home looking just as sad as when she arrived.

Now and then one of my kids goes down to the corner store and buys a joke book called Some Fun, shoving her dimes across the counter as solemnly as if she's paying a water bill. This book is about two inches thick, printed on grey blotting paper, and is full of fun, games, jokes and riddles. My kid gets no fun out of it, never laughs and can't understand the riddles or make the jokes work. But she reads it from cover to cover, her face a mask, finishing all the jokes on one page, looking briskly to the top of the next page, like a mother reading a letter from her only son. Often she'll read something to my wife and me at the supper table.

"When is a door not a door?" she'll say.

"I give up," I reply.

She peers out from her hair, her face wreathed in smiles. "When it's upstairs."

"When it's upstairs? Why can't it be a door when it's upstairs?"

She wraps her feet around the chair, sniffs, wriggles, disappears behind her hair, looks back at the book and reads the answer again. Then she says, "Oh. That was for another joke. It's, 'When it's ajar.'"

She resumes her smile. When everyone has started eating again, she asks, "What does ajar mean?"

The kids in the neighborhood read aloud to one another from this book. It's a peculiar social game that I watch with fascination. The objective of the kid being read to is to get away. The objective of the one doing the reading is to keep reading aloud as long as she can. The effect is heightened by the character of the joke book itself, which has a peculiar flavor of a Sunday school paper written by an old drunk.

A couple of days ago out in my back yard a little girl, wearing a lace curtain over her head, walked around at an ecclesiastical stroll with her nose about two inches from the joke book, reading jokes to another kid with long black hair who finally disappeared under a tent about a foot high and made of a bed sheet. The one with the book stopped at the tent without taking her eyes from the book.

" 'MIKE:' " she read, " 'For gosh sake, Jake, I heard you were dead.' "

The other kid's voice came up from under the bed sheet. "I'm going home to supper now." She came out of the tent and walked away.

The one with the book followed her, just as if she hadn't been insulted, head bowed over the page and still reading. " 'JAKE: They did say I was dead, Mike, but I knew it was someone else when I saw myself in the mirror.' "

Her friend stopped abruptly, turned around and looked into her face searchingly and said, "Can I play with your lizard cage to-morrow?"

"No," the first girl said, without looking up from her book. She turned a page. " 'MIKE: I'm in a terrible fix.' "

The one with the long hair said, "My mother says that she's going to buy me a lizard cage a hundred feet high with real people in it."

" 'JAKE: What's the matter, Mike?' "

"—and I won't let you play with it."

" 'JAKE:—' "

I don't know what the kids get out of this. Nobody thinks it's funny, including the one reading the book. Audience appreciation means nothing. If someone gets up and goes home, dragging all her toys, the reader just walks over to someone else who doesn't want to hear it either. Nothing discourages her, offends her or stops her.

Another thing about children's humor is that a joke can't be shredded too fine to spoil their enjoyment of it, especially adult jokes.

A little while ago I told my wife that joke about the accountant who drove his fellow employees crazy with curiosity every morning for thirty-five years peering into his desk drawer then closing it and locking it. When he died and they opened the drawer, they found a note reading: "The debit side is the one next to the window."

Both my kids laughed. When they were through, Mary said, "What does it mean?"

"Don't you know?"

"No."

"Then what are you laughing at?" I asked her.

"I thought it was a joke," she said.

I explained it to her the best I could. When I was through she laughed again, just as hard as the first time. About fifteen minutes later, she said, "Is that true?"

"Is what true?"

"Did a man lock a desk so that nobody could get into it?"

"No. I don't think so."

Mary laughed again. After the supper dishes were done she looked at six cartoons on TV without laughing, then went outside and started building a chair out of some wooden boxes. I heard her tell a friend of hers, "My daddy knew a man who couldn't remember what side of a desk he'd written on but it's a joke." They both laughed. As far as I know, she and the gang still laugh at this occasionally.

Although any contrived humor on the part of a kid is more related to cold-blooded curiosity than fun, they can really laugh at some things, the humor of which entirely escapes adults. I was watching a bunch of kids play one day when a plump little boy with slick black hair and enormous brown eyes got up from doing something, looked at his shirt, did a little pivot and said, "I'm a strawberry pie."

The whole gang went completely out of control, swept by some strange group hysteria, repeating to one another, "I'm a strawberry pie," ecstatically breaking things they'd been working on, rolling on the ground, punching one another, doing headstands and getting red in the face. This was followed by a period of silence, broken only by the sound of occasional halfhearted hammering by one kid who lay with his cheek resting on his hand, driving a nail through a board. A few minutes later they all started to fight, all hitting one another excitedly with roller skates and skipping ropes and wandering off home, some crying, others scurrying around shrubs.

A child's sense of humor is very different from an adult's. It's closer to our origins, and carries vestigial remains of life in the Mesozoic swamps, when lizards flew, mankind hid in holes, and the sound of laughter often made our ancestors sit very still trying to make themselves look like leaves. To pretend that a child's sense of humor is just like an adult's, only smaller and cuter, is one of those oversimplifications that is liable to end up in a few psychological split lips.

One lovely young mother I know with beautiful buck teeth has already nearly had them knocked out by following too literally the advice that "the mother-child relationship can be strengthened by peek-a-boo games and good-natured teasing." She poked her little girl right in the middle of a tantrum and said something like, "A-a-a-a-aticky-ticky-ticky," and the kid, all in one reaction, burst out laughing, burst out crying and took an ecstatic swing at her mother with a little tin steam shovel. Her mother spent the rest of the evening re-reading the book with a wet cloth over the bridge of her nose.

As a matter of fact, the author had specifically pointed out that laughter and humor are closely related to crying, anger and tensional behavior—which, I think, explains some of the humor of children that often baffles parents. In other words, kids aren't always feeling funny when they laugh.

Something that will always stand in the way of an adult's complete understanding of children's humor is the vast difference in the way adults look to children and the way adults look to themselves. A couple of weeks ago I picked up my wife at an afternoon tea, just in time to have a piece of cake and to see the hostess' little girl walk to within about three feet of one of the women guests, stand there staring at her for quite a while, like a tourist looking at an exhibit of medieval tapestry. The woman found it amusing enough to get into the act, pursing her lips and staring back at the child with her chin tucked in, until the kid started to laugh: not the kind of laughter we usually associate with children, but laughing way down in her throat. It sounded like something you might hear coming out of very deep grass, or a mossy hollow log.

The woman kept smiling but her eyes looked thoughtful, the way people's eyes look when they say, "No, I mean it. Give me your honest opinion," and get it. But she said stoutheartedly in a deep masculine voice, "Well, now, young lady, what's so funny?"

"You look like a bureau drawer," the little girl said, putting her head on the floor and laughing upside down, which sounded even worse than right side up.

The kid kept it up until her mother crossed the room hurriedly and picked her up by a leg and one arm, swung her playfully. "I think," she said, "Little Miss Tinker is getting a wee bit silly," took the guest in with a glance of a wise mother coping with a childish situation, and added, "How can she be a bureau drawer, she has no handles," and darted a stricken look back at the guest, a smooth round woman shaped like a salami. The mother's grip tightened noticeably on the kid, who flopped around laughing until she left the room in mid-air, singing "I can fly. I can fly. I can fly."

The fact that this youngster left everyone very thoughtful and vaguely embarrassed was typical of a large area of children's humor which tends to result in high-strung smiles and remarks about running along home now. A little while ago I was visiting some distant relatives whom I scarcely knew. We were all sitting around a small living room, each trying to remember just who one another was and how we were related, when a little boy with thin hair slicked sideways over a broad round head started to send his younger sister into fits with suave blasé remarks. If there's anything vaguely disturbing to an adult it's an eight-year-old being droll, although I'll admit that this kid's humor was wonderful, in a ghastly sort of way—like Shakespeare's clowns. In fact it belonged to about the same era, if not earlier.

He'd make his face smoothly blank, let his eyelids droop and say things in a flat monotone like "Whoops!" or "Pardon me, I thought I was a movie star," or "Sure, why not?" until his mother was practically in tears and saying desperately, "John, dear, won't you show us the model airplane you built today?" At that John would raise his eyebrows, spin on his heel, with one hand extended horribly, and say, "I couldn't really, you know," and everyone would nearly die of embarrassment, including his mother, although his sister would nearly come apart.

His father, a big black man with a belt down around his knees, had kept out of the reunion as long as he could but had finally come up from the cellar to shake hands with me. He took one look at his son in the middle of the living-room floor, with everyone peering into their biscuits as if trying to figure out how they were made, and said, "Oh, my God! How long has he been doing that?" and got me out onto the porch to show me some cement work he'd been doing.

In other words, I think we should approach the study of children's humor tentatively and with great reservations. A child's sense of humor may play an important role in mental hygiene, as psychology has stated, and it may, as one doctor put it, "keep the mind from overstretching." But let's not over-stretch this theory. A lot of children's humor is basically a part of the process of evolution and hinges on making adults disappear, and for adults to try to enter into the game is a move that defeats itself at the outset.

I'll always remember one time when I was living in a cottage on a rocky part of the shore of Georgian Bay, I was out for a walk one day along the big rocks. There were just two other people: two boys with smooth guileless faces, clambering around the rocks like goats.

I stood at the bottom of rock they'd gone up, wondering whether I'd try it, when one of the kids poked his head over the edge and said, "Do you want to know how to get up, mister? Put your left foot in that little ledge and your right foot in that hole."

"That one?" I said.

"Now put your hand there and your right knee in that crack."

"You—you mean like this?"

I was now perched there like an old rock formation and just about as immovable.

The kid studied me dispassionately. "Now put your forehead against this ledge and ease your knee out."

"Look—for—I can't move," I said. "What do I do now?"

He studied me a minute and said, "I guess you're too big."

He said it matter-of-factly but it suddenly struck both kids as funny. They disappeared, laughing—into the sky for all I know because I've never seen them again, although I've often looked for them, peering shortsightedly into groups of small boys. I let myself down with my fingernails, my forehead and the weave of my pants. I think it's roughly the predicament a lot of us will find ourselves in if we start leaning too heavily on children's humor.

THE LITTLE HATCHET STORY

With Occasional Questions by a Five-Year-Old Hearer

ROBERT J. BURDETTE (1844–1914)

And so, smiling, we went on: "Well, one day, George's father—"

"George who?" asked Clarence.

"George Washington. He was a little boy, then, just like you. One day his father—"

"Whose father?" demanded Clarence, with an encouraging expression of interest.

"George Washington's. This great man we are telling you of. One day George Washington's father gave him a little hatchet for a—"

"Gave *who* a little hatchet?" the dear child interrupted with a gleam of bewitching intelligence. Most men would have got mad, or betrayed signs of impatience, but we didn't. We know how to talk to children. So we explained, "George Washington. And his father told him—"

"Told who?"

"Told George."

"Oh, yes, George."

And we went on, just as patient and as pleasant as you could imagine. We took up the story right where the boy interrupted, for we could see he was just crazy to hear the end of it. We said, "And he was told—"

"George told him?" queried Clarence.

"No, his father told George—"

"Oh!"

"Yes, told him he must be careful with the hatchet—"

"What hatchet?"

"George's!"

"Oh!"

"With the hatchet, and not cut himself with it, or drop it in the cistern, or leave it out in the grass all night. So George went round cutting everything he could reach with his hatchet. And at last he came to a splendid apple-tree, his father's favorite, and cut it down and—"

"Who cut it down?"

"George did."

"Oh!"

"But his father came home and saw it the first thing, and—"

"Saw the hatchet?"

"No, saw the apple-tree. And he said, 'Who has cut down my favorite apple-tree?'"

"What apple-tree?"

"George's father's. And everybody said they didn't know anything about it, and—"

"Anything about what?"

"The apple-tree."

"Oh!"

"So George came up and he said, 'Father, I cannot tell a lie, I—'"

"Who couldn't tell a lie?"

"Why, George Washington. He said, 'Father, I cannot tell a lie. It was I cut down your apple-tree. I did—'"

"His father did?"

"No, no, no! George did. 'Father, I cannot tell a lie,' he said, 'I did it with my little hatchet.' And his father said: 'Noble boy, I would rather lose a thousand trees than have you tell a lie.'"

"Said he'd rather have a thousand apple-trees?"

"No, no, no! Said he'd rather *lose* a thousand apple-trees than—"

"Said he'd rather George would?"

"No, said he'd rather *he* would than have him lie."

"Oh! George would rather have his father lie?"

We are patient and we love children, but if Mrs. Caruthers hadn't come and got her prodigy at that critical juncture, we don't believe all Burlington could have pulled us out of the snarl. And as Clarence Alencon de Marchemont Caruthers pattered down the stairs we heard him telling his Ma about a boy who had a father named George, and he told him to cut down an apple-tree, and he said he'd rather tell a thousand lies than cut down one apple-tree.

RULES FOR WRITING TO CAMP NOOSA WOOSA

*Or, a correspondence course for parents beset
by Junior's cryptograms from the woods.*

EMILY AMBER

Thousands of children from the New York area are now at summer camps, ostensibly sent there to "get out of the hot city," to improve their physical skills and to learn what the psychologists call "the dynamics of group living," but *really* disposed of, as every parent knows, in order to give Mother and Daddy a well-earned vacation.

Because the young camper's ticket to his Sunday lunch (a meal which is usually the mainstay of the week) is an envelope addressed to his absent progenitors and because the parents seek weekly to remind their offspring of their existence, a peculiar, but fairly regular correspondence between the two generations ensues which lasts the normal eight-week camping season.

A set of twelve official rules for parents engaged in this letter-writing exchange has been formulated and is here presented.

Rule One: Accept the fact that this is a somewhat Kafka-like correspondence, in which the chances are that no direct question will ever be answered. One parent we know spent all summer doggedly asking her daughter how the poison ivy contracted just before departure had progressed. Perseverance was but partially rewarded one day when she received word: "The mud *did* help my bee sting."

Rule One-A: Nor should you expect the child to respond even obliquely to even the most dramatic recountals in your letters. The news that "I tripped over the switching-engine you forgot to pick up and broke my leg, which is now in a cast," will probably evoke an answer such as "Today we had hot dogs."

Rule Two: Prepare yourself for references to the consequences of events in which you have had no previous grounding, such as "There will be no more fireworks because of Timothy," or "I hope the cage I'm building for Adeline won't be too big to get through the door to my room." The prudent parent will save himself the energy of trying to elicit any further information about Timothy and would be wise to set about installing double bars on the door to Junior's room in case Adeline turns out to be either carnivorous or non-housebroken.

Rule Three: Banish all bourgeois inclinations to know with what sort of children your own child is associating. The best you can hope for is "In my bunk are Tommy, Walt, John, Peter," unless you are blessed with a particularly communicative youngster in which case you may also discover that "Peter stinks."

Rule Four: Take a quick refresher course at Dale Carnegie in order to learn how to feign enthusiasm over such occasionally detailed descriptions as that of the Camping Trip, the Big Event of the summer. For instance, "Our trip to Lake Tripanontang was great. We hiked in the rain for too hours. The wind blue down the pup tents. We rapped up in ponchoes. Mine has too wholes. The KLIM got wet and turned into MILK before we were reddy. Uncle Joe forgot the Spam. The green letters saying CAMP NOOSA WOOSA ran and our T-shirts look real neat now. We told gost stories."

Rule Five: Do not be too ambitious about your child's athletic developments. They are pretty cagy at these camps about arranging the swimming tests so everyone can pass them (what would they do with the little brats all day if they couldn't?). But a more usual report on sports will be like this one: "Yesterday Tommy and I played tennis. Nobody won."

Rule Six: Learn self-control and remember that one of the primary jobs of a parent is to encourage the child's creative expression. When you read "I am making a leather watch-fob for Daddy in handycraft," it would be wise to throw out your wrist watch immediately and buy a timepiece for which the handicraft object will be more appropriate. One harassed father whose daughter had written "My animals is chickens" and whose son had written "I am making a lanyard" got so confused he dutifully prepared himself for a barnyard.

Rule Seven: Be especially careful about your own letters *after* visitor's day. By this time you will have seen your child living under conditions which would hardly be passed by the Geneva Convention. But make no disparaging comment: not only does he think it "neat" but, more important, you don't want to admit to yourself that you were taken in by those narrow-angle photographs in the catalogue and, after all, you're paying for the privilege of having him there.

Rule Seven-A: Curb also such bitter remarks as "You won't eat baked beans at home" or "Don't they feed you anything but hot dogs?"

Rule Eight: Don't sit down and write an irate note to the principal of your child's school demanding to know why he hasn't been taught how to spell. Your child knows perfectly well how to spell, but he is a canny little creature and knows that his misspelling adds a certain picturesqueness to his sparse weekly epistles. With Machiavellian cunning, he will write "We arrived in one peace and were commented for good behaveyour." He is apt to be particularly inventive with such words as "councelor" and "misketoe" which appear frequently throughout the summer, and his imaginative flights should not be discouraged.

Rule Nine: The one sure-fire way to get an extra letter from your progeny is to disregard a direct request. The budding photographer, for instance ("I took a pictur of Jane, but she moved"), will repeat demands for film until satisfied.

Rule Ten: Be grateful to the camp for the way in which, as the catalogue promised, your child's horizons are being expanded. Respond enthusiastically to such bits of information as may appear from time to time in the letters of the especially literary child—"I can ty nots" or "I know four smoke signals." Both of these skills may some day prove very useful—who knows but that the entire family may find itself in a tough nautical situation or desperately lost in Prospect Park?

Rule Eleven: Don't worry too much about what you write to the child as the summer progresses. He won't read your letters anyway. But he likes getting mail. Some parents we know give up writing entirely after July 15 and just post empty envelopes. There have been no complaints.

Rule Twelve: Be careful to show your child's communications only to your childless friends. Otherwise you'll have to read *their* children's letters.

Excuse me, now. My child's last words to me were "When you get home I want you to sit right down and write me a letter so I know you arrived safely." It won't take me very long, because I composed it coming up in a taxi from the station. "Dear Junior, I'm fine. How are you? I had a hot dog. Love, Mom."

IN ONE EAR AND UPSIDE DOWN

PARKE CUMMINGS

The other evening I requested of our eldest child (masculine, aged twelve): "Go down to the cellar and fetch me a screw driver. And while you're there, put a shovelful of coal on the furnace."

He departed and, after a decent interval, returned and handed me the coal shovel. To one unfamiliar with the soothing sound of wool-gathering in a young person's mind this might seem a curious way of complying with the particular request. On the other hand, every experienced parent would admit that, considering the phrasing used, this outcome was practically inevitable.

What a child does—if he bothers to listen at all—is pick out a couple of key words from a command, and then couple them together by associative reasoning. In the instance given, it requires no trained psychologist to deduce that for him the key words were "fetch" and "shovel."

Maybe this was a lucky selection at that. For instance, if they had been "screw driver" and "furnace," the twisted and charred remains of that handy tool would undoubtedly have shown up in the ashes a couple of days later.

Of course, parental instructions and directions are practically infinite in variety, and it's an obvious impossibility to list every conceivable one and predict exactly how they'll be misinterpreted.

However, as a help to parents who may not have faced this problem as often as I have, I shall be happy to furnish them, gratis, *Cummings' Sample Case Histories of Loused-up Instructions:*

Instruction: "Clean up properly before you come to the table—and don't use those guest towels!" *Result:* Child goes and wipes hands on a guest towel.

Instruction: "Fetch me my sewing scissors. They're in the basket where the needles and thread are." *Result:* Parent is handed a spool of silk thread, sometimes with the inquiry: "Is this the color you said?"

Instruction: "Will you kindly turn that radio down lower?" *Result:* Usually none whatsoever. Occasionally the child may tune to a different station which has apparently stepped up its power from 50,000 to 100,000 kilowatts and moved its transmitter into the lot next door.

Instruction: "Clear the things off the dining-room table, and then get at your homework so you can finish it in time. I'll do the dishes." *Result:* Youngster waits for Mother to clear the table, finally does so himself after the request is repeated three times. Then starts to do the dishes and is amazed when Mother instructs him to start studying. Protests bitterly that she is always telling him one thing and then changing her mind.

Instruction (or threat, if you want to get technical): "There's going to be trouble if you persist in leaving the front door open every time you go in and out of the house!" *Result:* Child, manifestly alarmed, quickly goes to door and opens it.

Instruction: "Don't forget you have a dentist's appointment at three o'clock on the fourth." *Result:* Having absorbed the preceding examples, the reader is expected to figure this one out for himself.

While this list could be expanded indefinitely, I am confident that its basic pattern has been grasped, and that a smart parent will now see a way out. To counteract the child's natural tendency to get a request mixed up, you simply first mix it up yourself, leaving him to unscramble it and arrive at the correct result.

For instance, the other morning we wanted John to wash his neck, but we hesitated a long time before we finally framed the command. It was: "Scrub the soap thoroughly with a washcloth, and then hang up your neck."

Result: Cleanest his neck has been in six months. See how simple it is when you get the pitch?

LET ME HANDLE THIS IN MY OWN WAY

CASKIE STINNETT

I recall the evening well. I was sitting up late—it was nearly nine o'clock—and I was bringing in KDKA just as though it were in the next room. Des Moines had come in nicely earlier in the evening, but it was now cut off by static and fading badly.

"Son," my father called from upstairs, "turn that thing off and come to bed."

"But KDKA is coming in," I protested, "just like it was in the next room."

"Do you want me to come down there and attend to you?"

That was all there was to it. I pulled the switch, disconnected the batteries and went upstairs to bed.

Kids don't act like that now, and I can't figure out why. They aren't any smarter than they used to be, and heaven knows that parents are just as strict with them. Something subtle has happened, and if we are ever going to get discipline established again, we've got to examine our mistakes impartially and act cooperatively. I will recite a recent experience of my own, for the common good, and if any conclusions can be drawn from it, I will be pleased for having made a contribution.

In a three-hour period, from three to six o'clock, my three-year-old daughter: put the key to the car down the shower drain, lowered a fully loaded clothesline, put puppy biscuits in a bowl of jelly (strawberry), blazed a more or less permanent trail from the bathroom to the porch with a ribbon of toothpaste (ammoniated), cracked what she said she thought was a hard-boiled egg on the rug in the living room, smuggled her christening dress across the street to be put on a cocker spaniel and placed the neighbor's rotating lawn sprinkler on the window sill of his living room. It was this last act of vandalism that brought the call for action.

"March that young lady right over to Sibley's," my wife said, "and make her tell Mr. Sibley she's sorry. She will remember that longer than a spanking."

As we were going down the steps, the miscreant reached up and caught my hand. I recognized this as sound strategy, but you can't be cruel to a child that needs comfort.

"I love you more than mommy," she whispered.

I pretended not to hear, but I don't mind admitting I was surprised. I had thought all along it was the other way around. She looked up at me like the heroine in a Western B-picture when the hero rides up to save the girl, her old grandpappy and the ranch.

"I'm daddy's girl," she said, squeezing my hand.

I returned the squeeze.

"I want to kiss daddy," she said, pulling my hand toward her. When we got back home, my wife asked what had happened, and I said maybe we should forget it. Sibley was no bargain as a neighbor.

"What's that on the child's face?" my wife asked. "It looks like chocolate ice cream. It is chocolate ice cream."

What's a little chocolate ice cream? Is that anything to get so worked up about?

"Don't think she won't hear about this when she gets home!"

ADOLESCENCE, OR PLEASE KEEP IMOGENE UNTIL SHE IS THIRTY

BETTY MacDONALD

The tricky thing to remember about adolescents is that they seem so miserable doing what they are doing that you, their loving and be-wildered parents, assume that they would be happier doing something else. They wouldn't. Adolescents are going to be miserable no matter what they are doing but they would rather be miserable doing the things *they* choose. This is all so easy for me now that Anne and Joan are twenty-four and twenty-five, charming, intelligent, beautiful, com-panionable, adult and married. Don and I adore them and can't see enough of them, even if Don did design a Christmas card showing him on the roof shooting at the stork.

But during that long pull between fourteen and twenty (they were both married at twenty) it came over us with a flash, well really more like a punch in the stomach accompanied by the splash of tears, that the English are truly more civilized than we are and they know what they are doing when they send Imogene away to school—and by "away" I mean from Rangoon to England or vice versa—at age seven and bring her home reluctantly when she is thirty.

The summer Anne and Joan turned fourteen and fifteen and both bolted themselves in the bathroom for hours at a stretch and wore lipstick to bed, Don and I sent away for the catalogue of a fine school in Canada. It had the splendid English approach, we could tell, because the catalogue said, "No need for them to come home for any of the holidays—we will keep them all summer." Anne and Joan found the catalogue and cried, not because we didn't want them home in the summer but because the school demanded that all pupils have their hair chopped off even with the ear lobes and wear black oxfords with Cuban heels.

Frankly I do not know any easy answer to adolescence. About the only thing to do is to try to hang on to your sanity and pray much as you would if you were lost in a blizzard without a compass or were adrift in a leaky canoe and could hear the roar of the falls just ahead.

While you are hanging on I will reach down into the black pit of my experience and give you a few things to think about, in case they aren't already glaringly apparent:

1. Adolescents do not hate their parents. They merely feel absolute contempt, occasionally coated with condescending pity for them, their tiny brains, ridiculous ideas, unfair rules and obvious senility. They all refer to their father as "oh him" and their mother as "she": "*She* won't let me go, naturally. *She's* scared to death I might have a little fun for a change." "Who was that on the phone? *Oh him!* What did he want, his overcoat again?"

2. All adolescents are masters of the double- even triple-cross. This does not mean that they will grow up to be either Communists or politicians—it is merely an indication that in adolescence, loyalty is no long-term emotion, and best friends can turn brown quicker than gardenias.

3. All adolescents "go steady." Daughters with boys who appear to be oily, weak-chinned and untrustworthy. Sons with girls who appear hard-eyed, brazen and, if not downright immoral, certainly not wholesome sister types. No parent gets anywhere combatting these great romances. How can anyone as stupid as "oh him" evaluate a big wheel

like Billy? (A big wheel who lies on the couch more than the dog and has a vocabulary of thirty words.)

"It just so happens that Billy is left half on the football team and president of Squee-Gees, *the* high school fraternity."

What can "she" possibly know about a wonderful girl like Charlene (with her skin-tight skirts, fuchsia lipstick apparently put on with a putty knife, and scintillating conversation of "Gollee, Anne, Johnny may have the mind of a boy but he sure has the *body* of a *man!*")? *She* is just jealous "because Charlene was voted sweetheart of the Squee-Gee *four times*" (no wonder).

The thing that is so difficult for fathers to remember is that very few, if any, of the brilliant lawyers, bankers, doctors, architects or statesmen, a facsimile of which they desire for a son-in-law, ever took out girls when they were in high school. They were too shy and too busy studying to be brilliant lawyers, etc. Big wheels in high school are, always have been, and undoubtedly always will be the smooth, shifty-eyed, self-confident non-studiers.

The thing that comes as such a blow to the mothers is the fact that little Conroy is not attracted to Ermingarde Allen, who "has such pretty manners and will be very nice-looking when her skin clears up and after all her mother was my classmate at Bryn Mawr." (Conroy, who is shy and unsure, refers to Ermingarde, who is shy and unsure, as "that pimply creep.")

4. All adolescents telephone. This is part of the cohesive quality that makes them all eat in the same beanery, walk in bunches, knot up in hallways, keep in constant touch. United we stand—divided we might learn something. (You will not solve anything by having two telephones, "Wow, *two* telephones!" Anne and Joan's friends said, and kept them both busy.)

5. All adolescents intend to have the family car all of the time. To accomplish this they resort to the gentle nag or water-on-stone method, the smooth lie, or the cold tearful silence. They will always win if you try to reason or appeal. They have the least resistance to the cheerful impersonal "no."

6. Adolescents are not careful of their own possessions, but they are absolutely reckless with anything belonging to their parents. Don's gray flannel slacks, Don's shoes, my small radio, my toast-colored cashmere sweater, Don's bathing trunks (about four pairs), my jeans, our sweatshirts, our beach towels, hit the adolescent trail and were never seen again.

7. All adolescent girls would prefer to live in a bathroom.
8. All adolescent boys would prefer to live in a car.

Examining in retrospect that first long wet difficult winter when day-light was only on weekends and keeping warm was the motivating force, I am overcome by how wonderful Anne and Joan were. How co-operative and uncomplaining and hard working and dear. Of course, viewing things in retrospect does blunt corners and point up bright places, but they were such little girls to be getting wood, cook-ing dinner, making beds and smiling, and I repeat again they were such little girls and they did smile. I wondered if they were happy liv-ing on an island and leaving for school in the dark. After all, they were used to my large family and our hordes of friends, I told Don.

He said cheerfully, "Look at the Brontës, Saki, Ruskin, Lincoln. All great people who thrived on isolation."

I said, "When I was a little girl I always came home to a house smelling of gingerbread and filled with people."

Don said, "I always came home to a house smelling of funerals and filled with Methodists. I think Anne and Joan are lucky."

I said, "Perhaps we should have waited until they were older before moving to the country."

He said, "Living in the city doesn't solve everything. Think of all the city children who are alone because their parents are in Palm Springs or down at the Athletic Club in New York attending the Na-tional Convention of the Juvenile Delinquency Prevention Society. Anyway there weren't any houses for rent in the city. Remember?"

One stormy night Don met on the ferry and brought home to dinner a widower who lived by himself on the other side of the island. Anne, home from school with one of her fleeting unlocalized ailments, had stuffed and baked a salmon and made an apple pie. The man couldn't get over it. "That little girl, that wonderful little girl!" he said over and over again as he passed his plate for more salmon and watched Anne swishing competently around making boiled coffee and cutting the cheese.

Joanie said, "I'm wonderful too, aren't I, Mommy? I rowed out and bought the salmon from the fishing boat and I carried up a root so big Don can't get it in the fireplace."

"You don't know how fortunate you are," the old widower told Don and me, with tears in his eyes. "I've never seen anything like it." Anne and Joan glowed like little fireflies and in his honor after dinner, when they were doing the dishes, kept their fighting down to quiet slaps, hissed insults and one broken saucer.

Sunday morning the girls always climbed in our bed, Don lit the fire in the fireplace and we took turns going down and getting coffee, orange juice and the Sunday papers. After we had read the papers, accompanied by a great deal of shoving and spilling and jerking of the covers Anne and I got up and cooked a big Sunday breakfast. Kippered herring and scrambled eggs or clam fritters and bacon or shad roe or eggs scrambled with Olympia oysters no larger than a thumbnail. While Anne and I cooked, Joan and Don got wood and built the fires. We never bothered with Sunday dinner, preferring soup and sandwiches whenever we got hungry.

Sunday afternoons we took walks, gathered bark, wrote and acted out plays, popped corn, made fudge, sang into the recording machine, read aloud, helped with homework, took trips in the rowboat with the outboard motor, cleared land, fed the deer and played with the kittens. In spite of my occasional misgivings, we were a very happy, enthusiastic family and I was delighted that Anne and Joan had accepted Don so easily as my husband and their friend.

Then Satan, in the form of adolescence, entered the Garden of Eden and turned it overnight into a jungle. A jungle filled with half-grown, always hungry, noisy, emotional, quarrelsome, rude, boisterous, snarling animals.

The first manifestation was the hair. Anne had bright copper-colored curly hair which she wore shining clean and hanging shoulder length. Joan had pale blond curly hair which she wore shining clean, if I caught her, and hanging shoulder length. One early evening Anne began rolling her pretty hair into small wet snails, about six hairs to a snail, secured tightly with bobby pins crisscrossed like swords.

I said, "What are you doing to your hair?"

Sighing heavily she said, through a mouth filled with bobby pins, "Oh, you wouldn't understand."

"Why shouldn't I?" I said.

"Because you don't know anything about style and anyway you want me to look ugly."

"Your hair looks lovely just the way it is," I said unwisely.

"I knew you'd take that attitude," Anne said, beginning to cry. "I knew you'd get furious if I tried to fix my hair the way *everybody* is wearing it."

Joan said, "That's right, Mommy, *everybody* puts their hair up in pin curls. They all think we look like hags."

"And bags."

"And scrags."

"I'm not furious," I said, getting a little furious. "But I don't see much point in curling curly hair."

"You don't see any point in *anything!*" Anne sobbed. "You don't know anything about anything! You even like to live on this God-forsaken island."

Joan said, "Say, Laurie told me that Helen told him that Bobby likes you."

"When?" Anne said, sucking the tears back into her eye sockets and brightening up.

"Yesterday," Joan said. "I forgot to tell you."

"You stinker," hissed Anne. "And now I promised Jimmy I'd go to the Friday dance with him. I could kill you."

"Go ahead," Joan said calmly, "but if I'm dead I won't be able to tell you what else Laurie said."

"What?" Anne said.

"Say 'cross my heart I'm not going to kill you,'" Joan said.

"Don't be silly," Anne said.

Joan said, "All right then, promise you'll help me with my theme."

"I promise."

"Well," Joan said, "Laurie said that Helen said that Bobby is going to ask you to the Seaview Boys School football dance. What are you going to wear?"

"Something ugly and childish and old," Anne said bitterly. "And all the other girls are rich and will smoke and have on strapless formals."

"Karen Hendricks isn't rich," Joan said, "and she goes steady with the president of the sophomore class."

"Yes, but she doesn't live on a corny old island," Anne said.

"If I had red hair I wouldn't care where I lived," Joan said wistfully. "Say, the subject of my theme has to be Why I Want to Go to College."

"Ugh, what a repulsive title," Anne said.

"You promised you'd help me."

"I know," Anne said, "but it will have to be all lies."

"I'll get my notebook," Joan said.

"Wait," Anne said. "I have to finish pinning up my hair. I'll do yours too, if you want," she added generously.

"Oh, boy," Joan said rapturously.

From then on Anne and Joan and all their little female friends spent at least one third of their lives rolling their hair into the small snail curls. Over the snails they tied bandannas of different kinds— one year dishtowels, one year men's bandannas, one year woolen scarves, one year enormous silk squares. The strange thing was that except for special occasions such as the Friday night dances, Squee-Gee formals and Junior Proms, we never ever saw these curls unfurled. Their hair was pinned up when they left for school, it was pinned up again the minute they got home.

Saturday before last, my sister Mary's middle daughter, Sally, who is sixteen, came to see me, bringing three of her school friends. I flinched when I saw their hair, wound into little snails, each snail secured with the crisscrossed bobby pins. I decided to ask Sally, who is not my daughter and therefore doesn't feel called upon to give me the "diamond drill eye" or to turn all my simple questions into personal affronts, why adolescents keep their hair pinned up all the time. Stepping softly, I said, "Sally, would you answer a question for me?" Instantly she and her three friends exchanged looks and moved closer together.

She said suspiciously, "What do you want to know?"

I said, "Why do you keep your lovely blond hair pinned up all the time? In the past two years I've only seen it combed out twice."

She said, "Well, it comes out of curl."

"When?" I asked.

"At school," she said. "I comb it out as soon as I get to school in the morning."

"And you put it up again the minute you get home?"

"Of course," Sally said. "Somebody might come over."

"What if somebody doesn't?"

"Then it's all ready for dinner."

"Do you comb it out before dinner?"

"Daddy won't let us come to the table in pin curls. He's so darn crabby!"

"Then you put it up right after dinner?"

"Of course."

"Why?"

"Somebody might come over."

"Then you put it up again before you go to bed?"

"Of course."

"So it will be ready for school in the morning?"

"Uh, uh."

"Wouldn't it be easier to have a permanent?"

"Oh, no, permanents are corny."

I said, "What about riding back and forth on the ferry with those little wet snails all over your head?"

She said, "Oh, we combed our hair while we were waiting in line."

"How did it get curled again?" I asked. "The ferry ride only takes twelve minutes."

"We rolled it up while we were waiting for the ferry to dock."

"Are you going to take it down again before you get back on the ferry?"

"Of course, you don't expect us to ride on the ferry with our hair in pin curls do you?" Accompanying scornful laughter.

Of course everybody knows that adolescents, in spite of a repulsively overconfident manner, are basically unsure. We read it in books. It is pointed out to us in lectures. There are even articles about it in the newspapers. But you have to live with an adolescent to realize that in this half-ripe, newly hatched, wet-feathered stage they are not aware they are unsure. They consider themselves wise, tolerant, responsible adults. Adults so mature they have a phobia against anything childish. Thus the pleasant Sunday mornings in our bed came to a sudden end. Instead Anne and Joan rushed down and got the papers, fought over them shrilly for a while, then came into our room, sat on the bed, drank the coffee which we had gotten ourselves, and complained. "Gosh, you look hideous in that nightgown, Betty," was one form of greeting, followed quickly by, "Raining again!" Heavy sigh. "It seems like it has been raining for years and years." Another heavy sigh. "Do you think Tyrone Power's going to marry Lana Turner, Mommy?" They were both wearing Don's pajamas, their hair was of course in pin curls, their faces smeared with calamine lotion, their fingernails were long, ruby-colored and chipped, their eyes sad.

I said, "Let's get dressed, have breakfast, build a big fire in the fireplace and play charades."

"Charades? You mean that baby game where you act out words?" Anne said.

"It isn't a baby game," I said. "You remember we played it last summer."

"I don't want to play," Joan said. "It's too much like school work."

"I wish I had a pink Angora sweater," Anne said. "Marilyn has two. A pale blue one and a pale pink one."

"Two?" Joan said. "Are you sure? They're twenty-five dollars, you know."

"Marilyn's rich," Anne said. "She gets thirty-five dollars a month just to spend on clothes."

Don said, "I can't understand why we let the Russians into Berlin."

Anne said, "Marilyn's going to spend Christmas in Palm Springs."

I said, "Palm Springs is the last place I would want to spend Christmas. Who wants hot weather and palm trees for Christmas?"

"I do," Anne said wistfully. "I'm so sick of rain I could die."

"Me too," Joan said. "Marilyn's going to get her own car when she's sixteen."

Don said, "Of course Russia had the world bluffed and our policy of appeasement, uncertainty and double-talk isn't fooling anybody but ourselves."

I said, "Possessions don't bring happiness. Happiness is something you must find in your own self."

"Well, it would be a lot easier to find if I had a car of my own," Anne said.

Joan said, "If we had a car of our very own we could drive to California next summer."

"You could not," I said.

"Why?" they said together.

"Because I don't believe in young girls' driving around the country by themselves. It's not safe."

"Well, next summer we'd be fifteen and sixteen."

"That's not old enough to take a trip by yourselves."

"It certainly seems funny to me that we are always old enough to do what *you* want but never old enough to do anything *we* want."

Don said, "Listen to this, 'Peace is largely beyond the control of purpose. It comes as a gift.'"

I said, "Why don't you girls get dressed?"

Don said, "You never listen to anything I say."

I said, "I do too. But it's hard to concentrate on Russia when the girls are leaving for California in their own car."

Anne said, "Don't you think Joan and I are old enough to drive to California, Don?"

"What about South America?" Don said. "It's farther away." . . .

"Let's get dressed," I said, getting out of bed.

Leg shaving began the summer Anne was thirteen and before either of the girls had so much as one picker on their skinny legs. But leg shaving was considered sophisticated and so they scraped their legs almost as often as Don did his chin, and always with his razor.

After a while I got pretty foxy, and when I saw Anne and Joan come limping out of our bathroom, their legs sporting bloody ribbons of toilet paper like tails of kites, I would dash upstairs, wash out Don's razor and put in a new blade.

Then there were the clothes. So vitally important. Everything long and loose and pitiful. Boys' coats. Men's sweaters. Don's shirts. Boys' jeans and T-shirts. Wooden shoes, loafers, dirty saddle shoes. Exactly the right kind of white socks turned down an exact number of inches. The first high heels and the furious outburst in the shoestore—"You're glad my feet are so big because you know it hurts my feelings!"

No matter what garment I bought Anne and Joan the grass was always greener in somebody else's closet. They and their schoolmates exchanged clothes constantly. Anne and Joan would leave for school in one outfit, come home in another. It was hard for me to understand this because all the skirts, blouses, sweaters and coats were exactly alike and all made the girls look like figures in faded photographs of long-ago picnics.

Next in importance to clothes were eating and dieting. For weeks everything would be so-so. The girls would come home from school with their accompanying wake of Jeanies, Lindas, Ruthies, Sandys, Bonnies, Chuckies, Normies, Bills and Jims, go directly to the kitchen and the icebox door would begin to thump rhythmically like the tail of a friendly dog, as they devoured everything not marked with a skull and crossbones or frozen. During those intervals any old thing I cooked, stew, spaghetti or deep-fried pot holders, was greeted with "Is that *all* you made? We're starving."

Then one morning I would decide to get up early and cook something very nice for my growing girls and their long chain of Ruthies, Jeanies and so on, who apparently didn't care if they slept six in a bed or in the fireplace just so it was every night at our house. "I'll make French toast," I said fondly to Tudor as I flitted happily around getting out the real maple syrup and crowding another place on the table each time another gruesome little figure in a torn petticoat, bobby pins and calamine lotion appeared and asked me where the iron was.

When I had a stack of golden French toast about two feet high, ordinarily a mere hors d'oeuvre, I called loudly that breakfast was ready and sat down in my corner with a cup of coffee and a cigarette. After an interval the girls began straggling in, dripping with my perfume and, of course, wearing each other's clothes.

"Hurry and drink your orange juice," I said proudly. "I've made French toast."

"I hope you didn't cook any for me," Anne said loftily, sitting down at the table and unscrewing the top on a bottle of nail polish. "I'm dieting and all I want is one hard-boiled egg."

"Why do you always fix orange juice?" Joan said. "Tomato juice only has fifty calories."

The various Ruthies and Jeanies said to my offers of French toast, "None for me, thanks, Mrs. MacDonald. I'm just going to have black coffee"—or warm water and lemon juice, or a hard-boiled egg.

After they had gone I grimly dumped the lovely golden brown French toast into the raccoons' pan and decided that this was the last time I would ever get up and cook breakfast for my disagreeable little daughters and their ungrateful little friends.

After school the locusts arrived on schedule, but only the boys ate. The girls sipped tea. Then came dinner and no matter what I cooked, rare roast beef, brook trout, ground roundsteak broiled, it was never on their diet. Also I could count on either Anne or Joan or both of them saying, "So much! Why do you always cook in such enormous quantities?"

I don't know what diet they were on, but it was apparently the same one Mary's daughters and friends are using today, a special high school diet that calls for one plate of fudge, three Cokes and a pound of cheese eaten in private and one small celery stalk and half a grapefruit nibbled at the dinner table.

Anne and Joan and their friends talked a great deal about sophistication, tight strapless black evening dresses and long cigarette holders, but when boys appeared they screamed like gulls, laughed like hyenas and pushed one another and the boys rudely. One day I came into the living room and found Anne lifting a chair with two great big boys in it. I was horrified and that night I gave the girls lectures #10874598734 on Being a Lady—Nice Manners—Charm—Womanliness. They listened with half-closed cobra eyes until I had finished, then yawned and stretched rudely, shoved and pushed each other up the stairs, and locked themselves in our bathroom. The thing that troubled me the most was that none of Anne and Joan's friends was as rude as they were. All the Ruthies and Jeanies, etc., said please and thank you, stood up when I came in the room and wrote their bread-and-butter letters. I wondered what magic their mothers used and when, as they were at our house most of the time.

. Then one day Don and I were at a party and a strange man came up to us and said, "So you're the parents of Anne and Joan. They go skiing with us quite often, you know, and Mrs. Alexander and I think they are the *most charming girls* we have ever met. They are also very witty and very bright but, right at this point, it is their *manners* that impress us the most. You see, Carol," (I realized all of a sudden that this was one of the mysterious parents of Carol, quiet, exquisitely mannered Carol, who had been with us off and on, mostly on, for over a year) "ever since she entered adolescence has apparently been taking a behavior course from Al Capone." Of course we told him about Carol and how beautifully she behaved at our house and he went on and on about Anne and Joan, and then he said, "I can't keep this to myself," and rushed off and got Mrs. Alexander, and we went over the whole thing again. We all left the party looking years and years younger.

Anne and Joan had always been to my prejudiced maternal eyes, normally truthful children. Joan told me when she broke the windshield of the Alcotts' car. Anne told me when she spilled nail polish on my new bedspread. Joan told me when she cut off her eyelashes. Anne told me when she drank the cherry wine. They both told me when they took the candy out of the ten-cent store. Perhaps they each told me what the other did, but anyway I got the truth one way or another, most of the time.

Then came adolescence and the birth of the wilful, deliberate, bold-faced lie. The lie, told, I finally decided, to test parents out, to see what kind of fools they really were.

It began with the lost wallet. Anne and Joan were each given five dollars a week allowance. This was to cover carfare, school lunches, Saturday movies and occasional shopping trips. One Saturday Anne told me that she had lost her wallet with her "whole allowance in it." She cried a little when she told me and I felt niggardly and probing when I asked her for details. She was remarkably definite.

"It was in Frederick and Nelson's at the hat bar on the first floor at eleven in the morning last Saturday. I put the wallet on the counter right beside me while I tried on a hat and when I looked for it, it was gone. Probably taken by a shoplifter." While she was telling her story, Anne and Joan both fixed me with large innocent guileless blue eyes. Of course I believed them and gave Anne another five dollars. She snatched it eagerly but I was not suspicious.

The next Saturday the same thing happened. Almost the same story only this time it was Joan and the Vashon drugstore and the culprit probably "some poor starving farmer who needed the money."

I shelled out another five dollars.

Monday morning Velma, my cleaning woman, brought me Anne's green wallet which she had found behind the bed. In it were two one-dollar bills and the stubs of four loge seats in the Fifth Avenue Theatre.

When Anne came home from school I showed her the wallet and the theatre tickets and said sorrowfully, "You lied to me."

"I know it," Anne said cheerfully.

"Why?" I asked, my voice hoarse with emotion.

"I don't know," Anne said. "I guess I just wanted to see if I could. All the kids lie to their mothers."

"Very well," I said. "You owe me five dollars. You can pay me back two dollars a month. Did you lie to me too, Joan?"

Joan, who had her mouth full of apple, nodded brightly, vigorously.

"I'm very very disappointed in you," I said

"Well, my gosh," Joan said, "Carol's been lying to *her* mother for months and months—she *never* catches on." She made it sound as if I had taken unfair advantage.

"Then why does Carol always borrow money from me?" Anne said furiously. "She owes me about a million dollars."

I said, "You can pay me back two dollars a month too, Joan."

Anne said, "I'm going to get my money back from Carol if I have to choke her to death."

A few nights later, at dinner, Anne announced, "Gosh, we had a hard geometry test today."

"We had an algebra test," Joan said, taking a tiny uninterested sip of her milk.

"The geometry test was hard but I think I got an awfully good grade," Anne said, as she pushed her peas into a string of green beads encircling her mashed potatoes.

"How do you think you did in algebra, Joanie?" I asked.

"All right, I guess," Joan said. "I despise Miss Gantron but she's so senile she can't think up very hard tests."

"What did they have for lunch at school?" I asked conversationally.

Anne and Joan glanced at each other quickly, then said together, "Spaghetti—macaroni and cheese."

"Make up your minds," I said levelly. "Which was it—spaghetti or macaroni and cheese—surely they wouldn't have both?"

"The food at school gets more revolting every day," Anne said, taking a tiny bite of avocado. "Absolutely tasteless and always cold."

"The macaroni and cheese tastes just like Kem-Tone," Joan said.

"It's better than their vegetable soup," Anne said. "It tastes just like perspiration."

I said, "Speaking of perspiration, Aunty Mary saw you coming out of the Paramount Theatre this afternoon."

Ruthie said, "Oh, it couldn't have been us, Mrs. MacDonald. We were all at school. Weren't we, Jeanie?"

Jeanie said, "Sure they were, Mrs. MacDonald. Ask Kathy."

I said, "I don't have to ask anybody. I *know* you weren't at school and I *know* you aren't hungry for dinner because you have spent the day stuffing down popcorn and ice cream and candy and Cokes. Now CLEAR THE TABLE, WASH THE DISHES, DO YOUR STUDYING AND GO TO BED!"

Later on when Don and I were lying in bed reading and trying to take our minds off adolescence, I heard Ruthie say to Anne, who was of course taking her bath in our bathroom, "Gee, Anne, your mom's sure sweet. I wouldn't dare tell my mom I skipped school. She'd kill me."

Anne said, "Oh, *she's* all right, I guess. Do you think Bill really likes me?"

There was also the music—the loud, blatting, tuneless music that boomed out of the record player from the minute the girls opened their eyes in the morning until they closed them at night. Boops Bigwig, Doggo Conray, Morks Ogle—or whatever their names were—all sounded exactly alike to me and made "Walkin' My Baby Back Home" indistinguishable from "Paper Moon" or Don's chain saw. To Boops, Doggo, etc., Anne and Joan and their friends danced the Avalon, a sort of crippled drag performed with . . . a pained expression on the face. They listened to Frank Sinatra, Frankie Laine, Billie Holliday and King Cole. Listening required that they be draped over some piece of furniture surrounded by a litter of Coke bottles, apple cores, candy wrappers, cigarette stubs, cookie crumbs and shoes. Nobody ever wore shoes except outside. Even at formal dances the girls kicked off their shoes and got holes in *my* nylons.

I am not at all partial to heavy perfume, preferring light flowery scents, but I'm particularly not partial to heavy perfume slopped on by the handful at seven o'clock in the morning when I'm tentatively taking my first sip of coffee. Anne would come downstairs immaculate, pressed and perfect to the last hair but with the husky scent of Come Hither hovering over her like smoke over a genie. Once or twice I remarked mildly, "Andy, darling, don't you think that perfume is awfully, uh, well, penetrating for school?" She and Joan, who by that time had also made an appearance quite obviously pinned in many places but drenched in Aphrodisia, exchanged long-suffering looks and sighed heavily. Any further mention of the stench in the kitchen I knew would bring forth a torrent of "You don't *want* us to smell nice. You'd like it if we had B.O. or used Lysol perfume. *Everything* we do is wrong. *All* you do is criticize." Keeping as far away from them as I could and drawing heavily on cigarettes, I put their breakfast on the table and thought with pity of the teachers who had to put up with perhaps thirty-five, all smelling like that.

Of course Anne and Joan treated Don and me as if we were tottering on the edge of senility. We weren't even thirty-five but if we danced (never exactly a spontaneous outburst of animal spirits on Don's part) we became the immediate objects of a great deal of humorous comment. "Oh, look at them! Do you mean to say they really used to dance like *that?* He, he, he, ha, ha, ha, you look so funny!" If I occasionally came back at them and reminded them how funny *they* looked when *they* danced they wailed, "You're so crabby all the time. You're never any fun any more."

I don't know how or when Anne and Joan learned to drive, but I do know that each one, on the day of her sixteenth birthday, demanded to be taken to town so she could go through the ridiculous routine of a driving test and be given a license to drive her steady's father's car and to lend our car to any bonehead friend who wished to back it onto a busy street without looking, run it into a tree, turn a corner without seeing "that dumb truck," or put it in reverse by mistake when going very fast. After a time I became rather accustomed to answering the phone and having a small quavering voice say, "Mrs. MacDonald, this is Joanne and I've had a little trouble with the car, your car I mean, and there's a policeman who wants to speak to you."

Once when we had been up very late listening to "then I said to

KATE OSANN, COLLIER'S

"It's simple economics, George. All I want is enough money to spend."

Ted and Ted said to me" and then were kept awake further by the music of Morks and Doggo and further still by the pattering of big bare feet and shrieks and giggles and the thump of the refrigerator door and finally by my bedside light being switched on and Joan demanding, "Where have you put my down quilt? We're making up a bed for Evelyn and Ruthie on the porch," Don remarked with feeling, "What are we running here, a youth hostel? That Ruthie hasn't been home for two years. How come nobody wants to go anywhere but here? Why should we be the only ones with Coke bottles and shoes on the mantel? Where are the other parents? What are they doing?"

Yawning, I said, "Probably sitting around in their uncluttered houses saying, 'What is all this talk about the problems of adolescents? I don't find them any trouble at all.'"

Anne burst in and said, "Do you care if Carol smokes?"

"I don't care if she bursts into flame," Don said.

"Very funny," Anne said witheringly, "and *very old.*" Taking our only package of cigarettes she went out, slamming the door.

"Never mind," I said to Don, "someday they will marry and leave home."

"Are you sure?" Don said, as he sadly sorted over the butts on his ashtray, finally selecting a pretty long one. He examined it critically for a minute or two, then, with a sigh, struck a match and lit it.

ROOF SITTER

FRANCES EISENBERG

From the very beginning there were two things wrong with my brother Joe. He was shy and he was stubborn. This is the way he did. If somebody tried to make him not shy, then he got stubborn. Like the time when he was only four years old and he was supposed to be a butterfly in the Sunday school entertainment, and Miss Wilson tried and tried to push Joe out on the stage and make him flutter his wings, but he lay down on the floor and wouldn't get up no matter how much the other butterflies stepped on him.

And when he started to kindergarten and his teacher kept asking him to come up in front and tell the other children about his pets, Joe ran out of the room and hid downstairs in the boys' toilet until they had to call the janitor to get him out.

My mother had tried her best to make Joe not like he was, but when he was six years old she had to give up. She said she hoped he would outgrow it. And she asked Joe's teacher please not to try to draw Joe out any more because of the way it made him act. So after that everybody left him alone.

One morning in June just after school was out we got a telegram from Nashville saying that my father's Aunt Sadie was in a dying condition, and for them to come quick. At first my mother didn't know what to do, because she knew they wouldn't want any children there, and there wasn't anybody to leave us with. But she thought a while, and then all of a sudden she said, "Sarah Blevins."

"Who is that?" I asked. I was standing there watching my mother.

"She is a college student," said my mother. "She is Mrs. White down the street's niece, and she is staying with her and earning her way through college by taking care of children and things like that this summer."

So my mother hurried down to Mrs. White's house, and I went too, and Mrs. White was out in the yard, and she said that Sarah Blevins would be glad to take care of us while my mother and father were gone. "She is very good with children," Mrs. White said. "She has had some courses in child training at the university and she knows all about them. She will try out some new ideas on your children."

Then Mrs. White called Sarah Blevins out and she was a tall skinny girl with glasses on and a serious look. She told my mother that she would be glad to stay with us, and would give us the best of care. "How old are these children?" Sarah Blevins asked, looking at me, and stretching her mouth a little like a smile.

"This is Helen," my mother said. "She is nine. And Joe, her little brother, is nearly six."

"Oh, that's very fortunate," Sarah Blevins said, "because I have just finished a course in the child from six to twelve years, and that includes both of your children."

"Yes," my mother said. "But please be careful with little Joe. He is a very shy child, and doesn't like to be noticed. As long as he's left alone though, he's very nice. Just so you don't try to draw him into the limelight."

Sarah Blevins looked interested. "I'm very good on behavior problems," she said. "I will try to adjust your little boy. I have done a lot of field work on problem children."

My mother looked worried. "Oh, there's nothing wrong with Joe," she said. "He's just a little young for his age. If you let him alone he'll be all right."

"I'm sure we'll get along splendidly together," said Sarah Blevins, stretching her mouth at me again. She went into her aunt's house and came out with her clothes in a little bag, and we all hurried back to our house because my mother had to meet my father in town and catch the one o'clock train.

When we got to our yard Joe was playing under the sweet-gum tree. He had some rocks and little sticks, and when he saw Sarah Blevins he stared at her for a minute and went on playing.

"This is Joe," said my mother in a hurry. "Joey, this is Sarah Blevins. She is going to take care of you while mother is gone, and you must be a good little boy and do what she says." Then my mother went into the house to get ready.

Joe stared at Sarah Blevins again, and then he began to hammer a stick into the ground with a rock. Sarah Blevins went over to Joe and held out her hand. "How do you do, Joe," she said.

Joe began to look nervous. He twisted his head around so he couldn't see her, but she kept on holding her hand out for him to shake. When she saw he wasn't going to shake hands with her, finally she put her hand down. She looked at the sticks and the rocks he was playing with.

"Oh, a house," she said. "Joe is building a nice house. Who will live in your house when it is built? Is it a fairy house? Will a tiny fairy live in it?"

Joe put his arm up and hid his face. Then he went over and stood behind a bush where Sarah Blevins couldn't see him. All you could see was a piece of his head.

"He doesn't like for people to talk to him," I told Sarah Blevins. "Just the family. He's shy of people."

Sarah Blevins looked a little mad. "Yes, but that's very wrong to encourage him in it," she said. "That way he'll get conditioned and then it will be hopeless. He should be drawn out."

"He doesn't like to be drawn out," I told her. "That just makes him worse."

"Not if it's done right," she said. She began to pretend that she didn't know where Joe was. "There was a little boy here a minute ago," she said. "Where did he go? Maybe he had on a pair of magic shoes, or maybe he changed into a flower or a butterfly?"

Joe heard what she was saying and he squatted down quickly behind the bush. He tried to crawl into it, but it was full of stickers.

Just then my mother came out of the house with her hat on. She kissed me good-bye. "Joe is behind the bush," I told her.

My mother went over and kissed him good-bye. "Be a good boy," she told him. "Good-bye," she said to Sarah Blevins. "I know you're going to be fine with the children. Just take charge of things, and order what you need from the grocery. We'll be back by Wednesday at least."

Then she got into the taxi and rode away.

It seemed very lonely without her. Sarah Blevins stood still a minute, then she said, "I will just leave your little brother alone for the time being." And she took her bag and we went into the house and I showed her where to put her things.

After a while, when she had looked in the icebox to see what food there was, she got a piece of note paper and began to write on it. She told me she was writing out what for me to do every hour of the day and beginning tomorrow I must do exactly what it said. She stuck the paper on the kitchen door with some thumbtacks.

"Now you must take care of everything for a few minutes," she said. "I am going to run down to the grocery store and get some celery. Your little brother seems to be lacking in iron."

While she was gone I went out and hunted for Joe. He was digging holes in the back yard.

"Is she gone yet?" he asked. I knew he meant Sarah Blevins.

"She is gone, but she is coming back in a minute," I told him. "She has gone to get something for you to eat to give you iron."

"I don't want iron," Joe said.

"But listen, Joe," I told him. "She is supposed to take care of us, and we are supposed to mind her while mother and father are away. So don't be stubborn. Do what she says, and maybe they will bring us something nice."

"I don't like her," Joe said.

I didn't know what else to say to Joe. I could see that he was going to be stubborn, but I didn't know how to make him not be.

Pretty soon I could hear Sarah Blevins in the kitchen fixing the supper, and after a while she called us in to eat it.

It was mostly lamb chops and celery and carrots with nothing for dessert. All through supper Sarah Blevins talked to Joe. She asked him things like did he like furry kittens, and did he ever see a brownie, and things like that. But Joe was so hungry that he didn't hide anywhere. He would take a bite of whatever it was, and then he would put his head under the table to chew it so he wouldn't have to look at Sarah Blevins. And just as soon as he got through eating he went into the living room and turned on the radio to the Krunchy Krispy Kiddies hour and I went in there too, and we listened to it.

It had got to the place where the twins had sailed to the moon in their rocket ship and found the palace of King Zoozag, the moon king. While the twins were looking around for the moon pearl, King Zoozag's magician had caught them and locked them up in a dungeon with a ceiling that kept coming down closer and closer to crush the twins to pieces. It was very exciting. The roof was just above their heads and you could hear it giving awful creaks, and you could hear the king laughing an awful laugh, hahahaha, when all of a sudden Sarah Blevins came rushing in there looking like she was going to faint. She ran over and turned off the radio.

"My goodness," she said. She sat down in a chair and got her breath.

"No wonder," she said. "No wonder your little brother has got a complex if your mother lets him listen to such things as that. Especially at night."

Joe had been sitting up close to the radio listening with his mouth open, but when Sarah Blevins turned it off, he turned around and stared at her with his mouth still open.

"Now," Sarah Blevins said, after a minute, in a cheerful voice. "Let's tell stories. Shall we? First I'll tell a story, then Helen will tell one and then Joe will. Or maybe Joe would tell his first."

Joe kept looking at her for just a minute, and then he shook his head. But Sarah Blevins paid no attention to that. "Joe's going to tell us a story, Helen," she said. "Won't that be nice? I wish Joe would tell us a story about a little white rabbit. Don't you?"

"Yes, but he won't," I told her. "He doesn't like to talk before people."

"Oh, yes, Joe will. I know he will," Sarah Blevins said. She gave me a kind of a mad look. "Joe will tell us a story."

Joe put his head down in a corner of the chair, and pulled a cushion over it.

"You see," I said. "He won't."

"Shhhh," hissed Sarah Blevins, frowning at me. "Yes he will," she said out loud. "Just as soon as he thinks awhile he will. Let's be quiet and let him think. Oh, what a nice story Joe is going to tell us."

For a little while we were quiet and Joe didn't take his head out.

"Now," Sarah Blevins said finally. "Now I think Joe is ready to begin. But where is Joe?" she asked in a surprised voice. "Why, he was here just a minute ago. Where can he be? Is he behind the radio?" She went over there and looked. "No, he's not there. Is he behind the door? No." Then she went over to the chair where Joe was and lifted up the cushion. "Why *here* he is."

But before she could say anything else Joe slid out of the chair and ran upstairs.

"I guess he's going to hide in the bathroom," I told Sarah Blevins. "Sometimes he does that when ladies bother him because they can't go in there after him."

Sarah went to the foot of the stairs. "Joe's sleepy," she said in a loud voice. "I guess he wants to go to bed. He will tell us a story tomorrow. Goodnight, Joe."

Then she came back and sat down in the living room. She looked sort of mad. "Helen," she said, "you must keep quiet when I'm talking to Joe. What's wrong with him now is that he's heard people say he's shy so much that he thinks he is shy. So he acts shy. He isn't really shy, he only thinks he is. When he withdraws like this you must pretend it's just a game he's playing, or you must explain it to him like I did just now and make it reasonable. Have I made it clear to you? Do you understand?"

"I don't know if I do or not," I said.

"Well, it doesn't matter. Just so you keep quiet and let me manage your little brother my own way. By the time your mother comes back I'll have him adjusted. But you must co-operate."

"All right," I told her. Because it would be nice and my mother would be glad if she got home and Joe was talking to people and not running from them any more, and not being stubborn and singing little songs when they asked him to, and making speeches and things like that. So I would do like Sarah Blevins said, and be quiet and pretend I didn't know why he was hiding.

The next morning we had breakfast and I looked on the note paper to see what I was supposed to do. I was supposed to do Household Tasks for a half an hour. Sarah Blevins told me to go upstairs and make up my bed and then come down and play outdoors until lunch. So I went up and I began to clean up the bedroom, and I looked out of the window and saw Joe playing in the front yard. He had some marbles and he was putting them in a row on the grass.

Pretty soon I saw Sarah Blevins coming out there and she had some papers in her hands. "Hello, Joe," she said. She sat down on the grass beside him.

"May I play with you?" she asked, stretching her mouth into a smile at him.

Joe looked down at the ground and began to pick up the marbles one at a time. He would not look at Sarah Blevins.

"Would you like to play a game that I have here?" Sarah Blevins said. She put one of the papers down on the grass. "It's a game with pictures. Look. It's fun. Do you want to play it with me?"

Joe began to shake his head. He began to slide away from her a little toward the bush.

"See the little girl in the picture," Sarah Blevins told him, holding it up. "She is rolling a hoop. But something is missing. Can you take the red pencil and put in what is missing?"

Joe kept shaking his head and Sarah kept holding out the pencil to him. Finally Joe got up and ran to the bush and hid behind it. But Sarah went over there too and sat down. "It's nicer over here, isn't it, Joe?" she said. "Let's don't play that game then, let's play another one. Listen."

She took another piece of paper and began to read off of it.

" 'The sun was shining on the sea, shining with all its might.' Can you say that, Joe? Listen: 'The sun was shining on the sea, shining with all its might.' Now you say it."

But Joe began to look more nervous than ever, and he went around to the other side of the bush, and Sarah followed him around there. She kept on talking. "This is fun, isn't it, Joe?" she said. "It's like a game I know called Follow the Leader. Did you ever play that game?"

Joe began to look kind of wild. He looked for another place to hide. There wasn't any. He ran toward the front porch, but I guess he thought that wouldn't be any good, and all of a sudden he started climbing up the rose trellis. There weren't many roses on it, and it was kind of like a ladder. He went half way up and then he turned his head around to see if Sarah was coming.

This time she did not follow him. But anyway he climbed on higher until he got up to the porch roof, and then he crawled up on it and sat there and looked down at Sarah Blevins.

I spread up the bed in a hurry and went on downstairs and out into the yard to where they were. I wanted to see what Sarah was going to do next to adjust Joe.

Sarah was standing there on the ground looking up at the roof. Her face was red and she looked sort of mad, but she laughed and said to me, "Did you see Joe go up the trellis? He's playing that he's a little squirrel, I guess. Did you see him climb?"

"Yes," I said. I was not going to say anything else, because I was supposed to co-operate with her and keep quiet.

"I wonder how a little squirrel comes down off a roof," Sarah Blevins said. "Can you show us, Joe?"

We waited about ten minutes, but Joe did not come down. He went over and sat down behind the chimney. We could just see his legs and a piece of his blouse.

Then I forgot. "We could get the stepladder and get him down that way," I told Sarah Blevins. She gave me an awful mad look.

"Be quiet," she said under her breath. Then she said in a loud voice, "Why, we don't want to get a little squirrel down with a ladder. He will come down himself in a little while to get some nuts."

"Or maybe he thinks he's a bird," I said.

But Sarah Blevins didn't pay any attention to me. "I'm going to fix your lunch now, and when I get back I wouldn't be surprised if Joe is on the ground playing with you, Helen," she said. "Being a squirrel is fun, but after all it's nicer to be a little boy, isn't it?" And she took the papers and things and went into the house.

I sat down on the ground and looked up at Joe.

After a while I said, "Sarah Blevins has gone inside now, Joe. Why don't you come down off of the roof and surprise her?"

Joe got from behind the chimney. "No," he said. After a minute he asked, "When is she going home?"

"Maybe not till next Wednesday," I said. "So come on down and do what she says. We're supposed to."

"I'll come down next Wednesday," Joe said.

I could see that he was going to be stubborn and not come down off of the roof, and then Sarah Blevins couldn't adjust him before mother came back. I didn't know what to do, so I just sat there and tried to think of something.

After a while some children from the next block came skating along the sidewalk. "What are you doing, Helen?" they asked.

"Nothing," I told them. "Only sitting here waiting for my little brother Joe to come down off of the roof."

They came up in the yard and looked up at Joe's face, which was sticking over.

"What is he doing up there?" they asked.

"Just waiting. He's going to sit there until next Wednesday."

Just then an automobile with two men in it came driving slowly along the street. The men looked out at us and stopped the car. A fat one stuck his head out of the window. "Hey, kids," he said. "Having a big time with school out and everything?"

"Yes sir," we said.

"Well sir, how would you like to have your pictures on the Kiddies' Vacation page of the *Morning Journal* so all the other kids all over the city can see what fun you're having? Would you like that?"

"Yes sir," we told him.

So they got out of the car and the thin one had a camera. The fat one told us to stand in a row with our hands on each other's shoulders and pretend that we were skating. One of the other children said, "Hey, mister, can Joe be in the picture?"

"Sure, sure," the fat man said. "Who is Joe, your dog?"

"No," I told him. "He's my little brother. He's up there." I pointed up at the roof.

"Sure, Joe can be in it," the fat man said. "Hold everything, Bill," he said to the man with the camera. "Come on down, Joe," he said.

"He can't be in the picture if he has to come down to be in it," I told the man. "He's going to stay up there all the rest of this week and some more too."

"Ha, ha," laughed the fat man. "That's a new one, ain't it. All over town they're sitting in trees, but he's the first roof sitter. Well, I'll tell you what. We wouldn't want Joe to spoil his record, so we'll take a picture of him from the ground. The rest of you can stand around and be looking up at Joe. We'll give him some free publicity."

So we all stood around and pointed up at the roof, and the cameraman clicked the picture so quick that Joe couldn't hide his face or do anything about it. Then the man asked us our names and how old we were, what grades at school we were in, and then they got in their car and drove away. And the children from the next block hurried home to tell their mothers about having their pictures taken. And just then Sarah Blevins came to the door and said lunch was ready. "We have peanut butter sandwiches, Helen," she said. "Maybe Joe will come down and get some."

But he didn't. I went in and sat down at the table.

"A man took our pictures," I told Sarah Blevins.

But she didn't pay any attention. I guess she was thinking what to do next to adjust Joe. When we finished lunch she said we would just let Joe alone until he got hungry, and she put the dishes to soak and sat down and began to read a magazine.

I went outside and stayed in the front yard. So the afternoon went by and it was beginning to get dark, and after a while it was really dark, and still Joe was on the roof.

I went in the house to see if supper was ready and to ask Sarah Blevins what she was going to do.

"It's dark," I said, "and Joe is still up on the roof. He still won't come down."

"Go out and tell him that supper is ready," said Sarah Blevins. "But don't tell him to come down. He must decide that for himself. He must make up his own mind what he is going to do. If I make him come down now, everything will be ruined."

So I went out and told Joe supper was ready. "Don't you want any?" I asked him.

His voice sounded very weak and far away. "No," he said.

"Are you going to sleep up there?" I asked him.

"Yes," he said, and he sounded scared and stubborn at the same time.

I went back and told Sarah Blevins. "Very well," she said.

So we ate supper and it was bedtime, and I went upstairs. I went to the window of my mother and father's bedroom. The moon was shining and I could look down on the porch roof and see Joe, sitting up close to the chimney.

"Are you awake, Joe?" I asked him.

"Yes," his voice came up.

"Good night, then," I said. I went to bed and I felt awful. I thought well anyway he can't roll off, because the roof is wide and flat, but it would be hard and maybe he would be hungry. So after a while I got two pillows and a blanket, and I went to the window and dropped them down to Joe. I didn't care if I had promised Sarah to co-operate. I knew my mother wouldn't want Joe to sleep out of doors without a blanket. "Do you want something to eat, Joe?" I asked him low so she wouldn't hear.

"Yes," he said. "I want a peanut butter sandwich and some crackers."

So I went into the kitchen and when I went past the living room I told Sarah Blevins I was going for a drink of water, and I got some peanut butter sandwiches and a whole box of crackers, and I went back up to the window and let them down to Joe by a string.

"But you oughtn't to be so stubborn, Joe," I told him while he was eating them. "You ought to do more what people say and mind them better, or something awful might happen to you."

"I don't care," Joe said. He was fixing the blanket and the pillows. He lay down on them and went to sleep.

The next morning Joe was still on the roof. We talked to him from the upstairs window, but he turned his back because Sarah was there and he wouldn't say anything to her. "Your little brother is a very strange case," Sarah Blevins said to me. She told me to get a bottle of milk and let it down to him, because we couldn't have him starving. And she would think of what to do next.

About ten o'clock people began to drive past the house, and they would drive slow and point up to our roof. A few of them stopped their cars and got out and came up on the sidewalk and looked. "Little girl," they said to me, "is this where the little boy lives that's sitting on the roof, that his picture was in the *Journal* this morning?"

I went and got the paper, and there we all were on the vacation page, and under it it said "Out to establish new record," and "Little

Joe Marsden, 7, 342 Cedar Street, has joined the ranks of marathon sitters and declares that he will stay on his roof until next Wednesday afternoon."

You couldn't see much of Joe in the picture, only his head. But the rest of us were plain. I ran and showed the paper to Sarah Blevins. "Look!" I said. "Joe got his picture in the paper, and look out in the street at all the people."

Sarah looked and she turned sort of pale. She asked me some questions, but she didn't listen to what I said. She straightened out her mouth and looked mad. "I'm going out there and try one more time," she said. "And this is the last straw."

"You mean you're not going to try to adjust him any more?" I asked her, following her out into the yard, but she didn't answer me.

She looked up at him from the sidewalk. She changed her voice from mad to sweet. "Helen, do you believe in magic?" she said to me. "I do. I'm going to close my eyes and count to ten, and when I open them I believe Joe will be down off of the roof, standing right here on the grass." Then she shut her eyes and began to count.

By now there were two cars parked in front of the house and a fat man and a woman in one of them and his face was red and he acted funny. He made funny motions at Joe and he yelled, "Don't you do it, sonny. You stay there. She's just trying to get you down." But he didn't talk plain, and he smelled funny. "Shhhh," the woman in the car said, "shhhh." But she was giggling herself, and she acted nearly as funny as her husband.

"Six, seven, eight," Sarah was saying very slow.

But just then something funny seemed to happen to Joe. He looked down and saw the people looking up at him and he heard the fat man yelling, "Don't you do it, sonny." Then all of a sudden instead of hiding from them he began to jump up and down on the roof and yell at Sarah, "This is my house. Let me alone." And then he called her a bad name. "Go home, old jackass," he said.

Sarah opened her mouth and looked surprised. I guess she was surprised that Joe could talk. He had not said anything before her until now.

The fat man began to laugh as loud as he could. "That's telling her!" he said and he drove the car away, and he was sort of whooping as he went, and so was his wife. "That's telling her," they said.

The people in the other car stayed, though. Twice Sarah started to climb the trellis so she could talk to Joe better, but both times he said, "Let me alone," and looked like he was going to jump. So Sarah had

"I'll try to explain why you can't play your Old MacDonald record. There's a big, big storm outside and the wind is blowing very, very hard—hear it? . . . B-r-r-r! And somewhere that mean old wind blew a tree down on the electric wires and shut off the electricity and that's why our lights won't light, the toaster won't work and Mommy can't run the vacuum. Daddy called up the man and he said he's going to fix it real soon. So until it's fixed, nothing that has wires is going to work . . . Understand?"

"I wanna hear my Old MacDonald record."

---

to get down, and she went over and talked to a woman. She told her that in all the time she had worked with children she had never in her life seen one as stubborn as Joe. But she said if everyone had just let him alone she could have had him adjusted, but now everything was spoiled.

But nobody paid much attention to her because now Joe had turned out to be famous, because he was the only roof sitter in town, and nobody cared what Sarah thought.

The more people stopped and looked up at Joe the more I got proud of him and I would tell everybody I was his sister and that he had stayed up there all day and all night and was going to stay on until Wednesday, and everybody asked me questions about him and laughed, and about three o'clock some newsreel cameramen that were in town for something else took some pictures of Joe for the movies.

It was just after this that my mother and father came home. When they got out of the taxi my mother saw the people standing there and she began to look scared. "What is it?" she said. "What's happened?"

"Look, mother. Look, papa," I yelled, pointing up to the roof. "Joe's up there. He's been up there nearly two days. He had his picture in the paper, and the people have been coming to see him all day. He's famous now."

Then Sarah Blevins ran over and began talking fast, and she was really crying. She kept saying things about how she had tried to adjust Joe, and then these people began to come and notice him and encourage him, and everything was spoiled.

"And he called her a jackass," I said. "And this is the stubbornest he ever was in his life. But now he's not so shy any more. He didn't hide from the people. Aren't you glad Joe's going to be in the movies and everybody will get to see him?"

But my mother didn't seem to be glad. She stood there looking mad and disgusted. "I ought never to have gone off in the first place," she said.

"Joe, you ought not to have done that," my father told him. "You ought to know better." Just then he saw the roses that had been stepped on and smashed on Joey's way up, and he gave a mad sound. "I've a good notion to come up there and blister you good," he said.

But when Joe saw that Sarah was leaving he came down by himself. And Sarah went away with her little black bag, and she said she was so nervous she didn't know what she was doing. All the people went away, and that was the end of Joe being a roof sitter. He had to eat his supper and go to bed, even if it wasn't dark, and he couldn't have any of the box of candy they had brought from Nashville where they had left and come home because my father's Aunt Sadie had turned out not to be so sick after all.

But Joe was famous for several days and all over town children began sitting on roofs, trying to break the record. One of them, a little girl named Gladys Potts, sat on her garage roof for ninety-three hours, but a storm came up, and she had to come down.

Still, it seemed that all the attention he had got did not quite adjust Joe, because later when they asked him to be in a Sunday school play he said he wouldn't, and he didn't. Not even when they promised to give him some bananas afterward.

Own Your Own Home:

BEDS

SHIRLEY JACKSON

Our house is, as I have said, large, and the second floor has four bed-rooms and a bathroom, all opening out onto a long narrow hall which we have made even narrower by lining it with bookcases so that every inch of hall which is not doorway is books. As is the case with most houses, both the front door and the back door are downstairs on the first floor. The front bedroom, which is my husband's and mine, is the largest and lightest, and has a double bed. The room next down the hall belongs to the girls, and contains a crib and a single, short bed. Laurie's room, across the hall, has a double-decker bed and he sleeps on the top half. The guest room, at the end of the hall, has a double bed. The double bed in our room is made up with white sheets and cases, the baby's crib has pink linen, and Jannie's bed has yellow. Laurie's bed has green linen, and the guest room has blue. The bottom half of Laurie's bed is never made up, unless company is going to use it immediately, because the dog traditionally spends a large part of his time there and regards it as his bed. There is no bed table on the distaff side of the double bed in our room. One side of the bed in the guest room is pushed against the wall. No one can fit into the baby's crib except the baby; the ladder to the top half of Laurie's double-decker is very shaky and stands in a corner of the room; the children reach the top half of the bed by climbing up over the footboard. All three of the children are accustomed to having a glass of apple juice, to which they are addicted, by their bedsides at night. Laurie uses a green glass, Jannie uses a red glass, Sally uses one of those little flowered cheese glasses, and my husband uses an aluminum tumbler because he has broken so many ordinary glasses trying to find them in the dark.

I do not take cough drops or cough medicine in any form.

The baby customarily sleeps with half a dozen cloth books, an armless doll, and a small cardboard suitcase which holds the remnants of half a dozen decks of cards. Jannie is very partial to a pink baby blanket, which has shrunk from many washings. The girls' room is very warm, the guest room moderately so; our room is chilly, and Laurie's room is quite cold. We are all of us, including the dog, notoriously easy and heavy sleepers; my husband never eats coffee cake.

My husband caught the grippe first, on a Friday, and snarled and shivered and complained until I prevailed upon him to go to bed. By Friday night both Laurie and Sally were feverish, and on Saturday Jannie and I began to cough and sniffle. In our family we take ill in different manners; my husband is extremely annoyed at the whole procedure and is convinced that his being sick is somebody's fault, Laurie tends to become a little light-headed and strew handkerchiefs around his room, Jannie coughs and coughs and coughs, Sally turns bright red, and I suffer in stoical silence, so long as everyone knows clearly that I am sick. We are each of us privately convinced that our own ailment is far more severe than anyone else's. At any rate, on Saturday night I put all the children into their beds, gave each of them half an aspirin and the usual fruit juice, covered them warmly, and then settled my husband down for the night with his tumbler of water and his cigarettes and matches and ashtray. He had decided to sleep in the guest room because it was warmer. At about ten o'clock I checked to see that all the children were covered and asleep and that Toby was in his place on the bottom half of the double-decker. I then took two sleeping pills and went to sleep in my own bed in my own room. Because my husband was in the guest room I slept on his side of the bed, next to the bed table. I put my cigarettes and matches on the end table next to the ashtray, along with a small glass of brandy, which I find more efficacious than cough medicine.

I woke up some time later to find Jannie standing beside the bed. "Can't sleep," she said. "Want to come in *your* bed."

"Come along," I said. "Bring your own pillow."

She went and got her pillow and her small pink blanket and her glass of fruit juice, which she put on the floor next to the bed, since she had got the side without any end table. She put her pillow down, rolled herself in her pink blanket, and fell asleep. I went back to sleep, but sometime later Sally came in, asking sleepily, "Where's Jannie?"

"She's here," I said. "Are you coming in bed with us?"

"Yes," said Sally.

"Go and get your pillow, then," I said.

She returned with her pillow, her books, her doll, her suitcase, and her fruit juice, which she put on the floor next to Jannie's. Then she crowded in comfortably next to Jannie and fell asleep. Eventually the pressure of the two of them began to force me uneasily toward the edge of the bed, so I rolled out wearily, took my pillow and my small glass of brandy and my cigarettes and matches and my ashtray and went into the guest room, where my husband was asleep. I pushed at him and he snarled, but he finally moved over to the side next to the wall, and I put my cigarettes and matches and my brandy and my ashtray on the end table next to *his* cigarettes and matches and ashtray and tumbler of water and put my pillow on the bed and fell asleep. Shortly after this he woke me and asked me to let him get out of the bed, since it was too hot in that room to sleep and he was going back to his own bed. He took his pillow and his cigarettes and matches and his ashtray and his aluminum glass of water and went padding off down the hall. In a few minutes Laurie came into the guest room where I had just fallen asleep again; he was carrying his pillow and his glass of fruit juice. "Too cold in my room," he said, and I moved out of the way and let him get into the bed on the side next to the wall. After a few minutes the dog came in, whining nervously, and came up onto the bed and curled himself up around Laurie and I had to get out or be smothered. I gathered together what of my possessions I could, and made my way into my own room, where my husband was asleep with Jannie on one side and the baby on the other. Jannie woke up when I came in and said, "Own bed," so I helped her carry her pillow and her fruit juice and her pink blanket back to her own bed.

The minute Jannie got out of our bed the baby rolled over and turned sideways, so there was no room for me. I could not get into the crib and I could not climb into the top half of the double-decker, so since the dog was in the guest room I went and took the blanket off the crib and got into the bottom half of the double-decker, setting my brandy and my cigarettes and matches and my ashtray on the floor next to the bed. Shortly after that Jannie, who apparently felt left out, came in with her pillow and her pink blanket and her fruit juice and got up into the top half of the double-decker, leaving her fruit juice on the floor next to my brandy.

At about six in the morning the dog wanted to get out, or else he wanted his bed back, because he came and stood next to me and howled. I got up and went downstairs, sneezing, and let him out, and then decided that since it had been so cold anyway in the bottom half of the double-decker I might as well stay downstairs and heat up some coffee and have that much warmth, at least. While I was waiting for the coffee to heat, Jannie came to the top of the stairs and asked if I would bring *her* something hot, and I heard Laurie stirring in the guest room, so I heated some milk and put it into a jug and decided that while I was at it I might just as well give everybody something hot so I set out enough cups for everyone and brought out a coffee cake and put it on the tray and added some onion rolls for my husband, who does not eat coffee cake. When I brought the tray upstairs Laurie and Jannie were both in the guest room, giggling, so I set the tray down in there and heard Sally talking from our room in the front. I went to get her and she was sitting up in the bed talking to her father, who was only very slightly awake. "Play card?" she was asking brightly, and she opened her suitcase and dealt him, onto the pillow next to his nose, four diamonds to the ace, jack and the seven of clubs.

I asked my husband if he would like some coffee, and he said it was terribly cold. I suggested that he come down into the guest room, where it was warmer. He and the baby followed me down to the guest room, and my husband and Laurie got into the bed and the rest of us sat on the foot of the bed and I poured the coffee and the hot milk and gave the children coffee cake and my husband the onion rolls. Jannie decided to take her milk and coffee cake back into her own bed, and since she had mislaid her pillow she took one from the guest room bed. Sally of course followed her, going first back into our room to pick up *her* pillow. My husband fell asleep again while I was pouring his coffee, and Laurie set his hot milk precariously on the headboard of the bed and asked me to get his pillow from wherever it was, so I went into the double-decker and got him the pillow from the top, which turned out to be Jannie's, and her pink blanket was with it. I took my coffee cake and my coffee into my own bed and had just settled down when Laurie came in to say cloudily that Daddy had kicked him out of bed and could he stay in here. I said of course and he said he would get a pillow and he came back in a minute with the one from the bottom half of the double-decker which was mine.

He went to sleep right away, and then the baby came in to get her books and her suitcase and decided to stay with her milk and her coffee cake, so I left and went into the guest room and made my husband move over and sat *there* and had my coffee. Meanwhile Jannie had moved into the top half of the double-decker, looking for her pillow, and had taken instead the pillow from Sally's bed and my glass of brandy and had settled down there to listen to Laurie's radio. I went downstairs to let the dog in and he came upstairs and got into his bed on the bottom half of the double-decker, and while I was gone my husband had moved back over onto the accessible side of the guest room bed so I went into Jannie's bed, which is rather too short, and I brought a pillow from the guest room, and my coffee.

At about nine o'clock the Sunday papers came and I went down to get them, and at about nine-thirty everyone woke up. My husband had moved back into his own bed when Laurie and Sally vacated it for their own beds, Laurie driving Jannie into the guest room when he took back the top half of the double-decker, and my husband woke up at nine-thirty and found himself wrapped in Jannie's pink blanket, sleeping on Laurie's green pillow and with a piece of coffee cake and Sally's fruit juice glass, not to mention the four diamonds to the ace, jack and the seven of clubs. Laurie, in the top half of the double-decker, had my glass of brandy and my cigarettes and matches and the baby's pink pillow. The dog had my white pillow and my ashtray. Jannie in the guest room had one white pillow and one blue pillow and two glasses of fruit juice and my husband's cigarettes and matches and ashtray and Laurie's hot milk, besides her own hot milk and coffee cake and her father's onion rolls. The baby in her crib had her father's aluminum tumbler of water and her suitcase and books and doll and a blue pillow from the guest room, but no blanket.

The puzzle is, of course, what became of the blanket from Sally's bed? I took it off her crib and put it on the bottom half of the double-decker, but the dog did not have it when he woke up, and neither did any of the other beds. It was a blue-patterned patchwork quilt, and has not been seen since, and I would most particularly like to know where it got to. As I say, we are very short of blankets.

"I wish they'd hurry and finish building—it's beginning to be
badly in need of repairs."

HELP WANTED!

LEONARD A. PARIS

Of all the workroom tools I know,
    Mine are the dandiest;
Of all the tinkering fools I know,
    I'm the unhandiest.
I'd give my all to use an awl,
    But I'm a dope with it;
I have a lovely coping saw,
    But cannot cope with it.
In fact, you never saw a man
    Less ambidextrous.
I hope to heck a carpenter
    Moves in right nextr-ous.

DOUBLE THAT ORDER!

PARKE CUMMINGS

The other day I went into a local general store and stated: "I want six nail files."

The clerk looked at me curiously for a minute, and finally said: "Of course, it's none of my business, but why do you want so many?"

Drawing myself up to my full height, and looking him squarely in the chest, I replied, with quiet dignity: "To clean my nails with."

Again he regarded me with curiosity. "I assumed that," he admitted, "but why six?"

"I will explain," I said patiently. "When I take the six files home, my son, John, will immediately grab one of them, attempt to wedge loose a stuck part of his electric train with it, and break off the tip. He will then take a second file, use it more carefully, but mislay it. My young daughter will employ a third one to loosen a tough knot in her shoelaces. It will never be seen again. My wife, seeing three remaining files on my bureau, will assume I have more than I need, and appropriate one of them to make up for the one she left in the washroom of the Hotel Ardmont. The disappearance of the fifth file will never be explained. If I have good luck, this will still leave me a file with which—as I have previously stated—to clean my nails."

The clerk nodded understandingly. "It's pencils that go in our house," he said.

"In ours too," I said. What I was outlining to this fellow was the Theory of Protective Mass Purchasing, one to which I have long subscribed. This, of course, should not be confused with any system of quantity buying where the object is to get a cheaper unit price—as when you buy five bushels of grapefruit, half of which spoil. I paid the straight retail price for my half dozen files, and my saving was not a financial one.

My objective was purely one of availability. The law of averages operates inexorably with nail files—and other articles I shall mention —but, by buying in quantity, you at least give it a temporary knockout. You get it down on the floor and under control, overwhelmed by sheer force of numbers. It will, of course, eventually get up off the floor to plague you again, but that fleeting respite is all I ask for.

Drinking tumblers should be similarly mass purchased, but on a far more generous basis. To buy six tumblers for a family of four is the height of futility. Before the first meal, one will be spirited to the bathroom for a toothbrush container, a second will get broken, and a third will be appropriated by one of the younger children for mixing water colors—which means that, at dinner, some member of the family will have to use an old jelly glass or go thirsty. A dozen is the minimum plausible purchase, but two dozen is the figure I hold out for. And the number should go up in geometrical, not arithmetical, proportion. For instance, for a family of eight, you should buy eight dozen glasses, not four.

Anybody who allows himself to get down to one door key should, of course, be held for observation. Some member of the family will develop the theory that this article is the solution to a locked trunk in the attic. It will be lugged up there, mixed in with a quantity of other unidentifiable keys, and then either lost or thrown away in disgust when it doesn't work. This means that you will have to hire a locksmith, at a fancy price, to make an impression of your door lock, and furnish you with new keys. On the other hand, it is a relatively inexpensive matter to have any hardware store turn out duplicate keys for you *provided* you have one suitable to serve as a model. My personal feeling is that no family should have less than eight keys per door, at least three of which should be cached in the safe-deposit box.

Here are some further recommendations the next time you go to the store. (I am assuming a family of four-six. Up this accordingly if yours is larger.)

Hammers: Six. (Small children, you have noted, eat hammers.)

Hair combs: Three per person. People are constantly lugging combs out of the house and losing them. Certain types of combs simply evaporate in unfavorable weather.

Paring knives: Use your judgment here, but reflect that in a typical family a paring knife will be used for: cutting string; whittling a closet door that sticks; mumblety-peg; severing heavy wire; cutting flowers; repairing light sockets; sharpening pencils; opening packages; paring fingernails; cleaning corroded water pipes; prying off bottle tops; trimming loose branches off small trees and shrubs; miscellaneous repairs to sporting equipment, such as baseball bats, tennis rackets, skis, sleds, air rifles; and (occasionally) paring vegetables. From this you should be able to estimate the chances of a housewife finding one in her kitchen drawer, and in good repair, when she wants to use it.

Adhesive substances: (Scotch tape, court plaster, tire tape, etc.) If my recommendations go into effect, these will hereafter be sold in quarter-mile, half-mile, and mile units.

Paper: To draw on, I mean. A small home-type paper mill installed just off the garage may keep you abreast of the demand, though I doubt it. A gesture in this direction will be appreciated at the office in any case.

Radio sets: Two per room per child, with a spare gross in the basement—and two tickets, for you, to Atlantic City.

Mittens: Just take all they have in Susie's size. If other customers have to go without, that's their hard luck.

HOUSEKEEPING TIPS

CARL BUCHELE

Cake will not get stale if kept in a bright-colored box in the children's room.

Books on scientific topics will remain in better condition than whodunits.

Scratches on floors can be concealed nicely with Oriental rugs.

To keep children from listening to your conversation, direct it at them.

A quick-acting remedy for housewife's aching back is a suggestion to eat out and take in a show.

Children will not track their muddy feet through the kitchen if the front door is kept unlocked.

Woolly dresses are fine for removing dog hairs from chairs and sofas.

THE PETERKINS ARE OBLIGED TO MOVE

LUCRETIA P. HALE (1820–1900)

Agamemnon had long felt it an impropriety to live in a house that was called a "semi-detached" house, when there was no other "semi" to it. It had always remained wholly detached, as the owner had never

"Do you have something that will cause crab grass a very slow
and painful death?"

---

built the other half. Mrs. Peterkin felt this was not a sufficient reason
for undertaking the terrible process of a move to another house, when
they were fully satisfied with the one they were in.

But a more powerful reason forced them to go. The track of a new
railroad had to be carried directly through the place, and a station
was to be built on that very spot.

Mrs. Peterkin so much dreaded moving that she questioned whether
they could not continue to live in the upper part of the house and
give up the lower part to the station. They could then dine at the
restaurant, and it would be very convenient about travelling, as there
would be no danger of missing the train, if one were sure of the direction.

But when the track was actually laid by the side of the house, and
the steam-engine of the construction train puffed and screamed under
the dining-room windows, and the engineer calmly looked in to see
what the family had for dinner, she felt, indeed, that they must move.

But where should they go? It was difficult to find a house that satisfied the whole family. One was too far off, and looked into a tan-pit; another was too much in the middle of the town, next door to a machine-shop. Elizabeth Eliza wanted a porch covered with vines, that should face the sunset; while Mr. Peterkin thought it would not be convenient to sit there looking towards the west in the late afternoon (which was his only leisure time), for the sun would shine in his face. The little boys wanted a house with a great many doors, so that they could go in and out often. But Mr. Peterkin did not like so much slamming, and felt there was more danger of burglars with so many doors. Agamemnon wanted an observatory, and Solomon John a shed for a workshop. If he could have carpenters' tools and a workbench he could build an observatory, if it were wanted.

But it was necessary to decide upon something, for they must leave their house directly. So they were obliged to take Mr. Finch's, at the Corners. It satisfied none of the family. The porch was a piazza, and was opposite a barn. There were three other doors—too many to please Mr. Peterkin, and not enough for the little boys. There was no ob-servatory, and nothing to observe if there were one, as the house was too low, and some high trees shut out any view. Elizabeth Eliza had hoped for a view; but Mr. Peterkin consoled her by deciding it was more healthy to have to walk for a view, and Mrs. Peterkin agreed that they might get tired of the same every day.

And everybody was glad a selection was made, and the little boys carried their India-rubber boots the very first afternoon.

Elizabeth Eliza wanted to have some system in the moving, and spent the evening in drawing up a plan. It would be easy to arrange everything beforehand, so that there should not be the confusion that her mother dreaded, and the discomfort they had in their last move. Mrs. Peterkin shook her head; she did not think it possible to move with any comfort. Agamemnon said a great deal could be done with a list and a programme.

Elizabeth Eliza declared if all were well arranged a programme would make it perfectly easy. They were to have new parlor carpets, which could be put down in the new house the first thing. Then the parlor furniture could be moved in, and there would be two comforta-ble rooms, in which Mr. and Mrs. Peterkin could sit while the rest of the move went on. Then the old parlor carpets could be taken up for the new dining room and the downstairs bedroom, and the family could meanwhile dine at the old house. Mr. Peterkin did not object to this, though the distance was considerable, as he felt exercise would be good for them all. Elizabeth Eliza's programme then arranged that the dining-room furniture should be moved the third day, by which time one of the old parlor carpets would be down in the new dining room, and they could still sleep in the old house. Thus there would always be a quiet, comfortable place in one house or the other. Each night, when Mr. Peterkin came home, he would find some place for quiet thought and rest, and each day there should be moved only the furniture needed for a certain room. Great confusion would be avoided and nothing misplaced. Elizabeth Eliza wrote these last words at the head of her programme—"Misplace nothing." And Agamemnon made a copy of the programme for each member of the family.

The first thing to be done was to buy the parlor carpets. Elizabeth Eliza had already looked at some in Boston, and the next morning she went, by an early train, with her father, Agamemnon, and Solomon John, to decide upon them.

They got home about eleven o'clock, and when they reached the house were dismayed to find two furniture wagons in front of the gate, already partly filled! Mrs. Peterkin was walking in and out of the open door, a large book in one hand, and a duster in the other, and she came to meet them in an agony of anxiety. What should they do? The furniture carts had appeared soon after the rest had left for Boston, and the men had insisted upon beginning to move the things. In vain had she shown Elizabeth Eliza's programme; in vain had she insisted they must take only the parlor furniture. They had declared they must put the heavy pieces in the bottom of the cart, and the lighter furniture on top. So she had seen them go into every room in the house, and select one piece of furniture after another, without even looking at Elizabeth Eliza's programme; she doubted if they could have read it if they had looked at it.

Mr. Peterkin had ordered the carters to come; but he had no idea they would come so early, and supposed it would take them a long time to fill the carts.

But they had taken the dining-room sideboard first—a heavy piece of furniture—and all its contents were now on the dining-room tables. Then, indeed, they selected the parlor bookcase, but had set every book on the floor. The men had told Mrs. Peterkin they would put the books in the bottom of the cart, very much in the order they were taken from the shelves. But by this time Mrs. Peterkin was considering the carters as natural enemies, and dared not trust them; besides, the books ought all to be dusted. So she was now holding one of the volumes of Agamemnon's Encyclopædia, with difficulty, in one hand, while she was dusting it with the other. Elizabeth Eliza was in dismay. At this moment four men were bringing down a large chest of drawers from her father's room, and they called to her to stand out of the way. The parlors were a scene of confusion. In dusting the books Mrs. Peterkin neglected to restore them to the careful rows in which they were left by the men, and they lay in hopeless masses in different parts of the room. Elizabeth Eliza sunk in despair upon the end of a sofa.

"It would have been better to buy the red and blue carpet," said Solomon John.

"Is not the carpet bought?" exclaimed Mrs. Peterkin. And then they were obliged to confess they had been unable to decide upon one, and had come back to consult Mrs. Peterkin.

"What shall we do?" asked Mrs. Peterkin.

Elizabeth Eliza rose from the sofa and went to the door, saying, "I shall be back in a moment."

Agamemnon slowly passed round the room, collecting the scattered volumes of his Encyclopædia. Mr. Peterkin offered a helping hand to a man lifting a wardrobe.

Elizabeth Eliza soon returned. "I did not like to go and ask her. But I felt that I must in such an emergency. I explained to her the whole matter, and she thinks we should take the carpet at Makillan's."

"Makillan's" was a store in the village, and the carpet was the only one all the family had liked without any doubt; but they had supposed they might prefer one from Boston.

The moment was a critical one. Solomon John was sent directly to Makillan's to order the carpet to be put down that very day. But where should they dine? Where should they have their supper? And where was Mr. Peterkin's "quiet hour"? Elizabeth Eliza was frantic; the dining-room floor and table were covered with things.

It was decided that Mr. and Mrs. Peterkin should dine at the Bromwicks', who had been most neighborly in their offers, and the rest should get something to eat at the baker's.

Agamemnon and Elizabeth Eliza hastened away to be ready to receive the carts at the other house, and direct the furniture as they could. After all there was something exhilarating in this opening of the new house, and in deciding where things should go. Gayly Elizabeth Eliza stepped down the front garden of the new home, and across the piazza, and to the door. But it was locked, and she had no keys!

"Agamemnon, did you bring the keys?" she exclaimed.

No, he had not seen them since the morning—when—ah!—yes, the little boys were allowed to go to the house for their India-rubber boots, as there was a threatening of rain. Perhaps they had left some door unfastened—perhaps they had put the keys under the door-mat. No, each door, each window, was solidly closed, and there was no mat!

"I shall have to go to the school to see if they took the keys with them," said Agamemnon; "or else go home to see if they left them there." The school was in a different direction from the house, and far at the other end of the town; for Mr. Peterkin had not yet changed the boys' school, as he proposed to do after their move.

"That will be the only way," said Elizabeth Eliza; for it had been arranged that the little boys should take their lunch to school, and not come home at noon.

She sat down on the steps to wait, but only for a moment, for the carts soon appeared, turning the corner. What should be done with the furniture? Of course the carters must wait for the keys, as she should need them to set the furniture up in the right places. But they could not stop for this. They put it down upon the piazza, on the steps, in the garden, and Elizabeth Eliza saw how incongruous it was! There was something from every room in the house! Even the large family chest, which had proved too heavy for them to travel with, had come down from the attic, and stood against the front door.

And Solomon John appeared with the carpet-woman, and a boy with a wheelbarrow, bringing the new carpet. And all stood and waited. Some opposite neighbors appeared to offer advice and look on, and Elizabeth Eliza groaned inwardly that only the shabbiest of their furniture appeared to be standing full in view.

It seemed ages before Agamemnon returned, and no wonder; for he had been to the house, then to the school, then back to the house, for one of the little boys had left the keys at home, in the pocket of his clothes. Meanwhile the carpet-woman had waited, and the boy with the wheelbarrow had waited, and when they got in they found the parlor must be swept and cleaned. So the carpet-woman went off in dudgeon, for she was sure there would not be time enough to do anything.

And one of the carts came again, and in their hurry the men set the furniture down anywhere. Elizabeth Eliza was hoping to make a little place in the dining room, where they might have their supper, and go home to sleep. But she looked out, and there were the carters bringing the bedsteads, and proceeding to carry them upstairs.

In despair Elizabeth Eliza went back to the old house. If she had been there she might have prevented this. She found Mrs. Peterkin in an agony about the entry oil-cloth. It had been made in the house, and how could it be taken out of the house? Agamemnon made measurements; it certainly could not go out of the front door! He suggested it might be left till the house was pulled down, when it could easily be moved out of one side. But Elizabeth Eliza reminded him that the whole house was to be moved without being taken apart. Perhaps it could be cut in strips narrow enough to go out. One of the men loading the remaining cart disposed of the question by coming in and rolling up the oil-cloth and carrying it off on top of his wagon.

Elizabeth Eliza felt she must hurry back to the new house. But what should they do? No beds here, no carpets there! The dining-room table and sideboard were at the other house, the plates, and forks, and spoons here. In vain she looked at her programme. It was all reversed; everything was misplaced. Mr. Peterkin would suppose they were to eat here and sleep here, and what had become of the little boys?

Meanwhile the man with the first cart had returned. They fell to packing the dining-room china.

They were up in the attic, they were down in the cellar. Even one suggested to take the tacks out of the parlor carpets, as they should want to take them next. Mrs. Peterkin sunk upon a kitchen chair.

"Oh, I wish we had decided to stay and be moved in the house!" she exclaimed.

Solomon John urged his mother to go to the new house, for Mr. Peterkin would be there for his "quiet hour." And when the carters at last appeared, carrying the parlor carpets on their shoulders, she sighed and said, "There is nothing left," and meekly consented to be led away.

They reached the new house to find Mr. Peterkin sitting calmly in a rocking-chair on the piazza, watching the oxen coming into the opposite barn. He was waiting for the keys, which Solomon John had taken back with him. The little boys were in a horse-chestnut tree, at the side of the house.

Agamemnon opened the door. The passages were crowded with furniture, the floors were strewn with books; the bureau was upstairs that was to stand in a lower bedroom; there was not a place to lay a table—there was nothing to lay upon it; for the knives and plates and spoons had not come, and although the tables were there they were covered with chairs and boxes.

At this moment came a covered basket from the lady from Philadelphia. It contained a choice supper, and forks and spoons, and at the same moment appeared a pot of hot tea from an opposite neighbor. They placed all this on the back of a bookcase lying upset, and sat around it. Solomon John came rushing in from the gate.

"The last load is coming! We are all moved!" he exclaimed; and the little boys joined in a chorus. "We are moved! We are moved!"

Mrs. Peterkin looked sadly round; the kitchen utensils were lying on the parlor lounge, and an old family gun on Elizabeth Eliza's hatbox. The parlor clock stood on a barrel; some coal-scuttles had been placed on the parlor table, a bust of Washington stood in the door-way, and the looking-glasses leaned against the pillars of the piazza. But they were moved! Mrs. Peterkin felt, indeed, that they were very much moved.

SUMMER IS ICUMEN IN

PARKE CUMMINGS

A preliminary survey conducted by my staff of experts indicates that we are in for a truly memorable summer this year. The United States has a greater backlog of old jelly and pickle glasses than at any other time in its history, so that tenants of beach cottages will be well supplied with drinking glasses. The tin knife-and-fork supply is also adequate, and the consensus is that the 1908 mattress is one of the most durable articles ever produced and can be made to last at least another season by reinforcing it with seaweed or leaves.

Owners of these cottages, as well as of those in inland-lake areas, have spared no pains to make their tenants' summer stay a pleasant one. They have cut fresh supplies of sticks to prop up windows with broken sash cords, and soaped all grooves so that the windows will slide up and down easily. Missing panes have been replenished with pieces of cardboard tastily decorated, and in a wide variety of colors. As an added service, all loose or weak floor boards have been chalked with warning marks, and loose plaster on ceilings has been removed, so that the tenant can look up, perceive the laths and know that he has nothing to fear.

Ruts in driveways have been filled in with ample-sized boulders, so that there is no possible chance of cars' becoming mired during rainy spells; and garages have been cleared of tools and assorted debris, so that it is possible to get a car in far enough so that its entire hood is protected from the elements. And some landlords have purchased an entirely new supply of pails and dishpans to catch drippings from leaky roofs.

Our survey, in fact, has left only one question unanswered so far: Where do owners go for the summer, after they rent out their cottages? Unfortunately, we are handicapped by the fact that practically none of them ever seem to leave forwarding addresses.

SILENCE! BOTTLES!

RALF KIRCHER

Some time ago I invested in two bottles of White Rock. The contents of these bottles have long since been consumed. To a little soda water I add the juice of one lemon, thus producing a highly alkaline beverage which is said to be an excellent tonic, aiding digestion, stimulating the liver, toning the nervous system, and maybe even being good for the morals for all I know.

The point is that I bought this soda water and that I drank it, and why I should bother to tell you just how I drank it is beyond me. After all, I am old enough to buy soda water without a note from my mother and I will drink it any blamed way I want to!

What I really started out to tell you, before everybody started leering in that disagreeable way, is that each of these bottles has got a cunning label on it that bears the following inscription, "*I cost you no deposit but when empty please return me to your dealer to serve you again!*" Frankly I am getting tired of having these bottles address me in this intimate manner.

There they sit on the table at the foot of the cellar stairs where I simply have to look at them when I am on my way to the furnace. I switch on the light from the landing and there they are, patiently waiting for me. I look first at one and it says,

"*I cost you no deposit but when empty please return me to your dealer to serve you again!*"

I then look at the other bottle and it says,

"*I cost you no deposit but when empty please return me to your dealer to serve you again!*"

These two bottles, talking so confidently about how they do not cost me any deposit—flaunting their generosity in my face—always put me in an ugly humor, and by the time I have taken the ashes out of the furnace and am ready to go back upstairs I am not in any mood to take back-talk from a bottle. "I will take you back to the dealer when I am darned good and ready if I do not bounce you off a rock first," I snarl, and stomp back upstairs, my sunny disposition a shambles.

To tell you the truth, I am getting tired of having inanimate objects talking to me all the time. We have got some kind of minty-smelling grease in our medicine chest and it has a label on it that says, "*Rub me on briskly and watch soreness disappear!*" It used to be that such remedies would merely carry sober directions, but now half the things you pick up want to start a conversation or an argument. Rub me on briskly and watch soreness disappear, indeed! That stuff makes me sore all the time, but it is the kind of soreness that I could rub him on briskly 'til kingdom come and not get any relief.

The advertisements are also full of products that are forever wanting to start a discussion club. I am looking at an ad right now for what appears to be a kind of aspirin. This bottle has got a balloon over it, the kind you see in the funny papers, and it is shouting, "*Here's a hot tip, Big Boy!*" How do you like that? Who is a strange aspirin bottle to be calling me "Big Boy"? I am not a dignified person, and I am not one to stand on ceremony, but I at least expect respect from an aspirin bottle.

I also have at hand the advertisement for a cereal and the box is saying, "*Start your day with me, Mister!*" For some reason I consider this an insolent suggestion coming, as it does, from a cardboard box that is filled with patented shavings. I do not wish to appear testy but I am one Mister who will make it his business to start his day with something else entirely.

No, I do not think that I care very much for anything of this nature. And to tell you the truth I do not hold a much higher opinion of talking animals. I do not like the pictures of pigs who are full of glib advice on how to brush my teeth, or the pictures of cows who speak so highly and so immodestly of their own milk, or the pictures of dogs who exclaim, "*Zowie! I'm a new dog since I've been eating this double-nutritious, vitamin-fortified dog food!*" To me, these are animals that should be seen and not heard, and if I want advice I am not going to a dog, a cow, or a pig to get it.

That goes for all those bottles, tubes, jars, cartons and other containers that try to jolly me along with their first-person conversational gambits. Those White Rock bottles for instance. If they are smart enough to keep saying, "*I cost you no deposit but when empty please return me to your dealer to serve you again*"—if they are smart enough for that, they are smart enough to walk back.

THINGS

LESLEY CONGER

The Australian aborigines live beautifully uncluttered lives. They possess nothing that they cannot carry with them. Of course the necessity for being forever mobile has led them to some tempting extremes, such as infanticide. This may be going too far.

We, on the other hand, are veritably possessed by our possessions. We don't own them; they (like cats) own us. The books we intend to re-read, the gifts we don't dare discard for fear the giver will return to the scene of our crime, the souvenirs of occasions we remember perfectly well without tangible reminders, the souvenirs of occasions we have forgotten even with the souvenirs in plain view, the objects of sentiment from which all sentiment has fled, the things which will come in handy sometime, the things awaiting improbable repairs—they all have a claim on us.

I have a dream that comes to me sometimes, a fleeting daydream that plucks at my mind when I am cleaning drawers or rummaging deep in closets amidst old unstrung tennis rackets and cases of language records from which nobody has learned anything as far as I can recall. In this daydream a notification arrives for our family—a brief, imperative, unavoidable command (from some as-yet-unimagined source) ordering us to report somewhere, usually a continent or two away, for some fascinating job. The only condition attached is

NED HILTON, THIS WEEK

"I'm sorry, John. The decorator says you'll have to go."

---

that we arrive with no more luggage than two suitcases for the lot of us.

This is not a realistic sort of daydream. I could have other daydreams that would do the trick. A devastating fire (in our absence) would be utilitarian, for example, except that I doubt that our neighbors in the duplex would share my secret joy at being reduced to nomadism.

I am, in fact, alone. My husband is a saver—a saver of shells, postage stamps, interesting articles in magazines, old books, rocks, bones, feathers, eagles' claws, musical instruments he can't play. And children, naturally, are always savers; we have one room entirely full of baseball cards, bits of tinfoil, comics, last year's torn and flattened-out Halloween masks, old Christmas cards dating back to 1952, cereal boxtops for defunct free offers, toys with missing vital parts, and vital parts to missing toys.

But things have, I suppose, a certain psychological utility. In times of desperation they provide an anchor, an essential curb on those wild, savage, aboriginal impulses toward freedom. How often, I wonder, would my husband have been tempted to pack a suitcase and slip away in the dark of night for who knows what exotic destination? But to leave his rock collection behind! his seashells! his Indian baskets! his accordion! that Japanese flute! those old second-hand books he hasn't read yet! that bow for which there are no arrows! He would sooner flee naked, without his nylon shirts, his Harris tweed jacket, and his billfold.

Perhaps, then, it is good to have one half the adult family attached with that unreasoning, unreasonable attachment to useless personal belongings. How much of what stability the family possesses may depend upon the clogging inertia provided by material objects alone. Read those precious family memoirs of the Victorian era, and take note of the time absorbed in and pages devoted to the recollection and contemplation of *things*—that wonderful old clock that used to be great-grandfather's, that rocking-chair, that piece of faded needlework, those fragile cups and saucers (fragile! They have held the family together over half a century!), that quilt, that cradle.

Yes, if everybody lived out of suitcases, how simple would be the dissolution of the family over some trivial quarrel, some trifling difference! But think of dividing up the books, the photographs, the old back issues of the National Geographic Magazine, the children . . . the task is too herculean to consider. If my husband should ever take a notion to seek his freedom when the onerous obligations and the sheer noise of family life become too much for him, I know he would not disappear forever. Sooner or later he would come back; I would hear his stealthy step in the night, and I would creep out into the hall and catch him redhanded, trying to salvage from the closet that old stringless banjo that nobody in our family has ever learned to play.

I still have my daydream sometimes; it is comforting when the clutter and rubble rise above my eyebrows to imagine the delicious aerated simplicity of life unpossessed and unpossessing. But even should I make a break for it myself, I should be back; there is always that box of the children's early drawings and first school exercise-books —how could I bear to leave it behind?

Health (Good /Fair /Poor):

GIVING UP SMOKING

A. P. HERBERT

Thank heaven, I have given up smoking again!

This is the morning of the second day and the thing is now fixed. You can scarcely imagine the relief of it. How well I feel! What vitality and vigour!

I could bite through the leg of that chair, kick a hole through that table or run about knocking everybody's heads together. In fact, I have felt like doing these things since just after luncheon yesterday.

Gad! I feel fit. Homicidal, but fit. A different man. Irritable, moody, depressed, rude, nervy, perhaps; but the lungs are fine. And if I do bash somebody over the head it will at least be said in my defence that I had the strength of mind to give up smoking.

And then, the *mental* difference! The mind more active, the imagination less sluggish. True, at the moment I can think of nothing but pipes and cigars; but the mind is busy. True, I am now travelling through the Red Sea and the pipe is never so alluring in the tropics. True, also, I have a cruel sore throat. But these little accidents have really nothing to do with it. I have always meant to give up smoking for good, and now it just happens that I have.

What a filthy foolish habit it was. Have you ever examined the interior of a pipe just after a smoke—a good old long-service, 'favourite', disgusting pipe? Incredible! One might as well put a straw in the gutter and have a suck at that. Better, indeed, for the gutter as a rule contains no nicotine.

And what sentimental twaddle we used to talk about it! All this Baldwin-and-his-pipe stuff, for example. Mr. Baldwin ought to be ashamed of himself. Obviously he oversmokes; and that explains why

—I mean, I know myself exactly the effect it has on the brain. People say it's so 'English', and even women will say that they like to see their husbands smoking a pipe. Silly fools! They cannot know what they mean. The writers too, with their 'Odes to Tobacco', 'My Lady Nicotine', and so forth. 'My Lady Nicotine', forsooth! Might as well rhapsodize about 'My Lady Tannin' or 'My Lady Lipstick'.

'English', indeed! Bah! Is it really characteristic of our race to burn a vegetable substance in a small bowl just in front of the eyes and nose and then suck the residuary juices (which are toxic) into the mouth? Is this really a distinguishing mark of the pioneers of civilization? Again 'Bah!'

Gosh, I feel fit! And gosh, what a temper I'm in! Gosh, what an appetite! I could bite that lifebuoy through!

It pleases me to think of the time, trouble, and transport (to say nothing of cash) which I shall save—am saving already. The *stuff* one carried about! Every time one dressed, every time one went out, every time one changed one's clothes there was the same trouble: Have I got everything? One pipe (generally two), one tobacco-pouch (and is it full? and, if not, where's the tin?), the matches, the pipe-cleaners, the knife or Smoker's Companion for poking or cleaning. And some poor slaves, of course, carry cigarettes as well. What a lot of trash! Bulging out the pockets, spoiling the figure! Here I sit in my tropical suit, with empty pockets at last, a flat surface, and the right shape.

And free of that endless match-trouble. He does not notice it, maybe; but life for the pipe-smoker is really coloured by the number of matches in his box. He acquires a full box—elation; some one removes it—agony; it dwindles towards emptiness—growing anxiety; the last match flickers out—despair; no matches to be had anywhere—madness, murder, anything.

And then, the *labour* of pipe-smoking! In the bad old days when I smoked, that is to say, the day before yesterday, I used to sit in this same corner at the after end of B deck and write—and *smoke*. Naturally, in the Red Sea, one sits in a breeze if possible; and when the mind is being used the pipe goes out, I find, or used to find, about once in every two minutes; and one then ceased thinking and lit a match; and it was instantly extinguished by the breeze; and one lit two more and tried again; and then one got up, went round the corner and lit the pipe in the lee of the smoking-room; and then one returned, collected the thoughts and began work again.

Well, you will understand that on a morning when the breeze was fresh and the concentration-of-mind strong the pipe-lighting intervals amounted to a considerable period. You may say, of course, 'Well, if the mind is concentrating to that extent, why smoke at all?' But it is quite useless to ask silly questions of that kind. The answer is, 'One does'. Or rather, 'One did'.

All that, however, is now dead and done with. Today, a non-smoker, I sit here working away steadily without interruption, unless it might be to look at a passing flying-fish or porpoise or, once in a while, to pop into the smoking-room to read the wireless news or stand some poor devil the first drink of the day. No pipe-trouble, no breeze-trouble, no match-trouble.

No *dead*-match-trouble, for instance. What a problem—what to do with dead matches when sitting on deck! Being a tidy person and attached to the Chief Officer, I have never cared to drop them on deck, for this maddens him. Sometimes I thrust them tidily back into my match-box; and then ladies came along, borrowed my matches, extracted four dead men in succession, and reviled me. Nor was it any use to remind them that the match-box was mine, and that people who could not keep matches of their own deserved what they got. So I invented a third plan. I allowed the deads to accumulate in a little pile till they numbered six or seven, and I would then make a special expedition to the side of the ship and throw them overboard. But these little walks took time, you know; and what with walks to the rail and walks round the corner, lighting matches and lending matches, filling the pipe, cleaning the pipe, prodding the pipe, and knocking out the pipe, slipping down to the cabin for more tobacco, slipping into the smoking-room for more matches, I really shudder to think how much of the working-morning was occupied with smoking or trying to smoke.

'*Was*'—mark you. For all that is a thing of the past.

Never again. Still, it would be interesting, in a morbid sort of way, to know exactly what was the loss of efficiency, reckoned in man-hours or output units, of those bad old days. Some things one can measure quite accurately—the time taken, for example, in filling and lighting a pipe. Let us see. (I will just slip down to the cabin and get the things.)

Filling the pipe, I find, done leisurely and meditatively, takes forty-five seconds at least. But the tobacco-pouch was then to hand: allow fifteen seconds for routing about under tables and chairs and papers (it is generally more) and it works out at a minute, or about three or four full minutes every morning. Then there was finding the matches and lighting the four or five abortive matches—say ten seconds each or a minute altogether. Two minutes gone, you see, before we reached the actual business of lighting the pipe at all. First there is the little walk round the corner, then comes the lighting of the pipe. Now how long did that take? Let us see.

A-a-a-h! . . .

About a minute.

And how long did it take to smoke a whole pipe through?

Let us see . . .

CURE OF A HYPOCHONDRIAC

SEBA SMITH

(From Godey's Lady's Book, 1840)

As Mr. Seth Woodsum was mowing one morning in his lower haying fields, and his eldest son, Obediah, a smart boy of thirteen, was opening the mown grass to the sun, Mr. Woodsum looked up towards his house, and beheld his little daughter Harriet, ten years of age, running towards him with her utmost speed. As she came up, he perceived she was greatly agitated; tears were running down her cheeks, and she had scarcely breath enough to speak.

"Oh, father," she faintly articulated, "mother is dreadful sick; she's on the bed, and says she shall die before you get there."

Mr. Woodsum was a man of a sober, sound mind, and calm nerves; but he had, what sometimes happens in this cold and loveless world of ours, a tender attachment for his wife, which made the message of the little girl fall upon his heart like a dagger. He dropped his scythe, and ran with great haste to the house. Obediah, who was at the other end of the field, seeing this unusual movement of his father, dropped his fork, and ran with all his might, and the two entered the house almost at the same time.

Mr. Woodsum hastened to the bed-side, and took his wife's hand. "My dear Sally," said he, "what is the matter?"

"What is the matter?" echoed Mrs. Woodsum, with a plaintive

groan. "I shouldn't think you would need to ask what is the matter, Mr. Woodsum. Don't you see I am dying?"

"Why, no, Sally, you don't look as if you was dying. What *is* the matter? How do you feel?"

"Oh, I sha'nt live till night," said Mrs. Woodsum, with a heavy sigh; "I am going fast."

Mr. Woodsum, without waiting to make further inquiries, told Obediah to run and jump on to the horse, and ride over after Doctor Fairfield, and get him to come over as quick as he can come. "Tell him I am afraid your mother is dying. If the doctor's horse is away off in the pasture, ask him to take our horse, and come right away over, while you go and catch his."

Obediah, with tears in his eyes, and his heart in his mouth, flew as though he had wings added to his feet, and in three minutes time was mounted upon Old Gray, and galloping with full speed towards Doctor Fairfield's.

"My dear," said Mr. Woodsum, leaning his head upon the pillow, "how do you feel? What makes you think you are dying?" And he tenderly kissed her forehead as he spoke, and pressed her hand to his bosom.

"Oh, Samuel," for she generally called him by his Christian name, when under the influence of tender emotions, "Oh, Samuel, I feel dreadfully. I have pains darting through my head, and most all over me; and I feel dizzy, and can't hardly see; and my heart beats as though it would come through my side. And besides, I feel as though I was dying. I am sure I can't live till night; and what will become of my poor children?" And she sobbed heavily, and burst into a flood of tears.

Mr. Woodsum was affected. He could not bring himself to believe that his wife was in such immediate danger of dissolution as she seemed to apprehend. He thought she had no appearance of a dying person; but still her earnest and positive declarations, that she could not live through the day, sent a chill through his veins, and a sinking to his heart, which no language has power to describe. Mr. Woodsum was as ignorant of medicine as a child; he therefore did not attempt to do any thing to relieve his wife, except to try to soothe her feelings by kind and encouraging words, till the Doctor arrived. The half hour which elapsed, from the time Obediah started, till the Doctor came, seemed to Mr. Woodsum almost an age. He repeatedly went from the bed-side to the door, to look out and see if the Doctor was anywhere near, and as often returned to hear his wife groan, and say she was sinking fast, and could not stand it many minutes longer.

At length Doctor Fairfield rode up to the door, on Mr. Woodsum's Old Gray, and with saddle-bags in hand, hastened into the house. A brief examination of the patient convinced him that it was a decided case of hypochondria, and he soon spoke encouraging words to her, and told her although she was considerably unwell, he did not doubt she would be better in a little while.

"Oh, Doctor, how can you say so?" said Mrs. Woodsum; "don't you see I am dying? I can't possibly live till night; I am sinking very fast, Doctor. I shall never see the sun rise again. My heart sometimes almost stops its beating now, and my feet and hands are growing cold. But I must see my children once more; do let 'em come in and bid me farewell." Here she was so overwhelmed with sobs and tears as to prevent her saying more.

The Doctor, perceiving it was in vain to talk or try to reason with her, assured her that as long as there was life there was hope, and told her he would give her some medicine that he did not doubt would help her. He accordingly administered the drugs usually approved by the faculty in such cases, and telling her that he would call and see her again in a day or two, he left the room. As he went out, Mr. Woodsum followed him, and desired to know in private his real opinion of the case. The Doctor assured him he did not consider it at all alarming. It was an ordinary case of hypochondria, and with suitable treatment, the patient would undoubtedly soon be better.

"This is a case," continued the Doctor, "in which the mind needs to be administered to as much as the body. Divert her attention as much as possible by cheerful objects; let her be surrounded by agreeable company; give her a light, but generous and nutritive diet; and as soon as may be, get her to take gentle exercises in the open air, by riding on horseback, or running about the fields and gathering fruits or flowers in company with lively and cheerful companions. Follow these directions, and continue to administer the medicines I have ordered, and I think Mrs. Woodsum will soon enjoy good health again."

Mr. Woodsum felt much relieved after hearing the Doctor's opinion and prescriptions, and bade the kind physician good morning with a tolerably cheerful countenance. Most assiduously did he follow the Doctor's directions, and in a few days he had the happiness to see his beloved wife again enjoying comfortable health, and pursuing her domestic duties with cheerfulness.

But, alas! his sunshine of hope was destined soon to be obscured again by the clouds of sorrow and disappointment. It was not long before some changes in the weather, and changes in her habits of living, and neglect of proper exercises in the open air, brought on a return of Mrs. Woodsum's gloom, and despondency, in all their terrific power. Again she was sighing and weeping on the bed, and again Mr. Woodsum was hastily summoned from the field, and leaving his plough in mid furrow, ran with breathless anxiety to the house, where the same scenes were again witnessed which we have already described.

Not only once or twice, but repeatedly, week after week, and month after month, these alarms were given, and followed by similar results. Every relapse seemed to be more severe than the last, and on each occasion Mrs. Woodsum was more positive than ever that she was on her death bed, and that there was no longer any help for her.

On one of these occasions, so strong was her impression that her dissolution was near, and so anxious did she appear to make every preparation for death, and with such solemn earnestness did she attend to certain details preparatory to leaving her family forever, that Mr. Woodsum almost lost the hope that usually attended him through these scenes, and felt, more than ever before, that what he had so often feared was indeed about to become a painful and awful reality. Most tenderly did Mrs. Woodsum touch upon the subject of her separation from her husband and children.

"Our poor children—what will become of them when I am gone? And you, dear Samuel, how can I bear the thought of leaving you? I could feel reconciled to dying, if it was not for the thoughts of leaving you and the children. They will have nobody to take care of them, as a mother would, poor things; and then you will be so lonesome—it breaks my heart to think of it."

Here, her feelings overpowered her, and she was unable to proceed any farther. Mr. Woodsum was for some time too much affected to make any reply. At last, summoning all his fortitude, and as much calmness as he could, he told her if it was the will of Providence that she should be separated from them, he hoped her last hours would not be pained with anxious solicitude about the future welfare of the family. It was true, the world would be a dreary place to him when she was gone; but he should keep the children with him, and with the blessing of heaven, he thought he should be able to make them comfortable and happy.

"Well, there's one thing, dear Samuel," said Mrs. Woodsum, "that I feel it my duty to speak to you about." And she pressed his hand in hers, and looked most solemnly and earnestly in his face. "You know, my dear," she continued, "how sad and desolate a family of children always is, when deprived of a mother. They may have a kind father, and kind friends, but nobody can supply the place of a mother. I feel as if it would be your duty—and I could not die in peace if I didn't speak of it—I feel, dear Samuel, as if it would be your duty as soon after I am gone as would appear decent, to marry some good and kind woman, and bring her into the family to be a mother to our poor children, and to make your home happy. Promise me that you will do this, and I think it will relieve me of some of the distress I feel at the thought of dying."

This remark was to Mr. Woodsum, most unexpected and most painful. It threw an anguish into his heart, such as he had never experienced till that moment. It forced upon his contemplation a thought that had never before occurred to him. The idea of being bereaved of the wife of his bosom, whom he had loved and cherished for fifteen years with the ardent attachment of a fond husband, had overwhelmed him with all the bitterness of woe; but the thought of transferring that attachment to another object, brought with it a double desolation. His associations before had all clothed his love for his wife with a feeling of immortality. She might be removed from him to another world, but he had not felt as though that would dissolve the holy bond that united them. His love would still follow her to those eternal realms of bliss, and rest upon her like a mantle for ever.

But this new and startling idea, of love for another, came to him, as comes to the wicked the idea of annihilation of the soul—an idea, compared with which, no degree of misery imaginable, is half so terrible. A cloud of intense darkness seemed for a moment to overshadow him, his heart sank within him, and his whole frame trembled with agitation. It was some minutes before he could find power to speak. And when he did, it was only to beseech his wife, in a calm and solemn tone, not to allude to so distressing a subject again, a subject which he could not speak of, nor think of, without suffering more than a thousand deaths.

The strong mental anguish of Mr. Woodsum seemed to have the effect to divert his wife's attention from her own sufferings, and by turning her emotions into a new channel, gave her system an opportunity to rally. She gradually grew better as she had done in like cases before, and even before night was able to sit up, and become quite composed and cheerful.

But her malady was only suspended, not cured; and again and again it returned upon her, and again and again her friends were summoned to witness her last sickness and take their last farewell. And on these occasions, she had so often slightly and delicately hinted to Mr. Woodsum the propriety of his marrying a second wife, that even he could at last listen to the suggestion with a degree of indifference which he had once thought he could never feel.

At last, the sober saddening days of autumn came on. Mr. Woodsum was in the midst of his "fall work," which had been several times interrupted by these periodical turns of despondency in his wife. One morning he went to his field early, for he had a heavy day's work to do, and had engaged one of his neighbors to come with two yoke of oxen and a plough to help him "break up" the old mowing field. He was exceedingly desirous not to be interrupted for his neighbour could only help him that day, and he was very anxious to plough the whole field. He accordingly had left the children and nurse in the house, with strict charges to take good care of their mother, and see that nothing disturbed her through the day. Mr. Woodsum was driving the team and his neighbour was holding the plough, and things went on to their mind till about ten o'clock in the forenoon when little Harriet came running to the field, and told her father that her mother was "dreadful sick," and wanted him to come in as quick as he could, for she was certainly dying now. Mr. Woodsum, without saying a word, drove his team to the end of the furrow; but he looked thoughtful and perplexed.

Although he felt persuaded that her danger was imaginary, as it had always proved to be before, still, the idea of the bare possibility that *this* sickness *might* be unto death, pressed upon him with such power, that he laid down his goad stick, and telling his neighbour to let the cattle breathe awhile, walked deliberately towards the house. Before he had accomplished the whole distance, however, his own imagination had added such wings to his speed, that he found himself moving at a quick run. He entered the house, and found his wife as he had so often found her before, in her own estimation, almost ready to breathe her last. Her voice was faint and low, and her pillow was wet with tears. She had already taken leave of her dear children, and waited only to exchange a few parting words with her beloved husband. Mr. Woodsum approached the bedside, and took her hand tenderly, as he had ever been wont to do, but he could not perceive any symptoms of extreme sickness or approaching dissolution, different from what he had witnessed on a dozen former occasions.

"Now, my dear," said Mrs. Woodsum, faintly, "the time has come at last. I feel that I am on my death bed, and have but a short time longer to stay with you. But I hope we shall feel resigned to the will of Heaven. These things are undoubtedly all ordered for the best; and I would go cheerfully, if it was not for my anxiety about you and the children. Now, don't you think, my dear," she continued, with increasing tenderness, "don't you think it would be best for you to be married again to some kind good woman, that would be a mother to our dear little ones, and make your home pleasant for all of you?"

She paused, and seemed to look earnestly in his face for an answer.

"Well, I've sometimes thought of late, it might be best," said Mr. Woodsum with a very solemn air.

"Then you have been thinking about it," said Mrs. Woodsum, with a slight contraction of the muscles of the face.

"Why, yes," said Mr. Woodsum, "I have sometimes thought about it, since you've had spells of being so very sick. It makes me feel dreadfully to think of it, but I don't know but it might be a matter of duty."

"Well, I do think it would," said Mrs. Woodsum, "if you can only get the right sort of a person. Every thing depends upon that, my dear, and I hope you will be very particular about who you get, very."

"I certainly shall," said Mr. Woodsum; "don't give yourself any uneasiness about that, my dear, for I assure you I shall be very particular. The person I shall probably have is one of the kindest and best tempered women in the world."

"But, have you been thinking of any one in particular, my dear?" said Mrs. Woodsum, with a manifest look of uneasiness.

"Why, yes," said Mr. Woodsum, "there is one that I have thought of for some time past, I should probably marry, if it should be the will of Providence to take you from us."

"And pray, Mr. Woodsum, who can it be?" said the wife, with an expression, a little more of earth than heaven, returning to her eye. "Who is it, Mr. Woodsum? You haven't named it to her, have you?"

"Oh, by no means," said Mr. Woodsum; "but my dear, we had better drop the subject; it agitates you too much."

"But Mr. Woodsum, you must tell me who it is; I never could die in peace till you do."

GEORGE FEYER, MACLEAN'S, CANADA

"It is a subject too painful to think about," said Mr. Woodsum, "and it don't appear to me it would be best to call names."

"But, I insist upon it," said Mrs. Woodsum, who had by this time raised herself with great earnestness and was leaning on her elbow, while her searching glance was reading every muscle in her husband's face. "Mr. Woodsum, I insist upon it."

"Well, then," said Mr. Woodsum, with a sigh, "if you insist upon it, my dear—I have thought if it should be the will of Providence to take you from us to be here no more, I have thought I should marry, for my second wife, Hannah Lovejoy."

An earthly fire once more flashed from Mrs. Woodsum's eyes—she leaped from the bed like a cat; walked across the room, and seated herself in a chair.

"What!" she exclaimed, in a trembling voice, almost choked with agitation—"what! Marry that idle, sleepy slattern of a Hannah Lovejoy! Mr. Woodsum, that is too much for flesh and blood to bear—I can't endure that, nor I won't. Hannah Lovejoy to be the mother to my children! No, that she never shall. So you may go to your ploughing, Mr. Woodsum, and set your heart at rest. Susan," she continued, turning to one of the girls, "make up more fire under that dinner pot."

Mr. Woodsum went to the field, and pursued his work, and when he returned at the dinner hour, he found the family dinner well prepared, and his wife ready to do the honours of the table. Mrs. Wood-sum's health from that day continued to improve, and she was never afterward visited by the terrible affliction of hypochondria.

WHERE'S THE STUDIO AUDIENCE?

CASKIE STINNETT

We would like to exchange correspondence with someone who, like us, has had the measles, the whooping cough, or the mumps. There aren't many of us left and it may be good if we could get together, like the Civil War Veterans, and swap experiences. In a world full of inhibition, depression, hypomania, neuroses, schizophrenia, conversion hysteria, and conflict between inner and outer personalities, it may even be a good influence. Anyway, if you would like to hear about our case of German measles in 1923—and there were some rather interesting details—just drop us a line.

Our attention was brought to this subject recently when we offered ourself for a physical examination, and instead of a kindly old physician with a blood pressure gauge and a stethoscope there was a doctor, a nurse, and a notebook. Although the nurse held the notebook and undoubtedly has the only official report of the proceedings, our recollection of it is as follows:

"First, we'll check him for Babinski," the doctor said, seizing one of our feet and dragging a nail across the bare sole. We almost rolled from the couch.

"Extreme Babinski," the doctor dictated, "with possible symptoms of Osgood Slater's Disease."

"What about Whitman's Disease?" the nurse asked, picking up a vicious looking needle and purring softly.

"If he has it," the doctor replied with obvious satisfaction, "it would be so advanced an injection wouldn't help."

Rather petulantly, the nurse put the needle down. "How about Romberg?"

The doctor directed us to stand up, hold our feet together, close our eyes, and extend both arms. We did.

"Catch him, Doctor!" the nurse shouted.

They eased us back to the couch. "Not only Romberg," the doctor said, "but also locomotor ataxia."

"Bad?" the nurse inquired, her pad poised on our knee.

"So bad he probably whistles at crossings," the doctor replied.

The nurse jabbed us in the ribs. "Laugh it up," she said. "He doesn't pull a nifty like that often."

We were forcing a smile when the doctor approached with a pin. "This tests the integrity of the central nervous system," he explained. "Whenever you feel a pinprick, say 'Pin.'" He sank the pin in our thigh.

We said ouch.

"Uncooperative and refuses to take direction," the doctor dictated.

We were going to reply but the doctor effectively cut off any further comment by squeezing a minor nerve center between thumb and forefinger.

"You have Huntington's Teeth but I want you to take the test anyway," he said. "Put on the robe and walk down the hall until you come to Dental Lab."

We walked down the hall until we came to a taxi stand. The robe wasn't much but neither was the suit we left.

Later in the afternoon, we dropped in on our old family doctor for a check-up. When he put the thermometer under our tongue and got out his stethoscope, we felt perhaps he hadn't kept up with current medical progress, but when we left we felt like a million dollars.

YOU, TOO, CAN BE NERVOUS

DICK ASHBAUGH

I used to be calm and relaxed, but, thank heaven, I got over that. Now I'm nice and tense, and a credit to all my nervous friends. For a long time I had no idea what was wrong with me socially. I used to sidle into a crowd and open the conversation with something silly like, "Well, when you come right down to it, the old T formation is still——" Then I'd stop because nobody was listening. They were all looking sympathetically at a man named Harry.

Somebody would whisper, "Harry's just found out he's allergic to buildings painted yellow." They would all shake their heads, while Harry just sat there, staring into the middle distance.

"What are your allergies, old boy?" they'd ask me.

"Don't seem to have any," I'd anwer miserably. "Wear a thirty-five sleeve, vote a split ticket and eat about what I want."

"How about phobias? You can tell us. Botts is a dendrophobic—afraid of trees."

"I had an aunt once that wouldn't sweep under beds," I said, but they just walked away.

Finally some friends took me aside. "Get yourself some phobias or allergies," they whispered in my ear.

The doctor I went to looked at me sternly. "Do you cavil at peach fuzz?" he asked. "Find leather chairs repulsive? What would you do if somebody blew chicken feathers in your face?"

"Hit him on the nose," I said.

"H'm'm'm. Now, try to remember your ambitions as a boy."

"Well," I said, "for a time I wanted to be the man who rides on automobile fenders and listens to the engine while another man drives."

"Ever have a fear of falling downstairs?" he asked.

"Plenty of times," I replied, "but I got over it."

"How?" he asked coldly.

"Fell down some," I said. "It wasn't so bad as I thought."

"Difficult case," he said. "Carboneurosis, advanced stage. Stay away from felt hats, open doorways and all cooked foods. Leave the contents of your wallet with the receptionist and report back in thirty days."

I'm going back tomorrow. The boys are coming around tonight in their stocking feet and strap me to the stretcher.

You can't name *anything* I'm not afraid of.

THE ENCHANTED SHIRT

JOHN HAY

The King was sick. His cheek was red,
   And his eye was clear and bright;
He ate and drank with a kingly zest,
   And peacefully snored at night.

But he said he was sick, and a king should know,
    And doctors came by the score.
They did not cure him. He cut off their heads,
    And sent to the schools for more.

At last two famous doctors came,
    And one was as poor as a rat,—
He had passed his life in studious toil,
    And never found time to grow fat.

The other had never looked in a book;
    His patients gave him no trouble:
If they recovered, they paid him well;
    If they died, their heirs paid double.

Together they looked at the royal tongue,
    As the king on his couch reclined;
In succession they thumped his august chest,
    But no trace of disease could find.

The old sage said, "You're as sound as a nut."
    "Hang him up," roared the king in a gale—
In a ten-knot gale of royal rage;
    The other leech grew a shade pale:

But he pensively rubbed his sagacious nose,
    And thus his prescription ran—
The King will be well, if he sleeps one night
    In the shirt of a Happy Man.

         *   *   *

Wide o'er the realm the couriers rode,
    And fast their horses ran—
And many they saw, and to many they spoke,
    But they found no Happy Man.

They found poor men who would fain be rich,
    And rich who thought they were poor;
And men who twisted their waist in stays,
    And women that short hose wore.

They saw two men by the roadside sit,
    And both bemoaned their lot;
For one had buried his wife, he said,
    And the other one had not.

"I wouldn't stand over there, son."

At last they came to a village gate,
　A beggar lay whistling there;
He whistled and sang, and laughed and rolled
　On the grass in the soft June air.

The weary couriers paused and looked
　At the scamp so blithe and gay;
And one of them said, "Heaven save you, friend!
　You seem to be happy today."

"Oh yes, fair sirs," the rascal laughed,
　And his voice rang free and glad;
"An idle man has so much to do
　That he never has time to be sad."

"This is our man," the courier said;
　"Our luck has led us aright.
I will give you a hundred ducats, friend,
　For the loan of your shirt tonight."

The merry blackguard lay back on the grass,
    And laughed till his face was black;
"I would do it, God wot," and he roared with fun,
    "But I haven't a shirt to my back!"

HOSPITAL FOR LIARS

ANONYMOUS

(About 1870)

A few days ago I visited the fairly recently established infirmary for liars in a quiet location in upstate New York. Since it was known that a representative of the TIMES was due, I was met at the door by a pleasant-faced gentleman, who spoke with a slight German accent and introduced himself as the Assistant Superintendent.

"Will you kindly walk this way?" he said. After I had inscribed my name in the Visitors' Book, he began to explain the system under which the infirmary for the mendacious operates.

"It is very simple," he said. "The theory of the Institution is that the habit of mendacity, which in many cases becomes chronic, is a disease, like habitual inebriety. It can generally be cured. We take the liar who voluntarily submits himself to our treatment, and for six months we encourage him in lying. We surround him with liars, his equals and superiors in skill, and cram him with falsehood until he is saturated.

"By this time, the reaction has set in. The patient is usually starved for the truth. He is prepared to welcome the second course of treatment. For the next half year the opposite course is pursued. The satiated and disgusted liar is surrounded by truthful attendants, and by force of example and moral influence, brought to understand how much more creditable it is to say the thing which *is* than the thing which is *not*. Then we send him back into the world. I will show you how our patients live. We will go first, if you please, through the left wing of the hospital, where the saturating process may be observed."

He led the way across a hall into a large room, comfortably furnished and occupied by two dozen or more gentlemen who sat or stood in groups, engaged in animated talk. Near one group, I overheard parts of the conversation.

"My rod creaked and bent double," a stout red-faced gentleman was saying, "and the birch spun like a teetotum. I tell you, if Pierre Chaveau hadn't had the presence of mind to grip the most convenient part of my trousers with the boat hook, I should have been dragged into the lake in two seconds or less. Well, sir, we fought sixty-nine minutes by actual timetaking, and when I had him in and had got him back to the hotel, he tipped the scale, the speckled beauty did, at thirty-seven pounds and eleven-sixteenths, whether you believe it or not."

"Nonsense," said a quiet little gentleman who sat opposite. "That is impossible."

The first speaker looked flattered at this and flushed with pleasure. "Nevertheless," he retorted, "it's a fact, on my honor as a sportsman. Why do you say it's impossible?"

"Because," said the other, calmly, "it is an ascertained scientific fact, as every true fisherman in this room knows perfectly well, that there are no trout in Lake Mooselemagunticook weighing under half a hundred pounds."

"Certainly not," put in a third speaker. "The bottom of the lake is of a sieve formation. All fish smaller than the fifty-pounders fall through."

"Why doesn't the water drop through, too?" asked the stout patient, in a triumphant tone.

"It used to," replied the quiet gentleman gravely, "until the Maine Legislature passed an act preventing it."

"These sportsmen liars," said my guide, as we crossed the room, "are among the mildest and most easily cured cases that come here. We send them away in from six to nine weeks' time, with the habit broken up, and pledged not to fish or hunt any more. The man who lies about the fish he has caught, or about the intelligence of his red setter dog, is often in all other respects a trustworthy citizen."

"What," I asked, "are the most obstinate cases?"

"Undoubtedly the travellers and politicians. The more benign cases, such as the fisherman liars, the society liars, the lady-killer or bonnes fortunes liars, the Rocky Mountain and frontier liars (excepting the Texas cases), the psychical-research liars, and the miscellaneous liars of various classes, we permit, during the first stage of treatment, to mingle freely with each other. The effect is good. But we keep the politicians strictly isolated."

He was about to conduct me out of the room, by a door opposite, when a detached phrase uttered by a pompous gentleman, arrested my attention.

"Scipio Africanus once remarked to me—"

"There couldn't be a better example," said my guide, as we passed out of the room, "of what we call the forcing system in the treatment of mendacity. That patient came to us about two months ago. The form of his disease is a common one. Perfectly truthful in all other respects, he cannot resist the temptation to claim personal acquaintance and even intimacy with distinguished individuals.

"His friends laughed at him so much for this weakness that, like a sensible man, he put himself under our care. He is doing splendidly. When he found that his reminiscences of Beaconsfield and Bismarck and Victor Hugo created no sensation here, but were, on the contrary, matched and capped by still more remarkable experiences narrated by other inmates, he was at first a little staggered.

"But the habit is so strong, and the vanity that craves admiration on this score is so exacting, that he began to extend his acquaintance back into the past. Soon we had him giving reminiscences of Tallyrand, of Thomas Jefferson and of Lord Cornwallis. There happens to be in this Institution another patient with precisely the same trouble. Thus, not long ago, I heard our patient describing one of Heliogabalus' banquets, which he had attended as an honored guest. They are in active competition, driving through ancient history at the rate of about three centuries a week. Before long they will be matching reminiscences of the antediluvian patriarchs, and then they'll bring square up on Adam. They can't go any further than Adam. By that time, they will be ready for the truth-cure process. After a few weeks spent in an atmosphere of strict veracity, they'll go into the world again, perfectly cured."

On our way back to the reception room, we met a gentleman about forty-years old. "He is a well known society man," said the Assistant Superintendent, as he approached. "He was formerly the most politely insincere man in America. I am glad to have you see him, for he is a good example of a radical cure. We shall be ready to discharge him by the first of next week."

The cured liar was about to pass us, but the Assistant Superintendent stopped him. "Mr. Van Ransevoort," he said, "let me make you acquainted with this gentleman who has been inspecting our system."

"I am glad to meet you, Mr. Van Ransevoort," I said.

He raised his hat and made me an unexceptionable bow. "And I," he replied with a smile of charming courtesy, "am neither glad nor sorry to meet you, sir. I simply don't care a damn."

I stammered something, then said, "I suppose you are looking forward to your release next week?"

"Yes, sir," he replied. "I shall be rather glad to get out again. But my wife will be sorry."

I looked at the Assistant Superintendent. He returned a glance full of professional pride.

"Well, goodbye, Mr. Van Ransevoort," I said. "Perhaps I shall have the pleasure of meeting you again."

"I hope not, sir. It's rather a bore," said he, shaking my hand most cordially, and giving the Assistant Superintendent a nod as he passed on.

AL KAUFMAN, THE SATURDAY EVENING POST

"Are you sure you're taking that vitamin prescription?"

DIRGE

ANONYMOUS

To the memory of Miss Ellen Gee, of Kew, who died in consequence of being stung in the eye.

Peerless yet hapless maid of Q!
    Accomplished LN G!
Never again shall I and U
    Together sip our T.

For, ah! the Fates I know not Y,
    Sent 'midst the flowers a B,
Which ven'mous stung her in the I,
    So that she could not C.

LN exclaimed, "Vile spiteful B!
    If ever I catch U
On jess'mine, rosebud, or sweet P,
    I'll change your singing Q.

"I'll send you like a lamb or U
    Across th'Atlantic C.
From our delightful village Q
    To distant O Y E.

"A stream runs from my wounded I,
    Salt as the briny C
As rapid as the X or Y,
    The OIO or D.

"Then fare thee ill, insensate B!
    Who stung, nor yet knew Y,
Since not for wealthy Durham's C
    Would I have lost my I."

They bear with tears fair LN G
    In funeral R A,
A clay-cold corpse now doomed to B
    Whilst I mourn her DK.

Ye nymphs of Q, then shun each B,
  List to the reason Y;
For should a B C U at T,
  He'll surely sting your I.

Now in a grave L deep in Q
  She's cold as cold can B,
Whilst robins sing upon a U
  Her dirge and LEG.

"SPEAKING OF OPERATIONS—"

IRVIN S. COBB

Now that the last belated bill for services professionally rendered has been properly paid and properly receipted; now that the memory of the event, like the mark of the stitches, has faded out from a vivid red to a becoming pink shade; now that I pass a display of adhesive tape in a drug-store window without flinching—I sit me down to write a little piece about a certain matter—a small thing, but mine own—to wit, That Operation.

For years I have noticed that persons who underwent pruning or remodeling at the hands of a duly qualified surgeon, and survived, liked to talk about it afterward. In the event of their not surviving I have no doubt they still liked to talk about it, but in a different locality. Of all the readily available topics for use, whether among friends or among strangers, an operation seems to be the handiest and the most dependable. It beats the weather, or Roosevelt, or Bryan, or when this war is going to end, if ever, if you are a man talking to other men; and it is more exciting even than the question of how Mrs. Vernon Castle will wear her hair this winter, if you are a woman talking to other women. Wherever two or more are gathered together it is reasonably certain that somebody will bring up an operation.

Until I passed through the experience myself, however, I never really realized what a precious conversational boon the subject is, and how great a part it plays in our intercourse with our fellow beings on this planet. To the teller it is enormously interesting, for he is not only the hero of the tale but the rest of the cast and the stage setting as well—the whole show, as they say; and if the listener has had a similar experience—and who is there among us in these days that has not taken a nap 'neath the shade of the old ether cone?—it acquires a doubled value.

"Speaking of operations——" you say, just like that, even though nobody present has spoken of them; and then you are off, with your new acquaintance sitting on the edge of his chair, or hers as the case may be and so frequently is, with hands clutched in polite but painful restraint, gills working up and down with impatience, eyes brightened with desire, tongue hung in the middle, waiting for you to pause to catch your breath, so that he or she may break in with a few personal recollections along the same line. From a mere conversation it resolves itself into a symptom symposium, and a perfectly splendid time is had by all.

If an operation is such a good thing to talk about, why isn't it a good thing to write about too? That is what I wish to know. Besides, I need the money. Verily, one always needs the money when one has but recently escaped from the ministering clutches of the modern hospital. Therefore I write.

It all dates back to the fair, bright morning when I went to call on a prominent practitioner here in New York, whom I shall denominate as Doctor X. I had a pain. I had had it for days. It was not a dependable, locatable pain, such as a tummyache or a toothache is, which you can put your hand on; but an indefinite, unsettled, undecided kind of pain, which went wandering about from place to place inside of me like a strange ghost lost in Cudjo's Cave. I never knew until then what the personal sensations of a haunted house are. If only the measly thing could have made up its mind to settle down somewhere and start housekeeping I think I should have been better satisfied. I never had such an uneasy tenant. Alongside of it a woman with the moving fever would be comparatively a fixed and stationary object.

Having always, therefore, enjoyed perfectly riotous and absolutely unbridled health, never feeling weak and distressed unless dinner happened to be ten or fifteen minutes late, I was green regarding physicians and the ways of physicians. But I knew Doctor X slightly, having met him last summer in one of his hours of ease in the grand stand at a ball game, when he was expressing a desire to cut the umpire's throat from ear to ear, free of charge; and I remembered his name, and remembered, too, that he had impressed me at the time as being a person of character and decision and scholarly attainments.

He wore whiskers. Somehow in my mind whiskers are ever associated with medical skill. I presume this is a heritage of my youth, though I believe others labor under the same impression. As I look back it seems to me that in childhood's days all the doctors in our town wore whiskers. I recall one old doctor down there in Kentucky who was practically lurking in ambush all the time. All he needed was a few decoys out in front of him and a pump gun to be a duck blind. He carried his calomel about with him in a fruit jar, and when there was a cutting job he stropped his scalpel on his bootleg.

You see, in those primitive times germs had not been invented yet, and so he did not have to take any steps to avoid them. Now we know that loose, luxuriant whiskers are insanitary, because they make such fine winter quarters for germs; so, though the doctors still wear whiskers, they do not wear them wild and waving. In the profession bosky whiskers are taboo; they must be landscaped. And since it is a recognized fact that germs abhor orderliness and straight lines, they now go elsewhere to reside, and the doctor may still retain his traditional aspect and yet be practically germproof. Doctor X was trimmed up in accordance with the ethics of the newer school. He had trellis whiskers. So I went to see him at his offices in a fashionable district, on an expensive side street.

Before reaching him I passed through the hands of a maid and a nurse, each of whom spoke to me in a low, sorrowful tone of voice, which seemed to indicate that there was very little hope. I reached an inner room where Doctor X was. He looked me over, while I described for him as best I could what seemed to be the matter with me, and asked me a number of intimate questions touching on the lives, works, characters and peculiarities of my ancestors; after which he made me stand up in front of him and take my coat off, and he punched me hither and yon with his forefinger. He also knocked repeatedly on my breastbone with his knuckles, and each time, on doing this, would apply his ear to my chest and listen intently for a spell, afterward shaking his head in a disappointed way. Apparently there was nobody at home. For quite a time he kept on knocking, but without getting any response.

He then took my temperature and fifteen dollars, and said it was an interesting case—not unusual exactly, but interesting—and that it called for an operation.

From the way my heart and other organs jumped inside of me at that statement I knew at once that, no matter what he may have thought, the premises were not unoccupied. Naturally I inquired how soon he meant to operate. Personally I trusted there was no hurry about it. I was perfectly willing to wait for several years if necessary. He smiled at my ignorance.

"I never operate," he said; "operating is entirely out of my line. I am a diagnostician."

He was too—I give him full credit for that. He was a good, keen, close diagnostician. How did he know I had only fifteen dollars on me? You did not have to tell this man what you had, or how much. He knew without being told.

I asked whether he was acquainted with Doctor Y—Y being a person whom I had met casually at a club to which I belong. Oh, yes, he said, he knew Doctor Y. Y was a clever man, X said—very, very clever; but Y specialized in the eyes, the ears, the nose and the throat. I gathered from what Doctor X said that any time Doctor Y ventured below the thorax he was out of bounds and liable to be penalized; and that if by any chance he strayed down as far as the lungs he would call for help and back out as rapidly as possible.

This was news to me. It would appear that these up-to-date practitioners just go ahead and divide you up and partition you out among themselves without saying anything to you about it. Your torso belongs to one man and your legs are the exclusive property of his brother practitioner down on the next block, and so on. You may belong to as many as half a dozen specialists, most of whom, very possibly, are total strangers to you, and yet never know a thing about it yourself.

It has rather the air of trespass—nay, more than that, it bears some of the aspects of unlawful entry—but I suppose it is legal. Certainly, judging by what I am able to learn, the system is being carried on generally. So it must be ethical. Anything doctors do in a mass is ethical. Almost anything they do singly and on individual responsibility is unethical. Being ethical among doctors is practically the same thing as being a Democrat in Texas or a Presbyterian in Scotland.

"Y will never do for you," said Doctor X, when I had rallied somewhat from the shock of these disclosures. "I would suggest that you go to Doctor Z, at such-and-such an address. You are exactly in Z's line. I'll let him know that you are coming and when, and I'll send him down my diagnosis."

So that same afternoon, the appointment having been made by telephone, I went, full of quavery emotions, to Doctor Z's place. As soon as I was inside his outer hallway I realized that I was nearing the presence of one highly distinguished in his profession. A pussy-footed male attendant, in a livery that made him look like a cross between a head-waiter and an undertaker's assistant, escorted me through an anteroom into a reception room, where a considerable number of well-dressed men and women were sitting about in strained attitudes, pretending to read magazines while they waited their turns, but in reality furtively watching one another.

I sat down in a vacant chair, holding fast to my hat and my umbrella. They were the only friends I had there and I was determined not to lose them without a struggle. On the wall were many colored charts showing various portions of the human anatomy and what ailed them. Directly in front of me was a very thrilling illustration, evidently copied from an oil painting, of a liver in a bad state of repair. I said to myself that if I had a liver like that one I should keep it hidden from the public eye—I would never permit it to sit for its portrait. Still, there is no accounting for tastes. I know a man who got his spleen back from the doctors and now keeps it in a bottle of alcohol on the what-not in the parlor, as one of his most treasured possessions, and sometimes shows it to visitors. He, however, is of a very saving disposition.

Presently a lady secretary, who sat behind a roll-top desk in a corner of the room, lifted a forefinger and silently beckoned me to her side. I moved over and sat down by her; she took down my name and my age and my weight and my height, and a number of other interesting facts that will come in very handy should anyone ever be moved to write a complete history of my early life. In common with Doctor X she shared one attribute—she manifested a deep curiosity regarding my forefathers—wanted to know all about them. I felt that this was carrying the thing too far. I felt like saying to her:

"Miss or madam, so far as I know there is nothing the matter with my ancestors of the second and third generations back, except that they are dead. I am not here to seek medical assistance for a grand-parent who succumbed to disappointment that time when Samuel J. Tilden got counted out, or for a great-grandparent who entered into Eternal Rest very unexpectedly and in a manner entirely uncalled for as a result of being an innocent bystander in one of those feuds that were so popular in my native state immediately following the Mexican War. Leave my ancestors alone. There is no need of your shaking my family tree in the belief that a few overripe patients will fall out. I alone—I, me, myself—am the present candidate!"

However, I refrained from making this protest audibly. I judged she was only going according to the ritual; and as she had a printed card, with blanks in it ready to be filled out with details regarding the remote members of the family connection, I humored her along. When I could not remember something she wished to know concerning an ancestor I supplied her with thrilling details culled from the field of fancy. When the card was entirely filled up she sent me back to my old place to wait. I waited and waited, breeding fresh ailments all the time. I had started out with one symptom; now if I had one I had a million and a half. I could feel goose flesh sprouting out all over me. If I had been taller I might have had more, but not otherwise. Such is the power of the human imagination when the surroundings are favorable to its development.

Time passed; to me it appeared that nearly all the time there was passed and that we were getting along toward the shank-end of the Christian era mighty fast. I was afraid my turn would come next and afraid it would not. Perhaps you know this sensation. You get it at the dentist's, and when you are on the list of after-dinner speakers at a large banquet, and when you are waiting for the father of the Only Girl in the World to make up his mind whether he is willing to try to endure you as a son-in-law.

Then some more time passed. One by one my companions, obeying a command, passed out through the door at the back, vanishing out of my life forever. None of them returned. I was vaguely wondering whether Doctor Z buried his dead on the premises or had them removed by a secret passageway in the rear, when a young woman in a nurse's costume tapped me on the shoulder from behind.

As I jumped she hid a compassionate smile with her hand and told me that the doctor would see me now.

As I rose to follow her—still clinging with the drowning man's grip of desperation to my hat and my umbrella—I was astonished to note by a glance at the calendar on the wall that this was still the present date. I thought it would be Thursday of next week at the very least.

Doctor Z also wore whiskers, carefully pointed up by an expert hedge trimmer. He sat at his desk, surrounded by freewill offerings from grateful patients and by glass cases containing other things he had taken away from them when they were not in a condition to object.

I had expected, after all the preliminary ceremonies and delays, that we should have a long séance together. Not so; not at all. The modern expert in surgery charges as much for remembering your name between visits as the family doctor used to expect for staying up all night with you, but he does not waste any time when you are in his presence.

I was about to find that out. And a little later on I was to find out a lot of other things; in fact, that whole week was of immense educational value to me.

I presume it was because he stood so high in his profession, and was almost constantly engaged in breaking into members of the first families, that Doctor Z did not appear to be the least bit excited over my having picked him out to look into me. In the most perfunctory manner he shook the hand that has shaken the hands of Jess Willard, George M. Cohan and Henry Ford, and bade me be seated in a chair which was drawn up in a strong light, where he might gaze directly at me as we conversed and so get the full values of the composition. But if I was a treat for him to look at he concealed his emotions very effectually.

From this point on everything passed off in a most businesslike manner. He reached into a filing cabinet and took out an exhibit, which I recognized as the same one his secretary had filled out in the early part of the century. So I was already in the card-index class. Then briefly he looked over the manifest that Doctor X had sent him. It may not have been a manifest—it may have been an invoice or a bill of lading. Anyhow, I was in the assignee's hands. I could only hope it would not eventually become necessary to call in a receiver. Then he spoke:

"Yes, yes-yes," he said; "yes-yes-yes! Operation required. Small matter—hum, hum! Let's see—this is Tuesday? Quite so. Do it Friday! Friday at—" he glanced toward a scribbled pad of engagement dates at his elbow—"Friday at seven A.M. No; make it seven-fifteen. Have important tumor case at seven. St. Germicide's Hospital. You know the place?—up on Umpty-umph Street. Go' day! Miss Whoziz, call next visitor."

And before I realized that practically the whole affair had been settled I was outside the consultation room in a small private hall, and the secretary was telling me further details would be conveyed to me by mail. I went home in a dazed state. For the first time I was beginning to learn something about an industry in which heretofore I had never been interested. Especially was I struck by the difference now revealed to me in the preliminary stages of the surgeons' business as compared with their fellow experts in the allied cutting trades— tailors, for instance, not to mention barbers. Every barber, you know, used to be a surgeon, only he spelled it chirurgeon. Since then the two professions have drifted far apart. Even a half-witted barber—the kind who always has the first chair as you come into the shop—can easily spend ten minutes of your time thinking of things he thinks you should have and mentioning them to you one by one, whereas any good, live surgeon knows what you have almost instantly.

As for the tailor—consider how wearisome are his methods when you parallel them alongside the tremendous advances in this direction made by the surgeon—how cumbersome and old-fashioned and tedi- ous! Why, an experienced surgeon has you all apart in half the time the tailor takes up in deciding whether the vest shall fasten with five buttons or six. Our own domestic tailors are bad enough in this regard and the Old World tailors are even worse.

I remember a German tailor in Aix-la-Chapelle last year who under- took to build for me a suit suitable for visiting the battle lines in- formally. He was the most literary tailor I ever met anywhere. He would drape the material over my person and then take a piece of chalk and write quite a nice long piece on me. Then he would rub it out and write it all over again, but more fully. He kept this up at intervals of every other day until he had writer's cramp. After that he used pins. He would pin the seams together, uttering little soothing, clucking sounds in German whenever a pin went through the goods and into me. The German cluck is not so soothing as the cluck of the English-speaking peoples, I find.

At the end of two long and trying weeks, which wore both of us down noticeably, he had the job done. It was not an unqualified suc- cess. He regarded it as a suit of clothes, but I knew better: it was a set of slip covers, and if only I had been a two-seated runabout it would have proved a perfect fit, I am sure; but I am a single-seated design and it did not answer. I wore it to the war because I had nothing else to wear that would stamp me as a regular war correspondent, ex- cept of course, my wrist watch; but I shall not wear it to another war. War is terrible enough already; and, besides, I have parted with it. On my way home through Holland I gave that suit to a couple of poor Belgian refugees, and I presume they are still wearing it.

So far as I have been able to observe, the surgeons and the tailors of these times share but one common instinct: If you go to a new surgeon or to a new tailor he is morally certain, after looking you over, that the last surgeon you had, or the last tailor, did not do your cutting properly. There, however, is where the resemblance ends. The tailor, as I remarked in effect just now, wants an hour at least in which to decide how he may best cover up and disguise the irregularities of the human form; in much less time than that the surgeon has completely altered the form itself.

With the surgeon it is very much as it is with those learned men who write those large, impressive works of reference which should be permanently in every library, and which we are forever buying from an agent because we are so passionately addicted to weekly payments. If the thing he seeks does not appear in the contents proper he knows exactly where to look for it. "See appendix," says the historian to you in a footnote. "See appendix," says the surgeon to himself, the while humming a cheery refrain. And so he does.

Well, I went home. This was Tuesday and the operation was not to be performed until the coming Friday. By Wednesday I had calmed down considerably. By Thursday morning I was practically normal again as regards my nerves. You will understand that I was still in a state of blissful ignorance concerning the actual methods of the surgical profession as exemplified by its leading exponents of to-day. The knowledge I have touched on in the paragraphs immediately preceding was to come to me later.

Likewise Doctor Z's manner had deceived me. It could not be that he meant to carve me to any really noticeable extent—his attitude had been entirely too casual. At our house carving is a very serious matter. Any time I take the head of the table and start in to carve it is fitting to remove the women and children to a place of safety, and bystanders should get under the table. When we first started housekeeping and gave our first small dinner party we had a brace of ducks cooked in honor of the company, and, I, as host, undertook to carve them. I never knew until then that a duck was inclosed in a burglarproof case. Without the use of dynamite the Red Leary-O'Brien gang could not have broken into those ducks. I thought so then and I think so yet. Years have passed since then, but I may state that even now, when there are guests in for dinner, we do not have ducks. Unless somebody else is going to carve, we have liver.

I mention this fact in passing because it shows that I had learned to revere carving as one of the higher arts, and one not to be approached except in a spirit of due appreciation of the magnitude of the undertaking, and after proper consideration and thought and reflection, and all that sort of thing. If this were true as regards a mere duck, why not all the more so as regards the carving of a person of whom I am so very fond as I am of myself? Thus I reasoned. And finally, had not Doctor Z spoken of the coming operation as a small matter? Well, then?

Thursday at noon I received from Doctor Z's secretary a note stating that arrangements had been made for my admission into St. Germicide that same evening and that I was to spend the night there. This hardly seemed necessary. Still, the tone of the note seemed to indicate that the hospital authorities particularly wished to have me for an overnight guest; and as I reflected that probably the poor things had few enough bright spots in their busy lives, I decided I would humor them along and gladden the occasion with my presence from dinnertime on.

About eight o'clock I strolled in very jauntily. In my mind I had the whole program mapped out. I would stay at the hospital for, say, two days following the operation—or, at most, three. Then I must be up and away. I had a good deal of work to do and a number of people to see on important business, and I could not really afford to waste more than a week-end on the staff of St. Germicide's. After Monday they must look to their own devices for social entertainment. That was my idea. Now when I look back on it I laugh, but it is a hollow laugh and there is no real merriment in it.

Indeed, almost from the moment of my entrance little things began to come up that were calculated to have a depressing effect on one's spirits. Downstairs a serious-looking lady met me and entered in a book a number of salient facts regarding my personality which the previous investigators had somehow overlooked. There is a lot of bookkeeping about an operation. This detail attended to, a young man, dressed in white garments and wearing an expression that stamped him as one who had suffered a recent deep bereavement, came and relieved me of my hand bag and escorted me upstairs.

As we passed through the upper corridors I had my first introduction to the hospital smell, which is a smell compounded of iodoform, ether, gruel, and something boiling. All hospitals have it, I understand. In time you get used to it, but you never really care for it. The young man let me into a small room tastefully decorated with four walls, a floor, a ceiling, a window sill and a window, a door and a doorsill, and a bed and a chair. He told me to go to bed. I did not want to go to bed—it was not my regular bedtime—but he made a point of it, and I judged it was according to regulations; so I undressed and put on my night clothes and crawled in. He left me, taking my other clothes and my shoes with him; but I was not allowed to get lonely.

A little later a ward surgeon appeared, to put a few inquiries of a pointed and personal nature. He particularly desired to know what my trouble was. I explained to him that I couldn't tell him—he would have to see Doctor X or Doctor Z; they probably knew, but were keeping it a secret between themselves.

The answer apparently satisfied him, because immediately after that he made me sign a paper in which I assumed all responsibility for what was to take place the next morning.

This did not seem exactly fair. As I pointed out to him, it was the surgeon's affair, not mine; and if the surgeon made a mistake the joke would be on him and not on me, because in that case I would not be here anyhow. But I signed, as requested, on the dotted line, and he departed. After that, at intervals, the chief house surgeon dropped in, without knocking, and the head nurse came, and an interne or so, and a ward nurse, and the special nurse who was to have direct charge of me. It dawned on me that I was not having any more privacy in that hospital than a goldfish.

About eleven o'clock an orderly came; and, without consulting my wishes in the matter, he undressed me until I could have passed almost anywhere for September Morn's father, and gave me a clean shave, twice over, on one of my most prominent plane surfaces. I must confess I enjoyed that part of it. So far as I am able to recall, it was the only shave I have ever had where the operator did not spray me with cheap perfumery afterward and then try to sell me a bottle of hair tonic. Having shaved me, the young man did me up amidships in a neat cloth parcel, took his kit under his arm and went away.

It occurred to me that, considering the trivial nature of the case, a good deal of fuss was being made over me by persons who could have no personal concern in the matter whatsoever. This thought recurred to me frequently as I lay there, all tied in a bundle like a week's washing. I did not feel quite so uppish as I had felt. Why was everybody picking on me?

Anon I slept, but dreamed fitfully. I dreamed that a whole flock of surgeons came to my bedside and charted me out in sections, like one of those diagram pictures you see of a beef in the Handy Compendium of Universal Knowledge, showing the various cuts and the butcher's pet name for each cut. Each man took his favorite joint and carried it away, and when they were all gone I was merely a recent site, full of reverberating echoes and nothing else. I have had happier dreams in my time; this was not the kind of dream I should have selected had the choice been left to me.

When I woke the young sun was shining in at the window, and an orderly—not the orderly who had shaved me, but another one—was there in my room and my nurse was waiting outside the door. The orderly dressed me in a quaint suit of pyjamas cut on the half shell and buttoning stylishly in the back, *princesse mode*. Then he rolled in a flat litter on wheels and stretched me on it, and covered me up with a white tablecloth, just as though I had been cold Sunday-night supper, and we started for the operating room at the top of the building; but before we started I lit a large black cigar, as Gen. U. S. Grant used to do when he went into battle. I wished by this to show how indifferent I was. Maybe he fooled somebody, but I do not believe I possess the same powers of simulation that Grant had. He must have been a very remarkable man—Grant must.

The orderly and the nurse trundled me out into the hall and loaded me into an elevator, which was to carry us up to the top of the hospital. Several other nurses were already in the elevator. As we came aboard one of them remarked that it was a fine day. A fine day for what? She did not finish the sentence. Everybody wore a serious look. Inside of myself I felt pretty serious too—serious enough for ten or twelve. I had meant to fling off several very bright, spontaneous quips on the way to the table. I thought them out in advance, but now, somehow, none of them seemed appropriate. Instinctively, as it were, I felt that humor was out of place here.

I never knew an elevator to progress from the third floor of a building to the ninth with such celerity as this one on which we were traveling progressed. Personally I was in no mood for haste. If there was anyone else in all that great hospital who was in a particular hurry to be operated on I was perfectly willing to wait. But alas, no! The mechanism of the elevator was in perfect order—entirely too perfect. No accident of any character whatsoever befell us en route, no dropping back into the basement with a low, grateful thud; no hitch; no delay of any kind. We were certainly out of luck that trip. The demon of a joyrider who operated the accursed device jerked a lever and up we soared at a distressingly high rate of speed. If I could have had my way about that youth he would have been arrested for speeding.

Now we were there! They rolled me into a large room, all white, with a rounded ceiling like the inside of an egg. Right away I knew what the feelings of a poor, lonely little yolk are when the spoon begins to chip the shell. If I had not been so busy feeling sorry for myself I think I might have developed quite an active sympathy for yolks.

My impression had been that this was to be in the nature of a private affair, without invitations. I was astonished to note that quite a crowd had assembled for the opening exercises. From his attire and general deportment I judged that Doctor Z was going to be the master of the revels, he being attired appropriately in a white domino, with rubber gloves and a fancy cap of crash toweling. There were present, also, my diagnostic friend, Doctor X, likewise in fancy-dress costume, and a surgeon I had never met. From what I could gather he was going over the course behind Doctor Z to replace the divots. And there was an interne in the background, playing caddy, as it were, and a head nurse, who was going to keep the score, and two other nurses, who were going to help her keep it. I only hoped that they would show no partiality, but be as fair to me as they were to Doctor Z, and that he would go round in par.

So they placed me right where my eyes might rest on a large wall cabinet full of very shiny-looking tools; and they took my cigar away from me and folded my hands on the wide bowknot of my sash. Then they put a cloth dingus over my face and a voice of authority told me to breathe. That advice, however, was superfluous and might just as well have been omitted, for such was my purpose anyhow. Ever since I can recall anything at all, breathing has been a regular habit with me. So I breathed. And, at that, a bottle of highly charged sarsaparilla exploded somewhere in the immediate vicinity and most of its contents went up my nose.

I started to tell them that somebody had been fooling with their ether and adulterating it, and that if they thought they could send me off to sleep with soda pop they were making the mistake of their lives, because it just naturally could not be done; but for some reason or other I decided to put off speaking about the matter for a few minutes. I breathed again—again—agai——

I was going away from there. I was in a large gas balloon, soaring up into the clouds. How pleasant! . . . No, by Jove! I was not in a balloon—I myself was the balloon, which was not quite so pleasant. Besides, Doctor Z was going along as a passenger; and as we traveled up and up he kept jabbing me with the ferrule of a large umbrella which he had brought along with him in case of rain. He jabbed me harder and harder. I remonstrated with him. I told him I was a bit tender in that locality and the ferrule of his umbrella was sharp. He would not listen. He kept on jabbing me. . . .

Something broke! We started back down to earth. We fell faster and faster. We fell nine miles, and after that I began to get used to it. Then I saw the earth beneath and it was rising up to meet us. A town was below—a town that grew larger and larger as we neared it. I could make out the bonded indebtedness, and the Carnegie Library, and the moving-picture palaces, and the new dancing parlor, and other principal points of interest. At the rate we were falling we were certainly going to make an awful splatter in that town when we hit. I was sorry for the street-cleaning department.

We fell another half mile or so. A spire was sticking up into the sky directly beneath us, like a spear, to impale us. By a supreme effort I twisted out of the way of that spire, only to strike squarely on top of the roof of a greenhouse back of the parsonage, next door. We crashed through it with a perfectly terrific clatter of breaking glass and landed in a bed of white flowers, all soft and downy like feathers.

And then Doctor Z stood up and combed the débris out of his whiskers and remarked that, taking it by and large, it had been one of the pleasantest little outings he had enjoyed in the entire course of his practice. He said that as a patient I was fair, but as a balloon I was immense. He asked me whether I had seen anything of his umbrella and began looking round for it. I tried to help him look, but I was too tired to exert myself much. I told him I believed I would take a little nap.

I opened a dizzy eye part way. So this was heaven—this white expanse that swung and swam before my languid gaze? No, it could not be—it did not smell like heaven. It smelled like a hospital. It was a hospital. It was my hospital. My nurse was bending over me and I caught a faint whiff of the starch in the front of her crisp blue blouse. She was two-headed for the moment, but that was a mere detail. She settled a pillow under my head and told me to lie quiet.

I meant to lie quiet; I did not have to be told. I wanted to lie quiet and hurt. I was hurty from head to toe and back again, and crosswise and cater-cornered. I hurt diagonally and lengthwise and on the bias. I had a taste in my mouth like a bird-and-animal store. And empty!

It seemed to me those doctors had not left anything inside of me except the acoustics. Well, there was a mite of consolation there. If the overhauling had been as thorough as I had reason to believe it was from my present sensations, I need never fear catching anything again so long as I lived, except possibly dandruff.

I waved the nurse away. I craved solitude. I desired only to lie there in that bed and hurt—which I did.

I had said beforehand I meant to stay in St. Germicide's for two or three days only. It is when I look back on that resolution I emit the hollow laugh elsewhere referred to. For exactly four weeks I was flat on my back. I know now how excessively wearied a man can get of his own back, how tired of it, how bored with it! And after that another two weeks elapsed before my legs became the same dependable pair of legs I had known in the past.

I did not want to eat at first, and when I did begin to want to they would not let me. If I felt real peckish they let me suck a little glass thermometer, but there is not much nourishment really in thermometers. And for entertainment, to wile the dragging hours away, I could count the cracks in the ceiling and read my temperature chart, which was a good deal like Red Ames' batting average for the past season—ranging from ninety-nine to one hundred and four.

I shall never forget my first real meal! There was quite a good deal of talk about it beforehand. My nurse kept telling me that on the next day the doctor had promised I might have something to eat. I could hardly wait. I had visions of a tenderloin steak smothered in fried onions, and some French-fried potatoes, and a tall table-limit stack of wheat cakes, and a few other incidental comfits and kickshaws. I could hardly wait for that meal.

The next day came and she brought it to me, and I partook thereof. It was the white of an egg. For dessert I licked a stamp; but this I did clandestinely and by stealth, without saying anything about it to her. I was not supposed to have any sweets.

A little later on, seeing that I had not suffered an attack of indigestion from this debauch, they gave me junket. In the dictionary I have looked up the definitions of junket. I quote:

JUNKET, v. I. t. To entertain by feasting; regale. II. i. To give or take part in an entertainment or excursion; feast in company; picnic; revel.

JUNKET, n. A merry feast or excursion; picnic.

When the author of a dictionary tries to be frivolous he only succeeds in making himself appear foolish. In a hospital, junket is a custard that by some subtle process has been denuded of those ingredients which make a custard fascinating and exciting. It tastes as though the eggs, which form its underlying basis, had been laid in a fit of pique by a hen that was severely upset at the time. Hereafter when the junket is passed round somebody else may have my share. I'll stick to the mince pie *à la mode*. And the first cigar of my convalescence—ah, that, too, abides as a vivid memory! Dropping in one morning to replace the wrappings Doctor Z said I might smoke in moderation. So the nurse brought me a cigar, and I lit it and took one deep puff; but only one. I laid it aside. I said to the nurse:

"A mistake has been made here. I do not want a cooking cigar, you understand. I desire a cigar for personal use. This one is full of herbs and simples, I think. It suggests a boiled New England dinner, and not a very good one at that. Let us try again."

She brought another cigar. It was not satisfactory either. Then she showed me the box—an orthodox box containing cigars of a recognized and previously dependable brand. I could only conclude that a root-and-herb doctor had bought an interest in the business and was introducing his own pet notions into the formula.

But came a day—as the fancy writers say when they wish to convey the impression that a day has come, but hate to do it in a commonplace manner—came a day when my cigar tasted as a cigar should taste and food had the proper relish to it; and my appetite came back again and found the old place not so greatly changed after all.

And then shortly thereafter came another day, when I, all replete with expensive stitches, might drape the customary habiliments of civilization about my attenuated frame and go forth to mingle with my fellow beings. I have been mingling pretty steadily ever since, for now I have something to talk about—a topic good for any company; congenial, an absorbing topic. I can spot a brother member a block away. I hasten up to him and give the grand hailing sign of the order. He opens his mouth to speak, but I beat him to it.

"Speaking of operations——" I say. And then I'm off. Believe me, it's the life!

Draft Status:

A PLETHORA OF SERGEANTS

JOHN SACK

Books about the Army, I know, are supposed to dwell quite a long time on basic training. In the standard formula the author, or hero, is tormented at length by a most execrable villain: a sergeant, preferably master, a man suckled by werewolves and weaned on the blood of Fafnir, devoid of heart and stunted of brain: elephant lunged, Satan eyed, vulture clawed, volcano mouthed, and pledged in life to the humiliation, prostration and ultimate trituration of our hero (author). I wish, for the sake of tradition, that I could tell such a story, but alas! even the names of my sergeants I can hardly remember. During our sixteen weeks at Fort Dix, New Jersey, we had easily half a dozen of them; they passed through our lives like magazine salesmen, or soldiers on review. As soon as we learned the whims and foibles of one, he would be transferred to the Rangers, or put in for chemical school, or go off to the wars, and a new one would take his place. The fault was the Army's, I think; it's not that we had such a repellent platoon, although one boy had lice and another, a fellow named Hawkins, disappeared in the fourth week of training and was picked up by the Feds in Oklahoma City.

Of all our platoon sergeants, only one was really a sergeant. His name was Sergeant Powell, and he lasted about five days. The only thing I remember about Powell was his way of saluting, which was to bend back like a parenthesis, force his elbow in front of his face, and then hurl his hand from his forehead as if, like Oedipus, he were plucking out an eyeball. It was a breathtaking thing to see, if you didn't stand too close. "Allpresentandaccounted *for!*" Sergeant Powell would bellow, the word "for" shouted as on a golf course. Most of our sergeants were really corporals or PFC's, and one was only a private, like us: his name was pronounced *ka*-p'l-ch'k and was never spelled out, if indeed it could be. *Ka*-p'l-ch'k had finished Leadership School at Fort Dix, and was sent to us for practice. The quality of *ka*-p'l-ch'k's leadership was unusual, at best: once he was showing us (first squad) how to quell civil rioters (second squad) and, when the plucky insurgents broke our ranks and scattered us in dismay, he could only whine, "Now *stop* that!" and look very unhappy. A PFC whom I remember was Castellani, who looked like Mussolini. Castellani took his fatigues to a zoot tailor and walked around making muscles, but beyond that he is just a blur. Of all our sergeants the most fearsome, I guess, was a corporal whose name eludes me but was that of some fabled beast, probably Griffin. Corporal Griffin (if that's his name) was a good fellow but had just come back from Korea, and the stories he told kept us in a constant state of neurosis. "Back in Frozen Chosen," he would say, "we never usta sleep in sleepin' bags. We *usta* usta sleep in sleepin' bags, but da Chinks caught us in 'em and slit our troats." Corporal Griffin was very frightening. We breathed easier when he was discharged.

I know this is all very disillusioning, as it was to me, for I too had expected a sergeant hewn of brimstone and voiced like the howling baboon. If I *had* to find a termagant old sergeant to rack me through basic training, I suppose I would have chosen the sergeant who loaded us on the buses from Devens to Dix. "Now when I call your name," he roared, "sound off as if you never had a blank-blank in your life. [Don't worry what the word was. It didn't make much sense, anatomically.] When I say sound off, *sound off.* If your girl or wife walked in, you'd *yell.* Now everyone pretend your barracks bag is your girl, and SOUND OFF!" It was quite a severe tongue-lashing, seeing how we had done nothing wrong, and I shudder to think of his words if we had. Another dire sergeant would have been our company commander at Fort Dix, who was a sergeant before the war. Captain Damisch stood straight as an arrow and steady as a rock; and when something went wrong in our company he spake with the hollow voice of doom: "Men, there's two things we don't do in the Army. We don't discriminate a fellow because of race, creed or religion, and we don't leave gum in the washrooms." Or: "Men, there's two things we don't do in the Army. We don't discriminate a fellow because of race, creed or religion, and we don't sharpen pencils with bayonets." Captain Damisch's plea for tolerance came first in each exhortation, although, as far as I know, no fellow in our company was ever discriminated. We had two colored lieutenants in the company, and they were pretty nice guys. Lieutenant Moore, also known as The Kingfish, was happy as long as we remembered to carry pencils or, as he pronounced them, palcils. "Nah when everyone goes fall in," he'd drawl each morning, "doan fo'get yo' *palcils*." Lieutenant Collins, the other lieutenant, used to rattle all of us by wandering absent-mindedly into the barracks any time of day or night. As we leapt to attention he'd gaze vacuously around the room, mumble something like, "If you open *one* window, open 'em *all*," and ramble out again. Once he mustered the whole company to lecture us on putting hands in pockets. "It's not soldierly," said Lieutenant Collins, and then realized *his* hands were in *his*. He stared down blankly for a few moments and said, "But what *I* do is this. I jingle coins." Lieutenant Collins jingled furiously, but we weren't much convinced. He wouldn't have made a very terrifying sergeant, I think.

The platoon sergeant I remember best, because he was the first, is Corporal McHugh. McHugh was with us only three weeks, but he taught us everything about the Army a soldier has to know: how to make a bed with hospital corners (he called them Army corners) so a quarter will bounce in the center; how to close a rifle bolt without malforming one's thumb; why the Ninth Division patch is an octofoil, and which side goes up, and down; where to stamp, indelibly, each item of martial clothing; how to affix the centipedal straps of the Army field pack, which, next to the fourteen-count drill, is the hardest task military men are called on to do; and many other things like that. Corporal McHugh drilled us with infinite patience. "We shall now learn how to count off," he would say. "Is there any man in ranks"— and here he would gaze around, sizing up the educational background of each of us—"is there any man in ranks who cannot count to two?" *Right face* and *left face* he taught with similar caution. "Which is your right hand?" he would ask us each morning. Then: "Why?" It was not an easy question, as the reader can judge for himself, but I know now the answer that McHugh wanted: "Because Army Field Manual Such-and-Such says so, Corporal."

Corporal McHugh was a regular soldier and went by the book, and only once did we hate him for it. That day began pleasantly enough, with a tour of Dix by rubberneck bus: our guide, a PFC, pointed out the arts and crafts shop, the library "where you can hear the opera on

Saturdays," the golf course and swimming pools, the picnic grounds, the PX village complete with dancing school, and the bars of nearby Wrightstown. The outing drifted into the Red Shield Club of Wrightstown, where we had coffee and doughnuts, and where a homesy voice cooed through a loudspeaker: "Come in, boys, come on in. Some of you will want to know whether you can smoke. Well, *of course* you can smoke. Smoke anything you want to . . . cigars, cigarettes . . . you don't *have* to smoke, of course." We had been lulled into a fine euphoria, both smokers and abstinents, when Corporal McHugh broke the spell. "Dix is a great place when you got free time," he guffawed. "Too bad you guys won't get none!"

For the rest of that week, McHugh said, we would shine our barracks floor to marmoreal luster; the weekend would be set aside for the sewing of patches and the stamping of names; and any free time could best be dedicated to the insides of our gun barrels. That very night, in fact, we would be confined to the barracks to master the Prescribed Array of Military Footlockers.

We were a sullen crew that evening when Corporal McHugh showed up, his hands full of mimeographed plans. "Now there's a right way and a wrong way to lay out footlockers," he began. "This platoon, we're gonna do it the right way." The right way, copied from an Army manual, could be found on the corporal's mimeographed maps. Everything had its place, to the fraction of an inch. The tooth powder stood bolt upright but the toothbrush lay down, its shank to the right and its bristles to the rear. Immediately behind the toothbrush, and on line with its balance point, came the razor blade, its edges parallel to those of the footlocker. Abreast the razor blade was the razor, head to the leftward; the comb pointed its tines to the soap dish, one and one-fourth inches away; a single handkerchief lay quadruply folded; and the socks, tightly furled, were contiguous. We looked at the chart in dismay.

"I got more'n one hankachief," someone said. "I blows my nose like hell."

"Supposin' I use toothpaste instead?" another voice piped in. "How'm I gonna make the toothpaste stand up?"

"You don't *use* toothpaste," McHugh explained patiently. "Like it says here, you uses *powder*."

Tempers were rising. Half of us shaved with electricity, but the Army's mimeographed plan, evidently drawn in the days of the Cuban campaign, had sites for a razor blade, shaving brush, and a shaving stick. I for one had never heard of a shaving stick.

"You don't gotta *use* them," McHugh was arguing. "In fact, you *won't* use them. The stuff you *uses*, you hides somewhere. This stuff you buys special. You keeps it clean; it's for inspections."

"Oh brother!" said someone. Money meant a lot to us in those days. McHugh looked at our incredulous faces and tried to keep going.

"Now, another thing, all this stuff gotta be *uniform*. So now we're gonna have a vote, and figure what color toothbrush and everything we're gonna buy."

"Man, you knows what you can do wit' dat toothbrush," said a colored boy. All of us were ready to mutiny.

"*All right!* Don't vote!" roared McHugh. "I'll tell you myself what t'get! Lessee, the cigarettes in the corner, that's gonna be Kools. . . ."

"But I don't smoke!" said Faletti.

"Damnit you don't *gotta* smoke 'em," McHugh bawled, waving his plans in the air. "All you gotta do is *have* 'em!"

"Boy oh boy," said someone, "wait'll I tell my fambly! The Army's making me buy cigarettes!"

McHugh was shaking all over by now, and my wrathful bunkmates, deserting him, sulked to their footlockers. "They're pretty angry, Corporal," I said.

"Damnit, all this stuff is in the book!" said McHugh. "All I'm doin' is what's in the book."

"Well, maybe the book's just a guide."

"The book *ain't* no guide. The book's the book!"

"OK," I said, "but you have to admit it's sort of silly."

McHugh was simmering down. "Yeah," he said, "I guess it's sort of silly." For a few minutes he sat introspectively on my bunk. "I'm a funny guy," he said.

"Sure. We all are."

"Sometimes I feel different. I get temperamental. I'm moody."

"You're a man of many moods," I said.

"Yeah," said McHugh, "that's it. You got it." McHugh left our platoon soon after. He said he was going to the Infantry School at Fort Benning, Georgia. We had many sergeants after him, but none who lasted so long. I guess I sort of miss him.

INITIATIVE

HAROLD HELFER

"The trouble with you, Fluffy," I said, "is that you don't have any initiative. And you eat too much. You're always eating."

"I guess you're right," said Fluffy, munching on a piece of pie.

"All the guys in our boot camp outfit now are corporals or sergeants or something. All except you, Fluffy. You're still a private."

"You're right about that," agreed Fluffy amiably.

"And you know that the main thing a marine is supposed to have is initiative," I pointed out.

"That's the truth, all right," said Fluffy, leaning his imposing corpulence against one of Leyte's more stalwart palm trees.

"You don't even have the initiative to argue about it," I argued.

"I reckon I don't," sighed Fluffy. "I reckon you're right all the way around. I reckon I don't have any initiative."

"Maybe if you weren't so crazy about food you could get interested in something else," I continued. "Maybe you wouldn't be weighing any two hundred and twenty pounds, but you might find other things fascinating about life and the Marine Corps, even if you had to do it at, say, a downright skinny hundred and ninety-five."

"I guess you're sure right there," acknowledged Fluffy, stretching.

"I wouldn't be telling you this if I weren't your pal," I said.

I was, too. I liked Fluffy, all right. But he was lazy, indolent, and given to procrastination, and besides that, he didn't like to work. He never did anything unless he was told to, and then he didn't if he could possibly get out of it. The only thing he seemed to care about, the only thing that ever excited him, was food. The only time he wasn't goldbricking was at chow.

He always went back for second helpings, and sometimes thirds and fourths, and he used to come back to his tent with his dungaree pockets bulging with food items that some of the other leathernecks didn't want, and these he would stack away and munch on in his leisure moments, of which he always managed to have plenty. All of us guys tried to talk about interesting things, like women, and well, other things, but the only time Fluffy showed any conversational animation whatsoever was when the subject veered to chow.

Like I say, though, I considered myself his pal, and I didn't want to hurt his feelings, but I figured it was about time I had a heart-to-heart talk with him. Fluffy and I had been left behind to keep an eye on headquarters. Most of the other guys in our outfit, except for a few officers and the cooks, had gone out on one kind of a mission or other and wouldn't be back for quite awhile.

I was going to continue my lecture to Fluffy when I saw the Jap. "Duck behind the tree, Fluffy," I said. "I see a Jap."

I dropped to the ground and scampered away on my hands and knees for about twelve yards, until I was behind a jeep. Meanwhile, a shower of bullets was coming our way.

So not one, but a bunch of Japs, had infiltrated to our headquarters. I couldn't tell exactly how many there were because they were hiding in the fringe of the jungle growth, but I gathered there were at least a couple of dozen.

Behind his tree, Fluffy was leisurely taking pot shots at the little yellow men. I kept firing away for all I was worth.

Pretty soon the rest of the men at headquarters came out of their huts and tents to join in the show. A few got behind the jeep with me; some took cover behind trees; some behind the woodpile.

The Japs kept up a steady stream of fire. We did our best to match them. Occasionally we had the pleasure of hearing an Oriental groan.

Then I heard another kind of groan. From one of our men. It was Corporal Tom Watson. He'd taken an advanced position, having moved up behind a concrete mixer. Now he lay sprawled out on the ground.

He wasn't dead, though. We could see him stirring.

Apparently the Japs were aware of that, too. Part of their fire was now directed exclusively at him. Luckily, only his outstretched legs were actually exposed to the Japs.

But that wasn't too lucky, either. If you keep firing away at a man's feet, it isn't going to do him any good. Several of us made a break to go to Watson's rescue, but the Japs put up such an intense hail of bullets that we were driven back.

A second or two later, Fluffy left the sanctuary of his tree and darted over to the jeep. A mess of Jap bullets followed him every inch of the way along those dozen yards.

"You crazy fool," I bellowed. "You should've stayed there. But if you just had to come, why, in Hirohito's name, didn't you crawl?"

"I'm in a hurry—I have an idea," he said, all out of breath. "You guys will have to take cover somewheres else though. Why don't you get behind those bushes over there? I haven't got time to explain. Please hurry."

His voice was urgently pleading and before we quite realized what we were doing, I suppose, we obeyed him. Then he jumped up in the jeep and started the motor.

Crouching down as far as he could get and lowering his head, off he and the jeep went.

He headed straight into the teeth of the Jap fire. I heard some ping-pong noises that sounded very much like some of the Jap bullets were deflecting themselves off his helmet, but on he went regardless.

Suddenly, the jeep came to a stop. He was now alongside Watson. He leaped out of the jeep, picked the corporal up, put him in the back, and he was off again.

Coming back was a much more dangerous proposition because his back was exposed to the Japs—there was no protruding helmet. Fluffy must have realized it with all his enormous being because then he really pressed his foot down on the gas. He zoomed back toward us, a fat, sweating, panting bat out of hell.

The jeep screeched to a stop near the hut, and Fluffy, with the Jap bullets still whizzing around him like a nest of hornets, carried the wounded corporal inside. Pretty soon a medical corpsman was there to start administering aid.

He was just in time. The corporal had been shot in the chest and several times in the legs, and had lost a lot of blood.

A half-hour later a whole platoon of marines came back to camp, and we had no trouble in routing the Japs.

But of course, Fluffy was the hero of the day. Our second Looey even made a speech about him to the rest of the boys and said he certainly was going to recommend Fluffy for some kind of medal or other.

"I suppose my talk to you did some good after all," I said to Fluffy afterwards, trying my best not to gloat.

"I reckon so," said Fluffy.

"I'm glad to see you're a man that can take advice, Fluffy."

"I reckon I just saw red when I saw them Japs firing at Watson while he was so helpless," said Fluffy, leaning against a tree and munching on something. "And him the best pie-maker we got in camp."

PRIVATE WUMPERDOPP OF THE NEW ARMY

LARRY SIEGEL

Before Korea there was much talk that Army life had changed. It may not have changed as portrayed here, however.

News Item

York, Pa., Oct. 22, 1949 (Affiliated Press)—The Army told the mothers of America tonight that every youth drafted into the Army "will be treated as a human being, never a raw recruit."

A high ranking officer promised the mothers a recruit will be treated as a person "of individual dignity and feelings, entitled to courtesy and consideration."

The officer presented the following nine points:

(1) The recruit will be sent to a post "as near home as possible."

(2) His instructors will try "to establish a personal relationship with him."

(3) He will have explained the reason for everything he does which is new to him.

(4) No matter how or when he arrives, "someone will meet him" and he will be given "a chance to ask questions."

(5) His uniforms are individually fitted.

(6) The Army will insist that "he write home."

(7) He will be interviewed by his company commander and first sergeant, each of whom also will write a personal letter to his mother.

(8) The young man gets "an advance on his pay" immediately.

(9) Neither he nor his instructors will use profanity.

Scene I

(*The front steps of the Wumperdopp house. Julius Wumperdopp, nineteen, is standing with his right arm around his suitcase and his left arm around his mother. The day they have both been fearfully anticipating has arrived.*)

Julius: (manfully) Good-by, Mother, I'm off for the Army.

Mother: (tearfully) Good-by, Julius. I'll miss you, son.

Julius: And I you, Mother.

Mother: Are you taking the bus to camp?

Julius: No, it's balmy today; I think I'll walk.

Mother: Oh, Julius, I wish they were sending you to Fort Fenwick on Maple Street, instead of to that Camp Cadence all the way on the other side of town.

Julius: Mother, I told you they tried to get me into Fenwick, but it's filled. However, I heard the Cadence isn't bad; it's only twelve blocks from here.

Mother: (grasping his arm tightly and looking into his eyes) Twelve blocks! It might as well be twelve miles! Oh, Julius!

Julius: There, there, Mother. Before you look around, I'll be home. And don't forget, I'll write you. We'll all write you.

Mother: I know you will. And now, good-by. I'll miss you, son (she kisses him and scampers into the house, liberally expending tears along the way).

Julius: (to the closed door) And I you, Mother.

(Curtain)

Scene II

(*Twelve minutes later. The front gate of Camp Cadence. Julius, with bag in hand and awe in his eyes, approaches the nattily dressed military policeman on duty.*)

Julius: Hello there, my name is Julius Wumperdopp.

M.P.: (warmly) Why hello, Julius. We've been expecting you. My name is Fred.

Julius: Pleased to meet you, Fred.

M.P.: Did you have a nice trip?

Julius: Fair to middlin'. I had a little trouble breaking through the shopping crowd at Grand Avenue.

M.P.: That's too bad. But the important thing is that you're here now. The way I look at it, that's all that counts.

Julius: Well, Fred, where is he?

M.P.: Who?

Julius: The man who's supposed to meet me.

M.P.: Oh, I almost forgot. Sergeant Snead said he'd be a little late. Some last minute stuff turned up to detain him. But he promised he'd be here as soon as possible. I hope you don't mind.

Julius: (shrugging his shoulders) Well, I guess it's all right. I'll wait.

M.P.: I knew you'd understand.

Julius: (takes out a pack of cigarettes) Smoke, Fred?

M.P.: Heavens, no! There is nothing more detrimental to the lungs than nicotine. We in the New Army look down on it.

Julius: I see. (takes out a package of gum) Gum?

M.P.: Well . . . no. I'd better not. Not while I'm on duty. (Sergeant Snead, trim and bronzed, in an impeccably laundered suit of khakis, enters from the left. He stops and scrutinizes Julius' profile. Then, his entire face one huge smile, he hurries over.)

Snead: (seizing Julius' hand) Well, well, if it isn't . . . no, no, don't tell me! Let me guess! Julius! Julius Wumperdopp!

Julius: And you must be Sergeant Snead.

Snead: In person! My, my, you look splendid! You know, in those pictures your mother sent me, you seemed kind of . . . well, pale. But you're not at all. By George, it's grand seeing you!

Julius: Same here, Sergeant Snead. But I must say that your pictures don't do you any kind of justice. You're so bronzed! So alive! So clean-cut!

Snead: (blushing) Well, you know—good food, plenty of sleep, clean living. It adds up. But don't call me Sergeant Snead. The other fellows call me Salvatore. I wish you would too.

Julius: Okay . . . Salvatore.

Snead: And now, guess what I've got for you (reaches into his pocket).

Julius: For me? Gee, I don't know.

Snead: Aw, come on, guess.

Julius: I couldn't even try.

Snead: (takes out a roll of bills) Here you are, Julius.

Julius: What's this?

Snead: Your raise in pay. You earned it. Now you just follow orders and be a good soldier and . . . (he winks at him) who knows what you'll get next month.

Julius: (visibly touched) I don't know how to thank you, Salvatore.

Snead: Forget it, kid. And now the questions.

Julius: What questions?

Snead: The ones you're supposed to ask me. Go ahead, ask.

Julius: About what?

Snead: Anything, anything at all about Army life.

Julius: But I don't have any questions.

Snead: Aw, go ahead and try. Please do. Surely there must be something. There is nothing I want more than for you to ask me about things.

Julius: Sorry, I can't think of anything.

Snead: Well, that's all right. But Julius—(his face warms with feeling) if at any time, anywhere, anything bothers you, come to me. No matter where I am, no matter what I'm doing, come to me, and by George, I'll help you. All I want is questions. Trust in me, Julius. Have faith in me. Ask questions. Ask questions.

Julius: (completely overwhelmed) Thank you; I shall. But right now I don't . . . oh, yes, by the way I do have a question. At home I was looking through an Army manual, and there was a tactics problem that stumped me. Here it is: If a battalion leader had to go through a wooded area to attack an enemy strongpoint at dawn, would it be wiser for him to use his own mortars for overhead fire, call for artillery support, or get air cover?

Snead: I don't know. And now, shall we go to the barracks?

Julius: Sure thing (picks up his bag). I'd like to meet the rest of the gang.

Snead: (takes bag from him) Give me that. You don't think I'm going to let you carry that all the way, do you?

Julius: Okay, Salvatore. (to M.P.) Well, so long, Fred, see you around.

M.P.: Righto. Oh say, Julius, I'm going off duty in a little while. I'll take that stick of gum.

(Curtain)

Scene III

(*Several minutes later. An enlisted man's barracks. Sixteen maple beds with inner-spring mattresses line the walls. Next to each bed is a mahogany dresser. Overhead are fluorescent lights. Hanging on the walls around the huge room are pictures of Captain Twiddle, the Commanding Officer, in various poses. On one he is playing baseball with the boys. On another he is grinning impishly as he playfully ducks a private in the company swimming pool. On another—a more serious one—he is selling Baltic Avenue to a Pfc. over a Monopoly board. On all the pictures are the same penned inscriptions, "To the boys, my boys—members of our one great big, happy family. All my love and then some, Harold." As Julius and Snead enter from the left, Mrs.*

Primm, the barracks mother, is straightening a bed in the corner and humming.)

Snead: Hello, Mrs. Primm! Look what I've got! (points to a blushing Julius).

Primm: (walking over; her honest, matronly eyes twinkling) Oh, I'll bet that's Julius! Julius Wumperdopp! I do declare! But he doesn't look at all like his pictures! He's not a bit pale!

Snead: (clapping Julius on the back) That's what I told him!

Julius: (flustered) I'm . . . I'm pleased to meet you, ma'am.

Primm: My, my, let me fix my specs so I can take a good look at you (she fixes her specs). You do look grand! Just like . . . just like . . .

Julius: What is it, ma'am?

Primm: (breaking down) Just li . . .

Snead: (to Julius in a low voice) It's her son.

Julius: (in an anxious whisper) What happened to him?

Snead: It's terrible.

Julius: Was he killed?

Snead: Just as bad. He's in the Navy.

Julius: So?

Snead: (explosively) So! Did you hear what I said. He's in the Navy. Do you know what that means?

Julius: Gracious sakes! Tell me.

Primm: (pulling herself together) It's all right, boys. I'm okay now. Julius, my son Eliot, my only son Eliot is a sailor boy. They . . . they treat him like dirt. He's been away for over a month now, and he still didn't get a raise in pay. There's no one to care for him. They don't explain things to him. They don't make his bed. They . . . they . . . (she breaks down again).

Snead: (putting his arm around her) Easy, Mrs. Primm. Don't torture yourself like this.

Primm: I'll be all right (dabs her eyes with her apron).

Julius: Gee, I'm sorry, ma'am. You must be having a rough go of it.

Primm: Well, let's forget about it for now. Shall we? Let's talk about you. How was the trip?

Julius: Oh, it could have been better. I was held up.

Primm: Grand Avenue shopping crowds?

Julius: Yes, ma'am.

Primm: Land sakes! You'd think they'd do something about that. But I guess it's one of those things you boys have to put up with.

Julius: I'm firmly convinced of that, ma'am.

Primm: How is your mother, Julius?

Julius: Oh, she's fine.

Primm: The rest of the family?

Julius: As well as can be expected.

Primm: I'm glad. I do declare! I can't get over how well you look. I must hurry to my room and write your mother about it.

Julius: Do you have my address?

Primm: Of course, we all do (she walks away muttering, "He doesn't look a bit pale.").

Julius: (to Snead) She seems to be keen.

Snead: Oh, she's a pip. We've had her for four months now. I don't know what we'd do without her. The place was a mess before she came. But come, let's find you a nice bed.

Julius: Don't trouble yourself. Any one of these will do.

Snead: (carrying the bag and leading Julius to a bed) Now here's a good one. You've got cross ventilation and an excellent view of the parade grounds. Or else, this one over here . . . oh, hang it all!

Julius: What happened?

Snead: I dropped the bag on my foot. Oh, darn. Oh, fush. Gee whilikers! Oh, fishcakes!

Julius: Are you all right?

Snead: Yeah, I guess so. I'm sorry for the sudden outburst of profanity. I don't swear as a rule. None of us do. But sometimes . . . Well, you know, a fellow has to sort of let go.

Julius: (sincerely) I understand.

(The front door opens. Rugged, sunburned men in flawlessly fitting khakis dash into the barracks. Their eyes shine with the radiance that only comes from supreme happiness. They are whistling, laughing, and singing.)

Snead: (to Julius) Well, well, the men are back from the temperance lecture already. How'd you like to meet them, Julius?

Julius: Salvatore, nothing on the face of this earth would give me more pleasure than to meet the fellows, the gang with whom I'm going to share all this (he spreads out his hands as if to signify not only the barracks, but the camp and the whole army as well).

Snead: Very well said, Julius.

Julius: Thank you.

Snead: (raising his voice) Fellows, I want you to come over and shake hands with Julius Wumperdopp!

(The men run over and enthusiastically pump Julius' hand and wish him luck.)

Snead: How was the lecture, gang?

Mixed voices: Super! Whizz bang! Jim dandy! Peachy! The cats!

Snead: That's great!

Julius: Say, Salvatore, how's the chance of getting a uniform now?

Snead: Sure thing. Then after that we'll have dinner. You know . . . (winks at him) chow down, like the old Army used to say (they walk to the door).

Julius: After you.

Snead: No, after you.

(Curtain)

Scene IV

(*Twenty minutes later. The company dining hall. Gay, flowered curtains bedeck the windows. A little fountain with a statue of the regimental commander spurting water through his mouth is in the center. The floors are carpeted in Oriental style. In a corner is a juke box, which floods the room with popular music—that is, whenever Monk Monroe and his company jive combo are off duty. Cunning, hand-carved booths jut out from the walls. On each is a menu and a candle for midnight snacks. Trim blond waitresses hustle about taking orders. Snead and Julius enter from the right. Julius is immaculately attired in khaki. Every fiber of the material clings to an appropriate spot on his body. It fits him so perfectly that if it were of a lighter color, it could easily be mistaken for his skin.*)

Snead: (guiding Julius) This way, Julius. I'll take you over to Captain Twiddle's booth. He's probably anxious to see you.

Julius: Say, this place is nifty!

Snead: It's not bad. But, boy, you ought to see it when it's fixed up (they arrive at Captain Twiddle's table).

Snead: Harold, I want you to meet Julius Wumperdopp.

Twiddle: (rising and dabbing his mouth with a napkin) This is indeed a pleasure, Julius! Come closer to the light so that I can look at you (Julius obliges).

Twiddle: Hmm, just as I thought . . . pale as a ghost. But we'll take care of that. Plenty of fresh air, bathing. You'll be in the pink. But sit down, fellows.

Julius: This is swell of you, sir.

Twiddle: Aw, can the "sir" business. You'll make me blush. Call me Harold like everybody else does. Unless you want to call me "Noodles" like the girls here do (he laughs and pokes Julius playfully with his elbow).

Julius: Harold will be fine.

Twiddle: Now, what'll we have to eat?

Julius: It really doesn't matter. I like lobsters pretty much.

Twiddle: Bully! Lobsters it is! Oh darn, I just forgot. We're all out of lobsters. Used 'em up at the company picnic and community sing last night. How about some steak.

Julius: Suits me.

Twiddle: How do you want it?

Julius: It doesn't matter. I'm not a fussy eater.

Twiddle: Good, good! We need rugged men. What about you, Salvatore?

Snead: I was sort of counting on lobster myself, but if we don't have any . . . (he shrugs his shoulders) we don't have any. I guess it'll have to be steak.

Twiddle: (calls waitress) Two steaks, honey, and let 'em sizzle.

Waitress: You bet, Noodles (she slinks off).

Julius: Say, Harold, this is quite a set-up.

Twiddle: Fair. Fair. Needs a lot of fixing, though. I don't like the way the door is situated. Hell of a draft on the men near it. And the acoustics are awful. Some of the boys in the back can't hear the music too well. Needs lots of fixing.

Julius: How often do the men do K.P. around here?

Twiddle: K.P.? K.P.? Oh, K.P.! Kitchen police! Ha, ha, that's out. Oh, we had it going for a while, but the men didn't like it. It played all kinds of hell with their sleep and that sort of stuff. Of course, we do have an enlisted man on duty at all times checking the thermostat. Can't be lax, you know (waitress brings two large steaks and puts them down on the table).

Julius: Say, Harold, this is a bit of all right.

Twiddle: Like it?

Julius: I'll say.

Twiddle: I'm sorry we ran out of lobsters, though.

Julius: Forget it.

(Curtain)

Scene V

(*A few weeks later. The company orderly room. Twiddle is working on some papers when Julius walks in.*)

Julius: (coldly) Hello, Harold.

Twiddle: Julius, Julius! Come in!

Julius: (noticeably disturbed) Harold, there's something I must speak to you about.

Twiddle: What is it, Julius? Aren't they explaining everything you do to you?

Julius: Yes, they are, but . . .

Twiddle: Aren't you treated as a human being, never a raw recruit?

Julius: I'm not kicking on that score.

Twiddle: Don't you feel like a person of individual dignity and feelings, entitled to courtesy and consideration?

Julius: Yes, I do.

Twiddle: Have any of your instructors been using profanity?

Julius: Sakes alive, no!

Twiddle: Don't you like your buddies, your noncoms, your bed, the food, the company hayrides?

Julius: Oh, Harold, I like them all.

Twiddle: Well, speak up. What is it then?

Julius: (looking around) Are we alone?

Twiddle: (alarmed) Why yes.

Julius: Good. This isn't going to be easy to say. I don't know exactly how to begin.

Twiddle: (walks over to him) Julius, what's the matter?

Julius: Well, before I start, let me say that I have always thought you were a peach of a guy. I know that you have plenty of work to do around here. You have a whole company of men to take care of, and it's only natural for you to make mistakes.

Twiddle: For goodness sakes, what have I done?

Julius: It's what you haven't done.

Twiddle: Julius, please tell me.

Julius: You haven't written to my mother in three days. There, I said it.

(Silence follows; tense, awkward silence. Twiddle, his forehead glistening with cold sweat, paces the floor.)

Twiddle: (stopping suddenly) You're right; I haven't. I guess it had to get out sooner or later. Now mind you, I'm not making excuses, but I tried to write. Honest I did. I just couldn't find time.

Julius: Like. I said, I understand that you're busy. But three days . . . !

Twiddle: (extremely emotional) Julius, in my last letter to her—which was Wednesday, I think—I told her that there was a chance I wouldn't write for a few days. Things came up. I explained it to her. Doesn't she understand?

Julius: Oh, she says she does. But somehow by reading between the lines I could tell that she's upset about it.

Twiddle: What have I done? What have I done? (he buries his head in his hands)

Julius: (consoling him) Now look, Harold, I forgive you, and I understand. I realize how things turn up at the last minute.

Twiddle: You know what we're up against in the Army with last minute orders. Why, take yourself. Remember yesterday when the company was at the theater during Motion Picture Appreciation hour, and they suddenly pulled you right out of your seat to play Barnes of B Company in the semi-finals of the battalion checker tournament. You remember, don't you?

Julius: Of course I do. You're partly right. But my mother . . . Look, Harold, let me put it this way. Let's say, for example, that every commanding officer in the Army just put off writing to the mothers of the men. Just like that, they stopped. I know it sounds horrible, but let's say they did, just for argument's sake. Can you possibly imagine the consequences? Do you dare? All right, so the men themselves would still be writing. But do you think that for one moment the mothers are going to believe that their sons are in . . . well, good hands . . . unless they hear about it directly from the commanding officer? Let me tell you right now that you're darned right they won't. They'll worry. And how they'll worry! Harold, that's what my mother is doing right now. Of course, she doesn't mind the three days so much, but you know that once you start neglecting things . . .

Twiddle: (broken up) Stop! Stop! You're right! I've been wrong, so horribly wrong! Julius, I'll write at once.

Julius: I wish you would.

Twiddle: (his eyes shining now and his voice quivering) I promise.

Julius: (simply) Thanks, Harold. Oh by the way, is Jolly Sandy, the First Sergeant, around?

Twiddle: No, Julius, he's visiting one of the sick men. Don't tell me that he too . . .

Julius: Oh no, he's been writing regularly. Well, I guess I'll take off now.

Twiddle: Look! (he holds up a pen and sheet of paper, as if to signify that he's ready to write the letter)

Julius: Good boy! Well, so long. I want you to know that my mind is clear, and I'm ready to serve my country as it should be served.

Twiddle: Where are you going now?

Julius: Out.

Twiddle: Yes, but where and with who—whom? We'd like to know these things.

Julius: I'm going to see some girls.

Twiddle: (rising wrathfully) Girls! See here, *Private* Wumper-dopp, don't you realize you're in the Army? Don't you recall your soldier's oath? Don't you know your General Order, "I won't fraternize with girls"? Don't you realize this is a court martial offense?

Julius: (white-faced) I beg your pardon, sir, but I am speaking before Girl Scout Troop 23, my mother's troop.

Twiddle: (covered with confusion) Oh, I'm sorry, Julius. A thousand pardons. I hope you will forgive me.

Julius: I'm afraid I can't accept your apologies, Captain, I believe in forgiveness, but I cannot overlook your lack of faith in me. I'm afraid, sir, that I have no alternative but to resign from an Army which does not trust its men.

(*Captain Twiddle's arms fall to his side and his head drops hopelessly on his chest.*)

Any Charge Accounts:

HOW GAY WAS OUR CREDIT

ROBERT M. YODER

The two-tone, reversible credit letter, which I hope shortly to offer credit managers in a poisoned wrapper, is the result of puzzled dalliance with a large but coquettish department store. The clearest come-on you ever saw opened this affair—a note from the store, saying that some of the best people found it pleasant to charge things there. The flattering suggestion was clear that I was just the well-heeled, dependable type they liked to have in the store.

Well, inside of two months there came another letter. You wouldn't have known this rude smirch was from the same company. "When we extend credit," said this coldly formal ultimatum—and what a crass name for the relationship hinted in that first scented note—"we expect everything to be paid up at the end of the month. If you cannot do this, call on the sixteenth floor and make other arrangements."

This from the store that had so lately been straightening my tie and fluttering its best sixty-nine-cent handkerchief.

My two-way letter was born right then, and I think credit managers will go for it, as it saves printing up two forms. It can be used either as the beautifully airy Maybasket in which they invite you to come in and rumple the sales manager's hair or as the little snarl a little later which tells you to pay your bill at once. Goes like this:

"Perhaps you are one of the few really nice people who still are not using our handy credit service. We find you have owed us $6 since yesterday. Where is it? If you are not, if you still shop the old-fashioned way, why not try 'Charge-O' sometime, just for a fillip? It's so languorous you'll wonder why you ever bothered carrying bulky old currency which stretches the pockets.

"We have taken the liberty of issuing you one of our pretty charge-account cards, chosen to match your eyes. Just whisper, 'Charge it' to one of the subservient salespersons, and we do the rest. If we do not hear from you promptly on this matter, we will slap a lien on everything you own.

"Many of our customers don't like to soil their fingers writing inky old checks, and they find charging much more diverting.

"If they need cash while downtown, they just borrow ten or twenty from Uncle Walter, our jolly cashier. If you cannot afford to buy here, why don't you get your stuff out of trash barrels? We extend credit only under certain tight limitations, and hate every minute of it.

"Incidentally, if you are passing our store—and we do hope you won't—and find it convenient to turn your head, you may enjoy the display of emeralds in our North Window. It's just possible you might spot something there for your collection. If you are broke, as we suspect, and nobody will lend you the six skins, then get over here at once and see S. Legree Wunkle, in our Paupers and White Trash Department. But get here before sundown or we are listing you with the Credit Bureau as a financial untouchable.

"May we look forward to seeing you—if you aren't in Saratoga or Banff—the next time whim leads you to our street? And may we sign ourselves: 'Your friend'? P.S.: Don't look for your other shoes, as we had the marshal come and get them. We want our dough."

THE ECONOMICAL PAIR

CAROLYN WELLS

Once on a Time there was a Man and his Wife who had Different Ideas concerning Family Expenditures.

The Man said: "I am Exceedingly Economical; although I spend Small Sums here and there for Cigars, Wines, Theatre Tickets, and Little Dinners, yet I do not buy me a Yacht or a Villa at Newport."

But even with these Praiseworthy Principles, it soon Came About that the Man was Bankrupt.

Whereupon he Reproached his Wife, who Answered his Accusations with Surprise.

"Me! My dear!" she exclaimed. "Why, I am Exceedingly Economi-

AL KAUFMAN, THE SATURDAY EVENING POST

"In case you're interested, we're no longer keeping up with the Joneses—we've passed them!"

---

cal. True, I Occasionally buy me a Set of Sables or a Diamond Tiara, but I am Scrupulously Careful about Small Sums; I Diligently unknot all Strings that come around Parcels, and Save Them, and I use the Backs of old Envelopes for Scribbling-Paper. Yet, somehow, my Bank-Account is also Exhausted."

Morals:

This Fable teaches to Take Care of the Pence and the Pounds will Take Care of Themselves, and that we Should Not Be Penny-Wise and Pound-Foolish.

IT MAY COST A LITTLE MORE

CASKIE STINNETT

We've contended for a long time that this mass-assembly mania can be carried too far and now that it has happened we can't find the impulse to exult. It may be a little hard to grasp at first, but under our mass-assembly system one thing now often costs more than two. To illustrate, we'll relate what happened to us recently when we went to buy a slip cover for the front seat of the car.

"You want I should break a set?" the man in the auto-accessory department asked. It was as if we'd asked him to put the torch to his mother's cottage.

"The back seat has never been used," we explained, "because my wife prefers to give me instructions from the front seat." We laughed winsomely.

He didn't laugh.

"Half a set will run a good deal more than a full set," he said, noting with satisfaction that the smile had frozen on our lips. "We'll have to order it special, and that means special handling. They might even have to make it special, which would mean shutting down one machine for a whole day. A new car would be a lot cheaper—"

You would have thought that when we got to the garage later we would have been prepared for the installer, but we weren't.

"To install half a set," the garage man said, "will—"

"—Run a good deal more," we suggested.

"Exactly," he said, nodding to show his appreciation of our understanding. "Half a set requires special handling. Covers are put on by two men working as a team. Take out the back seat man, and there's nobody for the front man to talk to. He has to lower the window and talk to the other men in the shop. This slows everybody down. I'm glad you understand."

We took the slip cover home and put it on ourself. On the *car*, ourself. The only person we talked to was our wife and all we said was, "Hand me the pliers." It worked so well that we're thinking of installing half-sets for our friends. It sounds crazy—and it may take a while for the idea to catch on—but we plan on charging only half as much as for a full set.

CONTENTMENT

OLIVER WENDELL HOLMES

"Man wants but little here below."

Little I ask; my wants are few;
  I only wish a hut of stone
(A *very plain* brown stone will do)
  That I may call my own;
And close at hand is such a one,
  In yonder street that fronts the sun.

Plain food is quite enough for me;
  Three courses are as good as ten;
If Nature can subsist on three,
  Thank Heaven for three—Amen!
I always thought cold victuals nice,—
  My *choice* would be vanilla-ice.

I care not much for gold or land;
  Give me a mortgage here and there,
Some good bank-stick, some note of hand,
  Or trifling railroad share,—
I only ask that Fortune send
  A *little* more than I shall spend.

Honours are silly toys, I know,
  And titles are but empty names;
I would, *perhaps*, be Plenipo—
  But only near St. James;
I'm very sure I should not care
  To fill our Gubernator's chair.

Jewels are baubles; 'tis a sin
  To care for such unfruitful things—
One good-sized diamond in a pin,
  Some, *not so large*, in rings,
A ruby, and a pearl, or so,
  Will do for me—I laugh at show.

My dame should dress in cheap attire
  (Good, heavy silks are never dear);
I own perhaps I *might* desire
  Some shawls of true Cashmere—
Some narrowy crapes of China silk,
  Like wrinkled skins on scalded milk.

Wealth's wasteful tricks I will not learn,
  Nor ape the glitt'ring upstart fool;
Shall not carved tables serve my turn,
  But *all* must be of buhl?
Give grasping pomp its double care,—
  I ask but *one* recumbent chair.

Thus humble let me live and die,
  Nor long for Midas' golden touch;
If Heaven more gen'rous gifts deny,
  I shall not miss them much,—
Too grateful for the blessing lent
  Of simple tastes and mind content!

NOTHING OVER TEN CENTS

MARY HEATON VORSE

Not dreaming evil could befall me, I went into the five-and-ten-cent store—the one on Fifth Avenue opposite the Library. The simple collector's instinct drove me in, wishing only to add a few specimens to my already large collection of Early Woolworth. Feet on earth, eyes level, limbs and wind sound, I walked in. How could I know I would, as one in a trance, buy $12.90 worth of five-and-ten?

All I bought is downstairs now: four large boxes, which in the presence of my pitying family I am unable to open.

Let me try and trace what occurred to me: what fatal thing undermined the brain, what insidious poison blurred the judgment, what, in fact, could ail a person who could spend nickels and dimes to the extent of $12.90.

What, indeed, do those boxes contain? Piled menacingly and darkly upon one another, they take up the whole side of the sitting-room.

There are your huge packages marked: "GLASS FRAGILE DON'T DROP." I *know* that I bought no glass, that I hurried past opulent counters glittering with topaz, amethyst, crystal, and jade. But the spectacle of acres of glasses, some tall and beautiful and slim, thin, translucent green; tables of rich pigeon's blood; tables of glittering, suave amethystine; tables of glass refracting splintered light from topaz depths, unnerved me. This, all this, was within my grasp for five cents, or ten cents. I looked fixedly into a small sea of emerald green. Strange thoughts flowed through my mind. I said:

"I could buy you, but I will not buy you. I could buy tables of you. I could buy *all* of you." For I had wealth. I had over fifteen dollars in my pocket. Suddenly I, who was poor, became Crœsus. I was Millionaire.

Illusions of the power of great riches undermined my reason. Meantime on all sides of me were happy-faced women reaching out hands so rapidly that they seemed like centipedes. Some culled objects rhythmically, as though picking berries. Others snatched like the famished. Others grabbed in a furtive, animal way. As I looked at them, I saw they, too, were overcome with the riches of the earth. They were all as drunk, as drugged, as I, with riches and power. . . .

I consulted a modest list. I bought a whiskbroom. I bought two. Yes, I can now remember, as I retrace the fatal steps which I took; I remember it was first the brushes which seduced me, having escaped the dazzle of the glass (I know I must have escaped it, in spite of the boxes). It was the little intricate brushes made to get dust out of all sorts of strangely shaped corners, little brushes with which one might well have cleaned out cobwebby corners of one's brain, which undid me. Yet somewhere deep within me tolled the warning bell: "Why brushes shaped like S's? Why loops? You have no bottles shaped like summer squash."

Then my fancy was seized upon by the kitchen-utensils counter. What did I buy? I can't tell, nor does the sheet of yellow memorandum tell me anything. It's twelve feet long and closely marked with hieroglyphics standing for things which presumably are mine. I'm a plain and old-fashioned woman. I like a sharp, French cook's knife for slicing. I cut out biscuits with the top of a baking-powder tin. Yet I see myself, far off as through an alcoholic haze, buying cooky-cutters shaped like diamonds, hearts, and spades. I bought egg-slicers and horrid little things for cutting potatoes into queer shapes. I don't

LADIES!
BORROW UP TO $1500.
ON YOUR
HUSBAND'S SIGNATURE

CHON DAY, COLLIER'S

know what I bought; I only remember a New England-looking saleswoman who said to me accusingly:

"Modom, you have eighteen kitchen utensils."

These eighteen unknown utensils do not include the pots, the pans, the pot covers, the double-boilers, the coffee-percolators which I bought. Why did I buy them in pairs? Did I think for a moment: "Male and female created He them"? That I was carrying out the great harmonious design of creation?

It is here that oblivion swept over me. I came to later, just at the moment when I was stretching out my hand to buy a small china elephant with purple spots, in full flight, carrying on its back a crate of gaudy gumdrops. From some still undimmed fragment of my brain had come the warning that I, going out to tea, had no need of a spotted elephant. I swayed waveringly to the cashier's desk.

"Twelve-ninety, Modom," she said snappily. I asked for a chair. A fat woman opposite looked at me with a compassionate eye.

"Ain't it a fact," she said. "I came in to spend fifty cents, and I spent six dollars." I looked around and I saw that at least I was not alone. And then I realized that the great tower of Woolworth was builded not out of nickels and dimes, but was erected from dreams and madness, spun from visions and illusions. I realized that the sky-smiting tower was built from an impulse which has carved empires: the desire for loot.

I went away grasping convulsively a large paper bag with a ship in full sail upon it, bought who knows why.

THE THING

KEITH W. JENNISON

For many years I have been aware of a certain noisome "thing" that keeps looking over my shoulder, down into my pocketbook, and separating me from amounts of so-called extra money.

I am, of course, using the word "extra" in its loosest sense. What happens is this. Every once in a while, with my creditors thrown off stride by a larger installment than usual on the current indebtedness, I find myself in possession of a sum of money which I can with reasonable safety leave in my checking (special) account for a few days. Whenever this happens, the "thing," getting its information from God knows where, springs into action, and I am immediately relieved of the exact amount of the cache. It isn't being parted from the money that bothers me, although that is bad enough. What really worries me is how the "thing" finds out so precisely what the sum is.

It all began a long time ago. When the boys were born we started a savings account for them. With the help of various well-heeled aunts, uncles, and godparents, this sum was built up over the years to the tidy, compared to the boys, sum of $113.50. During the late fall of the first year we lived in the country they slept happily in a room that was extremely well ventilated even with the windows closed. When the January winds came whistling through the charming old hand-hewn clapboards it was obvious that the room had to be insulated. The estimate for materials and labor came to $133.50. Which we didn't have. But the boys did. One of them had had a twenty-dollar birthday the week before.

As the years came and went it became evident that, while we weren't exactly living beyond our income, we did seem to be living ahead of it. We tried a series of stern budgets designed to keep a little cash around the house, but we gave them up. It was uneconomical to have money. Every time there was a slight surplus in the budget something that cost exactly that amount went wrong with the car, which ran perfectly, with no need for repairs, as long as we had no balance at all.

Two summers ago we made a mistake in our checkbook. What made this particular mistake remarkable was that it appeared that we had one hundred dollars more than we thought we had. Five minutes after the bank confirmed this pleasant truth the cesspool backed up. We had to have a new ditch dug and new tiling put in. The local expert made us a special price of, naturally, one hundred dollars.

Last fall, out of the blue, one of the trade magazines called me to ask if I would write a piece for them. I would be delighted, I said. I did the piece and sent it in. They accepted it and sent me a check for three hundred dollars. I had told the boys' mother nothing about the matter, figuring I'd start wiping my glasses with ten-dollar bills and leave a trail of them around the house.

The night I got the check she met me at the station as usual, and as we were driving home she informed me that the school dentist had told her that Chris needed braces. If the job were done immediately, the dentist said, it would be short and inexpensive.

"How much?" I asked, having a talent for superfluous questions.

She told me.

I told her about my check.

"But who told the dentist?" she asked.

"It's a mystery," I said.

"And you know," Emily said, "it still is a mystery. I remember later that night you said that since you'd sold one piece maybe you could sell another, so you sat down to write the 'thing' out of our lives forever."

"I can remember four nights later, when I finished, too," I said. "I went to the bathroom to wash my hands, and there was no hot water."

"And you called the contractor to find how much a new hot-water heater would cost so you could know how much to expect to get for your piece."

"I was right, too, wasn't I?" I said.

"You certainly were," Emily said, "almost to the penny." She laughed. "How do you suppose we've gotten along as well as we have?"

"I don't call it well, exactly. You wouldn't say that a man treading water is speeding toward an objective, would you?"

"No, but think a minute. What do you really want to own that you haven't got?"

I glared at her. "Are you going to give me that health-is-wealth-and-money-won't-buy-happiness routine? I'll tell you exactly what I want. I want a Jaguar XK410 and enough money to sit around in the back yard with a Speedie-Sun-Tan collar on when there is weeding to be done."

"You do that anyway," she said with more accuracy than tact.

"I'd enjoy it more," I said stiffly.

"Well, I wouldn't," she said. "You'd be torquing and down-shifting and drifting all over the countryside, and I couldn't relax for a minute."

"Well, don't worry," I said. "I doubt if there is a Jaguar in my future."

A CRY FROM THE CONSUMER

WILBUR D. NESBIT

Grasshoppers roam the Kansas fields and eat the tender grass—
A trivial affair, indeed, but what then comes to pass?
You go to buy a panama, or any other hat;
You learn the price has been advanced a lot because of that.
A glacier up in Canada has slipped a mile or two—
A little thing like this can boost the selling price of glue.
Occurrences so tragic always thrill me to the core;
I hope and pray that nothing ever happens any more.

Last week the peaceful Indians went a-searching after scalps,
And then there was an avalanche 'way over in the Alps;
These diametric happenings seem nothing much, but look—
We had to add a dollar to the wages of the cook.
The bean-crop down at Boston has grown measurably less,
And so the dealer charges more for goods to make a dress.
Each day there is some incident to make a man feel sore,
I'm on my knees to ask that nothing happens any more.

It didn't rain in Utah and it did in old Vermont—
Result: it costs you fifty more to take a summer's jaunt;
Upon the plains of Tibet some tornadoes took a roll—
Therefore the barons have to charge a higher price for coal.
A street-car strike in Omaha has cumulative shocks—
It boosted huckleberries up to twenty cents a box.
No matter what is happening it always finds your door—
Give us a rest! Let nothing ever happen any more.

Mosquitoes in New Jersey bite a magnate on the wing—
Result: the poor consumer feels that fierce mosquito's sting:
The skeeter's song is silenced, but in something like an hour
The grocers understand that it requires a raise in flour.
A house burns down in Texas and a stove blows up in Maine,
Ten minutes later breakfast food in prices show a gain.
Effects must follow causes—which is what I most deplore;
I hope and pray that nothing ever happens any more.

COMPLAINT DEPARTMENT

KATHERINE BEST

Mr. Seeley shut himself in the telephone booth. He had a small matter of business to transact with T. J. Tinglefooter & Co.

"Raymond 9-4000," he said to the operator.

"Good afternoon," a smooth voice greeted him. "T. J. Tinglefooter & Co."

"About three days ago," said Mr. Seeley, "my wife bought some flour at your store. . . ."

"Just a moment, sir," the smooth voice said, "I'll connect you with the grocery department."

"Good afternoon. Grocery department, T. J. Tinglefooter & Co.," said another smooth voice.

"Yes," said Mr. Seeley. "I want to tell you about some flour my wife bought. . . ."

"What is the name, please?"

"Mrs. F. D. Seeley. S-E-E-L-E-Y. 479 Crosswood Avenue, Bronxville, New York. This flour you sent, it had worms."

"Do you wish to register a complaint?"

"I certainly do," said Mr. Seeley. "It had worms!"

"Just a moment, sir. I'll connect you with the complaint department."

"Good afternoon," said the complaint department, "T. J. Tinglefooter & Co."

"Is this the worm department?" asked Mr. Seeley.

"I beg your pardon."

"I ordered some flour from you people and it was all molded or something. It had worms and I want . . ."

"Will you spell it, please?"

"Worms. W-O-R-M-S," spelled Mr. Seeley.

"And what is the nature of the complaint, Mr. Worms?"

"Worms! *That's* not *my* name! *My* name is Seeley. S-E-E-L-E-Y. 479 Crosswood Avenue, Bronxville, New York."

"And the initials?"

"F. as in Frank, D. as in David."

"Thank you. What is the street address, please?"

"I just *gave* it to you. 479 Crosswood Avenue, Bronxville, New York. You know, four as in one, two, three, four. Seven as in one, two, three, four, five, six. . . ."

"Four, seven, nyun Crosswood Avenue. Thank you. And the town, please?"

"Bronxville. *Bronxville.* And unless those worms have carried it away, it's in New York State."

"Just a moment, Mr. Seeley. You did not receive the merchandise you purchased?"

"I *did!*" shouted Mr. Seeley. "The stuff was crawly with worms. It was spoiled, see? *Spoiled.* It had worms!"

"Do you wish a readjustment?"

"I most certainly do!" Mr. Seeley wiped the perspiration from his face. "I didn't order worms. I ordered flour."

"Just a moment, sir. I'll connect you with the readjustment department."

"Good afternoon. Readjustment department, T. J. Tinglefooter & Co." The voices were getting smoother.

"I have worms," said Mr. Seeley desolately.

"I beg your pardon, sir. What department did you wish."

"I don't know. It's like this. My wife ordered some flour and it had worms crawling all through it and I called up to see if you . . ."

"May I have your name, please?"

"F. D. Partment."

"Your street address?"

"794 Bronxwood Avenue."

"Your town?"

"Crossville."

"Your state?"

"Damned bad." Mr. Seeley rarely resorted to blasphemy.

"I beg your pardon. What number did you call?"

"New York."

"Thank you. What is the nature of the complaint?"

"You see, my wife bought the loveliest sack of flour you ever saw. It was all wrapped up in pretty white paper and we could hardly wait to open it. And what do you suppose had gotten in our lovely white sack of flour? Worms, old nasty, crawly worms." Mr. Seeley writhed in reminiscence.

"The merchandise was received in imperfect condition? Very good. What readjustment do you wish?"

"I want you to send me," said Mr. Seeley wearily, "some more flour without imperfect conditions crawling all around in it."

"Just a moment, sir. I'll connect you with the order depart . . ."

Mr. Seeley left the telephone booth and went fishing.

IF WE DIDN'T HAVE TO EAT

NIXON WATERMAN

Life would be an easy matter
  If we didn't have to eat.
    If we never had to utter,
    "Won't you pass the bread and butter,
Likewise push along that platter
    Full of meat?"
    Yes, if food were obsolete
    Life would be a jolly treat,
If we didn't—shine or shower,
Old or young, 'bout every hour—
    Have to eat, eat, eat, eat, eat—
    'Twould be jolly if we didn't have to eat.

We could save a lot of money
  If we didn't have to eat.
    Could we cease our busy buying,
    Baking, broiling, brewing, frying,
Life would then be oh, so sunny
  And complete;

"A copy of a Paris original what?"

  And we wouldn't fear to greet
  Every grocer in the street
If we didn't—man and woman,
Every hungry, helpless human—
  Have to eat, eat, eat, eat, eat—
  We'd save money if we didn't have to eat.

All our worry would be over
  If we didn't have to eat.
   Would the butcher, baker, grocer
   Get our hard-earned dollars? No, Sir!
We would then be right in clover
  Cool and sweet.
  Want and hunger we could cheat,
  And we'd get there with both feet,
If we didn't—poor or wealthy,
Halt or nimble, sick or healthy—
  Have to eat, eat, eat, eat, eat,
  We could get there if we didn't have to eat.

CHEAP CLOTHES FOR FAT OLD WOMEN

MARGHANITA LASKI

Although the chief business of the fashion journalist is to find flattering alternatives to the phrase I have chosen for my title, the practised wielding of a new and esoteric language has now become instinctive with her. I am not speaking of those copy-writers in the daily Press who offer Gowns for the O.S. Matron in a colour-range (*puce, saxe, eau-de-nil*) that has elsewhere disappeared from the spectrum. My study is of the specialized grammar and vocabulary of the fashion-writer in the glossy monthlies whose language, while representing the quintessence of glamour to thousands of women, must still be virtually incomprehensible to millions more.

Her grammatical usages really merit special research, and here I will refer only to my two favourites. First, the Hypnotic Imperative: *This season you will be wearing . . . , reading . . . , talking about . . .* The best example I ever met ran: *Because it's high summer you'll buy a new aeroplane painted blue to match the skies.* Second, the Omitted Conjunction in descriptions of intellectuals: *He lives in an old house in Essex, writes for 'Horizon', collects china cats . . .*

But it is in the bold misuse of our contemporary vocabulary that the art of the fashion-writer is seen at its best; and for those who may wish to penetrate into hitherto unexplored fields I append an all-too-short glossary. I should add that the abbreviation G.W. indicates a Glamour-Word, extremely evocative in the right context and of no real meaning whatsoever.

AMUSING: cheap.

BOLD: G.W.; e.g., *b. back-sweeping fullness.*

BRIEF, adj.: very short in length; e.g., *b. bolero, b. panties,* also briefest.

BULGE, UNSEEMLY: stomach fat.

CHARM, NOSTALGIC: G.W.

CLASSIC, n.: English garment (shoes, hat, suit) barely susceptible to fashion changes.

CRISP, adj.: G.W.; e.g., *a c. silhouette, c. touches of white.*

DEMURE: (of hats and hair-styles) those which symmetrically frame the face.

DERRIERE, n.: buttocks; e.g., *tuck in your d.*

DIGNIFIED: (i) of women: old; (ii) of clothes: for old women.

DRAMATIC: virtually unwearable, but photographs well.

-EST: intensive used instead of 'very'; e.g., *palest grey, softest and finest worsteds.*

EVERYWHERE: in a very few places; e.g., *sable stoles are e.*

FLATTERY: G.W.; e.g., *the f. of mink, diamonds, orchids against your skin.*

FRANKLY, adj.: would be ugly if we didn't tell you it wasn't; e.g., *a f. jagged hemline.*

FUZZ, UNSIGHTLY: superfluous hair on the legs.

GENEROUS: (i) the designer is making nothing out of the dress-length, e.g., *g. cuffs;* (ii) fat.

HAIRS, OBSTINATE OR RECALCITRANT: the un-wanted moustache; e.g., *tweak out those o. (or r.) h.*

HIGHLIGHT, n.: a noticeable accessory. Cp. SPOTLIGHT.

HUGGING: tight; e.g., *bosom-h., waist-h.*

HUSKY: suitable for out-of-door country wear.

IMPORTANT: G.W.

INDISPENSABLE: G.W.; e.g., *the i. pearl choker.*

-IZE: verbal suffix; e.g., slenderize, glamorize, accessorize.

JAUNTY: G.W.

LIGHTLY-BONED: of corsets (no corsets to-day are HEAVILY-BONED).

LIMITED INCOME, adj.: cheap.

MIDRIFF: stomach.

OLDER: (of women) old.

PUSH, vb.: fabric-fullness is *pushed* (occ. *pulled*) to the back, side or front; once arrived at the back, however, it becomes BACKSWEPT (formerly used only of vertically ascending hair).

SIGNIFICANT: G.W.

SOFTLY: G.W.; e.g., *s. rounded, s. draped, s. knotted.*

SPOTLIGHT, vb.: to add a noticeable accessory. Cp. HIGHLIGHT.

SUBTLE: G.W.; frequently *s. emphasis of . . .*

TEAM, vb.: to wear one thing with another; e.g., *t. your palest grey dress with the subtle flattery of a brief scarlet bolero.*

THAT, THOSE: adjs. of distaste and elimination; e.g., *eliminate t. unsightly bulge,* or, as above, *tweak out t. recalcitrant hairs.*

Finally I should, I suppose, give an example of the way in which my title, that epitome of the whole thing, can be translated. A professional could, of course, do better: I offer: *Limited Income Clothes for Dignified Maturity.* You see what a different impression you get right away?

Church, Clubs and Other Organizations:

LUKE AND THE LORD'S WORK

PAUL T. STURGES

Letty Abisher could get a white shirt on her husband on a Sunday morning, but by the time she was ready to go to church, he'd have it soiled. He'd either be under his car tightening something, or working the plunger on the kitchen sink.

She'd say, "Luke, are you going to church with me this morning?" real nice like, and he'd say, "No, Honey, some other time. This sink is getting stopped up and Sunday is the only time I got to fix things."

Then she would go to church with us. She never missed a Sunday. She'd say apologetic like, "I hate to be always imposing on you folks," and my wife would say, "What are neighbors for, Letty? You know you are welcome and you can go with us any time you feel like it." And Letty would sigh, "I think if I could get Luke interested in the Lord's work he'd go every Sunday."

Then my wife would see me winking at her, because it always was a joke with us how handy Luke Abisher was thinking up excuses for not going to church, and would change the subject. "My, you look pretty this morning, Letty. Pink just matches your complexion." And Letty would blush and say, "I like gay colors. People won't think I'm a widow."

Then we would go to church and Letty would sit on the edge of the pew with a tense look on her face wondering what mischief Luke was getting into at home. For Luke was about as handy around the house as a lobster with locked brakes, and she never did know what she'd find when she got home.

I remember once we heard Luke yelling, "Shut off the water," when we drove in our driveway next door. Letty tried to jump out of the car before I got it stopped, but my wife held her back. When I opened their door I saw the water running down the front stairs and walls and knew where Luke was.

He was in the upstairs bathroom holding his hand over a faucet with water squirting through his fingers.

"Shut off the water, Joe," he yelled, "I unscrewed this faucet and everything busted loose."

"Where's the shut off?"

"I don't know. You'll have to find it for me."

They had to paper every downstairs room but the kitchen. I am just giving it as a sample. Luke Abisher was always taking things apart on Sunday morning when his wife was in church. I don't think she heard half what the preacher said, worrying about Luke.

One Sunday I noticed she was paying attention with a sort of evangelical intentness to the sermon. It was called, "Doers, not hearers only," and was about people who think they have done their duty by the Lord when they come to church on Sunday. "God needs workers every day of the week, not just on Sunday," the preacher thundered.

Going home that Sunday Letty said, "I think that was a wonderful sermon. I wish Luke had been there to hear it."

"What was Luke doing today?" I asked, and my wife gave me a dig.

"Putting up storm windows," Letty said lamely. "Winter is just around the corner and Luke said it was the only time he had."

"Yes," my wife said. "The church was cold today. I wish they would fix that furnace before it is too late."

"Maybe Luke would fix it," Letty exclaimed. "I think if he got interested in something like that he would come to church. He gives willingly to the church and I know he is a Christian."

"Luke!" I blatted, and my wife gave me another dig. "Mrs. Abisher, the only thing wrong with that furnace is that they are burning some old cottonwood chunks that Deacon Spencer donated. There is no heat in them."

She wasn't even listening and I had a feeling then of trouble ahead.

When we got home Luke was up on a ladder balancing a storm window over his head. He had a red baseball cap on, his shirt tail was out and his khaki pants had a droop in them like they had a weight in the seat. When he heard my car in the drive he let loose the storm window and grabbed for his pants. The storm window fell on a cement walk two stories below.

He was trying to hitch up his pants and tuck in his shirt when he heard the crash. Luke had a funny shape, kind of like a spider. All his weight was in his middle and he hated suspenders. Holding pants on his bulge with a belt was like tying a string on a hard boiled egg. He tried it however, lost his balance and fell backwards.

He landed in a barberry hedge. Both the women screamed and I stopped the car. By the time I got there Letty was pulling him out. "Are you hurt, Honey?" she kept moaning.

Well, outside of a few scratches, Luke was okay as he lit bottom first in the hedge. But Letty kept fussing over him like women do with a man when they haven't any kids to mother. "You come right in the house," she said. "I'll get some mercurochrome. You can do those windows some other time."

"I'll finish them next Sunday," he said right off.

The next time I saw Luke he was going up to his law office. I run an electrical shop. "What's this I hear about the church furnace going haywire?" he said. I said, "Forget it, Luke. There's nothing wrong with that furnace except that they are burning chunks."

The next Sunday Letty came over to our house while we were still at breakfast. "Luke's taking us all to church this morning," she announced proudly.

"That's wonderful," my wife exclaimed. "Letty, how in the world?"

"I told him about the furnace," said Letty, her eyes dancing. "He wants to see what's wrong with it."

"There's nothing wrong with it," I said.

My wife gave me a withering look. I shut my big mouth.

But when Letty was gone she lit into me. "You always have to open your big trap. Letty has been trying to get her husband interested in church work for years, and now when she succeeds you tell her there is nothing wrong with the furnace."

"Well there will be if Luke starts monkeying with it," I said. "That guy knows about as much about furnaces as a cub bear."

"Well he seems to know how to run his own," she said.

"Are you forgetting the Sunday it blew up on him and he spent the rest of the day fanning soot out of the house?"

Her face got pale. "He wouldn't try that again?"

"Maybe he will put an old battery in the furnace to burn the soot out of the chimney," I reminded. "Remember that Sunday he set his roof on fire?"

"How could he do that sitting in church?" she said acidly.

Well it did look like Luke had kept his white shirt clean when we went to church. He had on a pale lavender tie, a dark suit and a gleam in his eye I didn't like. Letty looked like if she was any prouder she'd burst. We went in the side entrance and going up the steps my wife whispered, "Doesn't she look sweet. Leading him in like a brand snatched from the burning."

I didn't say anything because we were at the door. Luke passed his wife and mine in. Then he said, "You first, Joe," and patted me on the back when I went in.

Every Sunday they have greeters at the door from one of the women's circles and as I stepped in I heard Letty say in a proud voice, "Mrs. Girard, I want you to meet my husband." So this lady, who must have been a new member, shook hands with me and said, "I am glad to know you, Mr. Abisher." Letty's face dropped. "Oh, I'm sorry," she said, "I thought he was right behind me. This is Mr. Butler."

While I was shaking hands with the rest of the greeters, I saw Letty Abisher go to the door and look out and when she came in again her face looked like she'd seen a ghost.

"Joe, where did he go?" she asked in a haunted voice.

"I thought he was right behind me."

"Joe, you've got to find him," she said in a stricken voice.

"He probably just went down in the basement to check the furnace," I said.

"He's got his best clothes on," she said in a hollow voice. "Get him, Joe. We'll go in and sit down."

I went out the side door because the basement entrance is on the outside and comes up in the kitchen back of Fellowship Hall. The basement only goes under that part of the church and the part under the sanctuary was never dug out. I looked in the furnace room and coal bin and there was no sign of Luke!

So I went outside and went around the church thinking he might be hiding in the shrubbery. He wasn't there so I went back in the church. The women were in the back row.

They both looked up when I came in. I shook my head and I saw Letty's head drop on her chest like she was praying. I found out where Luke was when the preacher was praying. I heard something pop under the sanctuary and thought it was the furnace pipe buckling until from the corner of my eye I saw Letty's hand clutch her hand bag. Then I knew Luke was crawling around under the church.

I knew what it was like under there and I couldn't help but feel sorry for that little woman. I ran a lead under the sanctuary when we put in the electric announcement board out in front. It was dark under there and all full of sooty cobwebs. There was room to crawl under the furnace pipes in the back under the sanctuary but where the floor sloped down to the pulpit you had to lie down and wiggle under.

I don't think either one of us heard much what the preacher was saying after that listening for Luke. He was pretty quiet under there but made a few bobbles. Like the time he thumped the pipe while the choir was singing when there was a rest in the music. He bumped his head a couple times, too.

It quieted down after that and when church was out I found him down in the men's wash room. He looked like somebody had been using him for a swab to tar a roof.

He was trying to get the soot off his face with paper towels and cold water but it only came off in streaks.

When he saw me he grinned. "Joe, I found out what's wrong with that furnace. The asbestos paper has rotted off the pipes. It's lying on the ground. I checked them all."

"I heard you," I said.

"No fooling?" he said, stroking his chin thoughtfully. "I thought I was keeping pretty quiet."

"I knew when I heard something crack under my seat."

Luke smiled wryly. "I busted a flower pot," he whispered. "Ran into it in the dark. Joe, you ought to see the junk the janitor has stowed under there. Flower pots, urns, bean pots, an old roll of linoleum. Joe, that place should be cleaned out."

"Luke," I said, "you don't understand. People gave those things to the church. They would be offended if you threw them out."

"Well, what are they doing under the church?"

"Because people keep giving and they've got to find the room."

Luke frowned and twiddled with his chin. "Well, one thing's for sure, Joe. We've got to get some more insulation on those furnace pipes or the heat will be all going under the church. I almost suffocated under there."

"That costs money and we haven't got it," I said.

Luke tweaked his chin. "I'll furnish the asbestos paper if somebody will paste it on."

"We'd have to hire that done and labor is high," I said.

"Why couldn't the women put on a rummage sale and get rid of that stuff—those urns and things. I bet they could raise the money if

I furnished the materials, or I could do the work myself," he added. "Nights and Sundays."

That settled it for me. "Let's see what the women think of it," I said. "Why don't you run around back of the church and wait for us in the car," I hinted.

"That might be a good idea," he said, ruefully eyeing his clothes.

When Letty saw him she said, "Luke! Your best Sunday clothes! Why did you have to do it when church was in session?"

"I had to," he said. "I wanted to know which were the hot air pipes and which the cold. I thought it would be the only chance I had to find out when the furnace was on."

"It seems so, so irreverent," she sighed. "You crawling around under the church while people were worshipping."

"I was on my knees all the time," he said stoutly.

"Luke found why the furnace doesn't heat," I put in, and told them what Luke had in mind. I noticed Letty's eyes getting rounder all the while I explained and when I got done she said, "Luke, I think that is a wonderful idea. I am so glad to see you are getting interested in the Lord's work."

"Looks like there's plenty to do around here," he admitted.

Well, when I explained to some of the men that Luke was liable to be under the church the next Sunday pasting on asbestos paper I didn't have any trouble getting volunteers for the job. We worked nights all week and Luke helped and bought the paper. We had to string lights from the furnace room light socket. We had too many and blew a fuse on the main switchboard upstairs. I went up to put in a new fuse and Luke went along.

I opened the glass doors that enclosed the switchboard and screwed in a fuse. Luke said, "How do you know you got it right?" I said, "Because I know this switchboard by heart."

"Does anybody else know it by heart?" he asked.

"Sure. Angus McLeod knows it," I said.

"Does anybody else know how to run it?" he asked.

"Well," I said, "the choir director knows which switch to throw when they have choir practice Thursday night."

"Is that all?" he asked, pulling at his chin again.

"Look," I said. "That's enough. We don't want every Tom, Dick and Harry monkeying with that switchboard. They are liable to get a shock on those old jackknife switches. That's why we've got those doors on it."

"I don't think it is a very good system, Joe, if you ask me. I mean, what would happen if you and Angus didn't come to church? What would happen then?"

"Angus is the janitor. He's always here. I don't miss once in a blue moon. It's not liable to happen. Forget it."

"But it could happen," he persisted. "Joe, that board should have some identification on it so people would know what switch to push and what one to pull."

"Where would you find the room to do it?" I asked.

He looked at the switchboard and shook his head. It was put in when the church was built in 1909. There were three rows of big jack-knife switches with the fuses screwed in underneath. They were so close together you couldn't get a thumb between them.

"It doesn't seem right to me," he said. "Just you two guys running that switchboard. Somebody else should know."

"If we are going to get those pipes insulated by Sunday, Luke, we'd better be at it," I said, with a growing feeling of trouble ahead. "The switchboard can wait."

We got the job done in time and Luke was right on hand Sunday to see how the furnace worked. His wife didn't need a halter on him to lead him in the side door but I could see she looked worried. When we went in the sanctuary Luke was up to his old tricks.

He opened the swinging doors to the sanctuary and let us in first. When we went in the pew he did the same. That put him on the end of the pew by the right aisle, beside me.

"Don't you want to sit by your wife?" I whispered.

He just dropped his chin on his chest reverently.

I dropped mine too, but couldn't seem to concentrate on anything but Luke. What was he sitting on the aisle for? I peeked at Letty. She was sitting on the edge of the pew with a strained look on her face. She was worried too.

I found out what was troubling her when the head usher, Jim Mitchell, touched me on the shoulder and whispered, "Angus is sick today. Will you take care of the lights?"

I started to get up and Luke laid his hand on my knee. "Never mind, Joe," he whispered. "I'll take care of it."

"Do you know which one to throw?" I asked.

"Sure, Angus showed me how to work it."

As there was only one switch to throw, I thought I would let him and save argument. It was the light over the choir, a five-hundredwatter I strung in behind the ceiling cluster so the choir could read the music. The choir was coming in to the sanctuary and Luke started to get up. "It's the last switch on the right in the middle row," I whispered.

"Gotcha," he whispered back and slipped out the swinging doors.

The choir took their places and the light went on. I took a deep breath and thought the choir looked nice in their red robes. They sang and then the whole church stood up to sing the opening hymn. I never once thought of Luke until I noticed his wife was singing with her hymnal held upside down. I looked around and Luke was gone!

The hymn was, "Ye Servants of God," and in the middle of the second verse the organ quit. Those that could carry the tune went ahead and the rest stalled. The organist started to pull out stops and the choir director started to pump his arms for everybody to sing. Letty dropped her hymn book on the floor and when she was picking it up she looked up at me like a quarterback calling signals.

I read her signal clear as a bell. It was, "Go find Luke." I found him in the little vestibule where the switchboard was.

"How do you like it?" he said, waving with pride at the switchboard. "I got them all labelled."

He had pasted little white labels on the cross bars of the switch-handles. "They're jelly glass labels," he explained, "I got the idea from Letty."

"You better get another idea. You pulled the wrong switch."

"All I pulled was the one marked 'Choir practice,'" he said stoutly. "I pulled it because they were through in there."

"Well you better push it back. You got the organ."

He pushed it in and a fuse blew. I started to unscrew the dead fuse. "Get another," I said, and he said, "There isn't any."

"Take one off the board," I said. He unscrewed one and all the bracket lights in the sanctuary went out. "Look, you butterfinger," I said. "Get one they are not using."

"I did," he said. "I took the one over kitchen."

"The fuses are underneath," I said, trying to be patient. "Luke, why don't you go in the sanctuary and sit down while I straighten this out. Sit by your wife this time."

"Maybe I should put some chunks in the furnace first," he hinted. "Y'know Angus isn't here."

"I don't care what you do."

When I got the switchboard straightened out I went back and anchored myself in the end seat. Luke sneaked in when they were singing the second hymn. It was "Fight the Good Fight," and I wondered who picked out the music. Luke sang it too, his Adam's apple fluttering up and down as his falsetto voice rose and fell.

I thought he would settle down then but when I passed the collection plate to them I heard him say, "I smell smoke," and his wife said, "You stay where you are. Someone is burning leaves."

I touched her with the collection plate and she jumped.

He must have left when the ushers marched down the aisle with the collection. Everybody stands then and sings the doxology. When we sat down I noticed it was getting pretty warm in the church. Most of the women had their coats off and some even took off their hats. I couldn't concentrate on the sermon. I was wondering what Luke was up to now.

I found out when they were singing the closing hymn. It was "Who is on the Lord's Side?" and I figured it wasn't Luke because I heard him yelling, "Help! Fire!" It sounded kind of muffled, but Letty and I both heard it and slipped out through the swinging doors. She went through Fellowship Hall. I thought he was in the basement or on the roof.

He wasn't in the basement so I came up the back way and saw the smoke edging up from the roof. I called the fire department and went in to look for Luke.

I saw the spilled water on the kitchen floor and followed it. It led to the little room off the kitchen where the women fix salads and desserts for church suppers. There was a little cubby hole in the ceiling that led to the attic and there was Luke—stuck fast in the hole!

Letty was up on a stepladder grabbing at his waving legs and I could hear Luke's voice. It sounded muffled but I made out what he said. "Don't pull. Push. The fire's up here."

"Honey, you'll suffocate in that smoke," and she caught his legs and pulled. All she got was his pants. I saw those long shanks of his vanish like a gopher snake going down a hole.

Then I heard a tinny rattle and what looked like a bucket of water poured down that cubby hole and caught her square. If I ever saw a woman look mad it was Letty Abisher. I closed the door softly, figuring from here on it was a family affair and if Luke wanted to step in a pail of water and soak his wife to the skin trying to put out a roof fire from the inside, it was none of my business.

I went outside. The firemen were there and had no trouble putting

"Will the trousers hold a press? I do a lot of kneeling."

---

out the fire. It was just some leaves that had gathered in a gutter, that got touched off by some spark from those chunks burning. When the firemen had their ladders put back in the truck, I drifted in to the hallway between the kitchen and this room where they were. I couldn't help but listen.

"Please, Honey, throw me up my pants. They must be gone now."

"Not until you promise, Luke Abisher," she said firmly.

"I promise," he said in a weak voice.

I tiptoed out and found my wife. "Where's Luke and Letty?" she asked. "I can't find them anywhere."

"They'll be along in a minute," I said. "We'll get in the car and wait. And don't ask Letty how she got wet."

"Wet!" she exclaimed. "How did she get wet?"

"A little water got spilled when she snatched her brand from the burning," I said. "Just don't say anything. I think after this she'll have no trouble getting Luke to go to church on Sunday. She made him promise."

And she didn't. Luke got interested in the Lord's work and was elected to the Board of Trustees. He paid for a new switchboard for the church if I would put it in. He headed the committee to paint the church and found an endless number of things to do for the Lord.

One Saturday when I was putting on my storm windows I looked across the hedge and saw Luke putting his on. Before I thought, I said, "Some change—eh, Luke?—since you got stuck in that cubby hole."

"What do you mean?" he asked frowning.

"You used to do that work on S-S-Sunday," I stuttered, wishing I had never said it in the first place.

"What cubby hole are you talking about?" he asked.

"The one at the church . . . The time you made your wife a promise . . ."

"Oh, yes, I remember," he said grinning. "She made me promise to wear suspenders. See!" and he flung his coat back and hooked his thumbs under a pair of red suspenders.

GOD HIT A HOME RUN

ROBERT FONTAINE

Long ago when I was very young my mother and father and I moved to Canada, to the lovely city of Ottawa.

We settled down in one half of a double house, next door to my several unusual uncles, my grandfather, and my aunt Felice, all of whom spoke, as we did ourselves, a strange language. It was a mixture of corrupt French, literally translated idioms, and, in time, the salt of French-Canadian patois.

There are but few memories of the first years in Ottawa. They are only bright fragments, like the little pieces of colored glass in the small hallway window at the stair landing.

The time, however, that God hit a home run is very clear.

My father played the violin and conducted an orchestra for a two-a-day vaudeville theater, so he had little time for diversion. In what spare moments he had, he turned to baseball. In spite of his sensitive, debonair temperament, he loved the game. It refreshed him, perhaps, because it was so far from his métier.

I remember well how many times he begged my mother to go with him to the twilight games at Strathcona Park. There was just time for him to see a game between the end of the matinée and the beginning of the evening performance.

My mother seemed always too busy.

"I must get the dinner, you know," she would say, with the faint, calm, resigned, Presbyterian air she often assumed.

"Dinner!" my father would exclaim. "We will stuff our pockets with apples and cheese."

"What about the Boy?" my mother would ask.

My father would look at me.

"The Boy is already too fat. Regard him!"

"It is only," my mother would smile, "because he has his cheeks full of shortbreads."

If it was not dinner she had to cook, it was socks she had to darn or blouses she had to make for me, or the kitchen floor she felt the need of shining.

All this made my father quite sad, even though, at each invitation, my mother promised to accompany him "some other time." Still, he never abandoned the hope that he would, in time, have the warm joy of explaining the principles of the intricate game to her. I suppose he knew that she was proud of his artistic talents and he wanted her to be pleased with his athletic knowledge, too.

One warm Sunday in the summer, when I was five or six (who can remember precisely those early times of coming-to-life when every week is as a year?), my mind was occupied with the American funny papers and the eccentric doings of one Happy Hooligan, he of the ragged, patched coat and the small tin can on the side of his head.

My father came into the room where my mother was dusting the china on the mantel and shining the golden letters on the sign that proclaimed: *Jesus Christ Is the Unseen Guest in This House.*

There was, by the way, nothing else to do in Ottawa on a Sunday in those days but to dust religious signs and plates on the mantel or to read the papers. All stores were closed. All theaters were closed. There was prohibition, too, as I recall, so there was not even a bar where one could sit and dream. True, one could go across the Inter-Provincial Bridge to Hull, in Quebec province, and return with a secret bottle of wine, but it could not be served in public.

No, Sunday was the Sad Day in Ottawa.

But to return to my father. He spoke to my mother with some hesitation: "The Boy and I . . . we . . . we go to a game of baseball."

My mother turned from the plates and regarded my father coldly.

"On Sunday?" she inquired.

My father ran his finger the length of his nose, a gesture which always indicated an attempt at restraint. Then he removed the band from his cigar as nonchalantly as possible.

"But naturally," he replied. "Do I have some other time to go?"

"You can go, as usual, to the twilight games."

My father bit off the end of his cigar.

"Bah!" he exclaimed. "Baseball for seven innings only is like a dinner without cognac at the end. It is like kissing the woman you love good night by blowing it from your fingers. No. Baseball in the shadows, when the stars are appearing, is not in the true spirit of the game. One must have the bright sun and the green grass."

My mother looked at my eager, shining face and then looked back at my father.

"What is wrong," she asked, smiling faintly, "with kissing a woman you love good night by blowing it from your fingers?"

My father put his arm around her and laughed.

"The same thing that is wrong," he said, "with making from sour cherries an apple pie."

"You can't make an apple pie from sour cherries."

"*Eh, bien,* you can't kiss a woman good night this way . . . you can only kiss your fingers."

He touched his lips to the back of my mother's neck.

I coughed impatiently at this dallying. My mind was fastened firmly on baseball.

"Papa," I said anxiously, "we go now? Yes?"

"You come with us," my father said to my mother. "Eh? We will stuff our pockets with apples and cheese and make a picnic. Red wine, too, perhaps."

"And an onion," I said, loving onions.

"Some other time," my mother said hastily. "Certainly not on Sunday."

"Ah!" my father cried. "Always some other time. Do you promise some time soon?"

"Yes," my mother replied without much conviction. I suppose the thought of sitting on a hard bench for hours, watching that of which she knew nothing, frightened her. I felt, though, that in time my father's plaintive eagerness would win her over.

"Why," she questioned, as if to soften the blow, "do you not ask Uncle Louis or Uncle Felix?"

"Uncle Louis will be full and will chase butterflies across the diamond. Uncle Felix will wish to measure the speed at which the baseball arrives at the catcher. Besides, they are gone up the Gatineau to bring back the Boy's grandfather."

"Grandpa is coming?" I asked happily.

"Yes. He will stay next door as usual and sleep here."

I laughed. "Why is it that Grandpa stays next door and sleeps here?" My father shrugged.

"When you are old you sleep where you wish."

My mother was at the window, fixing the small jars of ivy that stood there.

"It looks like a thunderstorm coming," she said. "Grandpa and the uncles will get wet. You and the Boy, too, should not go out in a thunderstorm."

Our entire family was frightened to death of thunderstorms. At the first deep roll in the Laurentian Hills or up the Gatineau we huddled together in one room until the sun broke through, or the stars.

My father spoke bravely, though, on this occasion: "It will probably follow the river."

He did not mention the fact that there were three or four rivers it might follow, all of which came, in the end, almost to our back yard.

"Look!" my mother exclaimed, as a white flash lit the horizon's dark clouds.

"Bah!" my father said nervously. "Heat lightning."

"To me," my mother countered solemnly, "it looks like chain lightning."

"Chain lightning . . . heat lightning . . . it is miles away, *n'est-ce pas*? It is not here, is it?"

"*Maman*," I begged, "let us go please, before the storm begins."

"*Voilà*, a smart boy!" my father said proudly, patting me on the head.

My mother sighed and adjusted the tiebacks of the curtains.

"Very well," she said sadly, "but you know what Louis says—he pays too dear a price for honey who licks it off thorns!"

"Honey . . . thorns," my father repeated, rolling his eyes unhappily. "It is baseball of which we speak now."

"All right," my mother said. "All right. Only, just be careful. Don't stand under trees or near cows."

"No," my father agreed, "no cows and no trees."

He kissed my mother gently on the lips, and I naturally understood there would be no further discussion. I put on my best straw sailor, a white hat with the brim curled up and with a black elastic under the chin to keep the bonnet from the fury of any possible gales.

My mother regarded me with sadness, tucking in the string of my blouse. It was as if I were soon to be guillotined.

"It just doesn't seem right," she said slowly, "on Sunday."

My father lit his cigar impatiently.

"We must be going," he announced hastily. "The game will commence before we arrive."

My father took me by the hand. My mother put her arms around me and hugged and kissed me. It was as if I were going away forever to become a monk.

"Be careful," she said.

"Yes, *Maman*," I said dutifully.

"And pull up your stockings," she added.

On the trolley car going up Rideau Street I was happy. The wind blew through the open, summer seats and the sun was not too warm.

It is true I should have been in Sunday school at my mother's Presbyterian church, learning about the Red Sea turning back. Instead, I was on my way to the very brink of hell. For Hull, where my father whispered confidentially we were going, was well known to be a place of sinful living, and the sulphur that drifted daily from the match factories was enough to convince me of the truth of the report.

"Papa," I asked, "is it true Hull is wicked?"

"Not in the part where they play baseball," my father assured me.

A faint flash of lightning startled me a little.

"Papa. I have fear Uncle Louis and Uncle Felix and Grandpa will be struck by lightning."

My father smiled.

"Louis and Felix are too fast for the lightning."

"And Grandpa?" I plucked nervously at the tight elastic under my warm chin.

"Grandpa is too close a friend of the Lord to suffer from such things."

I felt better after this. I reasoned that if the Lord was a friend of Grandpa, then Grandpa would no doubt see that nothing happened to Papa and me.

We changed cars presently and were soon crossing the bridge into Hull and the province of Quebec.

I looked down the dirty, roaring falls that ran the factories.

"No sulphur," I observed.

"Not on Sunday," my father said.

This pleased me a great deal. On the one hand, Grandpa and the Lord were good friends. On the other hand, the Devil did not work on Sunday. I was in a splendid strategic position to deal with Evil.

We descended from the trolley on the main street of Hull.

"We can walk from here," my father informed me. "At the theater, they say it is not far out on this street."

Soon we found ourselves in the midst of hundreds of jabbering French-Canadians, all speaking so quickly and with such laughter and mockery that I could not follow them. The patois, too, was beyond my young understanding. What is more, every other building on the main street of Hull was one of swinging doors from which came the strong smell of ale, making my head dizzy.

"What do you say, Papa? What do they all say so fast?"

My father laughed.

"They say that Hull will beat Ottawa like a hot knife enters the butter! The pitcher of Hull will fan every batter of Ottawa. The batters of Hull will strike the ball every time into the Lachine Rapids, which is many, many miles away. In the end, they say, everybody will become full as a barrel of ale except the people from Ottawa. They will return home crying and drink lime juice and go to bed ashamed."

I clapped my hands happily at this foolishness which sounded like a fairy tale—the white balls flying by the hundreds, like birds, up the Lachine Rapids.

A man reeled by from a bar as I was pondering the flight of the baseballs. He began to shout loudly: "Hooray for Ottawa! Hull is full of pea soups. Down with Hull and the pea soups!"

The crowd picked him up and tossed him on high from group to group, laughing all the while, until, at last, he admitted Hull was the fairest city in all Canada and pea soup the most delicious dish.

I laughed joyfully. "It will be a good game, no?" I asked happily.

"*Mais oui,*" my father chuckled. "With the Hull and the Ottawa it is like with David and Goliath."

It had become quite cloudy and dark when we made our way through the grounds to the ancient wooden stand. In the gray distance the lightning continued to dance.

My father patted my head gently. "Heat lightning," he said uneasily.

"I know," I said. In spite of the fact that I knew Grandpa was a friend of the Lord and that the Devil had taken the day off, I nevertheless felt a little nervous. After all, I *had* skipped Sunday school for the first time. And we *were* so far from home!

My attention turned from the storm for a time as the Hull team began field practice amid great roars of approval that drowned out the rumbling thunder. The crowd began to chatter happily and proudly like many birds screaming in our back yard.

"All the world," I said, "speaks French here."

"*Mais oui,*" my father agreed. "In Hull all the world is French. In Ottawa it is mostly English. That is why there is so much desire to fight with each other."

"And we," I asked curiously, "what do we speak, you and me?"

"Ha!" my father exclaimed, patting my knee, "that is a problem for the French Academy!"

Since I did not know what the French Academy was, I placed my small chin in my hands and watched the Ottawa team as it came out on the field.

Groans and jeers now filled the air. Bottles, legs of chairs, programs, and bad fruit were thrown on the field like confetti at a wedding.

Two umpires and several groundkeepers cleared away the debris. One of the umpires announced through a megaphone:

"*Mesdames et messieurs,* we are the hosts. They are the guests. They are from Ottawa, but that is not a sin. We cannot always help where we live. It is requested not to throw bottles while the game proceeds as this is not the fair way we shall win. I am born in Hull and also my wife and four children and I am proud of it. But I do my honest duty to make a fair game. God save the King! *Play ball!*"

The game went on evenly and colorlessly for five or six innings. The darkness of the afternoon turned a sulphur yellow and the air became filled with tension.

The rumble of thunder grew louder.

In the seventh inning the Ottawa pitcher singled and stood proudly on first base. The bat boy ran out with a sweater. This is, of course, the custom in the big leagues, so that the pitcher will not expose his arm to possible chills.

To Hull, however, it was a fine opportunity to start something.

"Sissy!" someone shouted.

"Si . . . ssssssssssyyyyyyyyyy!" The crowd made one long sound as if the wind were moaning. Most of them probably did not know what the word meant, but it had a pleasant sound of derision.

The pitcher, O'Ryan, stepped far off first base in an attempt to taunt the Hull pitcher to throw, which he did.

O'Ryan darted back safely, stood arrogantly on the white bag, and carefully thumbed his nose.

The crowd jeered.

O'Ryan removed his cap and bowed from the waist in sarcasm.

Once more bottles, legs of chairs, programs, and overripe fruit came down on the field like hailstones.

Again the umpire picked up his megaphone and spoke:

"*Mes amis*," he begged, "they are the guests . . . we are the hosts."

A tomato glanced off the side of his head; a cushion landed in his face. He shrugged his shoulders, brushed himself off, and ordered wearily: "Play ball!"

The next pitch was hit and it was accompanied by a violent peal of thunder which almost coincided with the crack of the bat.

O'Ryan started for second base and was forced to slide when the Hull second baseman attempted to force him out. The second baseman, with his spiked shoes, jumped on O'Ryan's hand.

The Ottawa pitcher was safe by many seconds, but the crowd shouted insistently: "Out! *Out!*" with such anger that the umpire hesitated but a moment and then waved the astonished and stunned Irishman off the field.

Two thousand French-Canadian noses were instantly thumbed.

O'Ryan stood up dazedly and regarded his maimed hand. He brushed the dust from his uniform and strode quietly to the Ottawa bench. There he picked up several bats, swung them together for a while, and selected his favorite.

He pulled down his cap firmly, walked calmly to second base, and, with only a slight motion, brought the bat down solidly on the head of the Hull second baseman.

This was the signal for a riot. Spectators, umpires, players, peanut vendors—all swarmed across the field in one great pitched battle. In the increasing darkness from the oncoming storm they were as a great swarm of hornets, moving around the diamond.

My father and I, alone, remained seated. We did not speak for a long time.

I began to wish I had gone to Sunday school to have the Red Sea divided, or that I had stayed home with *Maman* and Happy Hooligan. I was coming to believe that Grandpa was not so good a friend of the Lord as he pretended and that if the Devil did not work on Sunday he had assistants who *did*.

My father spoke, at length, with the hollow sound of sin: "Poor *Maman* would be angry if she knew, eh?"

"*Mais oui*," I mumbled, fearfully watching the lightning tear the sky.

Papa tried to be calm and to talk lightly.

"Ah, well," he remarked, "it is not always so simple, eh, to tell the heat lightning from the chain lightning?"

"*Mais non*," I muttered.

"Also, in this case, one can see the storm did not follow the river."

"It followed *us*," I replied nervously, almost to myself.

"Well, we are safe here, no? We are, thank the good Lord, not in the melee. Here we are safe. When the fight is ended we will go home. Meanwhile we are safe. *N'est-ce pas?*"

"And the storm, Papa?" I queried, pulling my sailor hat down over my head as far as it would go.

"The storm," my father announced, as thunder sounded so loudly it shook the flimsy stand, "is mostly wind. It will blow itself away in no time."

I sighed. I will pray, I told myself. I will ask to be forgiven for going to the city of the Devil on Sunday. I will pray the good Lord forgive me, in the name of my grandfather, for forgetting to attend the opening of the Red Sea, also.

I had but managed to mutter: "Dear Lord . . ." when the sky, like the Red Sea, divided in two and there was hurled at us a great fiery ball, as if someone in heaven had knocked it our way.

Before I could get my breath, the dry, wooden stand was in flames.

"Dear Lord," I began again, breathlessly and hastily, "we are not so bad as all this . . . we only . . ." But my father had me by the hand and was dragging me swiftly on to the field.

By this time, the rioters had stopped banging heads and were wistfully watching their beloved stand disappear with the flames.

By the time we arrived home the storm was over and even the rain had stopped. We had been at a restaurant to eat and rest and had recovered a little when we faced *Maman*.

In fact I did not feel bad at all. I reasoned that the Lord had not been after my destruction but after the rioters who profaned his Sabbath with fighting. For if the Lord had been after me, He could, in His infinite wisdom, have made the ball come even closer.

"I told you we would have a thunderstorm," my mother said angrily.

"To me," my father replied meekly, "it looked like heat lightning."

"You know I don't like the Boy out in thunderstorms!"

"Ah, well, he is safe now. Eh, *bibi*? And Louis and Felix and Papa?"

"They are here."

"Good."

"A baseball game on Sunday is just not right," my mother went on, refusing to be deflected from the subject. "Look how pale and sick-looking you both are!"

My father coughed uneasily.

"Let us call down Grandpa and have some wine and shortbreads. Let us forget the rest. No?" He kissed my mother. She turned to me, relented a bit, and smiled.

"Was it a good game?"

I clapped my hands together excitedly. "It was wonderful, *Maman*! Everything happened!"

"Wine and shortbreads," Papa interrupted nervously.

"What do you mean, everything happened?" my mother asked, glancing sidelong at Papa.

"I must go up and see my poor father," said Papa. "It is now many months . . ."

"One moment," my mother cautioned. She turned and motioned for me to sit on her knee. My father sank wearily into a chair.

"Well?" my mother urged.

It was too wonderful and exciting to keep!

"*Maman*," I exclaimed, "God hit a home run!"

My father groaned. My mother's eyes widened.

"He what?" she asked, pale.

The words came rushing out: "He hit a home run and He struck the grandstand with His powerful lightning and then the grandstand burned to very small pieces, all of a sudden, and this was because everybody was fighting on the Sabbath and . . ."

My mother let me down slowly from her knee.

"Is this true?" she said to my father.

My father shrugged and waved his delicate hands helplessly.

"A small fire. The stand in Hull is made of . . ."

My mother jumped to her feet.

"Now, for heaven's sake, don't act silly."

"*Where?*"

My father lowered his eyes.

"Hull," he admitted slowly. "After all, they do not permit baseball on Sunday in Ottawa. If they permit you to breathe it is something. All the world knows that."

"Hull!" my mother whispered, as if it were a dreadful name. "Hull! No wonder! To take the Boy from Sunday school to Hull! And on Sunday! Hull!"

"*Maman,*" I said, tears coming into my eyes, "I will speak to the Lord . . ."

"Go," said my mother, and she sounded like a voice from the heavens, "and wash your dirty face."

"*Ma chère,*" my father said, trying to be pleasant, "does one always know where a storm will travel?"

"You," my mother ordered, "go wipe your shoes. Look at the mud you have tracked in!"

As Papa and I went our respective ways, heads bowed, we heard her whisper once more: "Hull!"

I knew then that she would never go to a baseball game with Papa. The memory of the Lord's home run which so barely missed us would remain, I thought, forever in her mind. She would know one of the places the Lord was going to strike and she would know now that His aim was very good, if not perfect.

I DON'T WANT TO PLAY

ROBERT THOMAS ALLEN

It seems to me that it's time textbooks on entertaining, etiquette and social activity in general started dealing with something that's just as vital as knowing how to seat people, address them, serve them, group them and talk to them. That's knowing how to leave them alone.

Too many people operate on the theory that, if guests, friends, members and congregations are to have a good time, somebody has to make a strenuous effort to arrange it. This isn't a criticism of believers in organized fun, good-fellowship and enjoyment; I think they're generally better social human beings than I am. What I'm criticizing is the belief itself—a naïve and mistaken conviction that all kinds of people, including me, can be rescued from dullness and made temporarily happy by careful programming.

I keep running into this sort of thing at picnics, dinners, evenings out, summer resorts, banquets and a lot of other places where people are not allowed to enjoy themselves in their own way and with whom they choose. Somebody is always stiffening programs with three-legged races, sing-songs and middle-aged-men's ball games; rousing people from deck chairs to go on bird-watching expeditions or trail rides; getting guests on their feet at banquets and making them march around the table and sit down beside some stranger labeled "Harry"; bringing variety into their friends' lives by getting them all playing some game they don't understand; and sitting back beaming at the sight of everyone having such a good time.

A few nights ago at a party I was having a wonderful conversation in a corner with a little rumpled mathematics teacher who claimed that children shouldn't be made to go to school, that mankind had no real existence, and that getting drunk was not an acquired habit but a basic instinct like love. Just as I was warming up with some ideas of my own, the hostess, a stout boisterous woman, walked up to me, said, "Here!" stuck an orange under my chin and burst out laughing.

"You'll find out what it's for," she shrieked, tapping me playfully on the head with a score card. "It's an icebreaker."

She yanked me to a line of guests in another room and stood me in front of a thin embarrassed-looking girl about a foot taller than I am. The hostess explained to her that she had to get the orange out from under my chin with her chin and stick it under somebody else's chin without using her hands.

I stood there holding the orange against my chest, smiling up at the girl encouragingly, like someone being cheerful about a broken neck. She looked at me as if she wished that instead of being such a good sport I would just go home. It didn't help when, after a horrible tussle for the orange, she got my glasses caught in her hair and walked off with them dangling down her back like a broken brooch. Everybody laughed hysterically.

In other words this woman broke up a good conversation and very nearly smashed my glasses just seeing that everybody had a good time. And she wasn't through yet. She was already handing out stubs of pencils and pieces of colored paper for the next game.

"I'll tell you what to do with them in a minute," she told me. She glanced into my face, looking pleased, and said, "I like to get people out of the corner and make them forget themselves."

This is a principle behind a lot of organized good-fellowship and it's about as scientific as some of the early cures for warts. Organized fun doesn't always help people forget themselves. It often does just the opposite. Party games, for instance, sometimes get people's minds on themselves so that they can't think of anything else for days. Any time I sit up in bed in the middle of the night thinking of myself and something I said or did at a party, it wasn't something I said while sitting in a corner; it was something I said in a game, standing in the middle of the room and coming apart with nerves. Like the time I got into a game of charades and had to do a book title called The Web of Passion. There are still people on my street who were at that party who just barely speak to me to this day.

And I'm not the only one. I have a neighbor, a military old gentleman as erect as a polo mallet, with such a distinguished appearance that people always take him for something like a retired university president or a nuclear physicist. Actually, he sells shirts and anything deeper than The Return of Lassie gives him a headache, but he enjoys a certain prestige because he seldom talks and it does nobody any harm. But his reputation was almost ruined when a big, tightly girdled woman with frizzy yellow hair held a party for a few of the neighbors, included him among the guests, and decided early in the party to make everyone just forget themselves with a few brisk games.

In point of fact, this man could forget himself for longer periods than anyone I've ever known. He had a way of standing for hours, eyes narrowed, hands clamped behind his back, staring at a tree or a rock formation. Anyone who didn't know him would think he was going back millions of years and piecing together the earth's origin. Then he'd take his bulldog pipe out of his mouth and say something like, "Found a perfectly good deck chair this morning. Not a thing wrong with it. Somebody just chucked it out with the garbage."

That evening, sitting out on his lawn watching the sunset, the evening breeze ruffling his thinning hair, he'd take his pipe out of his mouth, look at you sharply and say, "Little hole in the seat the size of my finger." He'd hold up his finger. "Nothing else wrong with it." It would be a moment before you'd realize that he'd been thinking about the deck chair ever since you saw him in the morning.

He was a happy outgoing personality if I ever saw one, until he went to this party where the hostess made everyone take off their shoes and pile them in a corner, then pushed all her guests into two lines and explained a game called Junior High. It consisted of running for a table and picking out a slip of paper bearing a number and the name of the capital of a country, multiplying the number by another number which was pinned to the lapel of the person behind you, running for another table and picking up a piece of celery in your teeth, dipping it in some kind of juice, whipping around and writing the product of the two numbers on a big sheet of cardboard, then running to a corner of the room and putting on your shoes and going to the end of your line.

In about twenty seconds my neighbor had caused a traffic jam that backed right out onto the veranda. The game had pretty well stopped while everyone watched him in a sort of awe as it became apparent that he couldn't remember anything, that he had multiplied six by nine and got one hundred and sixty-three, that he had practically no reflex action, had forgotten the capital of England, couldn't hold celery between his teeth, and turned out to be a poor sport when the hostess started shrieking excitedly, "No. NO! You can't put your shoes on yet. You haven't done it right. You don't pin the celery to the cardboard." He snapped up at her from the floor, "What the devil do you mean? You told me to pin it to the board just half a minute ago," got a crick in his back and let out a military oath that made everyone turn aside in embarrassment. It all revealed that he wasn't a grand old man after all.

In fact he became completely demoralized, and for days after that when we'd be standing out in our gardens, he'd suddenly look at me with a new anxious look in his eyes. It was clear he was thinking of himself instead of deck chairs. He'd say, "I've got a head for figures, you know, but not when people are shouting at me. When they start that, I just want to get into a room by myself. I get rattled. I'd make a poor jet pilot."

This hostess just about made an introvert out of him at the age of seventy-five, and probably would have if he'd gone to any more of her parties. But next time he just asked me, "Make my excuses, will you? Tell that woman I'm tied up in another matter."

But the point is, whenever anyone starts monkeying with human nature they usually cause more trouble than they cure, especially the kind of people who think you can work on the human character from the outside, like a pie crust, molding it into something more desirable for a few hours.

A lot of activities at my kids' Sunday-school class are presided over by a tall, pleasant young minister from New Brunswick who, out of real goodness of heart and a genuine desire to serve, believes that you always have to be doing something brisk about human nature or nobody will have a good time. I really like this man and respect him but I just automatically start hiding behind pillars when he appears.

I was at one of his affairs the other day when, following a picnic lunch, about fifty parents all sat around in a big circle next to the people they wanted to sit next to, talking and enjoying themselves. Then this minister came in, took one look around, saw that nothing was organized and, with the energy of a gym instructor, announced something about us all getting to know one another better. With that, he made everyone stand up, walk to the middle of the floor, tell a lot of people, who didn't care, who he was, what his work was, and where he came from. Everybody nearly died of self-consciousness, and the minister tried to make them feel at ease by making little jokes in a professionally projected voice and laughing heartily. When he got me up there, he caught me on that old one about what hand did I write with and what hand did I stir my tea with; when I said my right, he said he used a spoon himself and clouted me on the back and left me to grope my way back to my seat.

The thing is, he not only changed the mood of the ones who had been in the middle of the floor—all of whom, after they'd returned to their seats, sat looking unhappily into space—but worried the ones who hadn't been called yet about what he was going to do to them, so that they couldn't pay any attention to what was going on. On top of all this, he made a lot of people forget where they'd been sitting and they found themselves among people they didn't know and who wouldn't talk to them.

One time he told me with a sort of benign grimness, "I like to drag people out of themselves."

With all due respect for his intentions, if a guest is the type who is shy, sensitive and slow-witted, nobody is going to change him by dragging him out of himself; or if they do it's something I'd just as soon not see. I believe in leaving people in themselves. The place for people to come out of themselves is on a psychiatrist's couch.

A good host or hostess, in my opinion, not only doesn't bring guests out of themselves but deftly keeps them stuffed in, so that the only part that's showing is the best part—the part that should go to parties.

Not that all people who plan organized fun are trying for a quick psychological cure. Some just feel that a get-together of any kind is a failure unless everybody knows everybody else, and that the quickest way to bring it about is something that will make them all stand up and move away from the people they like.

One bright, brown-eyed young hostess I know has been doing this ever since I've known her. As soon as everyone is having a good time she pins strips of paper on them, divides them into two groups so that friends, acquaintances and people who get along well are not together, then puts one group in the dining room and the other in the kitchen. Then, as far as I know, she goes to a late movie, because I never see her again.

I've yet to see one of these games end any way but with a lot of people standing around in different rooms as if they were going through customs, waiting for something to happen. It never does.

It's even worse when the guests are in costume, in some sort of pageant, to which only the hostess has the key. One time she herded seven guys into a sort of den, seated us all on the floor around a pumpkin, and told us in a haunting, tremulous eerie monotone that we were all witches. Then she left us looking at the pumpkin and wondering how long it would be before the party broke up.

Among the witches were a chemical engineer from a tire factory, a commercial artist from Simpson's, an insurance salesman, a Hoffman Press operator, an auditor, a cop (dressed like a grandmother) and a linotype operator—none of whom had met one another until an hour ago and all of whom wished they hadn't even then. Only two guys tried to keep up the spirit of mummery. The Hoffman Press operator, a large man who, I think, was supposed to be a skeleton, gave one eerie cry and everyone stared at him until he just went back to staring at the pumpkin. But the really shattering sight was the linotype operator who was dressed as a baby, with a bottle and a rattle in one hand and a rubber nipple in his mouth. When he had arrived at the party he had cried and said he wanted more milk and everybody nearly died laughing. But springing this without warning on a large group of people, including a lot of women and several old friends, is one thing, keeping it up an hour later in a room with six strange men, including a cop dressed as a grandmother, is something else again. Every time he burst out crying, the cop scowled from under his lace cap and looked as if he would have liked to get him down at the station for five minutes at evening vespers.

I'd come as an old Rembrandt with a frame around my head. I'm usually tongue-tied at parties anyway, but if you want to see something really subdued you should see me sitting looking through a picture frame at a cop dressed as a grandmother, or even a cop dressed as a cop. On the other side of me was the chemical engineer, a big, handsome, sulky red-faced man who was supposed to be a cavalier.

I've never seen anything less gay than that group. We all sat there looking grimly at the pumpkin, the cavalier flipping little bits of lint off the rug with his rapier, the man dressed as a baby sucking his nipple thoughtfully, and the cop waiting for him to cry "mamma" just once more. It was as funny as a nervous breakdown. The hostess never did come back. We just all began to stand up after a half an hour or so to read book titles or shove our lace bonnets and picture frames back off our heads and say a few words to one another about the weather. We probably would have all been there yet, stark staring mad, if our wives hadn't looked in on us eventually and told us in some surprise that they were serving cake and coffee.

Of all the confused ideas about entertaining, I think the worst is that it's all right to invite anyone to a social affair, with complete disregard of tastes, background, interests, sensitivity, old feuds and delicately balanced relationships, and think that the whole thing will be a success as long as everyone is made to play games. I remember one time in Kitchener watching two principals in a feud chew their way along a string toward one another. A few days earlier they had been threatening to decapitate one another with shovels. For some reason one of them had a theory that he owned the other man's driveway. It had something to do with a survey made by William Lyon Mackenzie. They were always yelling at one another above the sound of the wind, leaves, the roar of their cars and the barking of a beautiful big police dog.

Actually, it should have been a man and his wife at either end of the string, but the hostess got the teams mixed up. These two guys made an agonizing effort to be good sports and pretend there was something human on the other end of the string, but soon they were beginning to reel the string in with their fists, without taking their eyes off one another. They would have probably been scoring the game with loose teeth if a couple of guests hadn't hollered, "Time's up!" and shouldered them apart.

Another thing about party games, from a purely practical point of view, they're not feasible. The essence of the fun in any game is a certain skill which implies a certain knowledge of the game. But there isn't time in an evening to learn most of the party games I run up against. The idea that somebody can learn a new game, play it, have some coffee and sandwiches and a good time all in one evening, is like expecting someone to spend Saturday afternoon learning algebra. It's even worse the way most people explain games.

I've noticed that people who explain games explain everything but the purpose of the game. A couple of weeks ago I was forced sullenly into a game involving cards, miniature plastic brooms and little wooden disks with numbers on them. For three hours I played without knowing once what I was doing. I don't know yet. I don't want to know either. But the point is, the hostess and her husband both started telling me everything about the game except what I was supposed to do—or, rather, why I was supposed to do it—and told me both at the same time. They not only didn't tell me what I was supposed to do, they told me all the things that would prevent me from doing it and would count against me.

"See," the husband would say, shuffling the cards, "if anybody gets a queen or three jacks before you've got thirteen, you make them take a card from the deck. Then you can pick up any of the cards you discarded, if they say they're going to try for more than twenty-one."

"You'll catch on as soon as you start playing," his wife said, completely disregarding the fact that I didn't want to play. "It's just like bridge, except that if you draw a three you become a lamppost, and you count with brooms and aces."

Every time I asked what I was supposed to do, she said, "You try not to be a lamppost. It's loads of fun."

I've been trying not to be a lamppost all my life. I still didn't know how it fitted into this particular game.

"We'll just play a couple of games so that you can get the hang of it," the husband said.

Eight games later they were looking at me with horribly polite little smiles and saying things like, "No, you see, if you're a lamppost you miss a deal."

As far as I could see, the only possible purpose of this game was to end it as quickly as possible, or, better still, never to have started it. The only thing that half saved the situation for me was my partner, a huge woman with a happy face as expressionless as an egg, who not only couldn't understand anything but couldn't hold her cards so that she could read them. She would fan all the cards out to the right instead of the left, so that she had seven blank corners to look at and had to peek behind each card or underneath it as if looking into a hot oven. The only difference was that she didn't use pot holders.

But I'm not criticizing games as games, but as artificial social devices. They don't work any better than any other form of social coercion or methodical taping-out of people's moods and prejudices. It's sometimes hard to figure out people who think they do.

One time I was at a Canadian picnic in Florida, arranged by a local club. The chief organizer, with unerring instinct, sensed immediately that people who liked one another were going to group together and in a flash of genius said that we'd all sit in the order of home provinces. With this one master stroke, he had people from Winnipeg sitting next to people they didn't know or like from Toronto; Argo fans sitting next to people from Ottawa; and Newfoundlanders and Albertans trying in vain to find something in common besides Canada.

People who don't like one another, don't like one another any better just because somebody arranges for them to meet. I stayed one time at a small beach community in Nova Scotia where I met a fussy, friendly, nervous printing salesman who was a born social arranger.

He felt that, for a writer, I just wasn't meeting enough people. All I wanted to do was to sit scowling at the gulls and occasionally talking to one little man I met, an old well digger who was full of fascinating stories of the things he thought about while he was below sea level.

But this printing salesman started arranging little soirées with people I didn't want to meet and who wanted to meet me even less. At one informal little get-together he introduced me to a big bald lawyer who looked at me as if waiting for me to make just one wrong move; a sour little member of the town council with ulcers and no use for writers; an Austrian sculptor with a duck-tail haircut and a wife who talked all night about a pregnant cat; a millionaire yachtsman who tried not to be a snob about people without yachts; and a retired librarian who had written several papers on Cromwell's England. The yachtsman thought the Cromwellian scholar was a square; the Cromwellian scholar thought the sculptor was a freak. Both the scholar and the sculptor thought people shouldn't have yachts or a million dollars. I thought nobody should have a wife with a pregnant cat. Nobody liked me. And the lawyer and the councilor got into a fight. Everybody got away as fast as possible to their sculpture, office, yacht and books. I don't know where the Cromwellian scholar went. On the last day, the printing salesman had us all make out little cards with our names and addresses on them and give them to one another. We all tore them up as soon as we got out of sight. At least, I presume the others did too—I've never heard from any of them.

All in all, making someone do something he wouldn't have thought of doing himself doesn't make him enjoy it. Dragging shy people out of their corners doesn't make them any less shy. The way to help shy people out is to leave them alone. Pushing people around, on any scale, is a form of tyranny, even if it's done with the best of intentions by means of hearty social gimmicks. In fact, this kind is the worst kind of tyranny: the kind with moral backing. Anybody who refuses to go along with the convention that you should not only enjoy yourself, but enjoy yourself a certain way, is generally regarded as a poor sport and the kind of guy who kicks dogs in TV plays and gets shown up in his true colors by a cowboy. If you ask me, hostesses who don't like people who don't like games, yet still invite them to their parties and try to make them play, would probably dynamite brook trout, and I give them fair warning that from now on I'm not going to play.

In fact, if it's the kind of party that needs something to break the ice, I'm going to skate right past it and go home.

"The main thing is not to let ourselves be fooled by the evidence."

STRICTLY BUSINESS!

PHILIP MINOFF

Ask any man to describe the typical delegate to a business convention, and he'll always wind up drawing a picture of someone else.

Yet, despite the popular impression (perpetuated by comedians, cartoonists and even some wishful conventioneers themselves) that the get-togethers are mere excuses for levity, libation and libertinism, most of these assemblages are serious, straightforward and deucedly predictable affairs. A few of the more foreseeable occurrences follow:

At least one salesman will be agonized to discover that he's left his sales charts and presentation at home. But when the week is over, he'll realize it really didn't make any difference.

Someone's badge will read "Prince Rainier IV."

The same conventioneers who greet each other with "Long time no see" will bid their farewells with "Abyssinia."

An inept lecturer will try, with the aid of a huge graph, to explain the rise and fall of the industry's fortunes during the past year, and will wind up being unintentionally funnier than Bob Benchley in his "Treasurer's Report."

If the meeting is in Atlantic City, at least half the delegates will keep complaining that it should have been held in Chicago.

One of the men—a newlywed—will bring his wife along.

The loud speaker will announce that the owner of a blue sedan with license plate number 512NN is requested to move his car from in front of the main entrance to the hall, and for some unknown reason, the owner will be cheered lustily as he sheepishly walks down the aisle to the exit.

A rough-cut, bellicose speaker with a booming voice will order the microphone turned off, with the phrase, "I don't need this thing!"—and he won't.

At least one delegate will come upon an empty auditorium and, upon inquiry, learn that the convention isn't scheduled to start until the *following* Monday.

Someone's badge will read "Bridey Murphy."

If the meeting is in Chicago, at least half the delegates will mutter that it should have been in Atlantic City.

At a meeting of sound engineers, the public address system will go out of order, and the incident will make every paper in the country (as well as the Miscellany column of Time magazine).

A chairman will wink at a friend in the third row before calling the meeting to order.

A delegate will smoke his very first cigar.

An enterprising young salesman from the midwest who received an effusive letter of commendation from the Big Boss in New York just a few weeks ago (and showed it to everyone, including his barber) will introduce himself to the B.B. and be mortified to find that the guy doesn't even remember his name.

Someone's badge will read, "The Son of Bridey Murphy."

At the end of the very last session, someone will suddenly rise to propose a standing vote of thanks to the chairman for a fine job. Everyone in the room will get to his feet, except for the building's aging janitor, who'll remain seated in a corner—watching the proceedings with a glum, wise look.

Al Kelly, the double-talk artist, will pose as an international expert (in the convention's particular interest) and before he has a chance to admit his hoax, will be elected vice-president of the industry's executive board.

If the meeting is in Boston, at least half the delegates will insist it should have been held in San Francisco.

A junior executive will be tabbed for greatness when it's discovered he was the only speaker at the convention who didn't use a Tele-PrompTer.

Someone's badge will simply bear his correct name and home city, and hundreds of his colleagues will peer at it for hours, trying to discover where the joke is.

If the meeting is in San Francisco, at least half the delegates will wonder what the executive committee had against Boston.

One cut-up will surreptitiously place a walnut strategically on the lectern just before the first downstroke of the chairman's gavel.

Hundreds of delegates will wonder why the peas served at home by their wives don't have that technicolor-green look. They'll *know* why when they take their first bite of the tasteless pellets.

One veteran conventioneer will get roars from several of his colleagues by referring to the main dish as "chicken tetrachloride."

A sergeant-at-arms will return home and be totally unable to explain to his wife what his function was at the convention.

If the meeting is being held in Minneapolis, at least one delegate will feel it was an outright case of discrimination against Sioux Falls.

At least one speaker will open his remarks with the question, "Can you hear me back there?" and a raucous joker in the very last row of the auditorium will yell, "No!"

If the convention is taking place in New York, and New York was the unanimous selection of every delegate present, there'll still be a few who insist it should have been held in the fall.

Hobbies:

THE ALL-PURPOSE FISHING STORY

CHARLES W. MORTON

The time has come to end the senseless competition among writers of fishing stories: the narrator hooks a fish and (a) catches it or (b) loses it. The only items in the story that are at all variable are the species of fish—and hence its size and habitat—and the kind of tackle used in his wisdom (or folly) by the narrator. These, along with a few details, would simply be left blank in the standardized fishing story, to be filled in as the facts warranted. Thus, whether it all took place at the headwaters of the Orinoco or the narrows of Spectacle Pond, much pencil chewing and time-consuming thought will be saved by adherence to the simple rules governing all fishing stories.

The fishing story must begin with a modest statement of the author's credentials: "I've fished for the mighty —— off Acapulco and the battling —— along the Florida Keys. I've seen a maddened —— swamp a dory off Wedgeport, but for sheer power and gameness I've seen nothing that can equal, pound for pound, a ——."

That's a perfectly workable opening paragraph for any fishing story. If the reader is foolish enough to doubt its validity when applied to some notoriously inert species, let him remember that the fill-in of the battle itself will prove everything that the narrator contends. It's bound to, for the narrator uses just the same fill-in for a rock cod, which behaves much like a boot full of water, as he would for a fifty-pound muskellunge.

After presenting his own credentials, the narrator must introduce his guide. Guides are always terse, monosyllabic men—which saves the author from writing much improbable dialogue and dialect. They grunt or they gesture, but that's about all. The narrator must assume at this point the disarming role of chump and leave the high strategy to Joe, the guide. ("We never did learn Joe's last name, but he taught us all there was to know about ——s.")

Another purpose of the guide is to wake the author up on that never-to-be-forgotten morning and give him his breakfast: "My head had hardly touched the pillow, so it seemed, before Joe woke me up. The delicious aroma of ——ing —— greeted my nostrils, and I lost no time in getting out of my blankets."

And so to that mysterious locality, known only to Joe, where the narrator has been assured he will have a chance to pit his cunning against the great-granddaddy of all ——s. It makes no difference whether Joe is a Kanaka or a Canadian, or whether they travel by express cruiser, mule, or pirogue—their destination always disappoints the narrator when he gets there: "It looked like the last place in the world to try for ——s, but Joe merely grunted and gestured vaguely at the water. '—— here,' he said. 'Big one.'"

Joe of course was right, the author ruefully confesses. His first lure, a —— (spinner, fly, minnow, or grapnel baited with a small shoat—it's all the same) had hardly touched the water when down went the rod, out screamed the line! It was all the author could do to keep his footing against that first wild rush of the ——.

The next two hours are crammed with action, while the author brings in one gigantic —— after another, certainly the biggest he has ever seen and one of them looking as if it would go for at least —— pounds on the club scales. But hold on. What's wrong with Joe? He seems disgusted. He grunts contemptuously. Bored stiff. The author, still the chump and slow to catch on, presses Joe for comment. Joe grunts. "Big —— still here," Joe replies, gesturing at the water, and the author begins to realize that Joe is talking about a —— of a size never reported in all the annals of —— fishing.

Comes the final cast. Nothing happens. No —— of any size seems to be interested. The length of this interval of writing depends on how much space the author is trying to fill. If need be, he can reminisce of bygone feats against giant clams, electric eels, or things that have nothing to do with ——s.

Suddenly, a few yards beyond the lure, the waters swirl: "Some vast, invisible force was causing a submarine upheaval. Spellbound, I watched a great tail appear for an instant as the monster lazily rolled over and submerged again. I turned to Joe. 'Don't tell me that was a ——!' I whispered. '——s don't get *that* big.' But Joe only grunted. 'Big ——,' he replied."

The author realizes that his tackle is far too light for a —— of this size. Joe had really known what he was talking, or grunting, about. But it's too late now. So: *down* goes that rod again, *out* screams the line. Even with a ——-pound drag, the ——'s rush carries all before it. Crash! The leviathan hurls himself far out of the water and comes down with an echoing splash. The author vainly tries to reel in precious line. "My rod bent almost double. Pandemonium reigned." Sooner or later, as the line races from the screeching reel, the author does a very foolish thing: "I tried to brake it with my thumb." Naturally enough, he gets a bad burn on his thumb. More leaps, lunges— a page or so of them.

"Suddenly, my line went ominously slack. I began frantically reeling in. '—— gone,' Joe grunted."

True enough. The tale is almost told. Remains only the unbelievable circumstance of the leader when the narrator finally winds it to the surface. Gut, wire, or ⅜ inch log chain, its condition never varies: "*Bitten clean through!* Mute evidence that the —— had met man's challenge—and won!"

They prepare to leave. "But suddenly the waters were convulsed again as the mighty —— broke the surface in all his majesty and, with a final derisive smack of his great tail, disappeared—still the Monarch of ——." (Spectacle Pond, the Upper Orinoco, Hillsboro Inlet, etc., etc.)

LETTER TO A MANUFACTURER (X)

H. F. ELLIS

Sir: I have just been carefully following your directions. After half an hour's preliminary work, I pushed the spindle R through the apertures BB[1]. Then I pulled the arm L sharply downward (*Page 2*) and, retaining my hold on R, worked DD gently past E, W and Q until it clicked into position at S. Keeping L depressed as instructed, I now attempted, by means of the knurled knob T at the side, to raise the pinion at O until it engaged the horizontal worm F.

But there is no knurled knob at the side.

"The first time I get a strike and you want to cheat me out of it
just because the ball went into the wrong alley!"

Did you know that? There is a knob, fairly well knurled, at the back,
but how can that be T? You can't reach it, for one thing, while still
depressing L, unless you let go of the end of the spindle R. And you
know very well—assuming you have ever tried to assemble this thing
yourself—what happens then.

On the off chance that I had all along been mistaking the back for
the side, I unclipped the two brackets U_1 and U_2 from what in that
case would no longer be the bottom, and fixed them on the old top—
or front, rather. This, of course, necessitated reversing the slotted
panel HH (*Page 1*), and while I was doing that, DD slipped out of S
and a small bright part rattled down. As far as I can tell by shining
a torch through the floor boards, it is either G or V.

At this stage I turned to *Page 3* and at once became convinced that
Diagram 9 is upside down. It is impossible to secure W to K, since
the so-called J would obviously be in the way if it had not already—
through my following *Page 1* too carefully—been wrenched clean out
of its socket. Putting J back the other way round, so that the bent bit

is on top, simply forces a small spring—would it be N or M?—out of the slot YY, and there is a clang from inside that bodes, in my limited experience of this kind of mechanism, no good. I had every right, in my opinion, to find out whether, by putting a foot on L, gripping R with my teeth and at the same time giving a slight twist to this knurled knob of yours, I could induce the spring to return to its original position. No one could possibly have foreseen that this would cause the whole base plate—now, of course, on top—to buckle upward and spew a number of brass screws into the fireplace. Nor was this all. Even the worm F turned—and as to the pinion, all one can say for certain is that it was no longer at O.

When this happened, I took a cold chisel CC—not included in the outfit—set it at about the point P and drove it through the apparatus from A to Z, maintaining "a firm even pressure throughout" (*Page* 4). Then I carefully tossed your directions out of a fourth-floor window.

May I suggest that it is now your turn to follow them?

A BEE STORY BY BRICKTOP

J. B. COLLIN

I had an improved back yard. I went through a seed store and bought a sample of everything that would grow in this climate. The result was a perfect tangle of flowers and things, from an overgrown sunflower to a forget-me-not.

Mrs. Bricktop, my wife, is very proud of our garden, and while gushing over it the other morning, a happy thought worked its way under her black hair: "What a delightful thing it would be to have a hive of bees, and raise our own honey, as well as everything else!"

I have always thought that woman inspired, ever since she convinced me that I couldn't do better than to marry her. This was an original, bold idea; a happy thought. I promised her a hive of bees, and went to business with a lighter heart, and firmer belief in the genuine-ness of home comforts and amusements.

I bought a hive of honey-bees and brought it home with me that very night. It was one of those patent hydrostatic, back-action hives, in which the bees have peculiar accommodations and all the modern improvements. It was a nice little hive, none of your old-fashioned barn-size affairs. It even had windows in it, so that the bees could look out and see what was going on, and enjoy themselves.

Both myself and Mrs. B. were delighted; and before dark I arranged a stand for the hive in the garden, and opened the bay-windows so that the bees could take an early start and get to business by sunrise the next morning. Mrs. B. called me honey several times during the evening; and such sweet dreams as we had!

We intended to be up early next morning to see how our little birds took to our flowers; but a good half-hour before we probably should have done so we were awakened by the unearthly yells of a cat. Mrs. B. leaped from her downy couch, exclaiming, "What can be the matter with our yellow Billy?" The yells of anguish convinced us that something more than ordinary was the matter with him, and so we hurried our toilets. We rushed out into our back yard, and, oh, what a sight met our astonished gaze!

The sight consisted of a yellow cat that appeared to be doing its best to make a pin-wheel of itself. He was rolling over and over in the grass, bounding up and down, anon darting through the bushes and foliage, standing on his head, and then trying to drive his tail into the ground, and all the while keeping up the most confounded yowling that was ever heard.

"The cat is mad," said Mrs. B., affrighted.

"Why shouldn't he be? The bees are stinging him," said I, comprehending the trouble.

Mrs. B. flew to the rescue of her cat, and the cat flew at her. So did the bees. One of them drove his drill into her nose, another vaccinated her on the chin, while another began to lay out his work near her eye. Then she howled, and began to act almost as bad as the cat.

It was quite an animated scene. She cried murder, and the neighbors looked out from their back windows and cried out for the police, and asked where the fire was. This being a trifle too much, I threw a towel over my head and rushed to her rescue. In doing so, I ran over and knocked her down, trod upon the cat, and made matters no better. Mrs. B. is no child on a wrestle, and she soon had me under her, and was tenderly stamping down the garden-walk with my head, using my ears for handles. Then I yelled, and some of the bees came to her assistance, and stung me all over the face.

In the meantime the neighbors were shouting, and getting awfully excited over the show, while our servant, supposing us fighting, opened the basement door and admitted a policeman, who at once

"It's all fixed. His pants fall down in the second round."

proceeded to go between man and wife. The bees hadn't got at Mrs. B.'s tongue yet, and she proceeded to show the policeman that I had abused her in the most shameful manner, and that I had bought a hive of bees on purpose to torment her into the grave. I tried to explain; but just then a bee stung the officer on the nose, and he understood it all in less than a minute. He got mad and actually lost his temper. He rubbed his nose and did some official cussing. But as this didn't help matters any, he drew his club and proceeded to demolish that patent bee-hive. The bees failed to recognize his badge of office, and just swarmed on him.

They stung him wherever he had no clothing, and in some places where he did have it. Then he howled, and commenced acting after the manner of the cat and its mistress. He rolled on the ground for a moment, and then got up and made for the street, shouting "fire." Then the bees turned to the people who had climbed upon the fence to see the fun. Then they had some fun. Windows went down, and some of the neighbors acted as though they thought a twenty-inch shell was about to explode.

By this time a fire-engine had arrived, and a line of hose was taken through the house into the back yard. One of the hosemen asked where the fire was; but just then one of the bees bit him behind the ear, and he knew. They turned a stream upon that half-wrecked bee-hive, and began to "play away" with one hand and fight bees with the other. But the water had the desired effect, and those bees were soon among the things that were. A terrible crowd had gathered in the meantime in front of the house, but a large portion of it followed the flying policeman, who was rubbing his affected parts, and making tracks for the stationhouse and a surgeon.

This little adventure somehow damaged our enthusiasm regarding the delight of making our own honey. During the next week we wore milk-and-water poultices pretty ardently, but not a word was said about honey; and now Mrs. B. has gone to stay a week with her mother, leaving me and the convalescent cat and the tickled neighbors to enjoy our own felicity.

NO NUTBURGERS FOR ME

ROBERT de ROOS

There is a conspiracy of monstrous proportions spreading through this kindly land. Its sinister tentacles already reach into every city and village and shadow every home. Unless you are vigilant, you may be the next victim. I refer, of course, to the diabolical assault being made on the American hamburger. The hamburger sandwich is being debauched. And, until now, not a hand has been raised in its defense.

The hamburger is a triumph of indigenous American cookery. Redolent with the savory juices of good ground beef, garnished with lettuce and tomato, the whole encompassed in a golden bun, it is one of man's greatest achievements. Prepared by loving hands, it is a delight, a meal which satisfies man's deepest yearnings. It restores his soul as it knits his tissues. It sends him on his way with a spring in his stride and a lilt in his voice, refreshed, joyous, alert, every sinew in tune with the Good and the Beautiful.

This is the superlative sandwich which has fallen into unworthy hands. On the oil-spattered griddles of misguided meat maulers, the hamburger has become a monument to grease and indigestion. A national institution has become a national disgrace. All, however, is not lost. It is not too late to rally the forces of decency. The edible hamburger shall not perish from the earth!

Now is the time to rally the national treasure and manpower. "We will fight on the beaches. We will fight on the airfields. We will fight in the streets." I forget who said that—or even if he said it exactly that way—but it pretty well sums up the idea. Unless the stout of heart gird to battle the forces of evil, the hamburger, as we have known it, is doomed.

I recently made a motor trip which took me twice across the country. I traveled the main highways, the habitat of the hamburger. I carried on scientific researches and samplings unprecedented in the hamburger field. I learned plenty:

1. A movement to make the hamburger into something else—almost anything else—is in full flower. The renegade horse players, fallen executives and disenfranchised butchers who operate hamburger stands are determined to add adulterants never meant by a wise Providence to be part of a hamburger. There should be a law to compel hamburger cooks to wear little signs stating what they are up to. If they are about to commit hamburgers containing wild rice, guava jelly, bran meal or soybeans, the customer, in common courtesy, should be warned. Cooks who put pickled beets or chopped potatoes in hamburgers should be arrested and held without bail.

2. I can make the best hamburger in the world. For the good of a noble cause, I will lend you my recipe; you'll find it later in this article.

3. Whimsey is running riot on the hamburger bourse.

I recall a visit I made to a small hamburger place in the Midwest. Friendly-like, I struck up a conversation with the waitress.

"Where's Nan?" I asked.

"Oh, Nan's went," said the waitress. She turned to the cook, a man with a lined face and sad eyes (all hamburger cooks look like Ray Bolger). "How long's it been since Nan's went?"

"She ain't been here for more'n a year," he said.

"I was interested in the name of your sandwich," I explained. "'Nanburger'—that's pretty cute. Now that Nan's gone, I imagine you'll have to change the name, won't you?"

"Can't," said the cook. "When you got a name like mine you stick with Nanburger. Name's Fred Sprockter. You think anybody's going to order a Sprockterburger? But I got the best burgers in town," he added. "I used to be a butcher and I cut my own meat."

"Nanburger" is a comparatively mild example in the roadside lexicon. I have been offered (and, for my sins, have ordered) prime-burgers, circleburgers (the stand was on a traffic circle), beefburgers, bar-b-burgers, chickburgers (cooked by a man named Chick), broil-burgers, chowburgers, charburgers, steakburgers, steerburgers, burn-burgers, chiliburgers, meaties, Beckyburgers, big burgers, tunaburgers, shrimpburgers, lambburgers (made of lamb, taste like ram), huski-burgers, chuckburgers, Wimpies, Wimpyburgers, barbecueburgers, chickenburgers, hi-hat-burgers and nutburgers.

In Carmel-by-the-Sea, California, there is a restaurant advertising a Grubmah—which I take to be a hamburger cooked backward, with results probably no worse than most. In the San Fernando Valley of California, there was once a place which advertised good-earth-burgers. I don't know what they contained. Locusts, probably. You can still buy a lucky-13-burger or a golfburger there. There once was a Meet-the-People-burger, named after a musical revue. There was also an oomphburger, which was a hamburger served with oomph.

Horsemeat-burgers were semipopular during the war years. Some were called whinnyburgers. Still available at various places are rabbit-burgers, porkburgers, sausageburgers, pickleburgers and kirschburgers. There is a Pardburger for dogs. Senator Claghorn once concocted a yamburger for Southerners. You can buy a brunchburger, a kiddie-burger, a jiffyburger, a Mexiburger, a tripleburger, a dogburger, a sea-burger and a fishburger. In Mexico, where *j* is pronounced like *h*, you might try ordering a *j*amburger. What you'd get, I don't know. Probably jam.

A place in California, called The Hippopotamus, features a bour-bonburger. The beef is marinated in 100-proof bourbon before it is broiled. For the life of me, I can't say why, but these things are actually popular.

So are cannibalburgers sold at the same place: raw scrapings from a top round, served on a toasted bun. On the side are onions, relish, barbecue sauce, salt and pepper, and roasted sesame seeds.

Ordering a hamburger in Texas is something like fraternizing with an H-bomb. "You jus' sit there and don' fret," said the cheery girl in a place on the road westbound out of Houston. "Cook'll make the best li'l old hamburger you ever did see."

Well, sir, that hombre just outdid hisself. That was no plain, or-dinary burger like you can get in Boston or Butte. No, sir, it was called a Tay-ex-us-burger, and it must have been close kin to the chiliburger (everyone's related in Texas).

What the waitress laid down in front of me looked like a fair-sized hill covered with snow. Turned out the cook had taken a couple of meat patties and fried them up and then laid them on two half sides of a toasted bun. Then he buried them in a reddish pile of chili con carne and splashed a liberal handful of raw, rarin'-to-go onions on top. Hotter than Vee-suvius in its prime!

"Hurry back now, honey," the waitress said when I left after downing that ole burger and 12 glasses of water. Three days later, as I finally bid the Lone Star State adieu, my mouth was still burning.

Near San Francisco, there is a purveyor of whizzburgers. The slogan of the place is: "A whizzburger every thirty seconds." There is an obvious opening here for a slo-burger—for people who are not in *that* much of a hurry. In the same general neighborhood there is a hamburger place which calls itself The Ground Cow.

Then there's Hamburger Hamlet in Hollywood, where you can buy a Burgundy-wine-burger and read on the menu: "Broil the burger, I pray you, as I pronounced it to you, trippingly on the tongue: but if you burn it, as many broilermen do, I had as lief the physician broil my foods. . . . I would have such a chef whipped for despoiling the art of the caterer. . . ." Which shows what happens when a hamburger dealer gets his hands on Shakespeare.

About that Burgundy-wine-burger: it's served with sautéed walnuts on a bun after the meat has been marinated in wine and broiled. The inventor of this atrocity, Marilyn Lewis, who runs Hamburger Hamlet with her husband, actor Harry Lewis, has since repented. "It's a dreadful thing," she says now. "I just wanted to see how far people would go. And darned if the wine-burger didn't become a sensation. To preserve our self-respect, we took it off the menu, but people still come in little gourmetish groups and order it."

Marilyn, the vixen, is now planning a burger-Stroganoff: a broiled burger dolloped with a sauce made of sour cream and mushrooms. On the strength of her experience with the wine-burger she foresees a great future for it.

And it was only natural, I suppose, that a sandwich so meatily succulent as the hamburger should be simulated by the vegetarians. There are about 4,000,000 vegetarians in the land, and what they eat is a vegetableburger. In it, various vegetable proteins are camouflaged to look like hamburger. A single plant turned out 1,500,000 pounds of the stuff last year.

Even a purist (like me) can excuse a few of the infinite variations on the hamburger theme—say tunaburgers, rabbitburgers and possibly dobbinburgers. Maybe the folks just don't have any good beef and must rely on substitutes. I am not one to laugh at poverty.

But I am also not one to laugh at recipe makers who are foisting a plague of would-be-burgers on a supine public. I ask your forgiveness for quoting this recipe: "Liver-sausage-burger—Brown slices of liver sausage in butter until well browned. Split buns. Toast if desired. Serve hot liver sausage between buttered halves of buns. Add onion, pickle, relish or chili as desired." So far as I know, the perpetrator of this recipe has never been brought to justice.

It's bad enough to be faced with these concoctions on the public ways of the country. But recipe makers, not content with turning the highways into one long assault on the alimentary tract, are urging housewives to commit outrages on the hamburger in the home.

The food sections of the newspapers are probably the worst offenders. Recipe makers of the fourth estate have, within the last few months, offered the following sandwiches, all under the cover name, "burger": 'tateburger, branburger, deviledburger, moreburger (that's what it said: *moreburger*), jumboburger, herbburger (with marjoram, thyme, garlic salt), mushroomburger and bohemianburger. (A bohemianburger includes minced dill pickles, pickled beets and chopped, cooked potatoes.)

There are other offenders, too. I shudder to report that a Hollywood press agent once had a movie starlet put gardenia petals instead of lettuce in a hamburger sandwich. And the possibilities are endless. How about a benzeeburger, with just a dash of Benzedrine? Or a catfishburger-on-a-bagel for Southern song writers who move to New York? Or a pineapple-upside-down-burger?

However, the hamburger gourmets go along with Tom Sims, the man who dreams up the Sunday comic-strip activities of Popeye, the Sailor, Olive Oyl and the rest of the people in the Thimble Theatre. As legal guardian of Popeye's sidekick, J. Wellington Wimpy, the world's number one hamburger addict, Tom tells me: "I have known Wimpy to make whaleburgers, but he resorts to such low practice only in emergencies, and never, to my knowledge, has he ordered a cheeseburger or any of the other so-called burgers served by places which have no consideration for their customers. My guess is he'd rather starve than eat a nutburger."

On the other hand, Wimpy's own hamburger recipe, as quoted by Sims, leaves something to be desired: "Without a penny in your pocket, walk into a café where you're not known. Bang on the table or counter and demand instant service. Order one or more hamburgers. Enjoy your hamburgers in a leisurely fashion. Then get up and talk your way out. Or be thrown out. You must avoid having to wash dishes; insult the waiter and, if necessary, the manager to ensure being ejected by force."

The newest rage to hit the roadside stands is the nineteen-cent hamburger, which comes under a dazzling variety of names usually lifted from the wives of the owners. These places specialize in cooking their Toni-burgers and Nancy-Lou-burgers ahead of time. The most that can be said for them is that their sandwiches are simple: just the grilled meat and a "sauce" containing tomato catsup and sweet relish in equal parts.

Nineteen-cent hamburgers are for people who want to pay nineteen cents for a hamburger. Texas oilmen go to Jack and Charlie's exclusive "21" in New York City, where they are told with some hauteur: "We do not serve hamburger sandwiches. If we did, the recipe would be the same as for the 'Hamburger 21.'"

When a waiter hollers, "Hamburger 21!" in the kitchen of the restaurant, a qualified hamburger chef leaps to his feet, chops up a couple of stalks of celery and mixes the pieces into a quarter pound of ground sirloin. While he's about it, he also mixes in two raw eggs. Then he adds salt and pepper, pats the meat into an oval shape and sautés it gently in butter. Served up with brown sauce and string beans, this dish fetches $3 at "21." The price shows what a good location can do.

Still another variety of hamburger is served up by some San Francisco restaurants named Joe's, New Joe's, Original Joe's and possibly New Original Joe's. These are Italian places, and they feature a hamburger consisting of a hefty chunk of ground meat with built-in onions. The chefs press the onions into a great rectangular patty of the meat, grill it and then slam it into a section of a loaf of French bread which has been split horizontally. You eat it either with a knife and fork or by hand. That's usually all there is to the sandwich, just the bread and the onioned meat, although sometimes a dash of catsup is added. You have to be careful with this concoction or the sharp crust of the bread will lacerate the roof of your mouth.

This Italian version, while tasty and a worthy try, is still not a real hamburger. That dish, I was told, was invented in the Pennsylvania

Dutch country. The way I heard it, a transplanted German came in one night from painting hex signs on his barns.

"Achtung!" he said to his wife. "Why ist der meaten geboilen day in and day outen? Ist tasten lousy the meaten geboilen."

"Look who getalken ist," his *Frau* replied. "Herr Geniusen mit Thomas Edison, the inventen feller. Out of mein kitchen gegetten." The good woman, however, stopped boiling the beef. She put it through a chopper and cooked it like steak. It was a dish of unsurpassed succulence and flavor. As it is to this day. Her husband was overjoyed.

"Ist das nicht free from bonen?" he asked.

"Yah. Das ist free from bonen," she replied.

"Ist das nicht good for chewen?"

"Yah. Das ist vergut for chewen."

"Ist das nicht ein tasten wallop?"

"Yah. Das ist ein tasten wallop."

As fame of the new delicacy spread, scores of names were suggested for it. "Why not call it 'Hamburg Steak' after Hamburg, Germany, which has the largest port in continental Europe?" someone asked, and the logic of this idea won the day.

Almost immediately, some unheralded benefactor put the steak between buns and thus invented the Hamburg sandwich. (Twenty minutes later, someone else changed the name from "Hamburg" to "Hamburger"—thus beginning the tampering which has been going on ever since.)

Loving hands and clever brains combined over the years to fashion subtle improvements in this succulent supersandwich. Unremitting research by public-spirited bakers led to the development of a magnificent bun. A bun flushed with the golden brown of the autumn leaves. A bright bun, a light bun, subtly sweetened, yet strong enough to bear honorably its precious cargo of savory beef, lettuce as crisp and cold as the ice film on a mountain lake, and the rich, ruby red of sliced tomato.

Most people never learn to make a proper hamburger. The pity is that most of them actually think there is nothing to learn. Now, with me it was different. As a youth, I served a long apprenticeship on the beach in my native village, Santa Monica, California, under the tutelage of Percy H. Baden. For my money, he was probably the best hamburger maker who ever lived. He used to charge fifteen cents for his hamburgers when his competitors sold theirs for a dime. That will give you an idea of the edge his hamburgers had on the field. It will also give you an idea of how long ago it was.

Baden was a fine man, and he had great respect for the hamburger sandwich. He used nothing but lean round steak, of course. He ground it himself. He also had some gadgets which looked like those things men smooth down concrete with. His were made of aluminum lined with asbestos, and he laid them, ever so gently, on top of his buns so they would toast evenly on the griddle.

He also had an oversize wooden pestle, flat on the bottom. He used it to press out the round patties on waxed paper for the sandwiches. Then he had a board with a hole the exact size of a hamburger bun in it; this was sort of a jig to ensure a standard cut when the buns were sliced. Buns come already sliced these days, of course, and Baden's gadgets are no longer necessary to make the world's best hamburger.

Here is my recipe for that best of all hamburgers. It leans heavily on the original Baden patents.

A Good Hamburger

Ground round steak or ground chuck
Buns
Crisp lettuce
Tomatoes in slices
Mayonnaise
Butter
Sweet relish
Salt and pepper
Onions—optional (can be sautéed separately or sliced raw)
One No. 2 can of sliced peaches unopened
Waxed paper, cut into six-inch squares

Have everything ready; you have to move fast when your hamburgers are nearing their final perfection.

First scoop out enough meat for a single patty. An ice-cream scoop can be used, although I like a little larger patty. Don't use too much meat, however, because the hamburger should have a good balance of flavors.

Put the meat ball on a piece of waxed paper. Cover with another. Smack this with the bottom of the can of peaches. Not too hard. When you remove the upper wax paper, you will have what appears to be a facsimile of a Japanese flag. The patty should be about a half inch thick and about four inches in diameter. Be sure to count your buns.

Beginners sometimes are carried away with the shaping and stamp out dozens of meat patties and then find they have only six or eight buns.

If you have a griddle, you're in business. Otherwise, heat two frying pans, big ones—one for the meat and the other for the buns. Bacon fat is fine for the meat pan. Get it hot and slap in the meat patty, being careful to retain the wax paper in your hands. Cook the hamburgers quickly. Meanwhile, heat the bun pan, a little hotter than medium. Don't put any fat in the bun pan. Put half a bun in this pan, split side down. Then—and this is a step of paramount importance, the very heart of the Baden secret—press gently down on the bun with your fingers and swish it around the pan. Repeat with each half bun as it goes into the pan for toasting. This swooshing around glazes the face of the bun. And it makes a tremendous difference in the taste of the final delectable product. I don't know why, but it does.

When the buns are evenly browned—the split sides will have the color of a properly done hot cake at this point—remove them from the pan and quickly butter them. Spread mayonnaise on the top half of the bun and add as much sweet relish as you want. Slap the cooked hamburger, which has been salted and peppered only at the last moment of cooking, on the bottom half of the bun.

If you have sautéed onions, spread them on top of the meat. If not, embellish the meat with a slice of tomato and then add the raw onion slice. Then the lettuce. Some people prefer dill pickle instead of sweet relish. That is optional. But no mustard. Mustard is for hot dogs. And the first lady who puts in any minced pickled beets is a dead pigeon.

Finally, place the top half of the bun over everything. Eat the hamburger. You will find it is the best hamburger in town. Especially if you used to be a butcher and cut your own meat.

MR. FRISBIE LEADS THE WAY

SCOTT CORBETT

Mr. Frisbie said it was a swell day, so how about getting together with the neighbors and taking a ride in the country? He said he would bring the gas, the Gunnisons could bring the tires, and the Baxters could furnish the car.

Mrs. Frisbie said no sir. She said she had a better plan for their Sunday outing. She said they were going to have it all alone. She said Nature would furnish the hills and dales and they would furnish the feet.

Her husband said did she mean they should take a hike?

She said well, why not? She said after all, what was the good of living only 10 minutes' walk from Rockhill Park if they didn't take advantage of the fact once in a while?

Mr. Frisbie said aw, Rockhill Park. He said they had driven through it so much he knew it like the back of his hand, so what fun would it be to walk around there? He said what he would like would be to plunge into the uncharted wilds some place way out a couple of miles from town.

After some discussion they compromised in the usual manner and went to Rockhill Park.

When they got to the edge of the park they decided they might as well cut through the woods over to the main shelter house, which would give them about a mile's walk for a starter.

After a while Mr. Frisbie said it was time they were reaching the shelter house. Twenty minutes later he said so again. Twenty minutes after that he said where the devil was that shelter house?

His wife said him and his uncharted wilds. She said if he asked her, it looked as if they were lost on the back of his hand, which was what he had said he knew Rockhill Park as well as.

While they were talking there was a crashing in the underbush near by and a Boy Scout troop went trooping past not more than 50 yards away.

Mr. Frisbie said ah-ha, all they had to do now was sneak along behind and follow the Boy Scouts to the shelter house. Mrs. Frisbie said how did he know they were going there, and he said where else did they ever go in Rockhill Park? He said had she ever seen the shelter house when it wasn't swarming with Boy Scouts?

Just then the scoutmaster spied them through the trees. He said company halt, one, two, and walked over to speak to the Frisbies. He said how did they do, might he ask where they were going? Mr. Frisbie said why, to the shelter house. He said splendid, because he would not have the boys know it for anything, but frankly he was lost.

The Boy Scouts eventually got both the scoutmaster and the Frisbies safely to the shelter house.

CASEY AT THE BAT

ERNEST LAWRENCE THAYER

It looked extremely rocky for the Mudville nine that day,
The score stood four to six with but an inning left to play.
And so, when Cooney died at first, and Burrows did the same,
A pallor wreathed the features of the patrons of the game.
A straggling few got up to go, leaving there the rest,
With that hope which springs eternal within the human breast.
For they thought if only Casey could get a whack at that,
They'd put up even money with Casey at the bat.

But Flynn preceded Casey, and likewise so did Blake,
And the former was a pudding and the latter was a fake;
So on that stricken multitude a death-like silence sat,
For there seemed but little chance of Casey's getting to the bat.
But Flynn let drive a single to the wonderment of all,
And the much despised Blakey tore the cover off the ball,
And when the dust had lifted and they saw what had occurred,
There was Blakey safe on second, and Flynn a-hugging third.

Then from the gladdened multitude went up a joyous yell,
It bounded from the mountain top and rattled in the dell,
It struck upon the hillside, and rebounded on the flat,
For Casey, mighty Casey, was advancing to the bat.
There was ease in Casey's manner as he stepped into his place,
There was pride in Casey's bearing and a smile on Casey's face,
And when responding to the cheers he lightly doffed his hat,
No stranger in the crowd could doubt, 'twas Casey at the bat.

Ten thousand eyes were on him as he rubbed his hands with dirt,
Five thousand tongues applauded as he wiped them on his shirt;
And while the writhing pitcher ground the ball into his hip—
Defiance gleamed from Casey's eyes—and a sneer curled Casey's lip.
And now the leather-covered sphere came hurtling through the air,
And Casey stood a-watching it in haughty grandeur there;
Close by the sturdy batsman the ball unheeded sped—
"That hain't my style," said Casey—"Strike one," the Umpire said.
From the bleachers black with people there rose a sullen roar,
Like the beating of the storm waves on a stern and distant shore,

"Kill him! kill the Umpire!" shouted some one from the stand—
And it's likely they'd have done it had not Casey raised his hand.
With a smile of Christian charity great Casey's visage shone,
He stilled the rising tumult and he bade the game go on;
He signalled to the pitcher and again the spheroid flew,
But Casey still ignored it and the Umpire said, "Strike two."
"Fraud!" yelled the maddened thousands,
And the echo answered "Fraud."
But one scornful look from Casey and the audience was awed;
They saw his face grow stern and cold; they saw his muscles strain,
And they knew that Casey would not let that ball go by again.
The sneer is gone from Casey's lip; his teeth are clenched with hate,
He pounds with cruel violence his bat upon the plate;
And now the pitcher holds the ball, and now he lets it go,
And now the air is shattered by the force of Casey's blow.
Oh! somewhere in this favored land the sun is shining bright,
The band is playing somewhere, and somewhere hearts are light.
And somewhere men are laughing, and somewhere children shout;
But there is no joy in Mudville—mighty Casey has "Struck Out."

HOW NOT TO DO-IT-YOURSELF

EUGENE RACHLIS

America being, among other things, the land of the articulate mi-
nority, it should come as no great surprise to anyone, except, perhaps,
a couple of million do-it-yourself addicts, that there is a sizable group
of men about the nation who not only do not do-it-themselves, but
who have never done-it-themselves, and have no intention of ever
doing-it-themselves. What's more, they wouldn't even care if the
whole do-it-yourself movement did-itself-in.

Members of what may be called the get-others-to-do-it-for-you
school come from as many walks of life as the do-it-yourselfers. They
include cab drivers, statesmen, teachers, business men, housewives,
newspaper men, baseball players and people. Although membership
is wide open, there are no small boys or newly-weds included. This
may be attributed to inexperience.

The anti-do-it-yourself movement includes many angry men, perhaps the most vehement being the one who is not so much against the achievement of the person who did-it-himself, as the sound of his voice as he talks about it.

"Nowadays," he says, "a man makes a chair, a desk, a house, puts a washer in a leaky faucet, builds a kayak, paints a crib, he spends the rest of his life and yours telling you about it. I wouldn't mind if they did-it-themselves. Live and let live. But why do they have to talk-about-it-themselves? And why, oh why, must they talk in hyphens?

"The minute he finishes his job he shuts down his turret lathe, calls in all his friends and neighbors and tells them all-about-it. What size adze-he-used, how much money-he-saved, and if he gets real metaphysical, mainly after two or three drinks which he made-them-himself, how the decline of the skilled craftsmen since colonial days is what's wrong with America.

"Me, I like skilled craftsmen. I also like unskilled craftsmen. Mainly because they never talked about their work. Of course, maybe their mouths were full of nails all the time and they couldn't talk. But they *were* quiet."

Another anti-do-it-yourself man does not object to talk per se; it is its pernicious influence on those near to him.

"So they talk, talk, talk," he says. "And your wife hears the talk and she wants to know why you can't save us a lot of money and maybe build a whole set of living room furniture because, God knows, the stuff they're selling nowadays just isn't any good and the prices they get for it is a scandal and for the price of a hammer and a saw and the material we could do much better by ourselves, and it would be relaxing and would give you something to do week-ends instead of sitting around drinking beer in your bare feet and listening to the ball game."

It may be significant that many of those now most fervently opposed to the do-it-yourself movement at one time did do-it-themselves. Now their power saws are found in the same closet as their darkroom equipment, the tennis racquets, the bamboo fishing rods and the Monopoly game.

"The last time I did-it-myself," one man said, "was when a fuse blew in our apartment soon after we were married. I unscrewed the fuse and put a penny in the hole and screwed the old fuse back. The lights went on right away.

"Of course, I've been told since that this represents a fire hazard. I've never been to the fuse box since. Always call an electrician."

A growing body of opinion holds to the view that, in the current economic situation, there is a lot of money to be saved not by doing-it-yourself but by calling in an electrician, a carpenter or a plumber when there is work to do around the house, or that buying a boat from a boat builder and furniture from Grand Rapids is like investing in Government bonds.

"I go to a store," says this branch of the anti-do-it-yourselfers, "I look around and pick the size and the color of the furniture I want. I make a small down payment. A few days later the stuff is delivered and we're using it."

"You do-it-yourself and, first, you get yourself a bunch of fruit boxes. That's for people to sit on while you are doing-it-yourself. Then, you invest in a lot of tools—a saw, a hammer, a power this and a power that. By the time you have set up a workshop so that you think maybe everything will go just right, the kids are screaming when can they ask their friends over to sit around the living room. They'd be ashamed to have their friends sit on fruit boxes.

"You order wood. It costs as much as a suite of furniture delivered. A few wrong turns with the saw, a power-drill with a mind of its own, and you've had it. You order more wood and naturally they're out of the exact kind you ordered last time and have in now something which nearly matches it, which it doesn't, and it costs a little bit more, which it does.

"The money invested by now would furnish a whole house. You could read the Encyclopaedia Britannica from A to Zygo in the time you've wasted and you'd still be friends with your wife and children, which I understand is the basis of good family relations."

Many men who do not do-it-themselves are quite frank in acknowledging that they are very unhandy men-around-the-house. Most of these men can be found in the middle-upper levels of the sciences, the arts and the professions. Rather than undo-it-themselves they would much prefer to call in a professional.

In temperament the man who does not do-it-himself is more gentle, more gregarious, more at ease with himself and his environment than the man who does-it-himself. When he is your host, you can safely discuss the weather, Faulkner, Willie Mays or children's summer camps. He does not have, as does the do-it-yourself man, the abstract look of one who is not really listening but merely waiting for the op-

"Nine times six is seventy-two—now will you stop bothering
Mother while she's working on the budget?"

portunity to slip in something like "By the way, notice the finish on
that little end-table there. Well, I was mixing * * *." And he's off in
a world where 220 AC gets involved with blueprints, the relative merits of cast iron and brass legs for a foam rubber sofa, gradations of
sandpaper and whose varnish is better than whose paint.

The let-others-do-it-for-me man is not excitable. He views his world
of factory-made furniture with complete calm. To a wifely suggestion
that perhaps the furniture needs upholstering he can, with infinite patience, indicate the yellow pages of the telephone directory under "U."
The sight of a hardware store does not move him. The whirring of
fractional horsepower motors may give him a mild headache, but nothing that aspirin won't cure.

It is only when reminded of recent sessions with a man who did-it-
himself and talked-about-it, or when too frequently exposed to the
home-made boats, bookshelves, desks and beds of others, that he may
express himself with feeling. At times like these his vocabulary is
limited. "Ahhhhh," he will say. No hyphens.

SCORE THIS, GUISEPPE!

SCOTT CORBETT

One thing I have never understood is how workmen in the building trades can go about their business so calmly. When I build or install anything, every moment is charged with drama. No Italian tenor was ever more excitable than I, ever lived more intensely, felt more keenly, suffered more miserably. Talk about running the gamut of the emotions! Compared to the four-lane jobs I run up and down on, the average gamut is a mere mice trail.

When I had finished insulating our attic recently, I realized that what had happened was too big to be material for a mere Great American Novel. It had a sweep to it and a violently tragic quality which was made to order for opera. All I had to do was get it set to some somber, brooding music shot through with flashes of fire, and the Metropolitan Opera House would be the next stop. Was ever situation more fraught with overtones of that great theme, the tragic struggle of Man against Fate? I can see it clearly now as a gripping tragic opera, 'Una Muova Falsitta,' ('One False Move').

After a brief, morbid overture, the curtain rises to disclose a gloomy attic. A trapdoor is pushed up (the Metropolitan could light this thing beautifully) and the tenor, Don Scotto, climbs cautiously up into the attic carrying a single light bulb on an extension cord. His light discloses several rolls of balsam wool insulation and some tools he has previously brought up.

He looks around the vast reaches of the dismal attic and sings the touching aria, 'I attico aparechi tutte enormi' ('This job looks tougher now than it did when I let that salesman sell me the insulation'). For a moment he is despairing, but then he plucks up his courage and sings the jaunty 'Bravado me non deserto che dice magazino' ('Remember that article in Beautiful Homes that told how easy it was') and he sets to work.

Almost before he has started, however, his wife, Donna Elisabeta, thrusts her head through the trapdoor. In a brilliant coloratura showpiece she announces, 'Don Roberto telefono importa' ('He says it's important'). A passionate duet follows in which Don Scotto refuses to stop and climb down to talk to Don Roberto, while Donna Elisabeta

MARY GIBSON, COLLIER'S

"Someone in Tourist Class whistled at me!"

---

insists he should. When he threatens to stab her with a pair of tin snips she flees, and then Don Scotto, repentant, rushes down through the trapdoor and is heard falling off the stepladder as the curtain descends.

After a brief overture reminiscent of the opening one, except that it probes even more deeply into the wellsprings of human misery, the curtain rises on Act Two. Back once more in the attic, Don Scotto broods darkly on Don Roberto's telephone call, which was not really as important as he pretended. Then, once again, he sets to work.

What follows is all action. It cries out for wild and exciting music with plenty of cymbals and kettle drums. Don Scotto lays boards on the cross-beams and inches forward on his stomach, under the rafters, straining forward to fasten the far end of a strip of insulation with his staple gun. Sweat pours off his forehead, his jaw works, his lips move in silent prayer ('O Dio mi bendo silento!'). His eyes blaze with excitement as he presses his gun against the insulation batt flange, then grow wide with horror as he makes a grim discovery— he is out of ammunition! And the box of staples is out of reach. He has to inch back to them and reload lying on his side. His voice breaks as he sings the plaintive 'Buorno non e necesario!' ('Why was I born?')

At this moment, Don Roberto arrives outside with a henchman, Don Basso. They are heard chaffing Donna Elisabeta, and Don Roberto begins the mocking 'I pagliacci credo savecchi?' ('Is that clown trying to save money again by doing it himself?') Don Scotto soon hurls defiance at Don Roberto out the attic window and the four voices blend in a quartet which is unquestionably the high point of the opera. Then Don Roberto and his follower depart, and Don Scotto vows vengeance in the terrible 'Trumpetto I Uno!' ('Next time we play bridge I'll trump his ace!')

Remember that all this is no mere contrived and implausible libretto such as most operas are burdened with. It is substantially, to all intents and purposes, exactly what happened to me. The great moment, of course, the rush of tragedy which had been impending all along, came in that instant when my foot finally slipped off a beam and went through the thin ceiling below. ('Una muova falsitta!') I reeled back from the horrid sight of the guest room floor as seen from the attic, and my final anguished cry (the curtain would of course fall at this point) was alone enough to inspire any composer.

Verdi did this sort of thing awfully well. I wish he were still around where I could get hold of him.

Intelligence Quotient:

YOU SEE BUT YOU DON'T OBSERVE

Tell your family that you are going to mention twenty-four different articles which they see and handle every day of their lives, yet there is not one of them who can answer all the questions about these articles correctly. Of course there will be a great deal of guessing done and it is perfectly fair provided that they guess the right answer. Obviously, the winner will be the one who answers most of these questions correctly.

1. Which way does the Jack of Hearts face?
2. Whose head is on the 1¢ stamp?
3. About how long is a cigarette?
4. About how long is a dollar bill?
5. How many matches are there in an ordinary "book" of matches?
6. What are the dimensions of a piece of typewriting paper?
7. Which way do you turn a radiator handle to turn the steam on?
8. How many prongs has a table fork?
9. What is pictured on the back of a $5 bill?
10. How wide is a newspaper column?
11. What are the colors of the auto license plates in your state?
12. How long is the standard make of writing pencil (approx.)?
13. Are the cutting edges of a pair of scissors straight or slightly curved?
14. Is there any dark blue in a match or candle flame?
15. Are the divisions on your radio dial all equal?
16. What kind of 6 is there on a man's wrist watch?
17. Is the postmark used to cancel the stamp?
18. In your telephone dial what letters are above the 4?
19. Is the coin return on a pay telephone on the right side?

20. Approximately how far apart are the two rails in a car track?
21. What color stripe is directly under the blue in our flag?
22. Are the propellers in an airplane in front or in back?
23. How many shoelace holes are there in a man's shoe?
24. Approximately what is the diameter of a silver quarter?

ANSWERS

1. To the right
2. Benjamin Franklin
3. 2¾ inches
4. 6⅝ inches
5. 20
6. 8½ × 11 inches
7. To your left (counterclockwise)
8. 4
9. The Lincoln Memorial
10. 2 inches
11.
12. 7½ inches
13. Slightly bent
14. Yes
15. No
16. There is no 6 there
17. Sometimes
18. G H I in New York
19. Left
20. 4 feet 8½ inches
21. White
22. Front
23. 12
24. 1 inch

MATCH 'EM UP

BORIS RANDOLPH

Match one word with another below and form a longer word each time. For instance: HORN matched with SHOE forms SHOE-HORN. COW matched with BOY forms COWBOY. All the words must be used up.

1. APPLE	9. BOOT	17. CAR	25. FIRE
2. ASH	10. BOTTLE	18. COW	26. FLOWER
3. BACK	11. BOW	19. CROW	27. FLY
4. BAG	12. BOY	20. DOG	28. FOOT
5. BAR	13. BRICK	21. DRUM	29. HAND
6. BAT	14. BRUSH	22. EAR	30. HANDLE
7. BED	15. BUG	23. EGG	31. HEAD
8. BOARD	16. CAKE	24. FEATHER	32. HEART

33. HOOD	45. NECK	57. POUND	69. SUN
34. HORN	46. NOTE	58. QUARTER	70. SWORD
35. HORSE	47. NUT	59. RAIN	71. TAIL
36. HOUSE	48. PAN	60. ROCK	72. THUMB
37. JACK	49. PEA	61. SAW	73. TOE
38. KNOT	50. PICK	62. SCREW	74. TOOTH
39. LAP	51. PIG	63. SHIP	75. TOP
40. LEG	52. PIN	64. SHOE	76. WATCH
41. LIGHT	53. PLANT	65. STAR	77. WHEEL
42. LINE	54. PLAY	66. STICK	78. WING
43. LIP	55. POCKET	67. STREET	79. WINK
44. NAIL	56. POT	68. STRING	80. YARD

ANSWERS

1-37 APPLEJACK
7-60 BEDROCK
9-40 BOOTLEG
10-45 BOTTLENECK
13-6 BRICKBAT
18-12 COWBOY
19-5 CROWBAR
20-76 DOGWATCH
22-21 EARDRUM
23-53 EGGPLANT
25-15 FIREBUG
27-77 FLYWHEEL
28-46 FOOTNOTE
29-4 HANDBAG
31-42 HEADLINE
32-68 HEARTSTRING
33-79 HOODWINK
39-78 LAPWING
41-36 LIGHTHOUSE
43-66 LIPSTICK
48-30 PANHANDLE
49-47 PEANUT
50-55 PICKPOCKET
51-71 PIGTAIL
52-24 PINFEATHER
56-2 POTASH
57-16 POUNDCAKE
58-3 QUARTERBACK
59-11 RAINBOW
61-35 SAWHORSE
63-80 SHIPYARD
64-34 SHOEHORN
65-8 STARBOARD
67-17 STREETCAR
69-26 SUNFLOWER
70-54 SWORDPLAY
72-62 THUMBSCREW
73-44 TOENAIL
74-14 TOOTHBRUSH
75-38 TOPKNOT

A PROBLEM IN RADAR

BORIS RANDOLPH

Each way you can spell the word RADAR on the screen below constitutes a RADAR signal. Beginning with each R, and going in every possible direction, how many signals (spellings) of RADAR can you get?

R	A	D	A	R
A	D	A	R	A
D	A	R	A	D
A	R	A	D	A
R	A	D	A	R

ANSWER

172

FAKE BETS

Fake bets are the most liable to remain unchallenged. On the other hand, players who can guess ways of out-witting the proponents of the bets may themselves win, if they get a favorable decision from the judges.

A variety of FAKE BETS is included herewith, together with the "catch" for each. Think up others yourself, as you go along; but be careful to choose bets that others won't catch you at, in case you are challenged!

1. I bet I can drink the contents of this glass while the glass is under this hat, without touching the hat.
2. I bet I can hold something in my hand for three minutes that you can't hold in your hand for thirty seconds.
3. I bet I can drop a lump of sugar into a cup of coffee without wetting the sugar.
4. I bet I can turn an egg completely around in an egg-cup without touching the egg.
5. I bet I can hand you any card which you continually think of out of your own pack of cards. You may shuffle the cards as much as you wish.

6. I bet I can draw a circle of not more than 3′ in diameter around you where you are now standing and you won't dare to get out of it!

7. I bet I can place two people so close together that they will be less than an inch apart yet they won't be able to touch one another.

8. I bet I can show you all something which you have never seen before and will never see again.

9. I bet I can put two different objects under two different hats, eat both objects and place them under the hats again.

10. I bet I can name a large animal that you all know that has four legs and flies.

ANSWERS

10. Name a horse.

9. Put two crackers under two different hats, eat both crackers and then put each hat on separately. The eaten objects (crackers) will, of course, be under the two hats.

8. Open up a walnut, show the nut to your audience, then eat the nut.

7. One person is on one side of the door and the other is on the other side. Both people leaning against the door.

6. If you draw a circle of chalk around the top of a man's pants you will be drawing a circle around him which he will not dare to get out of.

5. Of course you can. If you keep on handing him the pack of cards long enough, he is bound to receive the card he is thinking of. In handing him the full pack, you are naturally including his card, and hence living up to your claim.

4. This is done by placing the egg in an old-fashioned egg cup and blowing very hard at the bottom of the egg, causing air to get in between the egg and the cup and turn the egg around.

3. You can, if you just put uncooked dry coffee in the cup.

2. The thing you hold in your hand is an ice cube in a handkerchief. You can hold this comfortably for three minutes, and if anyone wants to try it, hand him the cube without the handkerchief.

1. Tilt the hat over to the side so that the glass of liquid is still under it. Suck liquid out through a straw.

HERE'S TEN BUCKS

BORIS RANDOLPH

The answers to the questions below are all words beginning with BUCK. BUCKle down to the job of finding them and see if you can make a perfect score.

1. What's a good cloth for binding a book?
2. An old favorite among songs is "The Old Oaken" what?
3. What can you call a cowboy besides a cowboy?
4. In what palace in London does the Queen of England live?
5. A good flour for pancakes is what?
6. What kind of ammunition are you likely to find on a hunter?
7. Ohio is sometimes known as what State?
8. What kind of carriage did some people ride in before the automobile was invented?
9. What did people sometimes make suits out of in pioneer days?
10. In the Middle Ages a man might defend himself with a sword and what kind of shield?

ANSWERS

7. BUCKeye
1. BUCKram
2. BUCKet
3. BUCKaroo
4. BUCKingham
5. BUCKwheat
6. BUCKshot
8. BUCKboard
9. BUCKskin
10. BUCKler

IT'S ALWAYS 1089!

Take any number of three digits (the first and last digit must differ by more than 1). Reverse the first and last digits and subtract one from the other. Now reverse the first and last digits and add one to the other. The answer will always be 1089!

Example

Take 638 638
Reverse the first and last digits 836
Take one from the other 198
Reverse the first and last digits and add 891
  The answer is 1089   ‾‾‾‾‾
                                  1089

This will work for any number from 100 to 1000 except those ending in 00 or those whose difference between the first and last digit is 1 or zero, viz: 736, 505, 978, 372, 666, etc.

Try this a few times and watch it always come out 1089!

FAMOUS SIMILES

Everyone knows such expressions as "Red as a beet", "Brown as a berry", "Deaf as a post", etc. In this game, the questioner suggests the word with all the trimmings added to it. Instead of saying "Brown", he should say "Brown as a ———". Instead of saying "Red", he should say "Red as a ———", or "Fit as a ———", etc. Here is a list of 50 trite similes that have been done to death in conversation:

Deaf as a post	Funny as a circus
Dumb as an ox	Happy as a lark
Bright as a dollar	Hard as a rock
Smart as a whip	Huge as an elephant
Blind as a bat	Light as a feather
Brown as a berry	Mad as a hatter
Busy as a bee	Mean as a miser
Clean as a whistle	Modest as a violet
Clear as a bell	Neat as a pin
Crazy as a loon	Nervous as a cat
Cross as a stick	Playful as a kitten
Dead as a doornail	Poor as a church mouse
Dry as a bone	Pretty as a picture
Fair as a rose	Proud as a peacock
Fat as a pig	Pure as a lily
Fit as a fiddle	Quick as a wink
Flat as a pancake	Quiet as a mouse
Fleet as a deer	Red as a beet

Sharp as a razor
Slippery as an eel
Slow as a tortoise
Sly as a fox
Sound as a bell
Sour as a lemon
Stiff as a board

Still as a mouse
Strong as an ox
Stubborn as a mule
Swift as an eagle
Thin as a rail
Tight as a drum

FOUND IN MARRIAGE

BORIS RANDOLPH

All of the words defined below can be formed from the letters contained in the word MARRIAGE. How many of them can you find? You may use a letter in any word only as often as it occurs in MARRIAGE itself. The number in parenthesis indicates the number of letters in the word called for.

1. A mother (2)
2. The man of the house (2)
3. A soldier (2)
4. A jewel (3)
5. An objective in life (3)
6. Something to put around a loved one (3)
7. Just any old tune (3)
8. The sign of Aries (3)
9. The edge of things (3)
10. Anger (3)
11. To sin (3)
12. How old you are (3)
13. To bring up (4)
14. Something two can play together (4)
15. Another form of anger (4)
16. An opera tune (4)
17. A word that means unusual (4)
18. An Arabian prince (4)
19. The Wise Men attending the birth of Christ (4)
20. A picture or likeness (5)
21. A girl named Margaret (5)

22. A girl named Mary (5)
23. Another girl named Mary (5)
24. Work-dirt (5)
25. A poet (5)

ANSWERS

1. MA	6. ARM	11. ERR	16. ARIA	21. MARGE
2. MR	7. AIR	12. AGE	17. RARE	22. MARIE
3. CI	8. RAM	13. REAR	18. EMIR	23. MARIA
4. GEM	9. RIM	14. GAME	19. MAGI	24. CRIME
5. AIM	10. IRE	15. RAGE	20. IMAGE	25. RIMER

SIMPLE ARITHMETIC

BORIS RANDOLPH

Here are three plus signs and two minus signs:

$$+ + + - -$$

Insert them in the row of figures below so that the answer will be right:

$$1\ 2\ 3\ 4\ 5\ 6\ 7\ 8\ 9 = 10$$

ANSWER

$$1 + 2 + 34 - 5 + 67 - 89 = 10$$

CALLING ALL CABS!

BORIS RANDOLPH

The answer to each question below is a word beginning with CAB. Get them all right and there's nothing wrong with your voCABulary.

1. What is a Spanish gentleman called?
2. A two-wheeled, two-seated, one-horse carriage is a what?
3. What do the men who advise the President form?
4. What famous navigator was a contemporary of Columbus?
5. A night club is also a what?
6. What generally brings up the rear on a freight-train?

7. What is a bedroom on a ship called?
8. An overseas telegram is often alluded to as what?
9. What is cole slaw made of?
10. Who wrote "Jurgen"?

ANSWERS

1. CABallero
2. CABriolet
3. CABinet
4. CABot
5. CABaret
6. CABoose
7. CABin
8. CABle
9. CABbage
10. CABell

ONE-WAY TRIP AROUND THE WORLD

BORIS RANDOLPH

Find the right starting letter, then keep counting a certain number from West to East for the succeeding letters and the round trip above will spell out twenty stopping places.

SOLUTION

Starting with the H in the upper left-hand part of the circle and counting seven every time you get HAWAII, ALASKA, MEXICO, CUBA, PERU, HAITI, CHILE, BOLIVIA, WALES, SPAIN, ITALY, EGYPT, SYRIA, IRAN, INDIA, TIBET, BURMA, SIAM, JAVA and KOREA.

ANIMALGRAMS

BORIS RANDOLPH

Add the three-letter animals below to the three-letter words beside them and form a six-letter word each time. You may rearrange the letters as you wish.

1. FOX plus ROD
2. GNU plus LEO
3. ELK plus COD
4. EWE plus BAR
5. COW plus EBB
6. CAT plus MOB
7. HOG plus TUB
8. APE plus SIR
9. DOG plus RUN
10. RAT plus SUN
11. YAK plus NEE
12. RAM plus ACE
13. SOW plus DIM
14. ROE plus ANT
15. PIG plus VAN

ANSWERS

1. OXFORD
2. LOUNGE
3. LOCKED
4. BEWARE
5. COBWEB
6. COMBAT
7. BOUGHT
8. PRAISE
9. GROUND
10. SATURN
11. YANKEE
12. CAMERA
13. WISDOM
14. ORNATE
15. PAVING

WE'VE GOT YOUR NUMBER

(Par: 5 min.)

The list below is made up of famous numbers. Each number has a definite meaning or significance. How many can you identify?

A. 5280
B. 32
C. 1066
D. 57
E. 40 and 8
F. 32.2
G. 1776
H. 3.1416

I. 7–11
J. 98.6
K. 99.44
L. 1492
M. 186,000
N. 212
O. 360
P. 2.80

ANSWERS

P. The par value of one pound Sterling, in terms of American dollars.
O. The number of degrees in a circle.
N. The boiling point of water—Fahrenheit.
M. The approximate speed of light in miles per second.
L. The date of Columbus' sailing.
K. Ivory Soap's purity.
J. The normal temperature of the human body.
I. Important numbers in a crap game.
H. Pi.
G. The date of the signing of the Declaration of Independence.
F. The acceleration of gravity.
E. Forty men and eight horses—French box car.
D. Heinz' Varieties.
C. The date of the Battle of Hastings.
B. The freezing point of water—Fahrenheit.
A. The number of feet in a mile.

LET'S PICK A FEW FLOWERS

BORIS RANDOLPH

Fifteen of the names given below are the names of flowers; the rest are not. Can you pick the flowers?

1. ECONOMY	16. SYRINGA
2. THRUSHBILL	17. VENUS FLY-TRAP
3. THRIFT	18. SYNCOPE
4. PHLOX	19. COCKATEEL
5. PRETTY JOE	20. PRISCILLA
6. BELL BUTTON	21. LARKSPUR
7. COLUMBINE	22. CROCUS
8. FIELDWIST	23. EDELWEISS
9. LUPINE	24. LAPIN
10. FELIX	25. ARBUTUS
11. HAREBELL	26. ALEMBIC
12. ANEMONE	27. NEMESIS
13. BUG-CATCHER	28. VERONICA
14. SWEET WILLIAM	29. NARCISSUS
15. PIERROT	30. TUMBLE-DOWN

ANSWERS

The flowers are 3, 4, 7, 9, 11, 12, 14, 16, 17, 21, 22, 23, 25, 28, 29.

DIZZY MAID'S SHOPPING LIST

BORIS RANDOLPH

Hankies, gloves, hose, compact, lipstick, together	$12.50
Hankies, gloves, hose, compact, boy friend, together	12.00
Hankies, gloves, hose, lipstick, boy friend, together	11.00
Hankies, gloves, compact, lipstick, boy friend, together	10.00
Hankies, hose, compact, lipstick, boy friend, together	10.50
Hose, gloves, compact, lipstick, boy friend, together	11.50

A dizzy maid with a method all her own for keeping accounts made out the above shopping list. Can you tell from the figures how much she spent on her boy friend, and, for that matter, on each of the other items she purchased?

ANSWER

Only $1.00 for the boy friend, but $1.50 for the lipstick, $2.00 for hankies, $2.50 for a compact, $3.00 for gloves, and $3.50 for hosiery. If you add up the totals and divide by 5, the number of times each item is repeated, you get $13.50, the cost of all 6 items. Subtract from this each total for 5 items and you get the cost of the missing 6th item on each line.

A CARNIVAL OF WORDS

BORIS RANDOLPH

All of the words defined below can be formed from the letters contained in the word CARNIVAL. How many of them can you find? You may use a letter in any word only as often as it occurs in CARNIVAL itself. The number in parenthesis indicates the number of letters in the word called for.

1. Atmosphere (3)
2. Moving truck (3)
3. Automobile (3)
4. Bow (3)
5. Italian street (3)
6. Metal container (3)
7. Social group (4)
8. Downpour (4)
9. Peruvian Indian (4)
10. Piece of Italian money (4)
11. Train track (4)
12. Abel's brother (4)
13. Opera tune (4)
14. Small bottle (4)
15. Wood fastener (4)
16. Liquid rock (4)
17. Persia (4)
18. Prevaricator (4)
19. Animal's bed (4)
20. Futile (4)
21. Waterway (5)
22. Competitor (5)
23. Clergyman (5)
24. Iron block (5)
25. Caucasian (5)
26. Insect form (5)
27. Pertaining to ships (5)
28. Liniment (6)
29. Sensual (6)
30. Pertaining to the skull (7)

ANSWERS

6. CAN	12. CAIN	18. LIAR	24. ANVIL	30. CRANIAL
5. VIA	11. RAIL	17. IRAN	23. VICAR	29. CARNAL
4. ARC	10. LIRA	16. LAVA	22. RIVAL	28. ARNICA
3. CAR	9. INCA	15. NAIL	21. CANAL	27. NAVAL
2. VAN	8. RAIN	14. VIAL	20. VAIN	26. LARVA
1. AIR	7. CLAN	13. ARIA	19. LAIR	25. ARIAN

MAGIC FIGURES

BORIS RANDOLPH

Turn your back and ask someone to write a row of figures using any number from 1 to 9 as often as he likes, something like this:

$$8\ 9\ 4\ 3\ 2\ 9\ 1\ 6\ 8$$

The row can be as long as desired.

Now have him add the digits as follows, keeping the total to himself:

$$8+9+4+3+2+9+1+6+8 = 50$$

And have him subtract the total from the original row, like this:

$$
\begin{array}{r}
8\ 9\ 4\ 3\ 2\ 9\ 1\ 6\ 8 \\
-\ 5\ 0 \\
\hline
8\ 9\ 4\ 3\ 2\ 9\ 1\ 1\ 8
\end{array}
$$

Now have him cross out any digit he likes, add up the rest and give you the total.

Though your back has been turned all the time you can instantly tell him the number he crossed out.

SECRET

Reduce the total given you to one digit as follows: If the total is 34 you add the 3 and the 4 and get 7; if the total is 256 you add the 2, the 5 and the 6 and get 13 and then add the 1 and the 3 and get 4. When you have this one digit subtract it from 9 and the remainder will be the number crossed out, unless the digit is itself 9, in which case the answer will also be 9.

KNOTS OR NOT KNOTS?

(Par: 2 min.)

See if you can unravel these without getting caught in the loops.

Imagine you are pulling the two loose ends of rope, in each of the sketches below. Would the rope become knotted, or not?

Underline the letter below each sketch which will make a true knot.

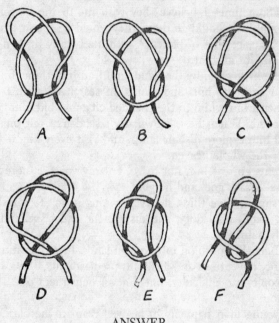

ANSWER

The only true knots are A and F.

AN ENIGMA

(From Godey's Lady's Book, 1839)

I am an invisible, irresistible, unreasonable, thing. Though nobody can see me, every body feels my power. I have done some good in my day, and plenty of mischief. I believe there is not a son, or a daughter, of Adam, to whom I have not been a trouble and a comfort. I am a source of perpetual delight to children, and of annoyance to their mammas. Sometimes I believe they wish me in the bottom of the ocean, though if I should go there, they would be the first to fish me up again. They get out of patience with me twenty times a day, but they like me, for all that.

I take the little child by the hand, and lead him through the green woods and over the hills and plains, in search of earth's beautiful things. Then I bring him to the crowded city, and bid him gaze at its many wonders. When he is grown up, I send him out on the wide ocean, bid him explore distant lands, and visit every kindred and nation under the whole heaven.

His parents entreat him not to go, but my voice is more powerful than theirs—I say "go!" and he goes.

Now I suppose you think it is very wrong in me to interfere with the young man's filial duty, and disturb the sweet spells of home—but it's my nature.

When I get the youth off into foreign lands, I run him into all sorts of fool-hardy adventures and awkward predicaments. I'm excellent at getting people into difficulty, but I never help them out; that's not my vocation.

If the young man happens to be well read in the classics, if his imagination has been warmed with the history and the poetry of the olden times, then I have him completely in my power—he is my willing captive. There is nothing which at my bidding, he will not do and dare, to obtain a sight of the relics of antiquity, and the places made famous in the glorious days of old. Ha! how I drive him about! He must encounter perils by sea, and perils by land—he must be choked by the sands of the desert, and suffocated by the simoon, and scorched by the tropical sun, and devoured by wild beasts, and robbed by wilder men; must starve, freeze, and encounter all manner of privations, only because I say so.

My favourite station is near the fountain of knowledge. Here I stand and call to every passer-by, to stop and taste the waters. If they approach near enough, I lay my soft, powerful hand upon them, and draw them, unresisting, to the well. Whoever tastes these waters, is sure to thirst again. The fountain is exhaustless, and the thirst that I create is equally so; none who once come, ever go away. So, as you may well suppose, I have by this time collected a vast multitude round it. There is one thing rather singular about this water; the first draught intoxicates—but "drink deep," and you will be quite sobered.

I am the constant companion, and counsellor, of men of science, ever urging them forward in the path of discovery. Sir Humphrey Davy was one of my especial favourites. But I worked him rather too hard, poor fellow! Once, when I was driving him through one of nature's hidden paths, a path never trodden by human foot before, he sunk down exhausted. I thought at first I had killed him; but he revived after a while, and I drove him on as fast as ever. The world may thank me for the treasures which he brought to light.

The great Herschel was another of my particular friends. Many a long night have I held his telescope for him, while he counted the stars. I was never tired, but he was sometimes; and then he would shut his weary eyes, and say he could look no longer; but I kept teasing him to try again. Aye, the "milky-way" would have been nothing but a "milky-way" to this hour, if I had not urged him on. I told him one night, after he had watched the planets a good while, that he had better look into that bright path in the heavens, and see what he could make of it. He looked a long time, but said he could see nothing new. "It may be," said he, "that its brightness is owing to a multitude of clustering stars, but if so, my glass refuses to show them."

"Then make one that will," said I. He fell to work; and I promise you I didn't let him have much rest, till he had constructed a glass of prodigious power. O, with what ecstasy he took his first look through it! What wonders burst upon him! Myriads of worlds, which no human eye had ever seen, now rolled before him. The "milky-way" was paved with suns!

I suppose you will say it was malicious, but in the midst of his ecstasy, I stooped down and whispered in his ear, "Ah! if you could only see a little farther!" I should have tormented him with the same suggestion if he had constructed a glass of ten times the power. I suppose it's cruel—but that's my way.

I am found in the parlour, the kitchen, and nursery. I tell the little boy to break his drum, and see what makes the noise. I bid the servant put her ear to the key-hole of the parlour door, while I set the lady to "watch her neighbour over the way."

The museums, picture galleries, caravans, theatres, processions, and all sorts of public shows, depend on me for success. When Lafayette entered the city, not a soul would have stirred to meet him, if I had not urged it.

When our red brethren paid our city a visit, the inhabitants turned out "en-masse" to witness their war-dance. It was I who sent them.

In short I am always moving among high and low, in great matters and small. They sometimes call me *idle*; but I am sure nobody is more busy. Sometimes I am called *impertinent*—this too I take to be a slander, for it is my vocation to pry into other people's affairs.

If, after this long description, you are in doubt as to my name, you will find it written in legible characters, on your own bright face.

ANSWER

I am curiosity.

USE YOUR VOICE—TAKE YOUR CHOICE!

(Par: 36)

Here is a little drill in words which are commonly mispronounced. How many can you pronounce correctly? This makes an excellent oral game.

1. Advertisement: Is it adver-TISE-ment or ad-VERT-isment?
2. Valet: Is it VAL-let or va-LAY?
3. Alternate: (noun) Is it ALL-ternit or alter-NAYTE?
4. Ignoramus: Is it ignor-RAM-us or ignor-RAY-mus?
5. Himalaya: Is it Hima-LAYER or Him-MAL-aya?
6. Asphalt: Is it AS-phalt or ASH-phalt?
7. Antique: Is it an-TEEK or an-TIK?
8. Creek: Is it CREEK or KRICK?

9. Comparable: Is it COM-parable or com-PAR-able?
10. Ego: Is it EE-go or EGG-o?
11. Gondola: Is it GON-dola or gon-DOLE-a?
12. Depot: Is it DAY-po or DEE-po?
13. Bassinet: Is it BASS-inet or bass-i-NET?
14. Apparatus: Is it appar-RAY-tus or appar-RAH-tus?
15. Hussar: Is it hoo-ZAR or huz-ZUR?
16. Greenwich: Is it GREEN-witch or GREN-nitch?
17. Dirigible: Is it DIR-igible or dir-IJ-ible?
18. Frequented: Is it FREE-quented or fre-QUEN-ted?
19. Gangrene: Is it gang-GREEN or GANG-green?
20. Illustrate: Is it ILL-ustrate or i-LUS-trate?
21. Dilemma: Is it DIE-lemma or di-LEM-ma?
22. Condolence: Is it CON-dolence or con-DOLE-ence?
23. Chauffeur: Is it SHO-fer or chauf-FEUR?
24. Tuesday: Is it TOOS-day or TIEWS-di?
25. Diphtheria: Is it dip-THERIA or dif-THERIA?
26. Environs: Is it EN-virons or en-VI-rons?
27. February: Is it FEBIEW-ary or FEBROO-ary?
28. Jonquil: Is it JON-quil or JONK-wil?
29. Khaki: Is it KAR-key or KAK-key?
30. Aerial: Is it AY-rial or AY-EE-rial?
31. Metamorphosis: Is it metamor-PHO-sis or meta-MOR-phosis?
32. Mnemism: Is it NEE-mism or MIN-imism?
33. Penitentiary: Is it peniten-TIARY or penti-TEN-shari?
34. Via: Is it VEE-a or VIE-a?
35. Often: Is it OFF-n or OFF-ten?
36. Oedipus: Is it ED-ipus or EED-dipus?
37. Laboratory: Is it LAB-ritory or LAB-o-ratory?
38. Kimono: Is it kim-MO-na or kim-MO-no?
39. Diamond: Is it DIE-mind or DIA-mond?
40. Irrefutable: Is it irre-FUTE-able or ir-REF-utable?
41. Vaccine: Is it VACK-sin or vac-SEEN?
42. Usual: Is it USE-zhal or YU-zhoo-al?
43. Oblique: Is it o-BLICK or o-BLEEK?
44. Despicable: Is it DES-picable or des-PICK-able?
45. Bicycle: Is it BI-seekle or bi-SI-kel?
46. Aerify: Is it AY-rify or AY-EE-rify?
47. Acumen: Is it ACK-umen or ac-CU-men?
48. Formidable: Is it for-MID-able or FORM-idable?

49. Quintuplets: Is it QUIN-tuplets or quin-TUP-lets?
50. Apparel: Is it ap-PAR-el or a-PAR-el?

USE YOUR VOICE, TAKE YOUR CHOICE

(answer key, printed upside down)

1. ad-VERT-isement	26. en-VI-rons
2. VAL-let	27. FEBROO-ary
3. ALL-ternit	28. JON-quil
4. ignor-RAY-mus	29. KAK-key
5. Him-MAL-aya	30. AY-EE-rial
6. AS-phalt	31. meta-MOR-phosis
7. an-TEEK	32. NEE-mism
8. CREEK	33. peni-TEN-shri
9. COM-parable	34. VIE-a
10. either is correct	35. OFF-n
11. GON-dola	36. ED-ipus
12. DEE-po	37. LAB-o-ratory
13. either is correct	38. either is correct
14. appar-RAY-tus	39. DIA-mond
15. hoo-ZAR	40. ir-REF-utable
16. GREN-nitch	41. VACK-sin
17. DIR-igible	42. YU-zhoo-al
18. fre-QUEN-ted	43. o-BLEEK
19. GANG-green	44. DES-picable
20. either is correct	45. BI-seekle
21. di-LEM-ma	46. a-VER-ify
22. con-DOLE-ence	47. ac-CU-men
23. SHO-fer	48. FORM-idable
24. TIEWS-di	49. QUIN-tuplets
25. dif-THERIA	50. a-PAR-el

GAME OF NO MYTHSTAKES

Have your guests identify each of the following mythological characters:

1. Minerva	6. Ceres	10. Vulcan
2. Apollo	7. Mars	11. Venus
3. Bacchus	8. Mercury	12. Atlas
4. Diana	9. Neptune	13. Hercules
5. Pluto		14. Cupid

ANSWERS

(Love)
(Strength)
(World)
(Beauty)
(Blacksmith)

(Ocean)
(Messenger)
(War)
(Season)

(Underground)
(Moon)
(Wine)
(Sun)
(Wisdom)

WORD SQUARE

BORIS RANDOLPH

Arrange the following sixteen letters into a four by four square so as to have four words reading vertically and four more reading horizontally.

D D E E E E G I N R S T T U W

Try it without the definitions below first, but if you need help, here they are: The words spell (though not necessarily in this order) to egg on, to require, to make senseless, to exhaust, the rise and fall of the sea, a border, a meat and vegetable dish, and a nuisance plant.

SOLUTION

NEED
URGE
TIDE
STEW

A TUBFUL OF FUN

BORIS RANDOLPH

Splash around as much as you like here and see if you can add the letters of the word TUB to each group of letters below and rearrange them to form a six-letter word every time.

1. ELS	6. DEG	11. ENN	16. GIN	21. LNO
2. AEP	7. BSY	12. CIS	17. ELM	22. ERS
3. ANR	8. ERT	13. GHO	18. ORT	23. DIR
4. ORS	9. EOS	14. NOT	19. ELR	24. ELN
5. AEY	10. ELL	15. ALR	20. EFF	25. CEK

ANSWERS

1. BUSTle	6. BUdgeT	11. UnBenT	16. TUBing	21. UnBolT
2. UpBeaT	7. sTUBby	12. cUBisT	17. TUmble	22. BUSTer
3. TUrBan	8. BUTter	13. BoUghT	18. TUrBot	23. TUrBid
4. roBUST	9. oBTUse	14. BUTton	19. BUTler	24. UnBelT
5. BeaUTy	10. BUllet	15. BrUTal	20. BUffeT	25. BUckeT

UNTRANSPOSED ANAGRAMS

In the following the words are used in various ways *without transposing the order of the letters*. Although they are not true anagrams they are very interesting, for they show how words may be divided. The words may be divided into two parts, the second part being frequently used *ahead* of the first part. See how many you can do: Number 1 has been done for you.

1. In spite of his 87 years the A̲ G̲ E̲ D̲ M̲ A̲ N̲ still M̲ A̲ N̲-A̲ G̲ E̲ D̲ to attend to his business.

2. Her _ _ _ _ _ _ _ _ _ told her that _ _ _ _ _ _ _ _ _ _ a convent was best for her sister.

3. The vigilant _ _ _ _ _ _ _ _ _ _ _ _ took the _ _ _, _ _ _ _ _ and other booty to the police station.

4. This _ _ _ _ _ _ _ is one whose sympathy for _ _ _ _ _ _ _ knows no bounds.

5. Her mother said, "I would really _ _ _ _ _ _ _ _ about your personal appearance if you were not so _ _ _ _ _ _ _ _ about money matters!"

6. The show commences at quarter _ _ _ _ _ but it is
   _ _ _ _ _ as much as half an hour late.
7. He was accused of _ _ _ _ _ _ _ _ _ _ _ _ but the other
   _ _ _’ _ _ _ _ _ _ _ _ _ won him a verdict of acquittal.
8. The optician found that in order to _ _ _ _ _ _ _ _ right
   he had to _ _ _ _ _ _ _ _ his glasses.
9. It was the _ _ _ _ _ _ for shad but with such high _ _ _ _
   _ _ he wouldn't dare take a chance with his little boat.
10. In 1776 the patriots indulged in fervid _ _ _ _ _ _ _ and
    at times it was difficult to tell whether a man were a whig _ _ _
    _ _ _ _.

ANSWERS

10. ORATORY—OR A TORY
9. SEASON—SEAS ON
8. READ JUST—READJUST
7. MANSLAUGHTER—MAN'S LAUGHTER
6. OF TEN—OFTEN
5. CARE LESS—CARELESS
4. KIND MAN—MANKIND
3. WATCHMAN—MAN, WATCH
2. INTUITION—TUITION IN

OVER AND OVER

BORIS RANDOLPH

The answer to each question below is a word beginning with OVER.
Be sure you don't OVERlook any of them if you want a perfect score.

1. Certain working clothes are called what?
2. Where does a soldier go when he goes abroad?
3. What do you have to do to catch up?
4. An arrogant person is what?
5. An opening piece of music is known as what?
6. What do you call it when the boss asks you to work an hour
   longer?
7. To conquer is to what?
8. From one day to the next is how long?

9. To what would you charge general business expenses?
10. A cloudy sky is what?

ANSWERS

1. OVERalls
2. OVERseas
3. OVERtake
4. OVERbearing
5. OVERture
6. OVERtime
7. OVERcome
8. OVERnight
9. OVERhead
10. OVERcast

JIGWORD PUZZLE

BORIS RANDOLPH

The two-letter words on the left below are the pieces. The spaces between each pair of letters on the right are where the pieces must go. Fit the right piece into the right space and you'll get a four-letter word each time. Example: Given the spaces O___L, D___H, and B___N, and the pieces OR, PA, and IS, you can fit the pieces in to make the words oPAl, dISh, and bORn. Of course, all the pieces (two-letter words) must be used up. That means you may have to switch one to another space now and then.

AM	AS				
IN	TO	1. A___M		9. F___D	
OX	IT	2. S___T		10. T___I	
AN	IF	3. L___E		11. E___Y	
US	AX	4. G___E		12. S___W	
HE	ON	5. B___E		13. R___H	
OF	ME	6. H___D		14. A___N	
BE	NO	7. F___Y		15. S___G	
		8. A___D		16. C___W	

ANSWERS

1. aTOm
2. sOFt
3. lIFe
4. gAMe
5. bITe
6. hANd
7. fOXy
8. aBEd
9. fINd
10. tAXi
11. eASy
12. sNOw
13. rUSh
14. aMEn
15. sONg
16. cHEw

HOW MANY?

BORIS RANDOLPH

Are you statistics-minded? Here is a chance to find out. Just check whichever you think is the right answer to each of the questions below.

HOW MANY

1. Keys on a typewriter? 29   39   49
2. Furlongs in a mile? 7   8   9
3. Full houses in a deck of cards? 560   1720   3744
4. Hours' difference between New York and Moscow? 6   7   8
5. Miles in a league? 3   5   7
6. People in the United States? 165 to 170 million   170 to 175 million   175 to 180 million
7. Dollars' worth of money in the United States? 25 to 35 billion   35 to 45 billion   45 to 55 billion
8. Tablespoons in a cup? 16   20   24
9. Whisky fifths in a gallon? 4   5   6
10. Amendments to the Constitution? 18   22   26
11. Air miles from San Francisco to New York? 2010   2200   2580
12. Sevens in a pair of dice? 5   6   7
13. Planets in the sky? 7   8   9
14. Pieces needed for a chess game? 24   28   32
15. Letters used for common Roman numbers? 5   6   7
16. Pecks in a bushel? 4   6   8
17. Feet in a fathom? 6   8   10
18. Inches of snow equal an inch of rain? 6   8   10
19. New nations admitted to the UN in 1955? 8   12   16
20. Pounds in a cubic foot of water? 62.3   100.5   115.7
21. Calories in a teaspoon of sugar? 16   32   48
22. People in the world? 2½ billion   3½ billion   4½ billion
23. Miles in a light year? 4,000,000,000   6,000,000,000,000   8,000,000,000,000,000

24. Years have the Academy Awards been given? 16   22   28
25. Signers of the Declaration of Independence? 26   56   106
26. Sheets in a ream? 500   750   1000
27. Miles to the moon? 238,857   520,462   755,420
28. Dollars earned by "Gone With The Wind"? 15,000,000   30,000,000   45,000,000
29. Years ago did King Solomon reign? 3000   4000   5000
30. Prime numbers (not divisible by others) between 1 and 100? 17   26   32
31. Quarts in a magnum? 2   3   4
32. Square miles in the United States? 3,022,387   4,621,408   5,204,561
33. Days did "Life With Father" run in New York? 1742   2431   3213

ANSWERS

33. 3213	21. 16	9. 5, of course!
32. 3,022,387	20. 62.3	8. 16
31. 2	19. 16	billion
30. 26	18. 10	7. 45 to 55
29. 3000	17. 6	million
28. 45,000,000	16. 4	6. 165 to 170
27. 238,857	15. 7	5. 3
26. 500	14. 32	4. 8
25. 56	13. 9	3. 3744
24. 28	12. 6	2. 8
23. 6,000,000,000	11. 2580	1. 49, generally,
22. 2½ billion	10. 22	with space bar

YOU'RE THE BOSS

BORIS RANDOLPH

You're the boss, and you want to get all the things on the left done. Which person on the right would you call for each job?

1. Cut a gem
2. Check a pedigree

1. Lexicographer
2. Philatelist

3. Grow some fruit
4. Identify a bug
5. Write a dictionary
6. Estimate some insurance
7. Get some shoes made
8. Mine some coal
9. Repair a barrel
10. Operate a roulette table
11. Get rid of a demon
12. Do some sewing
13. Examine some handwriting
14. Select some wines
15. Trade some stamps
16. Trade some coins
17. Lacquer some furniture
18. Read a face
19. Walk a tight rope
20. Dig up some ruins
21. Shoe a horse
22. Mend a tree
23. Hypnotize a person
24. Tend a stable
25. Ride a horse
26. Make some arrows
27. Cater for a party
28. Tell some fortunes
29. Herd some cattle
30. Make a clock

3. Cordwainer
4. Sommelier
5. Exorcist
6. Cooper
7. Calligraphist
8. Sempstress
9. Physiognomist
10. Lapidary
11. Mesmerist
12. Japanner
13. Numismatist
14. Genealogist
15. Farrier
16. Purveyor
17. Actuary
18. Equestrian
19. Collier
20. Pomologist
21. Dendrologist
22. Ostler
23. Soothsayer
24. Wrangler
25. Croupier
26. Funambulist
27. Horologer
28. Entomologist
29. Archaeologist
30. Fletcher

ANSWERS

30-27	25-18	20-29	15-2	10-25	5-1
29-24	24-22	19-26	14-4	9-6	4-28
28-23	23-11	18-9	13-7	8-19	3-20
27-16	22-21	17-12	12-8	7-3	2-14
26-30	21-15	16-13	11-5	6-17	1-10

HOW SMART IS YOUR THUMB?

JOSEPH LEEMING

Thumbless stunts can keep a party or a group of people amused for a long time. To prepare them, the players are given adhesive tape and help each other to tape their thumbs and forefingers together, making the thumbs on both hands useless.

Here are some stunts you can do:

1. Give each player a box, some wrapping paper, and a piece of string. Each person is to try to wrap up the box and tie the string around it.

2. Untie the shoelaces of each player. At a signal to start, each player must retie his laces. (Not easy!)

3. Give each player an orange and let him try to peel it.

4. Pair off the boys and girls. Give each boy a large handkerchief and tell him to put it around his girl's neck and tie a square knot in it.

The first person to accomplish any of these stunts is the winner.

GEOGRAPHY GAME

Read the following list of countries and places to your guests, and ask them to write down their location. For instance: Peru is in South America, Manitoba is in Canada, etc. Here is the list:

1. Albania	9. Finland	18. Ontario
2. Alberta	10. Honduras	19. Paraguay
3. Andorra	11. Guatemala	20. Siam
4. Bolivia	12. Klondike	21. Syria
5. Bulgaria	13. Latvia	22. Tibet
6. Ceylon	14. Madagascar	23. Turkey
7. Costa Rica	15. Morocco	24. Venezuela
8. Estonia	16. New Brunswick	25. Yukon
	17. Nicaragua	

ANSWERS

1. (Europe)	13. (Europe)
2. (Canada)	12. (Canada and Alaska)
3. (Between France and Spain)	11. (Central America)
4. (South America)	10. (Central America)
5. (Europe)	9. (Europe)
6. (India)	8. (Europe)
7. (Central America)	7. (Central America)
	6. (India)
14. (Island off Africa)	25. (Canada)
15. (Europe)	24. (South America)
16. (Canada)	23. (Asia Minor)
17. (Central America)	22. (Mongolia)
18. (Canada)	21. (Asia Minor)
19. (South America)	20. (French Indo-China)

The winner will be the one who locates most of these places correctly.

THE FAIR SEX

(Par: 18 min.)

Can you supply the following twenty-five masculine nouns with their corresponding feminine mates? For example: Man—Woman, Boy—Girl, etc. Here is the list:

1. Bachelor ....
2. Monk ....
3. Abbot ....
4. Duke ....
5. Horse ....
6. Drake ....
7. Deer ....
8. Gander ....
9. Ram ....
10. Marquis ....
11. Traitor ....
12. Executor ....
13. Chairman ....

14. Author ....
15. Poet ....
16. Aviator ....
17. Testator ....
18. Dog ....
19. Jury Foreman ....
20. Earl ....
21. Ox ....
22. Hog ....
23. Baron ....
24. President ....
25. Maharaja ....

ANSWERS

1. Spinster	14. Author (authoress seldom used)
2. Nun	15. Poetess or Poet
3. Abbess	16. Aviatrix
4. Duchess	17. Testatrix
5. Mare	18. Bitch
6. Duck	19. Foreman
7. Doe	20. Countess
8. Goose	21. Ox
9. Ewe	22. Sow
10. Marchioness	23. Baroness
11. Traitress	24. President
12. Executrix	25. Maharani
13. Chairman	

MIRROR DRAWING

JOSEPH LEEMING

Sit a player at a table and, in front of him, stand a book with the covers partly opened. Directly behind the book, on the side away from the person, lay a piece of writing paper. Just back of the paper stand a mirror, so that when the player looks over the book into the mirror, he can see the paper in the mirror, but can't see the actual paper.

Now give the person a pencil. Tell him to put his hand around the right end of the book and put the point of the pencil near the center of the paper. Then tell him to draw a square on the paper while looking into the mirror. After that, he is to draw two diagonals across the square.

When players try this for first time they seem to have no control over the pencil and draw the most peculiar designs!

QUOTAGRAMS

BORIS RANDOLPH

Without altering the order of the letters in each group below, switch the groups themselves around until they form a Bible quotation. Example: Given the groups ELI THE GHT LET REB, you could switch them around and get LET THE REB ELI GHT, which run together reads LET THERE BE LIGHT.

1. NHE INM CRE ART LEA ATE EAC
2. REE OUF THE LMA HAL KEY THS TRU
3. SGR ARD WAY ISH ORS RAN OFT THE ESS
4. DRE LET THR THE EAR IGN EJO THE ICE LOR ETH
5. ETH ING COM INT JOY ORN HEM
6. TFO THO TAK URL UGH IFE ENO RYO
7. HEE THE EAN ESS DBL EPT THE DKE LOR
8. LLN EAV ESS RTL UCO MFO EYO IWI OTL
9. EVE HAT SOR LLH WHA RAM OWE TSO EAL ANS THT EAP SHA
10. MIG HOW FAL THE HTY ARE LEN
11. HAT DWI OVE NGS LIK IHA EAD OHT
12. OHE HEA HAT HAT HET IMH ETH RST EAR ARL

SOLUTIONS

8. I will not leave you comfortless. *John*, 14.18.
7. The Lord bless thee, and keep thee. *Numbers*, 6.24.
6. Take no thought for your life. *Matthew*, 6.25.
5. Joy cometh in the morning. *Psalms*, 30.5.
4. The Lord reigneth; let the earth rejoice. *Psalms*, 97.1.
3. The way of transgressors is hard. *Proverbs*, 13.15.
2. The truth shall make you free. *John*, 8.32.
1. Create in me a clean heart. *Psalms*, 51.10.

9. Whatsoever a man soweth, that shall he also reap. *Galatians, 6.7.*
10. How are the mighty fallen! *II Samuel, 1.25.*
11. Oh that I had wings like a dove! *Psalms, 55.6.*
12. He that hath ears to hear, let him hear. *Mark, 4.9.*

MEN AT WORK

BORIS RANDOLPH

The answer to each question below is a word beginning with MEN. Get them all right and you're really MENtally alert.

1. What famous violinist has the first name of Yehudi?
2. A lying person is what?
3. Where is the best place to keep a lion?
4. What is the first thing you ask for in a restaurant?
5. That cool-tasting flavor in cough drops is generally what?
6. What is the opposite of Bolsheviki?
7. A famous Pennsylvania religious people are the what?
8. What's a good name for something threatening?
9. A wise and faithful teacher and counselor is a what?
10. If someone stopped you to beg for the price of a cup of coffee what would he be?

ANSWERS

1. MENuhin
2. MENdacious
3. MENagerie
4. MENu
5. MENthol
6. MENsheviki
7. MENnonites
8. MENace
9. MENtor
10. MENdicant

CROSTAGRAMS

BORIS RANDOLPH

WATER
SHOULD
QUICKLY
RELIEVE
THIS
TROUBLE

The above words are a sort of definition. The idea is to find an answer to this definition by selecting *one letter* from each word and reading them downwards. Thus, above, you would select T from WATER, H from SHOULD, I from QUICKLY, R from RELIEVE, S from THIS, and T from TROUBLE, and these, reading downwards, would spell THIRST, the answer called for by the definition. Following exactly the same method see if you can find the answers to the CROSTAGRAMS below.

1.	2.	3.	4.	5.
OFTEN	FROM	RECIPE	BIG	MAKES
LIES	MAN'S	FOR	WAR	FORTUNE
CLOSE	BELIEF	MAKING	ITEM	WITH
TO	STEMS	EVERY	THAT	HORSELESS
CARPETS	THIS	DAY	SETTLES	BOOK
		MERRY	ISSUES	MAKERS

6.	7.	8.
KEEPS	SOMETHING	EXISTS
THINGS	USUALLY	TO
GOING	SOUGHT	BURN
IN	BY	AND
MANY	MANY	QUICKLY
MACHINES	LONELY	BECOMES
	MAIDS	SMOKE

9.

ALTHOUGH
NOT
BASHFUL
STILL
TURNS
VERY
RED

10.

HOME
AS
GRAND
AS
MILLIONAIRES
MOVE
IN

ANSWERS

10. MANSION
9. LOBSTER

2. FAITH	4. BATTLE	6. ENGINE	8. TOBACCO
1. FLOOR	3. COMEDY	5. AUTHOR	7. HUSBAND

POSY POSERS

JOSEPH LEEMING

These questions are all answered by giving the names of flowers.

1. What flowers do we all have?
2. What do unmarried men often lose?
3. What did the professor do when he sat on a tack?
4. What do penniless people hope to do?
5. What flower is an American pin-up girl?
6. What flower is like a lot of birds?
7. What flower is some stage scenery made of?
8. What flower is an eyeful?
9. What flower describes a pretty girl who has had a quarrel with her boy friend?
10. What flower is a dressed-up wild animal?

ANSWERS

1. Tulips
2. Bachelor's buttons
3. Rose
4. Marigold
5. American Beauty
6. Phlox
7. Shamrocks
8. Iris
9. Blue bell(e)
10. Dandelion

Pets:

YOUR BOY AND HIS DOG

ROBERT BENCHLEY

People are constantly writing in to this department and asking: "What kind of dog shall I give my boy?" or sometimes: "What kind of boy shall I give my dog?" And although we are always somewhat surprised to get a query like this, ours really being the Jam and Fern Question Box, we usually give the same answer to both forms of inquiry: "Are you quite sure that you want to do either?" This confuses them, and we are able to snatch a few more minutes for our regular work.

But the question of Boy and Dog is one which will not be downed. There is no doubt that every healthy, normal boy (if there is such a thing in these days of Child Study) should own a dog at some time in his life, preferably between the ages of forty-five and fifty. Give a dog to a boy who is much younger and his parents will find themselves obliged to pack up and go to the Sailors' Snug Harbor to live until the dog runs away—which he will do as soon as the first pretty face comes along.

But a dog teaches a boy fidelity, perseverance, and to turn around three times before lying down—very important traits in times like these. In fact, just as soon as a dog comes along who, in addition to these qualities, also knows when to buy and sell stocks, he can be moved right up to the boy's bedroom and the boy can sleep in the dog house.

In buying a dog for a very small child, attention must be paid to one or two essential points. In the first place, the dog must be one which will come apart easily or of such a breed that the sizing will get pasty and all gummed up when wet. Dachshunds are ideal dogs for small children, as they are already stretched and pulled to such a length that the child cannot do much harm one way or the other. The dachshund being so long also makes it difficult for a very small child to go through with the favorite juvenile maneuver of lifting the dog's hind legs up in the air and wheeling it along like a barrow, cooing, "Diddy-app!" Any small child trying to lift a dachshund's hind leg up very high is going to find itself flat on its back.

For the very small child who likes to pick animals up around the middle and carry them over to the fireplace, mastiffs, St. Bernards, or Russian wolfhounds are not indicated—that is, not if the child is of any value at all. It is not that the larger dogs resent being carried around the middle and dropped in the fireplace (in fact, the smaller the dog, the more touchy it is in matters of dignity, as is so often the case with people and nations); but, even though a mastiff does everything that it can to help the child in carrying it by the diaphragm, there are matters of gravity to be reckoned with which make it impossible to carry the thing through without something being broken. If a dog could be trained to wrestle and throw the child immediately, a great deal of time could be saved.

But, as we have suggested, the ideal age for a boy to own a dog is between forty-five and fifty. By this time the boy ought to have attained his full growth and, provided he is ever going to, ought to know more or less what he wants to make of himself in life. At this age the dog will be more of a companion than a chattel, and, if necessary, can be counted upon to carry the boy by the middle and drop him into bed in case sleep overcomes him at a dinner or camp meeting or anything. It can also be counted upon to tell him he has made a fool of himself and embarrassed all his friends. A wife could do no more.

The training of the dog is something which should be left to the boy, as this teaches him responsibility and accustoms him to the use of authority, probably the only time he will ever have a chance to use it. If, for example, the dog insists on following the boy when he is leaving the house, even after repeated commands to "Go on back home!" the boy must decide on one of two courses. He must either take the dog back to the house and lock it in the cellar, or, as an alternate course, he can give up the idea of going out himself and stay with the dog. The latter is the better way, especially if the dog is in good voice and given to screaming the house down.

There has always been considerable difference of opinion as to whether or not a dog really thinks. I, personally, have no doubt that distinct mental processes do go on inside the dog's brain, although many times these processes are hardly worthy of the name. I have known dogs, especially puppies, who were almost as stupid as humans in their mental reactions.

The only reason that puppies do not get into more trouble than they do (if there *is* any more trouble than that which puppies get into) is that they are so small. A child, for instance, should not expect to be able to fall as heavily, eat as heartily of shoe leather, or throw up as casually as a puppy does, for there is more bulk to a child and the results of these practices will be more serious in exact proportion to the size and capacity. Whereas, for example, a puppy might be able to eat only the toe of a slipper, a child might well succeed in eating the whole shoe—which, considering the nails and everything, would not be wise.

One of the reasons why dogs are given credit for serious thinking is the formation of their eyebrows. A dog lying in front of a fire and looking up at his master may appear pathetic, disapproving, sage, or amused, according to the angle at which its eyebrows are set by nature.

It is quite possible, and even probable, that nothing at all is going on behind the eyebrows. In fact, one dog who had a great reputation for sagacity once told me in confidence that most of the time when he was supposed to be regarding a human with an age-old philosophical rumination he was really asleep behind his shaggy overhanging brows. "You could have knocked me over with a feather," he said, "when I found out that people were talking about my wisdom and suggesting running me for President."

This, of course, offers a possibility for the future of the child itself. As soon as the boy makes up his mind just what type of man he wants to be, he could buy some crêpe hair and a bottle of spirit gum and make himself a pair of eyebrows to suit the rôle: converging toward the nose if he wants to be a judge or savant; pointing upward from the edge of the eyes if he wants to be a worried-looking man, like a broker; elevated to his forehead if he plans on simulating surprise as a personal characteristic; and in red patches if he intends being a stage Irishman.

In this way he may be able to get away with a great deal, as his pal the dog does.

At any rate, the important thing is to get a dog for the boy and see what each can teach the other. The way things are going now with our Younger Generation, the chances are that before long the dog will be smoking, drinking gin, and wearing a soft hat pulled over one eye.

VAHAN SHIRVANIAN, THE SATURDAY EVENING POST

"Tell you what . . . I'll hold him and *you* give him the needle."

KINDNESS TO ANIMALS

J. ASHBY-STERRY

Speak gently to the herring and kindly to the calf,
Be blithesome with the bunny, at barnacles don't laugh!
Give nuts unto the monkey, and buns unto the bear,
Ne'er hint at currant jelly if you chance to see a hare!
Oh, little girls, pray hide your combs when tortoises draw nigh,
And never in the hearing of a pigeon whisper Pie!
But give the stranded jelly-fish a shove into the sea,—
Be always kind to animals wherever you may be!

Oh, make not game of sparrows, nor faces at the ram,
And ne'er allude to mint sauce when calling on a lamb.
Don't beard the thoughtful oyster, don't dare the cod to crimp,
Don't cheat the pike, or ever try to pot the playful shrimp.
Tread lightly on the turning worm, don't bruise the butterfly,

Don't ridicule the wry-neck, nor sneer at salmon-fry
Oh, ne'er delight to make dogs fight, nor bantams disagree,—
Be always kind to animals wherever you may be!

Be lenient with lobsters, and ever kind to crabs,
And be not disrespectful to cuttle-fish or dabs;
Chase not the Cochin-China, chaff not the ox obese,
And babble not of feather-beds in company with geese.
Be tender with the tadpole, and let the limpet thrive,
Be merciful to mussels, don't skin your eels alive;
When talking to a turtle don't mention calipee—
Be always kind to animals wherever you may be.

ARE CATS PEOPLE?

OLIVER HERFORD

If a fool be sometimes an angel unawares, may not a foolish query be a momentous question in disguise? For example, the old riddle: "Why is a hen?" which is thought by many people to be the silliest question ever asked, is in reality the most profound. It is the riddle of existence. It has an answer, to be sure, but though all the wisest men and women in the world *and* Mr. H. G. Wells have tried to guess it, the riddle "Why is a hen?" has never been answered and never will be. So, too, the question: "Are Cats People?" seemingly so trivial, may be, under certain conditions, a question of vital importance.

Suppose, now, a rich man dies, leaving all his money to his eldest son, with the proviso that a certain portion of it shall be spent in the maintenance of his household as it then existed, all its members to remain under his roof, and receive the same comfort, attention, or remuneration they had received in his (the testator's) lifetime. Then suppose the son, on coming into his money, and being a hater of cats, made haste to rid himself of a feline pet that had lived in the family from early kittenhood, and had been an especial favorite of his father's.

Thereupon, the second son, being a lover of cats and no hater of money, sues for possession of the estate on the ground that his brother had failed to carry out the provisions of his father's will, in refusing to maintain the household cat.

The decision of the case depends entirely on the social status of the cat.

Shall the cat be considered as a member of the household? What constitutes a household anyway?

The definition of "Household" in the Standard Dictionary is as follows: "A number of persons living under the same roof."

If cats are people, then the cat in question is a person and a member of the household, and for failing to maintain her and provide her with the comfort and attention to which she has been used, the eldest son loses his inheritance. Having demonstrated that the question "Are Cats People?" is anything but a trivial one, I now propose a court of inquiry, to settle once for all and forever, the social status of *felis domesticus*.

And I propose for the office of judge of that court—myself!

In seconding the proposal and appointing myself judge of the court, I have been careful to follow political precedent by taking no account whatever of any qualifications I may or may not have for the office.

For witnesses, I summon (from wherever they may be) two great shades, to wit: King Solomon, the wisest man of his day, and Noah Webster, the wordiest.

And I say to Mr. Webster, "Mr. Webster, what are the common terms used to designate a domestic feline whose Christian name chances to be unknown to the speaker?" and Mr. Webster answers without a moment's hesitation:

"Cat, puss, pussy and pussy-cat."

"And what is the grammatical definition of the above terms?"

"They are called nouns."

"And what, Mr. Webster, is the accepted definition of a noun?"

"A noun is the name of a person, place or thing."

"Kindly define the word 'place'."

"A particular locality."

"And 'thing'."

"An inanimate object."

"That will do, Mr. Webster."

So, according to Mr. Noah Webster, the entity for which the noun cat stands, must, if not a person, be a locality or an inanimate object!

A cat is surely not a locality, and as for being an inanimate object, her chance of avoiding such a condition is nine times better even than a king's.

Then a cat *must* be a person.

Suppose we consult King Solomon.

In the Book of Proverbs, Chapter XXX, verse 26, Solomon says: "The coneys are but a feeble folk, yet they make their houses in the rocks."

A coney is a kind of rabbit; folk, according to Mr. Webster, only another word for people.

That settles it! If the rabbits are people, cats are people.

Long lives to the cat!

DON'T BOTHER WITH THE ANTS

WILLIAM BIRMINGHAM

Last week I took my family off on a long-promised trip to the mountains. Our departure posed certain problems, which, in one way or another, are probably roughly similar to those experienced by any family which includes an eight-year-old boy.

A kindly neighbor dug out the following letter from his files. He said that it had been written to him in circumstances much the same as ours and he felt reasonably sure that if he again followed the instructions contained in the letter, he could solve most of our problems. This he did and the results were so successful that I am reprinting it here for the benefit of anybody who may be confronted with the same situation.

Dear Harry,

Wonder if you would take care of Bob's farm while we are away?

(1) Main thing is the turtles. Every once in a while you sprinkle dried bugs in their water for them to eat. A can of these bugs is usually next to the turtle bowl or under Bob's pillow.

(2) About the spiders. If you happen to catch a fly you might throw it in the mason jar. Personally I wouldn't unscrew the top for anything. They seem to multiply rapidly, and in a pinch, will get along eating each other.

(3) Bob's green caterpillars were taken off his tomato plants because they were chewing up the leaves. The only thing they will eat is tomato leaves. So if you feel as sorry for them as Bob does, tear off the top of the tomato plants once in a while and feed them. Personally, I wouldn't unscrew that jar either.

(4) I don't think it will be necessary to pull up the carrots every day to see how they are coming along, but I know that is part of the farming method used by Bob and it seems to stimulate the carrots . . . Ditto, the radishes.

(5) As far as the ants are concerned, don't bother with them. The holes in the top of the jar are for ventilation, and for some reason unfathomable to us, the ants seem to stay contained.

(6) The baby-food carton that makes the scratching noises has got a praying mantis inside. I don't know the plural of mantis, but I do know that the contents of the carton are plural. There are at least three hundred of them, in fact, and I suppose something ought to be done. Bob raised them from something brown and hard he brought in from the back yard and he says they will eat all the harmful bugs in the garden. For reasons best known to himself and the mantis—and the other two hundred and ninety-nine—he is reluctant to release them. Any disposal thoughts you may have on this will be considered mighty neighborly.

(7) The polliwogs. If you will go in the rear bathroom you will notice that the tub is full of water and that there are a lot of things swimming around. We gave Bob permission to do this in the interests of expediency. Fact is, he wouldn't leave until he knew they were under cover. Since they have gotten to be a sensitive subject around here, I am not inclined to ask him what they eat. If you can find out anywheres I wish you would throw them some.

(8) Last thought: If you come upon anything in the general neighborhood of his room that moves, will you please put it back in a mason jar. Then throw in some dried bugs, tomato leaves and carrots and screw the top on hard.

Many, many thanks,
Fred

KITTY! KITTY! KITTY!

RALF KIRCHER

Has anybody seen our cat?

I'm a fine one to be asking because personally I wouldn't give you the price of a catnip mouse for all the cats in Persia. It is not that I have anything against cats. Cats and I just do not have anything in common, that's all. Cats begin where I leave off, so to speak.

But we recently had a cat and one day it wandered away and Junior, who has faith in some of the darndest things, feels that maybe if I write a piece about the cat someone will see both the cat and the piece and bring it back. The cat, not the piece.

Let us get one point straight. I do not want the cat you have been trying to lose for years. I do not want a cat from that cunning litter out in your garage. There is only one cat that I want and that is the one we lost. If you have not seen it, forget the whole matter. I am not going to all this trouble just to be an easy mark for somebody who wants to unload an entirely different cat. If it isn't Smokey—Keep It!!

That is our cat's name—Smokey. I will try to describe it for you, though that will be difficult to do. Junior and I were talking about it the other evening and we figured that we would have a lot more luck if we could describe it as a purple cat with green spots, six legs, two tails, about four feet long, wearing bifocals, and carrying a box camera. A cat of that kind would be seen and would occasion comment and we could probably hope to track it down.

But Smokey is not an unusual cat. It is gray with a white face and with white feet and with a white spot on the end of its tail. It claims to be a tomcat. I would like to be able to tell you that it answers to the name of Smokey, but it doesn't. It doesn't answer to anything.

We got Smokey about two months ago in pretty much the way that we get everything else at our place. The children wanted a kitten and the wife wanted a kitten and I didn't want any part of a kitten. Knowing they had me outnumbered, and not wanting to occasion any premature howling, the family called a meeting in my absence, noted the presence of a quorum, and rushed through a decision to order a cat from one of our neighbors who owns a farm where the cat population runs in excess of forty-six to the acre. When I came home next evening, there was the kitten acting like he owned the place and making passes at the dog. I might say at this point that the dog didn't want a kitten either. The dog and I see eye-to-eye in the cat department.

Well, as I say, this kitten was acting as if he owned the place, which is typical, cats being no respecters of persons, traditions, seniority, the Bill of Rights, or anything else. It does not matter to a cat that we have lived in this house more than two years, and that it is our house in a heavily-mortgaged way, and that some things are sacred. A cat

will not give you two cents for such nonsense and will take full possession at once, sleeping in the best chairs, walking all over the furniture and across the bookcases, sneaking into any cupboard or closet
that is left open, meowing at the slightest inconvenience, and jumping at you from under beds. And not only will he do these impudent
things, but he will then show his contempt for you by walking off
when you decide to pet him, refusing to eat any food until he is certain that it was intended for somebody else, ignoring the bed you prepare for him, and playing with the lace curtains instead of the cunning
rubber mouse that cats are supposed to like. I do not think I am putting it too strongly when I say that a cat can show more insolence and
take more liberties than the average brother-in-law.

I resented all this and, to tell you the truth, Smokey seemed to
sense my animosity and left me pretty much alone. He found a way
to retaliate, however, and this he regularly did under the typewriter
stand in my study. I wasted a good bit of first-rate profanity in an
effort to correct that habit and I was often tempted to use certain
strong-arm measures that seemed like a good idea, but when I threatened Smokey the rest of the family would gather him to their bosoms
and say that after all he was only a sweet, little kitty and didn't know
any better, and don't be an old grouch. After a little of this I would
put the dog on the leash and take a long walk. The dog was a great
comfort to me through all of this.

And then, as I say, about two weeks ago Smokey disappeared. This
was a great tragedy and for several days there was scarcely an hour of
the day or night when one of us was not walking up and down the
street crying, "Kitty! Kitty! Kitty!" They even had me doing it, although I didn't call very loud, not wanting to annoy the neighbors.

But Smokey has not come back and so, at the request of Junior, I
am saying that if you see such a cat as this, let us know. I, personally,
have not contributed but I understand that the family has put together a small fund known, appropriately enough, as the kitty, and
this will be used to reward anyone who produces the right cat. But,
mind you, do not try to palm off any other cats on us. If it isn't Smokey,
we don't want it.

I'll say we don't.

MARTA THE DOG-LOVER

JOSEPH HENRY JACKSON

We had several reasons for believing, when Marta first came, that we had acquired what in the old-fashioned way my mother-in-law had always called a treasure. Her pleasantly ruddy complexion, her neat graying hair, her bright blue eyes—these spoke for themselves. Her former employers had written in the highest terms, and my wife liked the fact that Marta had kept the letters tidily, in clean envelopes. A few questions showed that she knew her way around a kitchen, and she said easily that one five-year-old was no trouble.

What settled things, really, was the way our cat, after one tentative look, jumped into Marta's lap and lay there purring. At the time, my wife took this for evidence that Marta loved cats; we did not know, though we learned, that this was not exactly true. Marta's was a kind of generalized affection, expressing itself in warmth toward cats to be sure, but extending beyond this in many directions, some unexpected.

From the first, her way with a meal was magical. There was the first breakfast she served: the eggs scrambled soft enough, and accompanied by bacon she had grizzled in her own special way, she told us. There were the buttermilk pancakes on another memorable morning, feather-light, though this was not altogether why Marta liked to make them. What interested her was the buttermilk itself. It was good for you, Marta explained; it changed the flora and fauna in your stomach. She had learned this, she told us, from the magazine put out by the Commuters' Union.

It was in her third week with us that our cat wandered away and did not come back, and our child was disconsolate. There was talk of finding a new one; for a time guppies were discussed, and there were mutterings about a dog. Marta had brightened at the mention of dogs, but we thought nothing special of that until she came back from shopping with the puppy.

She had felt in her bones that it would rain, she told my wife; the weather had been sulky all morning. So she had gone to the supermarket, which shared a coöperative parking lot with some other stores, and when she came back to the car after getting the parking-ticket violated, there was the pup, damp and miserable, cowering under the radiator, and Marta just scooped it up she said, a wet dog looks so bed-raggled.

"I just had to bring him home," she explained, "or I'd never of regretted it."

She told us immediately that she would take care of the puppy herself. It was healthy, she said. Anybody could see that; the whites of its eyes were as clear as a bell. Moreover, she understood about dogs; the people for whom she had worked in Southern California—a family named Trott—had been true dog-lovers. To be sure, a dog could be a lot of trouble, but Marta assured us she had mauled the whole thing over in her mind and would bear the blunt of it. And a puppy like this could never be half the work of the dog the Trotts had, an enormous Gray Dane so clumsy it had knocked over and broken a little statue of St. Venus de Milo. (The Trotts, Marta said, were really artistic people; Mrs. Trott had even hired a man to make a bust of her daughter's foot.)

A dog could easily be trained, Marta said, and she knew how. And with a young puppy you had a chance to begin from the beginning; you could start from scraps. She had learned all about it from a man who understood both dogs and horses; she had got to know him well when she took Mrs. Trott's little girl each week for her lesson at the Riding McCavity.

As the weeks passed, our house grew stranger all the time. There was a box with a blanket in the kitchen, and papers were strategically placed in each room. You had to have a system, Marta said; you couldn't go at it half-hazardly. Once she went to a movie made from a story by Albert Payson Terhune; she might learn something about dogs from it, she felt. But she came home in a bad humor. She explained that she should have known better. The movies were bound to spoil a story they made from a good book; they always gave them a twinge to jeeper them up.

Inevitably the puppy came down with something—though since it rapidly got well again, we never learned what. One of the troubles with dogs, Marta observed, was they couldn't tell you what was wrong with them. That, she felt, was the flaw in the ointment. And of course when a dog got really sick—well, you never knew; it could get a virex pneumonia, just like a person. Marta's sister's boy had told her all about it; he was studying medicine at Mark Hopkins, and he knew.

But the first glow of Marta's enthusiasm soon began to wane. Once our child reported, wide-eyed, that Marta had paddled the puppy with a rolled-up newspaper; on that occasion we looked up to see Marta in the doorway, her face flushed as she said indignantly that she hadn't thought a little girl would act the stew-pigeon. What it came to, Marta admitted to my wife, was that small dogs were really more trouble than large ones. Moreover, this puppy had been started wrong by somebody, and you couldn't teach a dog that had been spoiled; the cards were stagged against you.

It was not long after this that Marta came back from a downtown excursion without the puppy. As the cat had done, she said—and her round blue eyes were all gentle innocence—it had wandered off while she was in the supermarket. It was too bad, but anyway small dogs were more trouble than worth it. She must have known that we were in no mood for another dog, but she tried. Her look was almost wistful as she recalled her time at the Trotts' and how their big dogs— no nasty little puppies—had been such good company. "A full-size dog," she said, "is so friendly. Like, for instance, a lovely great big Sarah Bernard!"

LIVING WITH A DOG

ROGER ANGELL

There is a sports columnist for a New York newspaper who, on days when a double-header has been rained out or when Madison Square Garden is taken up with the antique show, likes to take a kick at dogs in his column. This fellow doesn't like dogs, and he says so. He doesn't understand dogs, has never lived with a dog, and wants no part of a dog. All this is perfectly O.K. with me; if he can't take dogs, he is at liberty to leave them alone and say so, and besides, six full columns a week is a lot of space for any man to fill with nothing but interviews with prize fighters and jockeys.

My beef with this sportswriter is over what he has to say about dog *owners*. It is his firm belief that a man who keeps a dog is first cousin to a heroin addict. A pet dog, he says, is nothing more than a shot in the arm to a man's ego—occasional evidence that he is a truly superior being. In keeping a dog around the house a man is merely making sure that there is at least one creature who will always love him, no matter what. He points out that a dog owner can drink up the rent money, snarl at his kids, beat his wife, and lie around in bed all day with a scratch sheet and still have the undying affection of his dog. The reason for this, he says, is simple: a dog is a singularly unprincipled and lazy animal who long ago discovered that a wag of the tail and a misty look in his eyes for his master would save him the trouble of going out and working for a square meal. A dog's loyalty is always reserved for the latest person to put down a dish of Red Heart for him.

All this, of course, is pure fantasy, as anybody knows who has ever had a dog around the house long enough to be on speaking terms with him. I know, because I am a dog owner of long standing and I have the scars—on my body, my furniture and my psyche—to prove it. I am prepared to explain to this dogless columnist exactly what living with a dog entails. I am rendering him this service entirely gratis, out of a simple desire to win more sympathy for dog owners, who, God knows, are in acute need of it.

First of all, let me confess that I am a patsy for a dog. I must be, or I wouldn't put up with the punishment. At the moment, the dog in my life is a muscular, rather numskulled English bulldog named Levi. He has been living with us for a year and a half now and I have just figured out, with pencil and paper, that the amount of my time I have given, almost entirely unwillingly, to attending Levi's odd needs and excessive demands, would have enabled me to write a long historical novel, lop fifteen strokes off my golf score, or become an expert on French brandies. In those eighteen months, for instance, I have four times (twice by pond, twice by sea) rescued our dog from drowning, simply because he is laboring under the insane delusion that he is a canine Weissmuller. I am not counting here the number of times I have fished him out of small streams and lakes he happened to tumble into merely because he was thinking of something else when he came across them. I once pulled him out of an open elevator shaft he had overlooked. I have pushed Levi about ten miles in my daughter's perambulator, simply because she once insisted that he join her on the seat and I, like a fool, thought it might be funny. Now *both* of them insist on it.

Consider, if you will, the absurd amount of inconvenience, wasted energy, and confusion involved in the mere act of taking Levi out of our apartment for a necessary breath of air. The signal for this is always relayed by my wife, who announces, "I think he wants to go out." Since this usually happens just as I am on the last chapter of the book I am reading or at the crux of an insanely funny story I am telling our guests, I am instantly upset and on the defensive. The dog, of course, has given no signal; he is either sleeping or thinking about swimming. "How do you know?" I ask my wife.

"Well," she says, "he just looks that way. You know, worried."

At this point, I have various choices. I can pooh-pooh the whole idea, pointing out accurately that the dog *always* looks worried, and just go on with what I was doing. In this case, Levi will invariably and disastrously prove my wife's point, usually on the bedroom rug. Or I can pretend to agree with my wife, but put the whole thing off. In this case, my wife plays her queen's pawn, the wifely gambit which never, never fails: "Oh, all right, then. *I'll* take him out." She doesn't, of course; *I* take him out, the way I should have in the first place.

Nor does the pother end there. If my daughter is around, she insists on accompanying me on this brief excursion. In wintertime, this results in a long struggle with snowsuit and zippers, a search for mittens, firm rejection of the suggestion that we also take along a tricycle and a couple of toys, and, not infrequently, tears. Even if the dog and I manage to get out of the apartment alone, we are apt to encounter trouble in the elevator, in the form of two elderly ladies, one of whom lives on the eighth floor, the other on the eleventh. Eighth Floor is convinced that my dog is the most vicious public enemy since Alvin Karpis. When she encounters him in the elevator, she flattens herself against the wall and murmurs, "Nice doggy" in an effort to save herself from instant dismemberment. The dog, of course, thinks she is the nicest lady he has ever laid eyes on and always tries to put his paws up on her stomach so that she can scratch his ears. Eleventh Floor, on the other hand, is just mad for Levi; the moment she meets him, she gets right down on all fours on the elevator floor and starts to talk baby talk to him—a habit which both Levi and I find hideously embarrassing.

This foolish state of affairs is not unusual; any dog owner (any city dog owner, at least) could offer a matching recital. The point is simple: a dog's capacity to inflate the ego of his owner is almost nil. His capacity to irk him, inconvenience him, put him at odds with his family and himself, and generally embarrass and belittle him is almost unbounded.

Take the case of Chloe and the Chicago railroad station. Chloe was a Saint Bernard we had during the war. I was stationed at an Army post in Denver at the time, where my wife and I and Chloe lived in a small one-story house. When I was ordered to ship out overseas, I received the usual fifteen-day furlough, and Chloe joined us on the train trip to New York. When our streamliner arrived in Chicago, I hurried up and retrieved Chloe from the baggage car, where she had spent a comfortable night. The three of us set off through the crowded Chicago Northwestern Terminal, following our porters toward the taxi which was to take us to our next train. Holding Chloe's leash, I had just started down the long, double flight of stairs which leads from the station's platform, when I was brought up short with a tremendous jerk. Looking back, I saw our dog, all four tremendous feet planted, looking down the flight of stairs with an expression of stark horror. "C'mon, Chloe," I said impatiently, twitching on the leash. But Chloe wasn't having any of *that*. This time I tugged; Chloe tugged back and I landed on my knees on the steps. I called my wife back for consultation. "It's perfectly simple," she said. "She's never seen a flight of stairs before."

"But that's stupid," I said. "She's a grown dog now—full grown. Besides, they're supposed to be Alpine dogs."

"Well, you'll just have to carry her," my wife said. "I'll meet you at the cab platform."

Chloe was only about a year old then, but she had her growth—and then some. I imagine she must have gone a good hundred and ten pounds. I unbuttoned my overcoat, collared the animal (who was trying to hide under a newsstand), and somehow heaved her into my arms and started a staggering journey down the stairs. I had taken about three steps down when Chloe let out a scream. It was no whimper, but a scream—a terrified, feminine, high-pitched yodel. I imagine every person in the station heard it. I couldn't see much with a Saint Bernard in my arms, but everyone I *could* see had stopped cold in his tracks and was staring at me. I continued downward and Chloe continued screaming at every step. By the time I reached the bottom, there were two M. P.'s with brassards and clubs waiting for me.

"Watcha doin' to that dog?" the sergeant said angrily.

I put Chloe down and straightened up with difficulty. "I was carrying her," I said.

"Oh, yeah? She don't look crippled to me. What was all that yellin' and hooraw for?"

"Yeah," said the other M. P. darkly. "I *like* dogs."

"She's scared of stairs," I said wearily. "She's never seen stairs before."

"Unh-huh," the sergeant said. "Let's see your dog tags, soldier."

I had to show my dog tags, my furlough papers, and then summon my wife over to back me up before I could get out of that station. It didn't seem likely at the time that Chloe would figure out another way to embarrass me but the following morning, when we arrived in the main concourse of Grand Central Terminal, she did. It was a less original way, but just as embarrassing.

It's not that I blame Chloe in the least. She was innocent in the whole affair, just as most dogs are more or less innocent when they get their owners into the most fantastic kind of trouble. After a while your well-broken dog owner just gets to expect that sort of thing. Just the other day I was telling a man about Chloe and those stairs and he came up with a similar Army dog experience. Worse, if anything.

Seems that this man had been stationed at a fort somewhere down South. He was a second lieutenant at the time, and had been for many, many months, largely because he and his commanding officer didn't get on very well. The man and his wife also had a dog at their house— a young puppy who was in the puppy stage of chewing up their slippers and clothes. They had a small family joke, based on an old James Thurber cartoon, whereby she pretended to blame her *husband* for all the damage the puppy did to their belongings. (This is a pretty complicated story, but all dog stories are complicated.) Anyway, one Sunday morning their doorbell rang, the lieutenant went to the door and was astonished to discover that his commanding officer had brought his wife over for a surprise social call—their very first. The lieutenant welcomed them and poured some coffee. They were attempting small talk when the lieutenant's wife, unaware that there were callers, opened her bedroom door upstairs. "John!" she shouted down, "have you been chewing the seat out of my pajamas again?"

The man explained to me that he and his visitors just sat there, in absolute silence, for a good ten seconds—long enough for him to realize that the whole thing was too complex, too hopelessly scrambled and implausible, for him to attempt any explanation. In the end all three of them simply pretended that the interruption hadn't taken place at all. After a minute or two of strained conversation, the C. O. and his wife got up and left. A week later the man was abruptly transferred to another outfit and shipped overseas.

In general, I guess dog and owner have an easier time of it in the country or suburbs than in the city, simply because it is easier for them to be independent of each other. My wife, however, once owned an old English sheep dog who managed to upset the smooth calm life of an entire community. He was a suburban dog who lived on a crowded hillside near Boston. He was also a kleptomaniac. He first evidenced this weakness by systematically collecting the food pans of every other dog in the neighborhood, bringing them home, and piling them up outside his own kitchen door. A few weeks later it began to appear that the local milkman had gone crazy. Every morning, instead of the usual two quarts of milk, my wife's mother would find a dozen or fifteen quarts piled up at the back door. A couple of days later the disease seemed to spread to the newsboy, who apparently was delivering everybody's *Boston Herald* to the same house. The milk company and the newsdealer were flooded with angry complaints, the delivery men were insulted and offered to quit, husbands blamed wives and mothers blamed children. After a week or so, of course, the culprit was discovered and was thereafter kept indoors in the morning. My wife's mother telephoned her apologies to everyone and tried to smooth ruffled feelings. "You know how dogs are," she said lamely. Nobody was particularly amused. I still remember the day of the first thaw that winter, when the snow on the road trickled away and revealed dozens of soggy newspapers and half-frozen bottles of milk which the busy dog had dropped on his rounds.

Finally I come to Fred. All the other dogs I have dealt with here were largely blameless and their mishaps involuntary. Fred, on the other hand, was a plotter. He never made a move in his life which he hadn't carefully thought out. Every one of his twenty-odd consecutive losing bouts with porcupines was calculated; he simply had decided that he was capable of handling a porcupine and nobody was going to teach him better. He was on separate terms (largely indifferent) with everyone in his rather large household, and he never deviated. His major studies in life, along with porcupines, included sheep-herding, the cultivation of a gallant and entirely fraudulent limp, the art of drinking beer out of nearly-empty bottles, and the fanning of a lifelong feud with his veterinarian.

I was there the day that Fred decided to Get the Vet. He was a pretty old dog by this time—a tremendous red dachshund whose entire muzzle and shoulders had turned white. I doubt that when I found him that morning, lying inert and helpless beside the kitchen steps, he had yet formulated his entire complex plan, but he was working on it. In any case, I was pretty worried. My parents, who owned Fred, were away on a trip, the veterinarian was twenty-five miles away, and I was pretty sure, after a careful examination, that I had a dying dog on my hands. I called my brother and we both tried unsuccessfully to coax Fred onto his feet. Then we found a burlap bag, tenderly laid the animal on it, and used this improvised stretcher to carry him to the car. Fred's eyes rolled alarmingly and he let out a few brave groans as we laid him on the floor of the sedan.

He lay there without moving throughout the long trip to the vet's, while I gently eased the car over the bumps and framed in my mind the sad telegram to my parents. When we got there, we unloaded our bundle and laid it gently on the floor of the vet's office. The doctor was unimpressed. He had been bitten several times during Fred's numerous porcupine-quill extractions and was a full partner in their feud. "Sick, huh," he said now without sympathy. He circled the prostrate dog warily. Suddenly he shouted. "*Get up, Fred!*" he yelled. "You old faker."

Fred rolled his eyes but didn't move. This obviously impressed the vet. Gradually, as he took Fred's temperature and listened with his stethoscope, his skepticism vanished and was replaced with genuine sympathy. "I guess he's really begun to slow down," he said sadly. I remarked that the dog's shoulder had seemed terribly sore. The vet now got down on his hands and knees to examine the shoulder. This was the closest he had allowed himself to come to Fred's jaws, and Fred now saw his chance. With a tremendous roar he threw himself into the air and slashed at the doctor's arm. The vet snatched his hand back just in time, staggered backward, and landed on the floor. Fred, who had not moved a muscle for the previous three hours, scurried rapidly across the room and crawled under a chair, from where he let loose some growling curses over his bad luck in having missed his target.

The vet, just as angry at having let himself be taken in, picked himself up and made up a prescription for Fred's heart (which seemed strong enough to *me*), and we took our leave. When I opened the car door, Fred leaped easily up into the back seat. He sat there the whole way home, looking out the window and chuckling quietly to himself.

Fred is dead now, but I wish somehow I could pass him along to that sports columnist for a few days' visit. The man would find that his ego, instead of being enlarged, would rapidly show signs of wear, but I think he'd enjoy it just the same. Perhaps he would decide, as I have, that for a man, taking on a dog is just like taking on a wife and raising a family. On the surface, it is a senseless thing to do, since it quickly deprives you of a good portion of your freedom, mobility, pride, and independence. There are moments when you remember this, but most of the time you know that you just couldn't get along without such a pleasantly cluttered life. Maybe the sportswriter wouldn't feel this way, though. I understand he is also a bachelor.

Will You Travel?

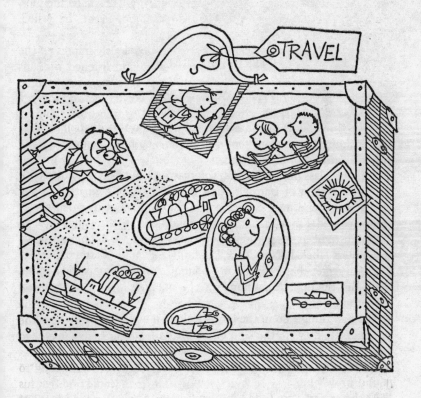

INTREPID AIRMAN, I

PATRICK CAMPBELL

I'll take three hours in the dentist's waiting-room, with four cavities and an impacted wisdom tooth, in preference to 15 minutes at any airport, waiting for an airplane.

You may class this as hysteria, you may regard it as ungenerous criticism of a system of transportation that has established itself as the fastest, safest and most convenient in the world. But where airplanes are concerned I'm a case for quiet conditions in the padded room.

I'm all right at the terminus; indeed, when I see people queueing at counters labeled "New York," "Chungking" and "Bermuda," I feel a certain regret that I too am not bound for similar romantic destinations. But the urge for far-flung travel evaporates as soon as I get into the airport bus.

The first thing I do in the bus is to look round at the other passengers to see if they are the kind of people with whom I should be content to die. They always, for some reason, fail to measure up to my standards. By the time we arrive at the airport, I have lost about a pound in weight.

At the airport I try to fall into conversation with the pilot or some member of the crew. I have a number of questions to ask—apparently offhand, casual questions, but they go to the root of the matter.

I wish to ask the pilot:

1. Are the very best engineers even now checking every inch of our airplane?

2. Have you, or any member of your family, ever been subject to giddiness, loss of memory or nervous attacks?

3. Will you drive it very fast?

4. Will it be necessary for us to travel at much more than 50 feet above the ground?

To the radio operator:

Can you, even if they send it out very quickly, be perfectly sure of understanding the Morse code?

And, finally, to the air hostess:

If anything goes wrong, would you be so kind as to inform me personally, some time in advance of the other passengers?

Reassured about these matters—and I must admit that all air crews are immensely reassuring—I enter the plane. I cannot decide whether it is better to sit in the front and bear the full brunt of the impact, or in the back and run the risk of being carried away when the tail unit falls off. I choose a central position, where I can watch the wings and see that the propellers are going round.

Five minutes after we are airborne, I disentangle my fingernails from the upholstery of the seat and release the safety belt which I had drawn so tight that it stopped my breathing. I sit back to enjoy the cloud panorama.

The door of the pilot's cabin opens—and the pilot himself comes out! What recklessness is this? He has left some half-fledged boy at the wheel! I watch with horror as he strolls down the aisle, chatting with passengers. I know what he's doing. He's telling them both engines have fallen off but he's saying it's all right.

When my turn comes, the pilot says, "Good morning—are you having a pleasant trip?" I merely nod, speechless. All I want him to do is to get back to his work and remove that mad office boy from the controls. I relax again as he shuts the door of his cabin behind him.

An hour goes by. I had a bad moment when the hostess leaned over and said something I was unable to hear. It sounded like, "We are falling into the sea." I was halfway out of my seat when I realized she was asking me if I would like some tea.

Suddenly we are losing altitude. I look down and the earth is carpeted with railway lines, red-brick houses, factory chimneys and telegraph poles. This is it.

The percussion valve in the port cylinder has blown out. This is the emergency landing. I sink the old nails right back into the upholstery and close my eyes. There is a bump, a faint screech—we have gone through a cow?—and then all is silent. We are alive, but where?

I open my eyes. We are on the apron outside the terminal building. They are pushing up a ladder to the door. I leave the plane with a

"Everyone in there is on the wrong train, Frank—— Hey! You're not Frank!"

---

slight swagger. Openmouthed sight-seers stand behind the railings. Well may they stare. They are looking at one of the intrepid birdmen of the modern era—in Dublin, a little more than an hour ago: now, as large as life, at Northolt airport.

What I say is that airplanes provide the safest, fastest, most convenient means of travel in the world.

OUR SHARED (?) LANGUAGE

DOUGLAS NEWTON,

(whom we must explain *is* an Englishman.)

All that the human race is or can ever hope to be it owes, some scientists tell us, to a curious pair of assets. One is a thumb working in opposition to the four fingers; the other is man's own astonishing invention, language. Any traveler will tell you, however, that of the two the thumb is by far the more precious possession. It means that he can always carry his own bags after he has failed to make himself understood by a porter who only—and obstinately—speaks a different tongue. Face an Englishman with a German, or an American with an Italian, and if nobody in the group knows more than his own language, they might as well all be dumb. For all practical purposes, they are. As a matter of fact the situation is even worse than it looks. Face an American with an Englishman—and very often they too become speechless.

It was only a freak of history that made English, the language of one of the smaller nationalities of the world, the language also of one of the most numerous. Let's face it, this need not have happened; there was nothing inevitable about it. If other colonists had arrived here earlier, faster, or had more children, the citizens of the United States might now be speaking Spanish, French, German, Gaelic, Polish, or Italian. But English it was—or was it? Is it? Do Americans speak English? In fact, do the English themselves speak English? The moment you take a close look at the rather ugly facts, hideous doubts creep in. It becomes appallingly plain that Oscar Wilde knew just what he was talking about when he remarked, "The Americans and the English have everything in common except a language." Like many of Oscar Wilde's witticisms, this is no joke. The awful truth behind it becomes more glaringly obvious every day.

Not only every day in the broad sense, but *any* day—in the particular. You challenge me? Very well. Let's agree this is not a question of the written language, which holds to the same forms, the same words, almost the same spellings and—so far, though who knows what the future may bring—the same alphabet. We are discussing here what comes out when an American and an Englishman meet, open their mouths, and give tongue. It is then that the real difficulties crop up. It is then that the bats begin to flitter in the transatlantic belfries.

Let us take as a test case a single day in the life of the Smith families—the Smiths who live in a suburb of London, and the Smiths who live in a suburb of Chicago. Mr. and Mrs. Smith in each case have three young children: Susan, John, and a baby who shall be nameless. Each Mr. Smith works in the city. Watch them closely, for in putting them through their paces we will not make them do anything unusual, nor will they use slang. They will talk and be described only in such terms as they would ordinarily use.

Mr. Smith overlies this particular Friday, so his wife has to return to their bedroom to knock him up a second time. A glance out of the window shows him a foggy autumn morning; however he throws back the eiderdown and gets up. Pulling on his dressing-gown, he hurries to the bathroom. The hot tap of the basin is out of order so he shaves leaning over the bathtub, and has his wash, using a flannel. Hopping on the bathroom scales in passing, he finds his weight registers twelve stone—rather heavy. Back in the bedroom he dresses hastily. Taking them from the chest of drawers, he puts on vest and pants first, followed by the socks he fastens with suspenders. After donning his shirt he goes to the clothes cupboard and selects a suit. Mr. Smith holds his trousers up with braces and, dressed and shod, slips on his jacket as he hurries downstairs.

Mrs. Smith and the kiddies are already at table in the dining-room, spooning up porridge. As Mr. Smith pulls up his chair, she informs him that an electric point in the kitchen has blown. Mr. Smith groans. "You cope, will you? Get the odd-job man to mend it."

Young Johnny chooses this moment to demand his pocket-money, while Susan sets up a cry

Mr. Smith oversleeps this particular Friday, so his wife has to return to their bedroom to call him a second time. A glance out of the window shows him a foggy autumn morning; however he throws back the covers and gets up. Pulling on his bathrobe, he hurries to the bathroom. The hot-water faucet of the washbowl is out of order, so he shaves leaning over the bathtub, and washes, using a washcloth. Hopping on the bathroom scales in passing, he finds his weight registers 150 pounds—somewhat overweight. Back in the bedroom he dresses quickly. Taking them from the dresser, he puts on undershirt and shorts followed by the socks he fastens with garters. After putting on his shirt he goes to the clothes closet and selects a suit. Mr. Smith holds his pants up with suspenders and, fully dressed, puts on his suit coat as he hurries downstairs.

Mrs. Smith and the kids are already seated in the dining room, eating their oatmeal. As Mr. Smith pulls up his chair, she tells him that an outlet in the kitchen is out of order. Mr. Smith groans. "You manage, won't you? Get the handy man to fix it."

Junior chooses this moment to demand his allowance, while Susan sets up a cry of "Can we go to the beach tomorrow?"

"No," replies Mrs. Smith; "it's

of "Can we go to the sea-side to-morrow?"

"No," replies Mrs. Smith; "it's too cold and in any case your bathing-costume has had the moth in it."

"You all treat me as if I was Father Christmas," complains Mr. Smith, passing Johnny a handful of coppers and change. "Make a long arm for the bread, would you?"

"Yes, Daddy. Brown bread or white?" asks grateful Johnny.

As Mrs. Smith sets a dish of eggs and bacon on the table, the baby wails.

"I'm sorry, darling, I'll have to change his nappy. You be Mum and pour the tea, please."

By the time she returns, the others have finished their toast and jam.

"May we get down?" the children ask. "Run along," replies Mr. Smith.

It's getting late. As he grabs his trilby, he accidentally knocks down his bowler, kisses his family and is off down the front-garden path and out onto the pavement.

"Oh, goodness," sighs Mrs. Smith. "He didn't take his overcoat or his mac, and I'm sure it's going to pelt. Put on your waders before you go to school, Johnny; and Susan, don't forget your galoshes. It's turning chilly; I'm going to change into a jumper."

too cold and in any case your bathing suit has moth holes in it."

"You all treat me as if I was Santa Claus," complains Mr. Smith, passing Junior a handful of pennies and change. "Pass the bread, will you?"

"Yes, Daddy. Whole-wheat or white?" asks grateful Johnny.

As Mrs. Smith sets a dish of eggs and bacon on the table, the baby wails.

"I'm sorry, darling, I'll have to change his diaper. You take charge and pour the coffee, please."

By the time she returns, the others have finished their toast and jelly.

"May we get up?" the children ask. "Go ahead," replies Mr. Smith.

It's getting late. As he grabs his felt hat, he accidentally knocks down his derby, kisses his family and goes down the walk and out of the yard onto the sidewalk.

"Oh, goodness," sighs Mrs. Smith. "He didn't take his topcoat or his raincoat and I'm sure it's going to pour. Put on your rubber boots before you go to school, Junior; and Susan, don't forget your rubbers. It's turning chilly; I'm going to change into a sweater."

Meanwhile Mr. Smith has reached the railroad station with just time to buy a paper at the

Meanwhile Mr. Smith has reached the railway station with just time to buy a paper at the bookstall. Getting out his season he hurries on to the platform. Without the time for his usual stop in the refreshment-room, he climbs into a carriage. The engine-driver and the stoker get to work, the guard clambers into the luggage-van, the station-master signals the engine-driver and the train pulls out. His neighbour, Mr. Jones, joins him. On the trip to town they talk about the sports season. Mr. Smith, a football fan, gives a brief assessment of various teams' prospects. Mr. Jones talks of the outlook for rugby.

On getting up to London, Mr. Smith decides to catch a bus, rather than take the tube, to his office. Boarding one at the terminus outside the station, he finds a seat downstairs.

Alighting at the nearest request stop, Mr. Smith walks to his office building and catches the lift, asking for the third floor. Entering his room, he is greeted by his secretary with the morning's post. He dictates a number of letters, and suggests she pass some on to another typist. The porter brings in his cup of tea, and Mr. Smith studies a few papers in preparation for the meeting at half-past ten. This takes place in the Board Room, and the firm's Managing Director presides. On leaving it,

newsstand. Getting out a commutation ticket, he hurries onto the platform. Without the time for his usual stop in the coffee shop, he climbs into a car. The engineer and the fireman get to work, the brakeman scrambles into the baggage car, the conductor signals the engineer, and the train pulls out. His neighbor Mr. Jones joins him. On the trip to town they talk about the sports season. Mr. Smith, a soccer fan, gives a brief assessment of various teams' prospects. Mr. Jones talks of the outlook for football.

On getting into New York, Mr. Smith decides to catch a bus, rather than take the subway to his office. Getting on one at the terminal in the station, he finds a seat downstairs.

Getting off at the nearest bus stop, Mr. Smith walks to his office building and catches the elevator, calling for the third floor. Entering his office, he is greeted by his secretary with the morning's mail. He dictates a number of letters, and suggests she pass some on to another stenographer. The office boy brings in his cup of coffee, and Mr. Smith studies a few papers in preparation for the meeting at half past ten. This takes place in the Conference Room, and the firm's President presides. On leaving it, Mr. Smith is told by the receptionist as he passes the switchboard that a call

Mr. Smith is told by the telephonist as he passes the switchboard that a call has been put through to his office. He hurries in and discovers that his solicitor is on the line. They agree to meet, but when?

"What about Monday week?" suggests the solicitor.

"That's a bad day," replies Mr. Smith; "what about a fortnight from today?"

The solicitor would prefer to ring back later to confirm this, and Smith agrees.

The rest of the family is about its usual pursuits. Johnny, daydreaming about half-term at his day-school, has cheeked his school-master. The furious man has awarded him a heavy imposition, and ordered him to stay in for break, while his friends ran about the playground pointing imaginary pistols and crying "Bang! Bang!" at each other.

Susan, a more amenable child, has passed a less eventful morning, apart from forgetting her plimsolls and gym-knickers, which has kept her out of the drill class.

Mrs. Smith's morning has included a session with the char, who was late. As so often, Mrs. Smith longs for a daily, and has already gone over the lino with the bumper before Mrs. Jenks turns up. The tags-and-bones man has called, so have the dust-

is waiting for him in his office. He hurries in and discovers that his lawyer is on the line. They agree to meet, but when?

"What about a week from Monday?" suggests the lawyer.

"That's a bad day," replies Mr. Smith, "what about two weeks from today?"

The lawyer would prefer to call back later to verify this, and Smith agrees.

The rest of the family is engaged in its usual pursuits. Junior, daydreaming about vacation at his public school, has sassed his teacher. The furious man has awarded him extra homework, and ordered him to stay in for recess, while his friends ran about the playground pointing imaginary pistols and crying "Bang! Bang!" at each other.

Susan, a more amenable child, has passed a less eventful morning, apart from forgetting her sneakers and gym shorts, which has kept her out of the gym class.

Mrs. Smith's morning has included a session with the cleaning woman, who was late. As so often, Mrs. Smith longs for a full-time maid, and has already gone over the linoleum with the dustmop before Mrs. Jenks turns up. The junkman has called, so have the garbage men, leaving, as usual, spilled garbage at the back entrance. However by eleven she is men, leaving, as usual, spilt rubbish at the back entrance. However by eleven she is on her way to the shops, carrier in hand and baby in his pram. Passing the carpark she meets her friend Mrs. Worseley, who has brought in the runabout, and stops for a chat. Then she drops in at the dairy, then gives her week-end order at the grocer's, including a stock of tins. She inspects the fishmonger's stock, but decides finally on a joint from the butcher. After paying the bread-bill at the confectioner's and making a call at the green-grocer's, she goes to the chemist's for a remedy for Mr. Smith's chronic catarrh. Slipping some letters from her hand-bag into the pillar-box, she finds her duties are over. She does a little window-shopping, meets more friends, and by one is home to give the children lunch.

Mr. Smith has his lunch at a pub with several office acquaintances. One, disconsolate because the boss has refused him a rise, orders a whiskey and soda; the others content themselves with their usual halves of bitter. Lunch is Vienna steak with runner beans and chips. The men refuse cheese and biscuits, but round off the meal with white coffee. As he leaves, Mr. Smith asks the barmaid for a packet of cigarettes.

On his way back to work Mr.

on her way to the stores, shopping cart in hand and baby in his stroller. Passing the parking place she meets her friend Mrs. Worseley, who has brought in the station wagon, and stops for a talk. Then she goes to the supermarket and stops at the dairy counter, then gives her weekend order at the grocery counter, including a stock of canned goods. She inspects the fresh-fish department, but decides finally on a roast from the butcher. After buying bread at the bakery counter and buying some fruit and vegetables, she goes to the drugstore for a prescription for Mr. Smith's asthma. Slipping some letters from her handbag into the mailbox, she finds her duties are over. She does a little window shopping, meets more friends, and by one is home to give the children lunch.

Mr. Smith has his lunch at a bar and grill with several office acquaintances. One, disconsolate because the boss has refused him a raise, orders a scotch and soda; the others content themselves with their usual bottles of beer. Lunch is Vienna steak with string beans and French fried potatoes. The men refuse cheese and crackers, but round off the meal with coffee with cream. As he leaves, Mr. Smith asks the waitress for a pack of cigarettes.

On his way back to work

Smith has his shoes polished. The afternoon passes quietly; he leaves at half-past five and takes the train home.

Johnny is working hard, but asks as his father comes in, "Dad, can I watch a program on the telly before I finish my prep?"

"No, Johnny; the rest of us want to listen to the wireless."

Mr. Smith switches on the radio-gram in the sitting room and before long it is time for dinner.

"Oh," says Mrs. Smith, "I forgot the table-mats and the water-jug." Johnny fetches them and the meal proceeds. Afterwards she distributes sweets to the children before bed-time.

Later, as the Smiths sit before the fire, Mrs. Smith retails the day's gossip. "Mrs. Braithwaite is very ill; Dr. Robson wants to call in Mr. Peddy, the surgeon, for a consultation. Mrs. Worseley's boy has a crush on some girl, and really it's just as well it's time for his call-up. The Joneses are thinking of taking in a lodger. There's going to be a whist-drive for the Church, and a bun-fight for the Sunday School; I told the vicar we'd go."

"What about tomorrow?"

"Let's pay a visit to Auntie Meg."

"Should we take the children to the flicks?"

"But there's always such a queue on Saturdays."

Mr. Smith has his shoes shined. The afternoon passes quietly; he leaves at half past five and takes the train home.

Junior is working hard, but asks as his father comes in, "Dad, can I watch a program on the TV before I finish my homework?"

"No, Junior; the rest of us want to listen to the radio."

Mr. Smith switches on the radio-phonograph in the living room and before long it is time for dinner.

"Oh," says Mrs. Smith, "I forgot the place mats and the pitcher." Junior brings them in and the meal proceeds. Afterward she distributes candy to the children before bedtime.

Later, as the Smiths sit before the fire, Mrs. Smith tells of the day's gossip. "Mrs. Braithwaite is very ill; Dr. Robson wants to call in Dr. Peddy, the surgeon, for a consultation. Mrs. Worseley's boy has a crush on some girl, and really it's just as well he's going to be drafted. The Joneses are thinking of taking in a roomer. There's going to be a bingo party for the Church, and a picnic for the Sunday School; I told the minister we'd go."

"What about tomorrow?"

"Let's pay a visit to Auntie Meg."

"Should we take the children to the movies?"

"That's true. Well, let's do the washing-up." As she washes the crockery and cutlery, Mrs. Smith stacks it on the draining-board; Mr. Smith goes through a couple of dish-cloths in the process of drying-up. A plate gets broken, but the pieces are soon tidied into the dust-bin. "Well," says Mr. Smith as he turns out the lights, "it's not been a bad day, and anyhow we can have a good lie-in tomorrow morning."

"But there's always such a line on Saturdays."

"That's true. Well, let's do the dishes." As she washes the dishes and silver, Mrs. Smith stacks it on the drainboard; Mr. Smith goes through a couple of dish towels in the process of dish drying. A plate gets broken, but the pieces are soon swept up and put into the garbage pail. "Well," says Mr. Smith as he turns out the lights, "it's not been a bad day, and anyhow we can sleep late tomorrow morning."

There you have the two Mr. Smiths and their families; all of them human, all of them thinking that they *share* the English language. That is, until they cross the Atlantic Ocean and are actually face to face.

At that point exasperation sets in, in the biggest way. It is not merely a matter of nouns; the disease of non-comprehension has by now infected the adverbs—and who can tell where it will next show its symptoms?

As it is, an American who asks an Englishman when some event will take place, and gets the answer, "Presently," expects it to happen. When it doesn't, he thinks dark thoughts of British inefficiency, dilatoriness and heaven knows what. But the Englishman means not "now" or "at once"; in his own terms he is saying "soon," or at least "in the foreseeable future." Similarly an Englishman in America asking for something to be brought "directly," and not getting it "directly," will begin to mutter about the service. He will be ignorant of the fact that he should have said, "right away."

Other misunderstandings are based on the very different lives and ideals of life the two nations maintain. To most Americans, warmth of manner is a part of good manners. They may not happen to feel it naturally at certain moments, but they believe the show of it oils the wheels of life. Everyone knows—and is perfectly correct in knowing—that the Englishman is brought up, whether he is naturally warmhearted or not, to take even the most extreme steps which will preserve his dignity. The American feels the Englishman is appallingly blunt.

To the American who refers tactfully to a late friend's being installed in a "casket" by a "mortician," the Englishman's use of the words "coffin" and "undertaker" is bound to seem brutally brisk. And an Englishman all set to meet an American "older man," and then presented to a rather badly preserved grandfather, is a fine example of bewilderment. You can almost see the questions revolving in his brain. If *this* is "an older man," he broods, what must a really *old* man be? And when does middle age begin?

Nothing of course will restrain well-disposed Englishmen from complimenting American ladies on their "homeliness." All they mean, poor wretches, is that the lady in question has all the comfortable qualities of home; that she is a "homebody." They have been making this mistake for a hundred and fifty years now, and being English it is one they are not likely to abandon. Tradition is of paramount importance to the English, and they don't like to give it up for the sake of mere accuracy.

It is English tradition which makes a good deal of English usage strike Americans as affected. It drives Americans to rage, bewilderment, or despair that an Englishman who spells his name "Featherstonehaugh" should pronounce it "Fanshaw." One American who had a heavy dose of Fanshaw talk at a dinner party in London was asked if he recommend any sights in the States.

"Of course," he told them. "The first thing you want to see is Niffels."

"How interesting," the English contingent said, "is there really a place called Niffels?"

"Certainly, Niffels," the American replied positively. "Spelt N-I-A-G-A-R-A F-A-L-L-S."

There is worse to come. The English are, it is perfectly true, terrible snobs. Americans are also very snobbish, but in different ways from the English, who concentrate on class distinctions. This was brought out when the Hon. Nancy Mitford, an English novelist, published an article about the British aristocracy. She quoted a linguistic study of "Upper Class British Usage," which pointed out that one of the main ways you can spot an English aristocrat when you see him is by his choice of words. It seems that the aristocrat eats *vegetables*, and *puddings*, not *greens* and *sweets*; he lives in a *house*—which is not necessarily a *home*; he is *sick* when he vomits, not *ill*. As physical decay sets in, he needs *false teeth*, not *dentures*; and should the worst befall, he goes *mad* not *mental*. Americans living in England were baffled by the conception of one vocabulary for the rich and another for the poor. They hardly knew whether to get *mad* or *mental*; they did know that they felt neither *sick* nor *ill*, just ready to throw up. Another wedge had been driven between English and American use of our—nominally—joint language.

The real crux of the matter is that the English as a group have a maddeningly defensive and possessive attitude to the language. Every Englishman believes that everyone in the world really understands English and hangs on to a pretense of incomprehension in a sheer desire to be irritating. Every Englishman also knows that no one but an Englishman born and bred will ever, ever learn to speak the language properly. It never occurs to the English that Americans outnumber them four to one, have been speaking the language for a long time, and are quite as at home with it as they are themselves. The result is that one of the highest compliments an Englishman feels that he can pay an American is to say; "But one wouldn't know from the way you speak that you were an American at all!" Nothing will ever persuade an Englishman that Americans have not distorted his language, either through willfulness or sheer ignorance. An American author living in England recently received proofs from her London publisher. A list of notes attached to the cover ran, "Please eliminate the following Americanisms and other mistakes." Of course, no Englishman, however often he hears them, will bother to distinguish one regional American accent from another; to him, the standard accent of every American is a hideous whine down the nose. It is not that he doesn't hear the difference; he does—but he just sees no reason to admit that it exists. Americans, he tells himself, talk Yankee, poor fellows; and that's all there is to it.

On their side, it is only fair to say that Americans have some equally well-dug-in beliefs about English speech. There is cockney English, which is hilarious. And there is the right-o-cheerio English, the kind with the monocle, which is fancy. Both kinds are "an English accent" —a phrase which never fails to cut an Englishman to the quick.

What's to be done? Are we to go on talking forever in our Yankee and English accents, saying "lorry" when we mean "truck," and "flashlight" when we mean "torch," and annoying each other silly in the verbal tug of war? Isn't there a Standard English we could all use? No.

There is probably only one consolation. Other nations that try to use English get in even worse tangles. When after World War II

English-speaking French diplomats appealed to the United States for wheat, using the English term, "corn," corn they got, quantities of ripe, superabundant, golden maize. For a whole year the French ungratefully munched corn bread, then rushed out to scribble on their walls with a patriotic fervor they had not felt since Napoleon— "YANCK GO HOM."

Some Americans—and some Englishmen too—would like to bring about a sort of linguistic Boston Tea Party, and split our language formally into American and English. It isn't likely this plan would work, though. There is a growing body of English people that feels secretly stimulated by American speech, knowing it is keeping the old language from dying on its feet. They manage to keep up to date, through movies and magazines—at least up to about last year's date. Whatever the minor difficulties may be, they feel the most important message is one they often hear from screen gangsters: "Keep talking!" Or, as they would say themselves, "Don't let me interrupt you."

A POE-'EM OF PASSION

C. F. LUMMIS

It was many and many a year ago,
　　On an island near the sea,
That a maiden lived whom you mightn't know
　　By the name of Cannibalee;
And this maiden she lived with no other thought
　　Than a passionate fondness for me.

I was a child, and she was a child—
　　Tho' her tastes were adult Feejee—
But she loved with a love that was more than love,
　　My yearning Cannibalee;
With a love that could take me roast or fried
　　Or raw, as the case might be.

And that is the reason that long ago,
　　In that island near the sea,
I had to turn the tables and eat
　　My ardent Cannibalee—
Not really because I was fond of her,
　　But to check her fondness for me.

LIFE'S DARKEST MOMENT

But the stars never rise but I think of the size
 Of my hot-potted Cannibalee,
And the moon never stares but it brings me nightmares
 Of my spare-rib Cannibalee;
And all the night-tide she is restless inside,
Is my still indigestible dinner-belle bride,
In her pallid tomb, which is Me,
In her solemn sepulcher, Me.

MARK TWAIN IN ITALY

(From "The Innocents Abroad")

In this connection I wish to say one word about Michael Angelo
Buonarotti. I used to worship the mighty genius of Michael Angelo

—that man who was great in poetry, painting, sculpture, architecture —great in everything he undertook. But I do not want Michael Angelo for breakfast—for luncheon—for dinner—for tea—for supper—for between meals. I like a change occasionally. In Genoa he designed everything; in Milan he or his pupils designed everything; he designed the Lake of Como; in Padua, Verona, Venice, Bologna, who did we ever hear of, from guides, but Michael Angelo? In Florence he painted everything, designed everything nearly, and what he did not design he used to sit on a favourite stone and look at, and they showed us the stone. In Pisa he designed everything but the old shot-tower, and they would have attributed that to him if it had not been so awfully out of the perpendicular. He designed the piers of Leghorn and the custom-house regulations of Civita Vecchia. But here—here it is frightful. He designed St. Peter's; he designed the Pantheon, the uniform of the Pope's soldiers, the Tiber, the Vatican, the Coliseum, the Capital, the Tarpeian Rock, the Barberini Palace, St. John Lateran, the Campagna, the Appian Way, the Seven Hills, the Baths of Caracalla, the Claudian Aqueduct, the Cloaca Maxima—the eternal bore designed the Eternal City, and unless all men and books do lie, he painted everything in it! Dan said the other day to the guide, "Enough, enough, enough! Say no more! Lump the whole thing! say that the Creator made Italy from designs by Michael Angelo!"

I never felt so fervently thankful, so soothed, so tranquil, so filled with a blessed peace, as I did yesterday, when I learned that Michael Angelo was dead.

But we have taken it out of this guide. He has marched us through miles of pictures and sculpture in the vast corridors of the Vatican; and through miles of pictures and sculpture in twenty other places; he has shown us the great pictures in the Sistine Chapel, and frescoes enough to fresco the heavens—pretty much all done by Michael Angelo. So with him we have played that game which has vanquished so many guides for us—imbecility and idiotic questions. These creatures never suspect; they have no idea of a sarcasm.

He shows us a figure, and says: "Statoo Brunzo." (Bronze statue.)

We look at it indifferently, and the doctor asks: "By Michael Angelo?"

"No—not know who."

Then he shows us the ancient Roman Forum. The doctor asks: "Michael Angelo?"

A stare from the guide. "No—thousan' year before he is born."

Then an Egyptian obelisk. Again: "Michael Angelo?"

"Oh, *mon Dieu,* genteelmen! Zis is *two* thousan' year before he is born!"

He grows so tired of the unceasing question sometimes, that he dreads to show us anything at all. The wretch has tried all the ways he can think of to make us comprehend that Michael Angelo is only responsible for the creation of a part of the world, but somehow he has not succeeded yet. Relief for overtasked eyes and brain from study and sight-seeing is necessary, or we shall become idiotic sure enough. Therefore this guide must continue to suffer. If he does not enjoy it, so much the worse for him. We do.

In this place I may as well jot down a chapter concerning those necessary nuisances, European guides. Many a man has wished in his heart he could do without his guide; but, knowing he could not, has wished he could get some amusement out of him as a remuneration for the affliction of his society. We accomplished this latter matter, and if our experience can be made useful to others they are welcome to it.

Guides know about enough English to tangle everything up so that a man can make neither head nor tail of it. They know their story by heart—the history of every statue, painting, cathedral, or other wonder they show you. They know it and tell it as a parrot would—and if you interrupt, and throw them off the track, they have to go back and begin over again. All their lives long they are employed in showing strange things to foreigners and listening to their bursts of admiration. It is human nature to take delight in exciting admiration. It is what prompts children to say "smart" things, and do absurd ones, and in other ways "show off" when company is present. It is what makes gossips turn out in rain and storm to go and be the first to tell a startling bit of news. Think, then, what a passion it becomes with a guide, whose privilege is every day to show to strangers wonders that throw them into perfect ecstasies of admiration! He gets so that he could not by any possibility live in a soberer atmosphere. After we discovered this, we never went into ecstasies any more—we never admired anything—we never showed any but impassible faces and stupid indifference in the presence of the sublimest wonders a guide had to display. We had found their weak point. We have made good use of it ever since. We have made some of those people savage at times, but we have never lost our own serenity.

The doctor asks the questions generally, because he can keep his countenance, and look more like an inspired idiot, and throw more imbecility into the tone of his voice than any man that lives. It comes natural to him.

The guides in Genoa are delighted to secure an American party, because Americans so much wonder, and deal so much in sentiment and emotion before any relic of Columbus. Our guide there fidgeted about as if he had swallowed a spring mattress. He was full of animation—full of impatience. He said—

"Come wis me, gentlemen!—come! I show you ze letter writing by Christopher Colombo!—write it himself!—write it wis his own hand! —come!"

He took us to the municipal palace. After much impressive fumbling of keys and opening of locks, the stained and aged document was spread before us. The guide's eyes sparkled. He danced about us and tapped the parchment with his finger.

"What I tell you, genteelmen! Is it not so? See! handwriting Christopher Colombo!—write it himself!"

We looked indifferent—unconcerned. The doctor examined the document very deliberately, during a painful pause.—Then he said, without any show of interest—

"Ah—Ferguson—what—what did you say was the name of the party who wrote this?"

"Christopher Colombo! ze great Christopher Colombo!"

Another deliberate examination.

"Ah—did he write it himself, or—or how?"

"He write it himself!—Christopher Colombo, he's own handwriting, write by himself!"

Then the doctor laid the document down and said—

"Why, I have seen boys in America only fourteen years old that could write better than that."

"But zis is ze great Christo——"

"I don't care who it is! It's the worse writing I ever saw. Now you mustn't think you can impose on us because we are strangers. We are not fools, by a good deal. If you have got any specimens of penmanship of real merit, trot them out!—and if you haven't, drive on!"

We drove on. The guide was considerably shaken up, but he made one more venture. He had something which he thought would overcome us. He said—

"Ah, genteelmen, you come wis me! I show you beautiful, oh magnificent bust Christopher Colombo!—splendid, grand, magnificent!"

He brought us before the beautiful bust—for it *was* beautiful—and sprang back and struck an attitude.

"Ah, look, genteelmen!—beautiful, grand,—bust Christopher Colombo!—beautiful bust, beautiful pedestal!"

The doctor put on his eyeglass—procured for such occasions.

"Ah—what did you say this gentleman's name was?"

"Christopher Colombo!—ze great Christopher Colombo!"

"Christopher Colombo—the great Christopher Colombo. Well, what did *he* do?"

"Discover America!—discover America. Oh, ze devil!"

"Discover America. No—that statement will hardly wash. We are just from America ourselves. We heard nothing about it. Christopher Colombo—pleasant name—is—is he dead?"

"Oh, corpo di Baccho!—three hundred year!"

"What did he die of?"

"I do not know!—I cannot tell."

"Small-pox, think?"

"I do not know, genteelmen!—I do not know what he die of!"

"Measles, likely?"

"Maybe—maybe—I do *not* know—I think he die of somethings."

"Parents living?"

"Im-posseeble!"

"Ah—which is the bust, and which is the pedestal?"

"Santa Maria!—*zis* ze bust!—*zis* ze pedestal!"

"Ah, I see, I see—happy combination—very happy combination, indeed. Is—is this the first time this gentleman was ever on a bust?"

That joke was lost on the foreigner—guides cannot master the subtleties of the American joke.

We have made it interesting to this Roman guide. Yesterday we spent three or four hours in the Vatican, again, that wonderful world of curiosities. We came very near expressing interest, sometimes—even admiration—it was very hard to keep from it. We succeeded though. Nobody else ever did in the Vatican museums. The guide was bewildered—non-plussed. He walked his legs off nearly, hunting up extraordinary things, and exhausted all his ingenuity on us but it was a failure; we never showed any interest in anything. He had reserved what he considered to be his greatest wonder till the last—a royal Egyptian mummy, the best preserved in the world perhaps. He took us there. He felt so sure this time, that some of his old enthusiasm came back to him—

"See, genteelmen!—Mummy! Mummy!"

The eyeglass came up as calmly, as deliberately as ever.

"Ah—Ferguson—what did I understand you to say the gentleman's name was?"

"Name?—he got no name!—Mummy!—'Gyptian mummy!"

"Yes, yes. Born here?"

"No! *'Gyptian* mummy!"

"Ah, just so. Frenchman, I presume?"

"No!—not Frenchman, not Roman!—born in Egypta!"

"Born in Egypta. Never heard of Egypta before. Foreign locality, likely. Mummy—mummy. How calm he is—how self-possessed. Is, ah—is he dead?"

"Oh, *sacré bleu,* been dead three thousan' year!"

The doctor turned on him savagely—

"Here, now, what do you mean by such conduct as this! Playing us for Chinamen because we are strangers and trying to learn! Trying to impose your vile second-hand carcases on *us!*—thunder and lightning, I've a notion to—to—if you've got a nice *fresh* corpse, fetch him out!—or by George we'll brain you!"

We make it exceedingly interesting for this Frenchman. However, he has paid us back, partly, without knowing it. He came to the hotel this morning to ask if we were up, and he endeavoured as well as he could to describe us, so that the landlord would know which persons he meant. He finished with the casual remark that we were lunatics. The observation was so innocent and so honest that it amounted to a very good thing for a guide to say.

There is one remark (already mentioned), which never has failed to disgust these guides. We use it always, when we can think of nothing else to say. After they have exhausted their enthusiasm pointing out to us and praising the beauties of some ancient bronze image or broken-legged statue, we look at it stupidly and in silence for five, ten, fifteen minutes—as long as we can hold out, in fact—and then ask—

"Is—is he dead?"

That conquers the serenest of them. It is not what they are looking for—especially a new guide. Our Roman Ferguson is the most patient, unsuspecting, long-suffering subject we have had yet. We shall be sorry to part with him. We have enjoyed his society very much. We trust he has enjoyed ours, but we are harassed with doubts.

CATCHING THE MORNING TRAIN

MAX ADELER (1841–1915)

I find that one of the most serious objections to living out of town lies in the difficulty experienced in catching the early morning train by which I must reach the city and my business. It is by no means a pleasant matter, under any circumstances, to have one's movements regulated by a time-table, and to be obliged to rise to breakfast and to leave home at a certain hour, no matter how strong the temptation to delay may be.

But sometimes the horrible punctuality of the train is productive of absolute suffering. For instance: I look at my watch when I get out of bed and find that I have apparently plenty of time, so I dress leisurely, and sit down to the morning meal in a frame of mind which is calm and serene. Just as I crack my first egg I hear the down train from Wilmington. I start in alarm; and taking out my watch I compare it with the clock and find that it is eleven minutes slow, and that I have only five minutes left in which to get to the depot.

I endeavor to scoop the egg from the shell, but it burns my fingers, the skin is tough, and after struggling with it for a moment, it mashes into a hopeless mass. I drop it in disgust and seize a roll; while I scald my tongue with a quick mouthful of coffee. Then I place the roll in my mouth while my wife hands me my satchel and tells me she thinks she hears the whistle. I plunge madly around looking for my umbrella, then I kiss the family good-by as well as I can with a mouth full of roll, and dash toward the door.

Just as I get to the gate I find that I have forgotten my duster and the bundle my wife wanted me to take up to the city to her aunt. Charging back, I snatch them up and tear down the gravel-walk in a frenzy. I do not like to run through the village; it is undignified and it attracts attention; but I walk furiously. I go faster and faster as I get away from the main street. When half the distance is accomplished, I actually do hear the whistle; there can be no doubt about it this time. I long to run, but I know that if I do I will excite that abominable speckled dog sitting by the sidewalk a little distance ahead of me. Then I really see the train coming around the curve close by the depot, and I feel that I *must* make better time, and I do.

The dog immediately manifests an interest in my movements. He tears down the street after me, and is speedily joined by five or six other dogs, which frolic about my legs and bark furiously. Sundry small boys as I go plunging past, contribute to the excitement by whistling with their fingers, and the men who are at work upon the new meeting-house stop to look at me and exchange jocular remarks with each other. I do feel ridiculous; but I must catch the train at all hazards.

I become desperate when I have to slacken my pace until two or three women who are standing upon the sidewalk, discussing the infamous price of butter, scatter to let me pass. I arrive within a few yards of the station with my duster flying in the wind, with my coat tails in a horizontal position, and with the speckled dog nipping my heels, just as the train begins to move. I put on extra pressure, resolving to get the train or perish, and I reach it just as the last car is going by. I seize the hand-rail; I am jerked violently around, but finally, after a desperate effort, I get upon the step with my knees, and am hauled in by the brakeman, hot, dusty and mad, with my trousers torn across the knees, my legs bruised and three ribs of my umbrella broken.

Just as I reach a comfortable seat in the car, the train stops, and then backs up on the siding, where it remains for half an hour while the engineer repairs a dislocated valve. The anger which burns in my bosom as I reflect upon what now is proved to have been the folly of that race is increased as I look out of the window and observe the speckled dog engaged with his companions in an altercation over a bone. A man who permits his dog to roam about the streets nipping the legs of every one who happens to go at a more rapid gait than a walk, is unfit for association with civilized beings. He ought to be placed on a desert island in mid-ocean, and be compelled to stay there.

ARAMINTA AND THE AUTOMOBILE

CHARLES BATTELL LOOMIS (1861–1911)

Some persons spend their surplus on works of art; some spend it on Italian gardens and pergolas; there are those who sink it in golf, and I have heard of those who expended it on charity.

None of these forms of getting away with money appeal to Araminta and myself. As soon as it was ascertained that the automobile was practicable and would not cost a king's ransom, I determined to devote my savings to the purchase of one.

Araminta and I lived in a suburban town; she because she loves Nature and I because I love Araminta. We have been married for five years.

I am a bank clerk in New York, and morning and night I go through the monotony of railway travel, and for one who is forbidden to use his eyes on the train and who does not play cards it *is* monotony, for in the morning my friends are either playing cards or else reading their papers, and one does not like to urge the claims of conversation on one who is deep in politics or the next play of his antagonist; so my getting to business and coming back are in the nature of purgatory. I therefore hailed the automobile as a Heaven-sent means of swift motion with an agreeable companion, and with no danger of encountering either newspapers or cards. I have seen neither newspaper reading nor card-playing going on in any automobile.

The community in which I live is not progressive, and when I said that I expected to buy an automobile as soon as my ship came in I was frowned upon by my neighbors. Several of them have horses, and all, or nearly all, have feet. The horsemen were not more opposed to my proposed ownership than the footmen—I should say pedestrians. They all thought automobiles dangerous and a menace to public peace, but of course I pooh-poohed their fears and, being a person of a good deal of stability of purpose, I went on saving my money, and in course of time I bought an automobile of the electric sort.

Araminta is plucky, and I am perfectly fearless. When the automobile was brought home and housed in the little barn that is on our property, the man who had backed it in told me that he had orders to stay and show me how it worked, but I laughed at him—good-naturedly yet firmly. I said, "Young man, experience teaches more in half an hour than books or precepts do in a year. A would-be newspaper man does not go to a school of journalism if he is wise; he gets a position on a newspaper and learns for himself, and through his mistakes. I know that one of these levers is to steer by, that another lets loose the power, and that there is a foot-brake. I also know that the machine is charged, and I need to know no more. Good day."

Thus did I speak to the young man, and he saw that I was a person of force and discretion, and he withdrew to the train and I never saw him again.

Araminta had been to Passaic shopping, but she came back while I was out in the barn looking at my new purchase, and she joined me there. I looked at her lovingly, and she returned the look. Our joint ambition was realized; we were the owners of an automobile, and we were going out that afternoon.

Why is it that cheap barns are so flimsily built? I know that our barn is cheap because the rent for house and barn is less than what many a clerk, city pent, pays for a cramped flat, but again I ask, why are they flimsily built? I have no complaint to make. If my barn had been built of good stout oak I might to-day be in a hospital.

It happened this way. Araminta said, "Let me get in, and we will take just a little ride to see how it goes," and I out of my love for her said, "Wait just a few minutes, dearest, until I get the hang of the thing. I want to see how much go she has and just how she works."

Araminta has learned to obey my slightest word, knowing that love is at the bottom of all my commands, and she stepped to one side while I entered the gayly-painted vehicle and tried to move out of the barn. I moved out. But I backed. Oh, blessed, cheaply built barn. My way was not restricted to any appreciable extent. I shot gayly through the barn into the hen yard, and the sound of the ripping clapboards frightened the silly hens who were enjoying a dust-bath, and they fled in more directions than there were fowls.

I had not intended entering the hen yard, and I did not wish to stay there, so I kept on out, the wire netting not being what an automobile would call an obstruction. I never lose my head, and when I heard Araminta screaming in the barn, I called out cheerily to her, "I'll be back in a minute, dear, but I'm coming another way."

And I did come another way. I came all sorts of ways. I really don't know what got into the machine, but she now turned to the left and made for the road, and then she ran along on her two left wheels for a moment, and then seemed about to turn a somersault, but changed her mind, and still veering to the left, kept on up the road, passing my house at a furious speed, and making for the open country. With as much calmness as I could summon I steered her, but I think I steered her a little too much, for she turned toward my house.

I reached one end of the front piazza at the same time that Araminta reached the other end of it. I had the right of way, and she deferred to me just in time. I removed the vestibule storm door. It was late in March, and I did not think we should have any more use for it that season. And we didn't.

I had ordered a strongly-built machine, and I was now glad of it, because a light and weak affair that was merely meant to run along on a level and unobstructed road would not have stood the assault on my piazza. Why, my piazza did not stand it. It caved in, and made work for an already overworked local carpenter who was behind-hand with his orders. After I had passed through the vestibule, I applied the brake, and it worked. The path is not a cinder one, as I think them untidy, so I was not more than muddied. I was up in an instant, and looked at the still enthusiastic machine with admiration.

"Have you got the hang of it?" said Araminta.

Now that's one thing I like about Araminta. She does not waste words over non-essentials. The point was not that I had damaged the piazza. I needed a new one, anyway. The main thing was that I was trying to get the hang of the machine, and she recognized that fact instantly.

I told her that I thought I had, and that if I had pushed the lever in the right way at first, I should have come out of the barn in a more conventional way.

She again asked me to let her ride, and as I now felt that I could better cope with the curves of the machine I allowed her to get in.

"Don't lose your head," said I.

"I hope I shan't," said she dryly.

"Well, if you have occasion to leave me, drop over the back. Never jump ahead. That is a fundamental rule in runaways of all kinds."

Then we started, and I ran the motor along for upward of half a mile after I had reached the highway, which I did by a short cut through a field at the side of our house. There is only a slight rail fence surrounding it, and my machine made little of that. It really seemed to delight in what some people would have called danger.

"Araminta, are you glad that I saved up for this?"

"I am mad with joy," said the dear thing, her face flushed with excitement mixed with expectancy. Nor were her expectations to be disappointed. We still had a good deal to do before we should have ended our first ride.

So far I had damaged property to a certain extent, but I had no one but myself to reckon with, and I was providing work for people. I always have claimed that he who makes work for two men where there was only work for one before, is a public benefactor, and that day I was the friend of carpenters and other mechanics.

Along the highway we flew, our hearts beating high, but never in our mouths, and at last we saw a team approaching us. By "a team" I mean a horse and buggy. I was raised in Connecticut, where a team is anything you choose to call one.

The teamster saw us. Well, perhaps I should not call him a teamster

"Says here a child can assemble this. Run out and borrow a child."

(although he was one logically); he was our doctor, and, as I say, he saw us.

Now I think it would have been friendly in him, seeing that I was more or less of a novice at the art of automobiling, to have turned to the left when he saw that I was inadvertently turning to the left, but the practice of forty years added to a certain native obstinacy made him turn to the right, and he met me at the same time that I met him.

The horse was not hurt, for which I am truly glad, and the doctor joined us, and continued with us for a season, but his buggy was demolished.

Of course I am always prepared to pay for my pleasure, and though it was not, strictly speaking, my pleasure to deprive my physician of his turn-out, yet if he *had* turned out it wouldn't have happened—and, as I say, I was prepared to get him a new vehicle. But he was very unreasonable; so much so that, as he was crowding us—for the seat was not built for more than two, and he is stout—I at last told him that I intended to run around and carry him home, as we were out for pleasure, and he was giving us pain.

I will confess that the events of the last few minutes had rattled me somewhat, and I did not feel like turning just then, as the road was narrow. I knew that the road turned of its own accord a half-mile farther on, and so I determined to wait.

"I want to get out," said the doctor tartly, and just as he said so Araminta stepped on the brake, accidentally. The doctor got out—in front. With great presence of mind I reversed, and so we did not run over him. But he was furious and sulphurous, and that is why I have changed to homeopathy. He was the only allopathic doctor in Brantford.

I suppose that if I had stopped and apologized, he would have made up with me, and I would not have got angry with him, but I couldn't stop. The machine was now going as she had done when I left the barn, and we were backing into town.

Through it all I did not lose my coolness. I said: "Araminta, look out behind, which is ahead of us, and if you have occasion to jump now, do it in front, which is behind," and Araminta understood me.

She sat sideways, so that she could see what was going on, but that might have been seen from any point of view, for we were the only things going on—or backing.

Pretty soon we passed the wreck of the buggy, and then we saw the horse grazing on dead grass by the roadside, and at last we came on a few of our townfolk who had seen us start, and were now come out to welcome us home. But I did not go home just then. I should have done so if the machine had minded me and turned in at our driveway, but it did not.

Across the way from us there is a fine lawn leading up to a beautiful greenhouse full of rare orchids, and other plants. It is the pride of my very good neighbor, Jacob Rawlinson.

The machine, as if moved by *malice prépense*, turned just as we came to the lawn, and began to back at railroad speed.

I told Araminta that if she was tired of riding, now was the best time to stop; that she ought not to overdo it, and that I was going to get out myself as soon as I had seen her off.

I saw her off.

Then after one ineffectual jab at the brake, I left the machine hurriedly, and as I sat down on the sposhy lawn I heard a tremendous but not unmusical sound of falling glass—

I tell Araminta that it isn't the running of an automobile that is expensive. It is the stopping of it.

Any Further Remarks?

FLOORWALKER IMPERSONATOR

SCOTT CORBETT

Mr. Frisbie said it was so nice out that he thought he wouldn't wear any hat when he went out to lunch. He said so silently, because he was sitting in his office alone at the time.

So he went hatless to lunch, and in the midst of lunch it occurred to him that the next day was March 20, which by a coincidence was the day he was once married upon.

The nearest department store was just around the corner, and so was Mr. Frisbie about three minutes later.

He strolled around looking at the available merchandise, and he had not been there any time at all until a large woman came up to him and said where would she find garters?

Mr. Frisbie said in the usual place, madam. He said that to himself too, however. Out loud he said he didn't know, he wasn't—er—and she looked annoyed. She said oh, wasn't he a floorwalker? He said no, and the large woman walked away after giving him a look which as much as said well then why didn't he stop masquerading as one.

Mr. Frisbie wished he had worn a hat. He edged along counters trying to look interested in what was in the showcases, but it didn't do any good. Another woman wanted to know where she could find children's earmuffs, red ones? It was too much trouble to keep explaining about himself, so Mr. Frisbie took a shot in the dark and said third floor, madam, and hoped he was right, or at least close.

He had got as far as the cosmetics counter when he noticed that a floorwalker was looking at him sort of askance, as if he suspected him of being a rookie floorwalker who had strayed into the wrong department.

Mr. Frisbie was about to ask him where he would find men's clothes, so as to show the man he wasn't a floorwalker, too, when the man suddenly cleared his throat and said, where would he find men's clothes?

Mr. Frisbie said wasn't he a floorwalker? The man said no, wasn't *he*? Then they had a good laugh, which drew disapproving glances from nearby lady customers, who obviously felt that store employees should not stand around together guffawing on company time.

Mr. Frisbie said he bet if they stood there for a minute someone would ask them something. People did. They sent a woman to the basement for thimbles, and a man up to the seventh floor for furniture, and then Mr. Frisbie said come to think of it he believed the store only had six floors. His co-worker said never mind that, get the snappy old gent coming with the cane and the derby who would probably want to know where he could find silk negligees.

Then the old gent came up to them and said, could he help them? He was a real floorwalker, just coming back from lunch, and after Mr. Frisbie had left in a hurry he wondered if the old gent ever heard anything from that man they sent to the seventh floor.

DAVE GERARD, THE SATURDAY EVENING POST

"While you're up—would you look at the roast, give the peas a stir, salt the potatoes, make some coffee, open a can of peaches, and set the table?"

THE CATFISH

OLIVER HERFORD (1863–1935)

The saddest fish that swims the briny ocean,
   The Catfish I bewail.
I cannot even think without emotion
   Of his distressful tail.
When with my pencil once I tried to draw one,
   (I dare not show it here)
Mayhap it is because I never saw one,
   The picture looked so queer.
I vision him half feline and half fishy,
   A paradox in twins,
Unmixable as vitriol and vichy—
   A thing of fur and fins,
A feline Tantalus, forever chasing
   His fishy self to rend;
His finny self forever self-effacing
   In circles without end.
This tale may have a Moral running through it
   As Aesop had in his;
If so, dear reader, you are welcome to it,
   If you know what it is!

HOW TO TELL BAD NEWS

ANONYMOUS

Mr. H., on returning from a long business trip abroad: Ha! Steward, how are you, my old boy? How do things go on at home?
   Steward: Bad enough, your honor; your dog's dead, sir.
   H: Poor Mag! So he's gone. How came he to die?
   S: Overeat himself, sir.
   H: Did he? A greedy dog; why, what did he get he liked so well?
   S: Horseflesh, sir; he died of eating horseflesh.

H: How came he to get so much horseflesh?

S: All your father's horses, sir.

H: What! Are they dead, too?

S: Ay, sir; they died of overwork.

H: And why were they overworked, pray?

S: To carry water, sir.

H: To carry water! and what were they carrying water for?

S: Sure, sir, to put out the fire.

H: Fire! what fire?

S: O, sir, your father's house is burned to the ground.

H: My father's house burned down! and how came it to set on fire?

S: I think, sir, it must have been the torches.

H: Torches! what torches?

S: At your mother's funeral.

H: My mother dead!

S: Ah, poor lady! she never looked up, after it.

H: After what?

S: The loss of your father.

H: My father gone, too?

S: Yes, poor gentleman! he took to his bed as soon as he heard
of it.

H: Heard of what?

S: The bad news, sir, and please your honor.

H: What! *more* miseries! *more* bad news!

S: Yes, sir; your bank has failed, and your credit is lost, and you
are not worth a shilling in the world. I make bold, sir, to meet you
at the train, for I thought you would like to hear the news as quickly
as possible.

WORDS ARE FUNNY—THEY WON'T STAND STILL!

WILFRED FUNK

Words are odd things. Strange hieroglyphics that we scribble down.
Noises that come out of our mouths. I've heard that the actual breath-
force of a word is only about one millionth of a horsepower. But
weak as that sounds, a whispered word can lose a friend for you. Or
put you in jail.

Or even start a riot, as a word once did in Dublin.

Here's what happened.

About a hundred years ago it was an open insult to use the word "shirt" before ladies, so "smock" was invented. But in the course of time "smock" grew disreputable and "shift" was substituted for "smock." Then over the years even "shift" became vulgar. If you can believe it, when the word "shift" was said out loud by an actor in a Dublin theater as recently as 1907, the audience broke up in wild disorder.

In these Bikini days a lady doesn't own much underwear of any kind, at least in comparison with the seven or more petticoats that were *de rigueur* in the 1890's. But whatever she owns isn't called by that vulgar name "underwear." Our modern girl wears "underthings" or "undies" or, as they used to say in times past, indescribables, irrepressibles, ineffables, unutterables, unmentionables, unwhisperables. Within the memory of my generation drawers became step-ins, and later, panties, although it is puzzling to know why stepping into these articles presents a more decent picture than drawing them on. As a matter of fact, "lingerie" is about the nicest way for retailers today to get around this whole embarrassing subject.

You are sitting down, for instance, to a chicken dinner. You say you prefer "white meat." You don't like "dark meat." Why "white" and "dark"? Ah, these phrases cover up two sordid words.

In the era after the Civil War no one ever said "leg" or "breast" out loud, not even referring to poultry. Some phrase had to be invented in order to specify a portion, and "dark meat" and "white meat" got around the untidy situation. Why, even the legs of the tables then were often covered with chintz to prevent an exposure that might be offensive to the more delicate sex.

Americans first became known for their delicacy in the 1830's or 1840's. In that period the word "chair" suddenly became taboo in mixed company. It was too closely connected in men's imagination with the part of a woman's body that sat on it. So the name was changed to "seat." But soon "seat" began to be associated with the "backside" (a circumlocution) and for a while people had only an anonymous piece of furniture on which to rest their *derrières* (another circumlocution).

We may be amused at this Victorian coyness, for we feel we are sophisticated. We don't resort to subterfuges in our speech. We meet this part of life with a direct eye and a frank phrase.

Or do we, always?

Again, from the French *toile*, which means "linen," the word *toilette*, "linen closet," is derived. In English we turned this word into "toilet" as a pleasanter name for quite another place, but because of its associations the word is hardly used anymore in polite society. Neither men nor women go there. Men "wash their hands" while women "powder their noses."

Of course the meaning of a word is a convention—something a group of people have agreed upon. If enough people think certain words are vulgar, they are. Often people change their minds and gutter words become comparatively proper.

There were at least three important eras in history when words that had a sexual tinge fell into disrepute.

The most intense period of Puritanism in the United States was during the time after the Civil War, when legs were "limbs" and covered to the shoe tops. And breasts became "bosoms." And even the word "woman" grew too suggestive and was changed to "female." You know that the first institution of higher education for women was called Vassar Female College. But this was too strong for some stomachs and was expurgated from *Godey's Lady's Book*, the fashion and etiquette magazine of the day. In these same proper decades one never "went to bed." Imagine daring to say the word "bed" out loud in front of a lady! One "lay down" or "went to sleep."

Again, don't feel too superior about all this. You may recall that when Do Hupfelt's delightful song "Let's Put Out the Lights and Go to Bed" was sung over the radio in the 1930's, the censors made him change the title to "Let's Put Out the Lights and Go to Sleep."

Right now in various parts of our country words which even sound like the tabooed Saxon words are considered highly improper. For example, not long ago two women in the south wanted a man arrested for mentioning a bull calf in their presence. According to H. L. Mencken the word "bull" is still *verboten* in the Ozark mountains. Farmers there have a terrible time getting around this obscene term. A bull is called a "gentleman cow," a "top cow," "that cow critter," or just "the old man." The word "bullfrog" is repulsive to them. And one fastidious minister told his flock that Moses was found in the "flags." He balked at the word "bulrushes."

There are two kinds of birds in the Ozarks, "girl birds" and "boy birds."

There are deep reasons behind our fear of words. From earliest history, human beings have believed that there was a direct connection between a thing and its name. Speak of the devil and he is sure to appear. Mention a person you hate or fear and he is likely to arrive. For this reason the Greeks didn't allow their word for cemetery to be associated with death. They named their burying-ground *koimeterion* —that is, "a sleeping place." And the Furies or the Avenging Gods who terrified them, they called, of all things, the *Eumenides*—"the kindly ones"!

We call the art of giving pleasant names to unpleasant or dangerous matters "euphemism," from the Greek *eu*, "well," and *phemizein*, "speak."

But you are a modern. You take no stock in this superstitious nonsense about words. You don't think that merely saying a word will summon disaster.

Are you sure? Let's say you are taking off in a plane from Chicago to the West Coast. The weather is bad. There was a terrible accident on this same flight a day ago . . . a crash in the mountains in which all aboard the plane were killed.

I challenge you to turn to your seat companion and say: "I've never had a plane accident in my life."

Possibly you'll take my dare if the occasion arises, but I'll make a small bet that you'll look around for some wood to knock on!

This superstition about the power of words comes out of the mists of the ages. Thousands of years ago in ancient Egypt the skills of reading and writing were kept a secret of the temple. Word magic gave the priests a hold over the common people. In the Dark Ages the arts of communication were taught only in the monasteries and were again associated with the mysterious rites of religion.

Even in the days of Queen Elizabeth I of England few people could read or write. Most girls had to sign their marriage contracts with a cross. The ability to read and write was thought to be connected with black magic.

We think we can smile at such simplicity. But again we had better not smile too broadly. We are still afraid to say certain words out loud.

When a man discusses his will, how often do you hear him say "When I die"? Isn't it usually "when I'm not around"; "if anything should happen to me"; "if I should get hit by a taxi"? And, as a matter of fact, it isn't too often that a man dies. He "passes away" and becomes not the "dead" but the "late" Mr. Brown. The "deceased." He is not removed to an undertaking establishment but to a "funeral chapel" where he is taken care of by a "mortician" and is carried to the "cemetery," not to the graveyard, in a "casket," not a coffin. The word "coffin" has not appeared in an advertisement for years. To suggest death might invite death.

But we shouldn't feel overly ashamed of our cowardice. The Malays purposely have no name for "tiger," lest the sound of it summon or offend him. The ignorant people of Madagascar never mention the word "lightning" for fear it might strike. Russian peasants have no name for their enemy, the bear. They speak of him as the *myedvyeardy*, or "honey eater," in order to propitiate him. And when a peasant in Hungary meets a mother with a new baby he is likely to say "What an ugly child," in order to placate the evil spirits and make them less jealous. When you start on a skiing trip in Germany your friends will never say, "I hope you don't get hurt." They will say instead, "Hals und Beinbruch," literally, "fracture of the neck and leg."

Coupled with a wish to avoid unpleasant word associations is one to invoke the magic of words for a beneficial purpose—to dignify an activity or a situation.

Nowadays, for instance, the garbage collector is a "sanitary engineer" and his conveyance is a "table-waste disposal truck." The old-fashioned ratcatcher is a "rodent exterminator" and the dogcatcher is a "canine control officer."

Many gas stations refer with pride to their "lubritoriums." Even floorwalkers prefer the title "aisle managers"; and the devised term "realtors" has put the real-estate agent up a social notch.

The old-time corn-doctors first became "chiropodists," and today they are getting to be "podiatrists." Your publicity is no longer handled by a press agent. He is now a "public relations counsel." The drivers of milk wagons are "salesmen"; the poor are "underprivileged"; criminal children are "juvenile delinquents"; servants became "help," help, "maids"; fake pearls are "simulated pearls"; and junkmen are "waste-material dealers." And where do you go for a drink if you ever have one? To a saloon? Not on your life! That vulgar word went out with prohibition. You now have one in "a cocktail lounge," "a café," "a tavern," or, at worst, "a bar."

In these days important prisoners aren't prisoners. They are kept in "protective custody." Dictators have stopped killing their enemies. They merely "liquidate" them. And they never conquer a country. They "liberate" it. Big business men aren't fired, they "resign," or they don't return from a "leave of absence." Radio and television programs aren't paid for by anybody. They come to you "through the courtesy of the sponsor."

Of course the advertising fraternity has long since taken advantage of this necromancy, for they discovered that the right word *can* alter things, at least in the minds of their customers, and they practice their magic on us every day.

For example, you are not asked to buy a large amount of a product. You are sold the "economy size." And how long has it been since you have seen used cars advertised as second-hand cars? They are "reconditioned" or "repossessed." And one Californian promoted his second-hand tires as "experienced tires"! Do you read about a sale of cheap dresses any more? Certainly not. They are "inexpensive" or "very low priced." Few are listed even as bargains. Rather they are "priced at only" so much. Suits are for "men and young men." There are no old men.

One time an experiment was tried. Two counters were arranged with men's hats of identical make displayed on each. On one counter was set a sign saying "Tyrolean." The other counter had no sign. Three times as many men purchased the hats called "Tyrolean" than those that were unnamed.

Another similar experiment was conducted. In the way described above, two lots of nylon stockings, all of the same brand and shade, were placed on two tables. One lot had no label, while the other bore the sign "Gala." Ten times as many of the Gala ones were sold.

Yes, in every area of life, and on every social level, the word magic of the ancients is still with us.

A DESPERATE RACE

J. F. KELLEY

(About 1850)

Some years ago, I was one of a convivial party that met in the principal hotel in the town of Columbus, Ohio, the seat of government of the Buckeye state.

It was a winter's evening, when all without was bleak and stormy and all within were blithe and gay,—when song and story made the circuit of the festive board, filling up the chasms of life with mirth and laughter.

We had met for the express purpose of making a night of it, and the pious intention was duly and most religiously carried out. The Legislature was in session in that town, and not a few of the worthy legislators were present upon this occasion.

One of these worthies I will name, as he not only took a big swath in the evening's entertainment, but he was a man *more* generally known than our worthy President, James K. Polk. That man was the famous Captain Riley, whose "Narrative" of suffering and adventures is pretty generally known all over the civilized world. Captain Riley was a fine, fat, good-humored joker, who at the period of my story was the representative of the Dayton district, and lived near that little city when at home. Well, Captain Riley had amused the company with many of his far-famed and singular adventures, which, being mostly told before and read by millions of people that have seen his book, I will not attempt to repeat.

Many were the stories and adventures told by the company, when it came to the turn of a well-known gentleman who represented the Cincinnati district. As Mr. — is yet among the living, and perhaps not disposed to be the subject of joke or story, I do not feel at liberty to give his name. Mr. — was a slow believer of other men's adventures, and, at the same time, much disposed to magnify himself into a marvellous hero whenever the opportunity offered. As Captain Riley wound up one of his truthful though really marvellous adventures, Mr. — coolly remarked that the captain's story was all very well, but it did not begin to compare with an adventure that he had, "once upon a time," on the Ohio, below the present city of Cincinnati.

"Let's have it!"—"Let's have it!" resounded from all hands.

"Well, gentlemen," said the Senator, clearing his voice for action and knocking the ashes from his cigar against the arm of his chair,— "gentlemen, I am not in the habit of spinning yarns of marvellous or fictitious matters; and therefore it is scarcely necessary to affirm upon the responsibility of my reputation, gentlemen, that what I am about to tell you I most solemnly proclaim to be truth, and—"

"Oh, never mind that: go on, Mr. —," chimed the party.

"Well gentlemen, in 18— I came down the Ohio River, and settled at Losanti, now called Cincinnati. It was at that time but a little settlement of some twenty or thirty log and frame cabins, and where now stand the Broadway Hotel and blocks of stores and dwelling-houses, was the cottage and corn-patch of old Mr. —, the tailor, who, by the bye, bought that land for the making of a coat for one of the settlers. Well, I put up my cabin, with the aid of my neighbors, and put in a patch of corn and potatoes, about where the Fly Market now stands, and set about improving my lot, house, etc.

"Occasionally I took up my rifle and started off with my dog down the river, to look up a little deer or bar meat, then very plenty along the river. The blasted red-skins were lurking about and hovering around the settlement, and every once in a while picked off some of our neighbors or stole our cattle or horses. I hated the red demons, and made no bones of peppering the blasted sarpents whenever I got a sight of them. In fact, the red rascals had a dread of me, and had laid a good many traps to get my scalp, but I wasn't to be catched napping. No, no, gentlemen, I was too well up to 'em for that.

"Well, I started off one morning, pretty early, to take a hunt, and travelled a long way down the river, over the bottoms and hills, but couldn't find no *bar* nor deer. About four o'clock in the afternoon I made tracks for the settlement again. By and by I sees a buck just ahead of me, walking leisurely down the river. I slipped up, with my faithful old dog close in my rear, to within clever shooting-distance, and just as the buck stuck his nose in the drink I drew a bead upon his top-knot, and over he tumbled, and splurged and bounded a while, when I came up and relieved him by cutting his wizen—"

"Well, but what has that to do with an *adventure?*" said Riley.

"Hold on a bit, if you please, gentlemen; by Jove, it had a great deal to do with it. For, while I was busy skinning the hindquarters of the buck, and stowing away the kidney-fat in my hunting-shirt, I heard a noise like the breaking of brush under a moccasin up 'the bottom.' My dog heard it, and started up to reconnoitre, and I lost no time in reloading my rifle. I had hardly got my priming out before my dog raised a howl and broke through the brush toward me with his tail down, as he was not used to doing unless there were wolves, painters (panthers), or Injins about.

"I picked up my knife, and took up my line of march in a skulking trot up the river. The frequent gullies on the lower bank made it tedious travelling there, so I scrabbled up to the upper bank, which was pretty well covered with buckeye and sycamore, and very little underbrush. One peep below discovered to me three as big and strapping red rascals, gentlemen, as you ever clapped your eyes on! Yes, there they came, not above six hundred yards in my rear, shouting and yelling like hounds, and coming after me like all possessed."

"Well," said an old woodsman, sitting at the table, "you took a tree, of course."

"Did I? No, gentlemen, I took no tree just then, but I took to my heels like sixty, and it was just as much as my old dog could do to keep up with me. I run until the whoops of my red-skins grew fainter and fainter behind me, and, clean out of wind, I ventured to look behind me, and there came one single red whelp, puffing and blowing, not three hundred yards in my rear. He had got on to a piece of bottom where the trees were small and scarce. 'Now,' thinks I, 'old fellow, I'll have you.' So I trotted off at a pace sufficient to let my follower gain on me, and when he had got just about near enough I wheeled and fired, and down I brought him, dead as a doornail, at a hundred and twenty yards!"

"Then you skelp'd (scalped) him immediately?" said the back-woodsman.

"Very clear of it, gentlemen; for by the time I got my rifle loaded, here came the other two red-skins, shouting and whooping close on me, and away I broke again like a quarter-horse. I was now about five miles from the settlement, and it was getting toward sunset. I ran till my wind began to be pretty short, when I took a look back, and there they came, snorting like mad buffaloes, one about two or three hundred yards ahead of the other: so I acted possum again until the foremost Injin got pretty well up, and I wheeled and fired at the very moment he was 'drawing a bead' on me: he fell head over stomach into the dirt, and up came the last one."

"So you laid for him, and—" gasped several.

"No," continued the "member," "I didn't lay for him, I hadn't time to load, so I laid my *legs* to ground and started again. I heard every bound he made after me. I ran and ran until the fire flew out of my eyes, and the old dog's tongue hung out of his mouth a quarter of a yard long!"

"Phe-e-e-ew!" whistled somebody.

"Fact, gentlemen. Well, what I was to do I didn't know: rifle empty, no big trees about, and a murdering red Indian not three hundred yards in my rear; and what was worse, just then it occurred to me that I was not a great ways from a big creek (now called Mill Creek), and there I should be pinned at last.

"Just at this juncture, I struck my toe against a root, and down I tumbled, and my old dog over me. Before I could scrabble up—"

"The Indian fired!" gasped the old woodsman.

"He did, gentlemen, and I felt the ball strike me under the shoulder; but that didn't seem to put any embargo upon my locomotion, for as soon as I got up I took off again, quite freshened by my fall! I heard the red-skin close behind me coming booming on, and every minute I expected to have his tomahawk dashed into my head or shoulders.

"Something kind of cool began to trickle down my legs into my boots—"

"Blood, eh? for the shot the varmint gin you," said the old woodsman, in great state of excitement.

"I thought so," said the Senator; "but what do you think it was?"

Not being blood, we were all puzzled to know what the blazes it could be; when Riley observed,—

"I suppose you had—"

"Melted the deer-fat which I had stuck in the breast of my hunting-shirt, and the grease was running down my leg until my feet got so greasy that my heavy boots flew off, and one, hitting the dog, nearly knocked his brains out."

We all grinned, which the "member" noticing, observed,—

"I hope, gentlemen, no man here will presume to think I'm exaggerating?"

"Oh, certainly not! Go on, Mr. —" we all chimed in.

"Well, the ground under my feet was soft, and, being relieved of my heavy boots, I put off with double-quick time, and, seeing the creek about half a mile off, I ventured to look over my shoulder to see what kind of chance there was to hold up and load. The red-skin was coming jogging along, pretty well blowed out, about five hundred yards in the rear. Thinks I, 'Here goes to load, anyhow.' So at it I went: in went the powder, and putting on my patch, down went the ball about half-way, and off snapped my ramrod!"

"Thunder and lightning!" shouted the old woodsman, who was worked up to the top-notch in the "member's" story.

"Good gracious! wasn't I in a pickle! There was the red whelp within two hundred yards of me, pacing along and *loading up his rifle as he came!* I jerked out the broken ramrod, dashed it away, and started on, priming up as I cantered off, determined to turn and give the red-skin a blast, anyhow, as soon as I reached the creek.

"I was now within a hundred yards of the creek, could see the smoke from the settlement chimneys. A few more jumps, and I was by the creek. The Indian was close upon me: he gave a whoop, and I raised my rifle: on he came, knowing that I had broken my ramrod and my load not down; another whoop! whop! and he was within fifty yards of me. I pulled trigger, and—"

"And killed him?" chuckled Riley.

"No, sir! I missed fire!"

"And the red-skin—" shouted the old woodsman, in a frenzy of excitement.

"Fired and killed me!"

The screams and shouts that followed this finale brought landlord Noble, servants and hostlers running up stairs to see if the house was on fire!

STORY OF A NEW HAT

ANONYMOUS

A business man had purchased a new stiff hat, and he went into a saloon with half a dozen friends to fit the hat on his head. They all took beer and passed the hat around so all could see it. One of the meanest men that ever held a county office went to the bartender and had a thin slice of Limburger cheese cut off, and when the party were looking at the frescoed ceiling through their beer glasses, the wicked person slipped the cheese under the sweat-band of the hat, and the man put it on and walked out.

The man who owned the hat is one of your nervous people who is always complaining of being sick, and who feels as though some dreadful disease was going to take possession of him and carry him off. He went back to his place of business, took off his hat and laid it on the table, and proceeded to answer some letters. He thought he detected a smell, and when his partner asked him if he didn't feel sick, he believed he did. He then turned pale, and said he guessed he would go home.

He met a man on the sidewalk who said the air was full of miasma, and in the street car a man who sat next to him moved away to the end of the car and asked him if he had just come from Chicago. The man with the hat said he had not, when the stranger said they were having a great deal of small-pox there and he guessed he would get out and walk, and he pulled the bell and jumped off.

The cold perspiration broke out on the forehead of the man with the new hat, and he took it off to wipe his forehead, when the whole piece of cheese seemed to roll over and breathe, and the man got the full benefit of it, and he came near fainting away. He got home, and his wife met and asked him what was the matter. He said he believed mortification had set in, and she took one whiff as he took off his hat, and said that she should think it had.

"Where did you get into it?" said she.

"Get into it?" said her husband. "I have not got into anything; some deadly disease has got hold of me and I shall not live."

She got his clothes off, soaked his feet in mustard water, and he slept. The hat was lying on the centre-table, and the children would come in and get a smell of it and look at each other with reproachful glances, and go out and play. The man slept and dreamed that a small-pox flag was hung in front of his house, and that he was riding in a butcher's wagon to the pest-house. The woman sent for a doctor, and when the man of pills arrived she told him all about the case.

The doctor picked up the patient's new hat, tried it on, and got a sniff. He said the hat was picked before it was ripe. The doctor and the wife held a *post-mortem* examination of the hat and found the slice of Limburger. "Few and short were the prayers they said."

They woke the patient, and to prepare his mind for the revelation that was about to be made, the doctor asked him if his worldly affairs were arranged in a satisfactory condition. He gasped and said they were. The doctor asked him if he had made his will. He said that he had not, but he wanted a lawyer sent for at once. The doctor then asked him if he felt as though he was prepared to shuffle off. The man said he had always tried to lead a different life, and tried to be done by the same as he would do it himself, but that he might have made a mistake some way, and that he would like to have a minister sent for to take an account of the stock.

The doctor brought to the bedside the hat, opened up the sweat-band, and showed the dying man what it was that smelled so, and told him he was as well as any man in the city. The man pinched himself to see if he was alive, and jumped out of bed and called for his revolver, and the doctor couldn't keep up with him on the way downtown.

The last we saw of the odoriferous citizen he was trying to bribe the bartender to tell him which one of those pelicans it was that put that slice of cheese in his hat.

IT ISN'T THE HEAT, AND IT ISN'T THE HUMIDITY, EITHER

JOHN BAILEY

Nature has equipped our body with a remarkable body-cooling mechanism which keeps our body cool. Except in hot weather. In hot weather this remarkable body-cooling mechanism doesn't seem to work.

However, there are a number of simple rules, published each year, which will help us to beat the heat, such as increasing salt intake, wearing loose clothing and holding your head under the faucet.

Not that I agree with all of them. For instance, one familiar rule is: DON'T SLEEP WITH AN ELECTRIC FAN DIRECTED AT YOUR BODY. On hot nights I sleep with two electric fans directed at my body and with my head sticking out of the window. So far, the only ill effect I've noticed is a little rain in my face.

But the rule, EAT PLENTY OF LETTUCE, is a good one. Nobody ever saw a hot rabbit. If you work in an open-pit mine or a blast furnace, especially, you should eat plenty of lettuce. I hate to tell you how much.

DRINK COOL LIQUIDS—NOT COLD. Personally, I drink plenty of ice-cold liquids and intend to keep on doing so. The danger seems to be that you will cool off your stomach. Well, that's what I'm after, a cool stomach.

Bathing is helpful, but not everyone can take a shower during a busy day. If you work in an office, try dipping a Turkish towel in ice water and wrapping it around your neck. This will give you a cool neck. A glass of cold water poured slowly over the head is refreshing too. It is wise to remove all the papers from your desk before doing this.

If your boss is away on a business trip or not looking, try lying on the floor with your shoelaces untied. Remember that muscular activity produces heat. Let's not have any muscular activity.

A little vinegar dabbed on the wrists and temples will have a cooling

HOW TO TORTURE YOUR HUSBAND

effect. Take a bottle of vinegar to the office and keep it in your desk drawer. And make sure it's vinegar.

AVOID TOO MUCH DIRECT SUNLIGHT. White reflects sunlight instead of absorbing it. If you are required to be out of doors a lot, it is a good idea to paint the top of your head white.

A GUEST AT THE LUDLOW

BILL NYE (1850-1896)

We are stopping quietly here, taking our meals in our rooms mostly, and going out very little indeed. When I say we, I use the term editorially.

We notice first of all the great contrast between this and other hotels, and in several instances this one is superior. In the first place, there is a sense of absolute security when one goes to sleep here that can not be felt at a popular hotel, where burglars secrete themselves in the wardrobe during the day and steal one's pantaloons and contents at night. This is one of the compensations of life in prison.

Here the burglars go to bed at the hour that the rest of us do. We all retire at the same time, and a murderer can not sit up any later at night than the smaller or unknown criminal can.

You can get to Ludlow Street Jail by taking the Second avenue Elevated train to Grand street, and then going east two blocks, or you can fire a shotgun into a Sabbath-school.

You can pay five cents to the Elevated Railroad and get here, or you can put some other man's nickel in your own slot and come here with an attendant.

William Marcy Tweed was the contractor of Ludlow Street Jail, and here also he died. He was the son of a poor chair-maker, and was born April 3, 1823. From the chair business in 1853 to congress was the first false step. Exhilarated by the delirium of official life, and the false joys of franking his linen home every week, and having cake and preserves franked back to him at Washington, he resolved to still further taste the delights of office, and in 1857 we find him as a school commissioner.

In 1860 he became Grand Sachem of the Tammany Society, an association at that time more purely political than politically pure. As president of the board of supervisors, head of the department of public works, state senator, and Grand Sachem of Tammany, Tweed had a large and seductive influence over the city and state. The story of how he earned a scanty livelihood by stealing a million of dollars at a pop, and thus, with the most rigid economy, scraped together $20,000,000 in a few years by patient industry and smoking plug tobacco, has been frequently told.

Tweed was once placed here in Ludlow Street Jail in default of $3,000,000 bail. How few there are of us who could slap up that amount of bail if rudely gobbled on the street by the hand of the law. While riding out with the sheriff, in 1875, Tweed asked to see his wife, and said he would be back in a minute.

He came back by way of Spain, in the fall of '76, looking much improved. But the malaria and dissipation of Blackwell's Island afterward impaired his health, and having done time there, and having been arrested afterward and placed in Ludlow Street Jail, he died here April 12, 1878, leaving behind him a large, vain world, and an equally vain judgment for $6,537,117.38, to which he said he would give his attention as soon as he could get a paving contract in the sweet ultimately.

From the exterior Ludlow Street Jail looks somewhat like a conservatory of music, but as soon as one enters he readily discovers his mistake. The structure has 100 feet frontage, and a court, which is sometimes called the court of last resort. The guest can climb out of this court by ascending a polished brick wall about 100 feet high, and then letting himself down in a similar way on the Ludlow street side.

That one thing is doing a great deal toward keeping quite a number of people here who would otherwise, I think, go away.

James D. Fish and Ferdinand Ward both remained here prior to their escape to Sing Sing. Red Leary, also, made his escape from this point, but did not succeed in reaching the penitentiary. Forty thousand prisoners have been confined in Ludlow Street Jail, mostly for civil offenses. A man in New York runs a very short career if he tries to be offensively civil.

As you enter Ludlow Street Jail the door is carefully closed after you, and locked by means of an iron lock about the size of a pictorial family Bible. You then remain on the inside for quite a spell. You do not hear the prattle of soiled children any more. All the glad sunlight, and stench-condensing pavements, and the dark-haired inhabitants of Rivington street, are seen no longer, and the heavy iron storm-door shuts out the wail of the combat from the alley near by. Ludlow Street Jail may be surrounded by a very miserable and dirty quarter of the city, but when you get inside all is changed.

You register first. There is a good pen there that you can write with, and the clerk does not chew tolu and read a sporting paper while you wait for a room. He is there to attend to business, and he attends to it. He does not seem to care whether you have any baggage or not. You can stay here for days, even if you don't have any baggage. All you need is a kind word and a mittimus from the court.

One enters this sanitarium either as a boarder or a felon. If you decide to come in as a boarder, you pay the warden $15 a week for the privilege of sitting at his table and eating the luxuries of the market. You also get a better room than at many hotels, and you have a good strong door, with a padlock on it, which enables you to prevent the sudden and unlooked-for entrance of the chambermaid. It is a good-sized room, with a wonderful amount of seclusion, a plain bed, table, chairs, carpet and so forth. After a few weeks at the seaside, at $19 per day, I think the room in which I am writing is not unreasonable at $2.

Still, of course, we miss the sea breeze.

You can pay $50 to $100 per week here if you wish, and get your money's worth, too. For the latter sum one may live in the bridal chamber, so to speak, and eat the very best food all the time.

Heavy iron bars keep the mosquitoes out, and at night the house is brilliantly lighted by incandescent lights of one-candle power each. Neat snuffers, consisting of the thumb and forefinger polished on the hair, are to be found in each occupied room.

Bread is served to the Freshmen and Juniors in rectangular wads. It is such bread as convicts' tears have moistened many thousand years. In that way it gets quite moist.

The most painful feature about life in Ludlow Street Jail is the confinement. One can not avoid a feeling of being constantly hampered and hemmed in.

One more disagreeable thing is the great social distinction here. The poor man who sleeps in a stone niche near the roof, and who is constantly elbowed and hustled out of his bed by earnest and restless vermin with a tendency toward insomnia, is harassed by meeting in the court-yard and corridors the paying boarders who wear good clothes, live well, have their cigars, brandy and Kentucky Sec all the time.

The McAllister crowd here is just as exclusive as it is on the outside.

But, great Scott! what a comfort it is to a man like me, who has been nearly killed by a cyclone, to feel the firm, secure walls and solid time lock when he goes to bed at night! Even if I can not belong to the 400, I am almost happy.

We retire at 7:30 o'clock at night and arise at 6:30 in the morning, so as to get an early start. A man who has five or ten years to stay in a place like this naturally likes to get at it as soon as possible each day, and so he gets up at 6:30.

We dress by the gaudy light of the candle, and while we do so, we remember far away at home our wife and the little boy asleep in her arms. They do not get up at 6:30. It is at this hour we remember the fragrant drawer in the dresser at home where our clean shirts, and collars and cuffs, and socks and handkerchiefs, are put every week by our wife. We also recall as we go about our stone den, with its odor of former corned beef, and the ghost of some bloody-handed predecessor's snore still moaning in the walls, the picture of green grass by our own doorway, and the apples that were just ripening, when the bench warrant came.

The time from 6:30 to breakfast is occupied by the average, or nonpaying inmate, in doing the chamberwork and tidying up his stateroom. I do not know how others feel about it, but I dislike chamberwork most heartily, especially when I am in jail. Nothing has done more to keep me out of jail, I guess, than the fact that while there I have to make up my bed and dust the piano.

Breakfast is generally table d'hote and consists of bread. A tin-cup of coffee takes the taste of the bread out of your mouth, and then if you have some Limburger cheese in your pocket you can with that remove the taste of the coffee.

Dinner is served at 12 o'clock, and consists of more bread with soup. This soup has everything in it except nourishment. The bead on this soup is noticeable for quite a distance. It is disagreeable. Several days ago I heard that the Mayor was in the soup, but I didn't realize it before. I thought it was a newspaper yarn. There is everything in this soup, from shop-worn rice up to neat's foot oil. Once I thought I detected cuisine in it.

The dinner menu is changed on Fridays, Sundays and Thursdays, on which days you get the soup first and the bread afterward. In this way the bread is saved.

Three days in a week each man gets at dinner a potato containing a thousand-legged worm. At 6 o'clock comes supper with toast and responses. Bread is served at supper time, together with a cup of tea. To those who dislike bread and never eat soup, or do not drink tea or coffee, life at Ludlow Street Jail is indeed irksome.

I asked for kumiss and a pony of Benedictine, as my stone boudoir made me feel rocky, but it has not yet been sent up.

Somehow, while here, I can not forget poor old man Dorrit, the Master of the Marshalsea, and how the Debtors' Prison preyed upon his mind till he didn't enjoy anything except to stand off and admire himself. Ludlow Street Jail is a good deal like it in many ways, and I can see how in time the canker of unrest and the bitter memories of those who did us wrong but who are basking in the bright and bracing air, while we, to meet their obligations, sacrifice our money, our health and at last our minds, would kill hope and ambition.

In a few weeks I believe I should also get a preying on my mind. That is about the last thing I would think of preying on, but a man must eat something.

Before closing this brief and incomplete account as a guest at Ludlow Street Jail I ought, in justice to my family, to say, perhaps, that I came down this morning to see a friend of mine who is here because he refuses to pay alimony to his recreant and morbidly sociable wife. He says he is quite content to stay here, so long as his wife is on the outside. He is writing a small ready-reference book on his side of the great problem "Is Marriage A Failure?"

With this I shake him by the hand and in a moment the big iron storm-door clangs behind me, the big lock clicks in its hoarse, black throat and I welcome even the air of Ludlow street so long as the blue sky is above it.

THE NIGHT THE STATION GOT LOST

HUGH A. MULLIGAN

No sir, Mister. This line ain't never lost a train yet, so don't you worry none. She'll be along sooner or later. Mostly later, I suspect, with that storm blowing up ahead. May be late, but she ain't lost. You can bet your blue-chip railroad stock on that. The old Boston & Kennebunkport is mighty particular about lost anythings. Lost a station once, and they ain't never got over it.

Yep, lost a station—whole town in fact. It was the darndest thing you ever heard of. Raised a heck of a ruckus. FBI was called in to help look, and for a time there the old B & K was in a peck of trouble with the state Public Service Commission and the Interstate Commerce Commission, but it died down after a time. Government folks don't like railroads to go misplacing towns and stations; messes up their rate schedules and what not. You'd think it was their station, the way they acted. Come to think of it, it wasn't anybody's station, except maybe Goldie's. You see, Goldie's the fellow that started it all.

This town that got lost wasn't like ordinary towns. No sir. Had no churches, no schools, no stores, no post office. Nothing like that, not even streets. Matter of fact, it had no people. Just a railroad station with a great big red-and-yellow sign that said "Valhalla Corners."

Of course, Valhalla Corners wasn't like other stations in every respect. What I mean is nobody ever got on or off there, or consigned any freight there. And nobody ever saw it on a timetable, or even a map for that matter, but it was there just as sure as you're sitting here waiting for the 10:17. Probably surer, since it's past midnight already and the 10:17 don't make too good a witness.

Anyway, Goldie came here as division super after old Flatwheel Farrington got crippled in the big pile-up outside Augusta. His whole name was Marrowbie K. Goldrick, but he just told us to call him Goldie, because he said he wasn't one of those bosses that stood on formality. Well sir, Goldie was a practical joker. That's what he called himself. He said he was one in a million. To my way of thinking, that's too high a percentage for humanity to bear.

I mean it wasn't no pastime or hobby the way some fellows does it. With Goldie, it was steady business. Why, he wasn't off the train five minutes before we got a sample of what was in store for us for the next five years. After he'd been handshook all around, he began telling us how nice it was to be up in Hemlock Gap with some real soot-and-cinder veterans for a change. We just nodded in a friendly way, because that's what all the new brass hats say when they first get here, and the conversation was chugging along a familiar roadbed, until all of a sudden Shorty—he's the schedule maker and rate fixer for the Mountain Division—shoots up out of his chair like a Roman candle. Looked and sounded like a Roman candle too, what with all that smoke and flame leaping up around the traffic files and him screaming like the spinster that saw the snake at the lawn party. And there was Goldie, the new boss, laughing as if he was seeing his first "Our Gang" comedy.

Know what he'd done? While the introductions was being made, he slipped his cigarette lighter out and set fire to the big time-chart Shorty had been working on for more than a week, getting ready for daylight-saving time to go off. Then he just stood back and laughed and laughed.

That's the way it went all winter. The morning paper'd have the pages glued together or last week's sport page slipped in the middle. You found your shoes nailed to the locker floor or flypaper in the pockets of your overcoat. Legs got loose from desks and tables. There was sand in the inkwells, tickets rearranged in the racks, desk drawers nailed tight, letters to you from lonely hearts clubs. Everything you could imagine.

Well sir, it took us about six months to get wise to Goldie's ordinary everyday pranks. Got so we could schedule them pretty well, even figure out who was due next. That's when he got started on his scientific stunts, the ones that took some time and planning.

Like the night he loosened the wheels on the baggage cart. Not all the way off, but just enough so they'd hold up for a few yards before everything went boom. Of course, it would be a Friday night he'd pick. Right smack dab at the height of the weekend rush, with all them co-eds carting suitcases home from college and those skiers heading off to the mountains. Top of that, the train was late and the engineer was bellowing at Henry to load up quick so he could make up the time. I tell you, it was a picture. There was the 5:51 Bangor-direct snorting and puffing like a bull in clover. There was all them pretty little girls straddling their suitcases, and the skiers with all that lumber leaning against them. And there was the baggage cart, loaded near to the roof with chickens and trunks and parcels and what not, and Old Henry, our baggage clerk, bent over in front tugging at the handle. Then all of a sudden there was a terrific crashing, like the station had collapsed. The girls was screaming at the fellows. The fellows was screaming at the conductor. The baggage cart was on its belly in the middle of the platform, flatter than a toboggan, and Henry was chasing the wheels up and down in every direction. It was a sight. Chickens flying in and out the eaves, people scampering and tripping over skis and sometimes over skiers. Out on the tracks there was trunks and bundles and chicken cages three feet deep. The engineer was cussing his head off. So was Henry, and he was a temperate man, mighty temperate. And echoing above all this, came the shrill call of that cawing gooney bird in the office. It took more than a mite of coaxing to keep Henry from quitting his job right there and then, and hang the retirement pay.

Then the Swede arrived. And he was to be the inspiration for Goldie's greatest achievement.

The Swede was an engineer sent up from Augusta to break in with the Mountain Division. Might have made a good man any place else, but he was made to order for Goldie. The blaze made by Shorty's schedule was nothing compared to the one the Swede's straw suitcase made when Goldie got done with his handshaking stunt. You remember, the one with the cigarette lighter. Always good for a laugh. So were all the others, and they started all over again, from the nailed-up shoes right down to the exploding cigar. Swede never give a frown or a smile.

When he found his new work gloves oozing with wheel oil, he just shook his big blond head and muttered, "What do you know about that. Ay moest 'ave spilt some earl in my gloeffs!" And when his favorite corncob blew up like a thirsty boiler, he jabbered, "Yumpin' yimminy. Ay never buy that terbaccy again."

Swede had been pulling a slow freight less than a month when Goldie hit on his real Lulu. I call it that, 'cause I think it's the only one really rated the title. We hadn't seen much of him for a few days. Guess he was inside the office mapping it out. Great one for strategy, that Goldie. One day though he come busting out, arms all aflutter and voice shrieking like a rusty brake wheel. "Gather round, lads," he cried. "This is it! My masterpiece. The Swede'll never catch on." Then he told us Swede was being promoted to a passenger run, the 10:17.

"What's so comical about that?" asks Abner. "Seems to me he'd be just the man . . . always on time, careful with the equipment and reports every last wheeze in his boiler to the shops."

"Wait a minute," cuts in Goldie. "You haven't heard my plan yet. You all know where Beaver Lake is, don't you?"

Of course we did. It's a logging town up in the hills, about halfway between Orsank and Middletown. Four trains a day; six Sundays and holidays. Good ski country and enough freight with the sawmills and pulp plants.

"Then you must know where that old fur-curing factory is?" continues Goldie. "Out of business now, but the siding is still there. In serviceable condition too, according to our maintenance reports, but I'm having it checked again, just to be sure. Here's the plan: that siding leaves the main drag about a mile after Beaver Lake, circles two miles through the woods out to the old fur place, then comes back on the main line about a mile before Beaver Lake.

"Get it? One of those overlapping sidings. Begins in one place that comes back to the main line again just ahead of where it started. The Swede'll never catch on. It'll kill him."

He was laughing so hard somebody had to give him a glass of water before we could make head or tail of it.

"You don't get it?" he says in a disappointed tone. "It's really very simple. Look, when Swede starts highballing it out of Beaver Lake, we'll have the switchman throw him into that siding. See what happens? Instead of staying on the main line, he'll circle out to the old fur-curing plant then back into Beaver Lake. Two Beaver Lakes in one night. It'll drive him nuts!"

We had our doubts. Goldie assured us Swede would never know what was happening. He had never been north before and would hit there around midnight. It's a dark patch of woods coming out of Beaver Lake. A new engineer could easily mistake a siding for the main line.

"What about the train crew?" demands Shorty. "Night or day those fellows can feel the tracks under their feet."

"Oh," says Goldie with a pixie grin, "that's where you boys come in. We have to work this together. I took care of my end. Spoke to the agent at the Lake this morning. The switchman's all primed. Now it's up to you to tip off the trainmen."

"How about the passengers?" injects Silent Tom, the government mail clerk. "They got eyes too, you know."

"Won't be any passengers second time around," snaps Goldie. "All interested in Beaver Lake will have gotten off the first time. Besides, he'll only stop in Beaver Lake once. Second time around, we'll give him the green."

I asked how it would work on the return haul and he says "Like a charm. Like a charm. The very same thing. Into Beaver Lake, out of Beaver Lake. Into the siding, out to the old fur place, then back into Beaver Lake again. It can't miss."

It didn't either, from the looks of the Swede's face the morning after his first trip on the 10:17. He was sitting in the office when we came back from our coffee session down at the shops. For a cold day, there seemed to be a lot of perspiration on his face. Probably some sort of chill, because his hand shook as he read over the timetable chart. None of us dared say a word, except good morning, and he didn't answer that. All of a sudden, he got up and began pacing back and forth, like a switcher doing ramp duty. On a quick impulse, he sidled up to my desk and almost whispered, "That 10:17 be one Yell of a run, don't she?"

I coughed a little to get my face straight and confessed I had never been on the train. That didn't seem to satisfy, so he went back to floor pacing. Next, he tried Henry, who had been trying his darndest to look busy but had been out of practice so long he forgot how it was done. "Ayfer been yup to Bee-fer Lake?" I heard Swede ask.

"Can't say as I have," says Henry, burying his face in a drawer to keep from ripping out all over the place, while the rest of us found sudden need to hunt up a file folder or check on the thermometer outside. Swede didn't try any others, so we had to wait on the train crew and the agent at Beaver Lake to fit the pieces together.

Seems he hit there right on time, little past midnight, dropped off a couple of hunters and some egg crates, then pulled out. Mile or so up the pike he thundered through the switch into the siding, circled the old factory and was back in Beaver Lake in less than five minutes. Agent said he was afraid Swede would fall out of the cab the way he was leaning into the roadbed to see if it was really Beaver Lake again. They say you could smell burnt out brake lining the rest of the night the way he stopped.

"What the blazes are you stopping for," the agent roared. "Don't you see that green?"

"Ya. Ya. Sure," Swede stammered. "But ain't this Bee-fer Lake? I yam supposed to stop here."

"It's Beaver Lake all right and you already have stopped here."

Swede looked for sympathy from the fireman beside him but got nothing more than the bored look most veterans reserve for newcomers. "Ya. Ay guess maybe Ay don't feel so good tonight," he murmured. "Ay yumpy all over."

He mumbled and grumbled all the way back about "Bee-fer Lake," the crew told us, and when he hit it a second time on the return run, he reached for the brake bar again, but didn't stop. He just leaned forward in his seat peering out into the night, and held that pose the rest of the trip, like he expected two or three more Bee-fer Lakes to come popping out of the darkness.

But worse than that came out of the darkness—Valhalla Corners. Goldie thought of it three days later. He come charging out of his office shouting, "Call up the stockholders. Declare a dividend! This line has got a new station! The old B & K is growing every minute. Make way for Valhalla Corners, U.S.A."

We should have guessed it. It was the new name for Beaver Lake second time around. As usual, Goldie had it all plotted out: the bright red-and-yellow sign, a red wig for the agent over at the Lake, and little details like moving the newsstand and rearranging the baggage carts and trash baskets. He thought of everything.

The next morning Swede come into the office and I never saw any-one looking so bad. His eyes was all blurry and bloodshot. His face was white as goat's milk. And it would be me he'd pick on when he finally decided to talk. "Ayfer hear of Val-yaller Corners?"

"Nope," I gulped. "Can't say's I have. Where is it?"

The goat's milk curdled. "Oh," he moaned. "It been sum'vere. Aye tank."

Then he spun around on his heel and was gone. He never men-tioned Valhalla Corners again. Not ever to the train crew. But he saw it every night. Sometimes it was Beaver Lake first and Valhalla Cor-ners second; other times the ghost station came first, then the Lake. The signals never permitted a stop, but Swede often slowed down enough to let the mystery of it fill his big eyes with terror. Especially on the nights when it was Valhalla Corners first on the way up and then first again on the way back!

I guess it ended the only way it could have. The mail special took care of it. Funny part is, the whole thing was Goldie's idea. He sug-gested a special mail train to run Christmas packages up to that Army camp near Middletown, and the brass hats went strong for the idea. It was scheduled out of here about 10:25, only eight minutes after Swede's train, so I don't see how Goldie ever forgot. Maybe it was all the excitement over the opening run. The general manager and his whole staff come up, plus all the public-relations people and the Army bigwigs. You know how people carried on in wartime. But this was one celebration they never got over.

The way I heard it, Swede made up his 10:17 and was out of here lickety-split, on the dot, as per usual. It was beginning to snow and get fierce when the special roared through here a few minutes later, with Goldie grinning and waving from the observation deck. The general manager was just running over his speech in his mind when they got to Beaver Lake and whistles start tooting up ahead.

"What train is that?" he asks, and Goldie told him it was the 10:17. He didn't think twice about it. Neither did the Swede, who by this time was barreling through the siding back towards Beaver Lake again. Only this time the way was blocked by the special, which had stopped for a mail pickup. Swede gave a tug at the whistle. The general manager lost the thread running through his speech. "Pretty busy division you have here, Mr. Goldrick. What train is that back there?"

"The 10:17," gasped Goldie as the light struck.

"How nice," said the G.M., returning to his musing. Goldie took advantage of the silence and lit out for the door. "For gossake," he shouted, "somebody pull that switch. Do you hear me? Somebody throw that switch." It was a fatal direction, but the switchman was already long accustomed to Goldie's whims. He did as directed. Goldie should have remembered the agent had orders to switch only once, then let the 10:17 go on its way. When he called for another one, that's what he got. Into the siding went the special, all the way out to the fur plant, then back into Beaver Lake again, right behind the 10:17.

Whistles up ahead again. The general manager stuffed the speech into his brief case. "What train is that?" he demanded in querulous tones.

"The 10:17," mumbled Goldie, all meek and beaten.

"What did you say?"

"The 10:17 . . ."

"But I thought that was behind us!"

"I know," sighed Goldie. "It's just one of those things . . ."

"One of what things?" roared the executive. "What's going on here? How many 10:17's are there? First it was in front of us, then behind us, now in front of us again. Trains don't jump over one another. They run on tracks . . . steel tracks. They can't play leap-frog. I've been in this business 35 years. I ought to know. Do you hear?"

His voice rumbled through the car like a loud-speaker, each new quiver of wrath bringing redder hues to the bald spot on his oval-shaped crown. "Yes sir," shivered Goldie, "I'll go see what I can do." And with that, he ran down on the steps shouting frantically for someone to "throw that blasted switch." They did.

When whistles tooted mournfully from behind, the general manager sprang into action. A conductor came on the run to answer his summons. "What time is it?" the G.M. barked.

"It's 24:03," replied the conductor with a smart flip of his watch.

"Find out what train that is behind us and be quick about it if you like your job!" The conductor dashed up to the doorway and back with hardly time to turn around. "The 10:17," he announced crisply, and never quite recovered from the barrage of profanity that greeted him. Goldie leaned out into the night, pleading with the switchman.

They never did settle how many times the two trains went around that circle. The agent says at least three. The switchman claims five. Others go as high as seven or eight. I do know that someplace in there the general manager calmed down long enough to find out the name of the station they were passing through.

"Val-hal-la Cor-ners," reported the brakeman, squinting at the sign through the snowflakes.

"Valhalla WHAT?"

"Corners, Valhalla Corners. It says."

"But . . . but . . . but that's impossible! Ridiculous! We don't have any station by that name."

"Yes sir. But that's what the sign says."

"I don't care what the sign says. I ought to know. I'm general manager of this line and I've been here 35 years."

His report must have been a beauty. Within 48 hours the whole Union Station force, from callboys to president, was up here asking more questions than Dr. Kinsey and the income tax combined. They rode all over, interviewed hundreds of people—farmers, lumberjacks, hoboes, hunters and what not. Didn't do any good. Nobody ever heard of Valhalla Corners. Then the railroad dicks arrived, went over this place like customs agents hunting the crown jewels. Next the FBI and the ICC. Never a trace of Valhalla Corners. It had vanished in the old pot-bellied stove over at Beaver Lake in a fragrance of burnt shellac and crackling of good pine.

Before the probe busted up, the president of the line apologized to Goldie and said a lot of nasty things about the general manager. Goldie was real nice about it. He told the president not to be too hard on the general manager, because you know how it is around the holidays. Fellows get to celebrating. Saved the general manager's job too, but the man never appreciated it. Some people are like that.

We saw Swede only once after that. He came in and cleaned out his locker. Didn't even wait for his paycheck. Suppose half a dozen

HOW TO TORTURE YOUR HUSBAND

And Nothing Can Be Done About It

assorted Beaver Lakes and Valhalla Corners was too much for him in one night. Guess you can't blame him there. Got a card from him about a week ago. He's in the Peruvian jungles. A missionary of some sort. Come to think of it, he did get awful religious towards the end there.

And Goldie? Oh, he's the same. Never changes. Got a new engineer in the other night. Guess that's why the 10:17's late. Heard Goldie talking to the sign shop this afternoon. Said something about "Utopia Junction." Whatever that means.

THE TWINS

HENRY S. LEIGH

In form and feature, face and limb,
   I grew so like my brother,
That folks got taking me for him,
   And each for one another.
It puzzled all our kith and kin,
   It reach'd an awful pitch;
For one of us was born a twin,
   Yet not a soul knew which.

One day (to make the matter worse),
   Before our names were fix'd,
As we were being wash'd by nurse
   We got completely mix'd;
And thus, you see, by Fate's decree,
   (Or rather nurse's whim),
My brother John got christen'd *me*,
   And I got christen'd *him*.

This fatal likeness even dogg'd
   My footsteps when at school,
And I was always getting flogg'd,
   For John turned out a fool.
I put this question hopelessly
   To every one I knew—
What *would* you do, if you were me,
   To prove that you were *you*?

> Our close resemblance turn'd the tide
> Of my domestic life;
> For somehow my intended bride
> Became my brother's wife.
> In short, year after year the same
> Absurd mistakes went on;
> And when I died—the neighbors came
> And buried brother John!

THE ALL-PURPOSE GHOST STORY

CHARLES W. MORTON

A single all-purpose form for the ghost story ought to be welcomed by authors' leagues everywhere. Writers who find the standardized fishing story a convenience (page 510) will fare even more briskly with the ghost story in blank. It practically writes itself, once you get the thing going.

"I don't believe in ghosts—yet how else to account for what happened to me that night in ——?"

This model opening sentence is adjustable in various ways, but the main point must be made at the very beginning: It's a ghost story; eerie doings impend. Once he understands that, the reader will find something spooky in even the most commonplace details.

With the full gullibility of the reader thus fired at the take-off, the ghost-story writer need only breeze along, filling in the blanks as he goes.

"It was late in the afternoon when I finally reached ——," he continues. "I had been ——ing hard all day and I was looking forward to a ——, a good ——, and the possibility of —— the next morning."

Any reader who will stick with a ghost story, once he knows it for that, is a highly suggestible personality. He creates his own atmosphere for himself out of anything the author sees fit to tell him, so it matters little what the layout at —— proves to be.

"There was nothing about the outward appearance of No. —— that was in the least unusual, but as I mounted the steps and rang the bell I had a sudden feeling of ——. I noticed, too, that a —— across the street seemed to be eying me rather closely, but I must confess that I thought nothing of it at the time."

Just who the author's host will be at No. —— is easily settled. It can be an old friend, though a landlady would do just as well—but only one in either case. ("I realized when Blank answered the door himself that his servants must have left and that we were alone in the house. . . .") You can't afford to have too many people around in a story of this kind.

The reader ought to have built up a fair head of steam by this time and be ready to assign odd meanings to any old statement. "The hall was brightly lighted" will worry him as much as no lights at all. If the author reports a window open, the reader wonders who opened it. Was it Blank? Why was it open?

A few such details set the reader up for the first really scary development—the extraordinary change in Blank (or the landlady): "The warmth of my welcome was like old times, but I was hardly prepared for Blank's appearance. He was much ——er than when I had last seen him; his ——, which I had remembered as downright ——, was now quite ——. His ——s, too, were no longer as I had known them. All in all, he seemed like a man who had ——ed, if I may be permitted the word."

Reader and author alike are thoroughly frightened by the way Blank is looking, and here is just the moment to plant another disturbing trifle: "I could not help noticing, as we exchanged greetings, Blank's ——; it was very old, as I could tell at a glance, and of curious workmanship." (This item could be almost anything—Blank's clock, teapot, set of false teeth, or what you will. It may be that nothing will come of it anyhow, but there it is, if the author finds later on that he needs it. Meanwhile, it sets the reader to breathing noisily.)

"The room to which Blank showed me seemed cheery enough," the story goes on "but I was struck by the huge —— which occupied almost one entire wall. Once or twice, as I turned suddenly and looked at it, I could have sworn that it was ——ing, but this, of course, was absurd. ——s simply do not ——, I told myself."

Let us not linger over Blank's dinner (unless the author fancies himself as a food-and-drink expert), and the conversation over the cigars can be cut short, too. Blank himself certainly won't be allowed to give the story away at this juncture, and the author is still feeling, the effects of a hard day's ——ing. The sooner both men are in bed, the better. Thus:

"So far as I could tell, my room was just as I had left it, but the ——

seemed even larger than before. Its bulk dwarfed everything else, and I was uncomfortably aware of it as I dropped off to sleep.

"I have no way of judging how long I slept, but suddenly I was wide awake. The room was pitch black; all was still. Then I heard, faintly and as at a great distance, the sound of ——ing. It was as if a very —— ——, or a ——, were being ——ed, far away. I cannot describe the feeling of ——, of ——, of sheer ——, that swept over me. The ——ing grew louder. It seemed to be coming from the general direction of the vast —— that I have mentioned. My —— was ——. I tried to ——, but to no avail. Suddenly I realized that I could see taking form in the darkness the unmistakable outlines of a —— (italics)!

"At that point I must have —— —— altogether, for the next thing I knew, it was —— ——, and Blank was ——ing —— —— —— jug of hot water.

"I —— —— —— ——, Blank —— —— —— ——, and the house was sold. Shortly afterwards, I came upon this story in my evening paper:

"'Workmen ——ing an old house at No. —— Street discovered today in the wall of a bedroom the mummified remains of a ——. Police are investigating.'"

THE OLD CLOCK

JAMES NACK

(About 1880)

Two Yankee wags, one summer day,
Stopped at a tavern on their way;
Supped, frolicked, late retired to rest,
And woke to breakfast on the best.

The breakfast over, Tom and Will,
Sent for the landlord and the bill;
Will looked it over; "Very right—
But hold! what wonder meets my sight!
Tom! the surprise is quite a shock!"
"What? wonder where!" "The clock! the clock!"

Tom and the landlord in amaze
Stared at the clock with stupid gaze,

And for a moment neither spoke;
At last the landlord silence broke:

"You mean the clock that's ticking there?
I see no wonder, I declare;
Though may be, if the truth were told,
'Tis rather ugly—somewhat old;
Yet time it keeps to half a minute,
But, if you please, what wonder's in it?"

"Tom, don't you recollect," said Will,
"The clock at Jersey near the mill,
The very image of this present,
With which I won the wager pleasant?"
Will ended with a knowing wink,
Tom scratched his head, and tried to think.
"Sir, begging pardon for inquiring,"
The landlord said, with grin admiring,
"What wager was it?"

                    "You remember
It happened, Tom, in last December,
In sport I bet a Jersey Blue
That it was more than he could do
To make his fingers go and come
In keeping with the pendulum,
Repeating, till one hour should close,
Still *here she goes—and there she goes,*—
He lost the bet in half a minute."
"Well, if I would, the deuce is in it!"
Exclaimed the landlord; "try me yet,
And fifty dollars be the bet."
"Agreed, but we will play some trick
To make you of the bargain sick!"
"I'm up to that!"

                    "Don't make us wait;
Begin, the clock is striking eight."
He seats himself, and left and right,
His finger wags with all his might,
And hoarse his voice, and hoarser grows,
With *"here she goes—and there she goes!"*

"Hold!" said the Yankee, "plank the ready!"
The landlord wagged his finger steady,
While his left hand, as well as able,
Conveyed a purse upon the table.
"Tom, with the money let's be off!"
This made the landlord only scoff;
He heard them running down the stair,
But was not tempted from his chair;
Thought he, "The fools! I'll bite them yet!
So poor a trick shan't win the bet."
And loud and loud the chorus rose
Of *"here she goes—and there she goes!"*
While right and left his finger swung
In keeping to his clock and tongue.

His mother happened in to see
Her daughter; "Where is Mrs. B——?
When will she come, as you suppose?
Son!"
"Here she goes—and there she goes!"
"Here!—where?" the lady in surprise
His fingers followed with her eyes;
"Son, why that steady gaze and sad?
Those words—that motion—are you mad?
But here's your wife—perhaps she knows
And"—
"Here she goes—and there she goes!"

His wife surveyed him with alarm,
And rushed to him and seized his arm;
He shook her off, and to and fro
His fingers persevered to go.
While curled his very nose with ire,
That *she* against him should conspire,
And with more furious tone arose
The *"Here she goes—and there she goes!"*

"Lawks!" screamed the wife, "I'm in a whirl!
Run down and bring the little girl;
She is his darling, and who knows
But"—
"Here she goes—and there she goes!"

"Lawks! he is mad! what made him thus?
Good Lord! what will become of us!
Run for a doctor—run—run—run
For Doctor Brown, and Doctor Dun,
And Doctor Black, and Doctor White,
And Doctor Grey, with all your might."

The doctors came, and looked and wondered,
And shook their heads, and paused and pondered.
Till one proposed he should be bled,
"No—leeched you mean"—the other said.
"Clap on a blister" roared another,
"No—cup him"—"No, trepan him, brother!"
A sixth would recommend a purge,
The next would an emetic urge,
The eighth, just come from a dissection,
His verdict gave for an injection;
The last produced a box of pills,
A certain cure for earthly ills;
"I had a patient yesternight,"
Quoth he, "and wretched was her plight,
And as the only means to save her,
Three dozen patent pills I gave her,
And by tomorrow, I suppose
That"—
"Here she goes—and there she goes!"

"You are all fools," the lady said,
"The way is, just to shave his head,
Run, bid the barber come anon"—
"Thanks, mother," thought her clever son,
"You help the knaves that would have bit me,
But all creation shan't outwit me!"
Thus to himself, while to and fro
His fingers persevere to go,
And from his lips no accent flows
But "here she goes—and there she goes!"

The barber came—"Lord help him! what
A queerish customer I've got;
But we must do our best to save him—

So hold him, gemmen, while I shave him!"
But here the doctors interpose—
"A woman never,"—
                    "There she goes!"

"A woman is no judge of physic,
Not even when her baby *is* sick.
He must be bled," "no—no—a blister"—
"A purge you mean"—"I say a clyster"—
"No—cup him"—"leech him"—"pills!—pills!—pills!"
And all the house the uproar fills.

What means that smile? what means that shiver?
The landlord's limbs with rapture quiver,
And triumph brightens up his face—
His finger yet shall win the race!
The clock is on the stroke of nine—
And up he starts—"'Tis mine! 'Tis mine!"
"What do you mean?"

                    "I mean the fifty!
I never spent an hour so thrifty;
But you who tried to make me lose,
Go, burst with envy, if you choose!
But how is this! where are they?"

                    "Who?"
"The gentlemen—I mean the two
Came yesterday—are they below?"
"They galloped off an hour ago."
"Oh, purge me! blister! shave and bleed!
For, hang the knaves, I'm mad, indeed!"

H. J. TALKING

R. G. G. PRICE

(*From Punch Magazine*)

I

My name is Harmony Jenkins and a scientist is what I mainly am.
It is a good life, plenty of variety and prestige, and one never knows

but what one might turn out useful as well as just happily occupied. My line is psychological physics, though I am far from being narrow-minded and enjoy a good experiment even if off my beat. For example, I once mixed equal quantities of all the chemicals in my laboratory, first forecasting the result by the Law of Averages. It should have come to a black sticky mixture smelling of camphor, but before I was half-way through there was an explosion, and my wife asked me not to start again owing to comment among the neighbours, those on the side where the bath landed taking any occasion to be critical.

She is far from encouraging about my work, as there are rifts between us, one being that her people bridle if you refer to them as relations and not relatives, while my people bridle if you refer to them as relatives and not relations. However, I was advised this was not enough for a divorce, not even when we had the fire. It was quite a small fire to begin with. We kept it in a stove. But one day my wife got obstinate about the Seven Wonders of the World. She stuck to it they were chosen annually by the Swedes. She got so obstinate she took the fire out of the stove and heaved it here, there and everywhere, as some people say. I should have thought it burnt enough for two divorces.

When my wife was at home—before she got hold of me, most of her family were net makers. They had a large net in the middle of the floor, and all worked at their own bits, hoping that in time it would all be one big net; but what with Uncle Ted doing purl and Uncle Jobbett plain, and what with quarrels, and Aunt Endor not doing her share, and Aunt Hedwig making larger holes than the others to finish sooner, it never seemed to get much forrarder. The kids used to get worked into the net, and then cutting them loose made gaps which led to arguments, until it was decided that the parents should always repair the damage. There was one of my wife's family, called Syd, who refused to go into the net and took a night-school course and became a shoe shiner, but the family used to go and stay with him, taking the net with them, and it covered his pitch so that the customers got their shoes caught in it, which was bad for trade. He issued a notice saying his family had gone home, but by then the goodwill had vanished.

Science is not very expensive if you don't spend money on it. During a long experiment I put the apparatus into pawn, where it fizzes away, costing me nothing, not at least till I come to get it out. I expect you are wondering what I do with it when I have finished a piece of research. Well, quite a lot of it can be worked into the next experiment with a little ingenuity, such being test-tubes and string. Some of it, however, is ad hoc, and when done with I use it for presents. On her last birthday I gave my wife a rat suffering from measles. I had been investigating whether it was curable, which it did not seem to be. Since my next job was to study the effect of heat on memory I could not work the rat in, as being sick its memory might be defective before it even went into the oven. Nothing spoils science like not having everything average and normal to begin with. I once ruined a test of the influence of electric shocks on concentration by not noticing that the child I had borrowed was wearing rubber-soled shoes.

I never take my scientific equipment with me on a fishing trip, not because of its size but because of its lack of cosiness. I always like a fishing shack to be homely, and that is why I go in so much for breakages. A piece of furniture which looks as if it had just come from the makers has no appeal for me whatever. Until a cup has been chipped that cup does not accompany me on a holiday. Some of my cups have edges like saws. Nobody feels they need live up to them. Things are different at home, where I have a good deal of trouble with my wife over mats which she likes about the table to go under things. To try to cure her I put a doormat on the table when we had friends to dinner. It said "Welcome" and had room for three places and a soup tureen, but it never improved her much. She differs from me in liking a table polished. I like a table you can put your elbows on without them slipping. If anyone lent me a shack with a polished table in it I should go out first thing and buy some emery paper. By the way, as to the fish I catch on holidays. That depends where the shack is. If it is on a river I go for salmon and trout, while if it is on the coast I go more for lobsters. I bear all fish fairly easily as eating, but fish I have caught myself and can count as free fish I bear easiest of all.

II

At one end of my laboratory I keep my tenant, B. Smith, who is also a scientist, specializing in solar biology. Solar biology is something quite new. For years the books have said there just couldn't be life on the sun, but as B. Smith points out, the scientific method is to verify your hypotheses. Of course, it makes it easier for him that he knows there can't be life on the sun owing to the heat, but his work is to prove it. He spends a lot of time looking at the sun through a telescope, but even the largest telescope would not show animals if they were small or lived under ground or something like that. Some people might just give it up, but B. Smith is conscientious; he writes a regular article for a scientific journal giving a day-to-day record of animals he has not seen through his telescope, but impartially pointing out that this is not watertight proof they do not exist.

Perhaps this year B. Smith might come fishing with me. He agrees with me on almost everything, except that he goes further than I do about breakages, and how they make things free and easy in a shack. He likes to haul a chunk of the ceiling down and let it lie about. He usually does it by standing on the table with an ice-pick. In some moods he digs away until he has extracted a tile, and when it is cold we have to scramble up on the roof and cover the hole with the table-cloth to keep the snow out. Another thing B. Smith doesn't agree with me about is my wife. He says I don't treat her consistently rough enough, but let up from time to time. He says if I gave him the run of her with his ice-pick he could smarten her up no end.

B. Smith sometimes behaves what he calls "debonairly." He flicks bits of fluff off his lapel until his finger-joints ache and hums with his teeth shut. He has a theory that this makes him irresistible to women. My wife told him it didn't and said the effect it had on her was worse than hiccoughs, but he turned nasty and said she wasn't a woman he would wish not to be resisted by. It was only my pointing out to her he was a tenant that stopped her biting him, that being one way she has in a dispute; another is divorcing, and it makes her wild she can't divorce him. He knows this and sometimes his treatment of her is unbridled to the last degree. It is nothing to B. Smith to spread stories about that she is tattooed with a ready-reckoner, once causing her to have her clothes torn off when passing the Stock Exchange.

Some people pay bills before they happen, scared of getting into debt. B. Smith is like that. He passes a shop, sees a piano, thinks he might have a piano sometime, goes in and pays for it, and tells them he will send for it later on. Then he goes sour on the idea; the piano hangs over him. He looks round the laboratory and thinks of all the things he will have to get rid of to make room for it. So he thinks he had better sell it, but the only shop that will buy it is another piano shop, and the only thing he can buy at the piano shop is a piano, and so it goes on. He just won't take cash for fear he might spend it and get into debt. Buying pianos new and selling them secondhand eats up the money, which is why he has to take another job on the side. At night, when there is not much doing in solar biology, he gives my wife and me lessons in memory training. He reads a lot of numbers out of the telephone book and we wait ten minutes and try and write them down. He charges pretty heavily for it, but if we didn't take the lessons he would have no money to pay the rent.

B. Smith once used to write advertisements for the end of books. Publishers often make you think you have got a really long book when it is quite short, and the way they do this is by having a lot of advertisements at the back. Generally speaking they have advertisements with a good deal of reading in them, solid advertisements, but when they haven't been publishers very long they have few of their own books to advertise, and don't seem much class. So people like B. Smith write advertisements for them, and if anyone wants any of the books they say that owing to the demand they are out of print. Some of the advertisements he wrote were for the Fundamental Classics Library, containing all the books he had ever read, described at great length, *The Gravedigger's Encyclopaedia* and the works of a divine he called "Doctor Artemus Saggett." There were twelve volumes of *Sermons on Sundry Offertories* alone. He once got his own back on my wife by including her in the advertisements of a series of biographies which contained Messalina, Lucrezia Borgia and Constance Kent.

III

Scrupulous readers will have noticed that I have frequently referred to my wife but never to my children, and some conclude that I am destitute of same, such conclusions being so rash as to be laughable. I have at least four children, my vagueness being caused by the twins as a lark pretending to be triplets and referring frequently to each other, as if they were being additional outside the room. The eldest, a he-child, is called Secundus, my wife regarding my suggestion of Primus as disrespectful to her. Secundus, or "Two" as he is nicknamed, is a very small-built child, which is convenient, as he fits easily into small cheap pieces of apparatus when I am experimenting. He is thought by some to be slightly odd in manner, having been brought up for several years with three owls, to test whether they would teach him to see in the dark. The test was a failure, but interesting all the same, as they taught him to hoot, which through laziness he is apt to do instead of speaking, especially for the responses in church. The twins come next and are called Medius and Media, being of opposite sexes. Apart from being like each other there is really not much to the twins, though they served as a basis of one experiment, which showed that if you pushed a pin into a twin the other did not much care. Our last child is a more striking character and called Junissimus, being the youngest. He is full of fun and pranks, such as stuffing cushions with barbed-wire and filling folded umbrellas with sneezing-powder, causing people to think that they have caught colds from the rain when they raise them. Junissimus is a very strong child and has an annoying habit of taking the garden-roller and rolling the rock garden right into the ground so that it looks like a crazy paving. He is also apt to roll visitors as they come up the path, and we have had to have a notice printed saying "ALTHOUGH THERE IS NO NEED TO BEWARE OF THE DOG BECAUSE WE HAVE NO DOG BEWARE OF A SMALL BOY PUSHING A GARDEN-ROLLER NOR DO WE WANT CANVASSERS."

Recently we have been trying an educational experiment with our family, dividing them equally into an Experimental Group and Control Group. The Experimental Group are taken to various places of interest, given milk and orange juice, have stories read to them and very expensive tutors. The Control Group do their lessons in a cellar; they learn mainly Latin grammar and arithmetic, and live on fever diet. Both groups are then sent in for an examination, and the Experimental Group do much better, this proving several things, among such being that environment is more important than heredity, that modern methods are good methods and that food is important.

We have some difficulty in deciding what careers the children are to follow when they grow up, as my wife wishes them to go into the family business, and this means starting a business for them to go into; while I want them to marry money, and for this it is necessary to learn such subjects as horse-riding, dancing, and simple accountancy. If all four marry money it will easily be seen that the money can be less than if only one does. B. Smith is writing a book on choice of careers, and when finished this should be of great assistance to us. It tells you—what few other books on the subject mention—the drawbacks to each career; for example, under VET, being bitten, under SAILOR, the sea, etc. The problem of discipline in a large family is very difficult, and until B. Smith discovered that the children were sensitive about their personal appearance it seemed insoluble; but now all that is needed if a child is naughty is to forbid it to wash or to brush its hair for a fortnight, serious cases being dealt with by smearing them liberally with the cheaper kinds of jam.

What with a house and family and science and self-indulgence, straitened is what my circumstances would be if I were not fortunate enough to have a Financial Flair. I devote two hours each day to the Flair, this being ample to provide me with all I want to spend in the other hours. My method is this. I open the daily paper and look down the lists of engagements; then I write to the parties and threaten to forbid the banns, this being something that anyone can do and being difficult to live down even if unjustified. I cannot ask outright for money, as this might be considered blackmail, so I just wait for them to make an offer. Some are hard and dare me to do my worst, but many think it better to play for safety and send me gifts which I convert into stocks and shares. Investments, I should explain, are of two kinds: those which pay you so much every year (and these I keep) and those which do not pay you but just go up and down; these I keep until they go up, when I sell them, and the difference between the price I gave for them and the price at which I sell them is called profit, and I live on it. It sometimes happens that shares go down all the time, and in this case I use them as presents, and people feel that they must return my gifts and frequently give me good solid things, and if these are worth more than the price I originally paid for the shares here again we have a profit. Some people find it is cheaper to live by making themselves into a company, and others stay mainly with friends, but I find that the Flair produces ample for my simple needs and saves me the embarrassment of being announced by butlers as Harmony Jenkins and Co.

There is one thing which strains my Flair to limits and this is income-tax, which even my scientific training does not enable me to master completely, and I have on several occasions paid same. While I find the best way of dealing with income-tax is losses and depreciation of plant, for some reason I cannot convince inspectors that if finance is my business my plant must be capital, and that I should be allowed depreciation at standard rate quite apart from what is actually lost or gained.

Once I set up as an Income-Tax Consultant, and by means of an enticing brochure acquired many clients whose fees more than balanced the amount of tax I had to pay; but this was not a method which would work very often, and the next year I was again down in my accounts. Tax officials, though amiable and industrious, are narrow-minded and apt to turn down good suggestions even if they might benefit the revenue—among such being that I should place my Flair at the disposal of the Government, my idea being that if when threatening to forbid banns I did it on official note-paper my percentage of failures would be far fewer, and the profits would be shared with the Treasury. I also suggested that if I managed to get ten new tax-payers I should go tax-free myself, something not unlike this principle being applied in many kinds of trade.

THE FOX AND THE STORK

BRET HARTE

(From "Aesop Improved")

A fox one day invited a stork to dinner, but provided for the entertainment only the first course, soup. This being in a shallow dish, of course the fox lapped it up readily, but the stork, by means of his long bill, was unable to gain a mouthful.

"You do not seem fond of soup," said the fox, concealing a smile in his napkin. "Now it is one of my greatest weaknesses."

"You certainly seem to project yourself outside of a large quantity," said the stork, rising with some dignity, and examining his watch with considerable *empressement*; "but I have an appointment at 8 o'clock, which I had forgotten. I must ask to be excused. *Au revoir*. By the way, dine with me tomorrow."

The fox assented, arrived at the appointed time, but found as he fully expected, nothing on the table but a single long-necked bottle, containing olives, which the stork was complacently extracting by the aid of his long bill.

"Why, you do not seem to eat anything," said the stork, with great *naïveté*, when he had finished the bottle.

"No," said the fox, significantly, "I am waiting for the second course."

"What is that?" asked the stork, blandly.

"Stork stuffed with olives," shrieked the fox in a very pronounced manner, and instantly dispatched him.

Moral:

True hospitality obliges the host to sacrifice himself for his guests.

THE PIG IN A POKE

A Tale

(From The Wit's Magazine, 1784)

A farmer's lease contained a flaw;
To mend it, he appealed to law.
Dear-bought experience told him plain,
That law without a fee was vain;
And that, to clear his counsel's tone, he
Must bribe o'er with meat or money.
　One morn he calls his clown in chief,
"Here, take this pig to Lawyer Brief."
The clown (unlike his wife, they say)
Could both be silent, and obey;
　The pig secured within a sack,
At ease hung dangling from his back;
Thus loaded, straight to town he went,
With many an awkward compliment.

A half-way house convenient stood,
Where host was kind, and ale was good;
In steps the clown, and calls to Cecil—
"A quart of stout, to wet my whistle!"
Eased of his load, he takes a chair,
And quaffs oblivion to all care.
　Three artful wags accost the clown,
And ask his errand up to town.
With potent ale his heart grows warm,
Which, drunk or sober, meant no harm;
He tells them plainly whence he came,
His master, and the lawyer's name;
And, ere the circling mug was drained,
Showed what the prostrate sack contained.

Whilst two the witless clown amuse,
With merry tales, and mournful news,
A third removes the sack unseen,

And soon sets free the guest within.
But, lest our clown the trick should trace,
A well-fed cur supplies the place.
The point cleared up of what's to pay,
Our clown in peace pursued his way.
Arrived, he makes his awkward bow,
With many a *Wherefore*, and *As how*.
"Heaven bless your honour many a year!
Look what a pig I've brought you here."
The sack untied without demur,
Forthwith out gently crept the cur.

Both stood aghast with eager eyes,
And both, no doubt, looked wondrous wise.
The clown, who saw the lawyer foam,
Swore 'twas a pig when brought from home.
And, wondering at the queer disaster,
In haste returned to tell his master.
    Well pleased to see him take the bait,
The wags his quick return await.
What peals of noisy mirth prevail,
To hear him tell the mystic tale!
The devil is in it, they all agree,
And seem to wonder more than he.

From them to Cecil he repairs,
To her the strange event declares.
Meantime the wags, to end the joke,
Replace the pig within its poke.
The rustic soon resumes his load,
And, whistling, plods along the road.
    The impatient farmer hails the clown,
And asks, "What news from London town?
The pig was liked, they made you drink?"—
"Nay, master! master! what d'ye think?
The pig (or I'm a stupid log)
Is changed into a puppy dog"—
"A dog!"—"Nay, since my word you doubt,
See here: I'll fairly turn him out."

No sooner was the sack untied,
Than a loud grunt his word belied.

"Death," cries the farmer, "tell me whence
Proceeds this daring insolence?
Make haste, take back this pig again you
Presuming elf, or, zounds! I'll brain you!"
   The clown of patient soul and blood,
Awhile in silent wonder stood;
Then briefly cried, with phiz demure—
"Yon lawyer is a *witch* for sure!
How hoarse his voice! his face how grim!
What's pig with us is dog with him.
Heaven shield my future days from evil!
For, as I live, I've seen the devil."

CHIEFLY ABOUT HUGH TROY

H. ALLEN SMITH

Practical jokers are as common as bum spellers around a newspaper shop. Hoaxing, in fact, seems almost a part of the business. I have worked on more than a dozen newspapers and each of them had at least one practical joker on the premises.

My initiation into Journalism was by way of a fairly common joke. It came on the second day of my employment at the Huntington Press. I remember that it was a steaming afternoon and I was applying myself to the hen scratches used in proofreading when Mr. George Wood, foreman of the composing room, stepped into the editorial department and engaged the managing editor in conversation.

"I've got to have that nonpareil spaceband," said Mr. Wood, "and I've got to have it right away. You'll have to find somebody to send."

The two of them looked at me, and I was all eagerness to serve. At last they decided I was trustworthy and the managing editor told me to trot down to Rox Cartwright's print shop and get a nonpareil spaceband for Mr. Wood.

Rox Cartwright's print shop was a good half mile away but I got there in handy time. Mr. Cartwright was a tall, solemn man, and when I told him I had come to get a nonpareil spaceband for Mr. Wood, he looked me up and down and said:

"Where's your truck at?"

I assured him I had no truck, whereupon he sighed heavily and led me around to the rear of his shop. There he dug an old wheelbarrow from a pile of junk and pointed out a huge piece of machinery as being the nonpareil spaceband. I helped him load it on the wheelbarrow, thanked him, and started off with it.

The nonpareil spaceband proved a greater burden than I had ever been called upon to handle before, but I tugged and shoved and sweated until, at last, I arrived in the alley alongside the newspaper office.

Mr. Wood came into the alley, took one look at my unwieldy cargo, and began to purple the neighborhood with strong language.

"Take it back!" he cried. "Take it out of my sight! Take it back to Rox Cartwright and tell him for me that he's gettin' old. I said nonpareil spaceband, and what does he send me! A pneumatic slug line! Heavenly God!"

The trip back with that pneumatic slug line was much worse than the original journey. I could only make it a few feet at a time, and nothing but a single hope bore me up. I figured that the genuine nonpareil spaceband would not likely be as heavy as the pneumatic slug line Rox Cartwright had given me by mistake.

Finally I reached the print shop, gasping for breath, barely able to tell the proprietor what Mr. Wood had said.

Rox Cartwright shoved the wheelbarrow to the rear of the shop and dumped the huge hunk of iron—actually part of an old flat-bed press —onto the ground. He was looking over an even bigger chunk of machinery when human compassion caused him to turn and examine me.

It must have been fairly obvious that I would never be able to stand up under another trip with a nonpareil spaceband. Rox Cartwright stood and studied the thing over in his mind a bit, then he spoke:

"You better go on back to the shop. This is a little joke they played on you. You go on back and tell George Wood that enough is enough, and also tell him for me that he's an old goat. There is no such thing as a nonpareil spaceband, and if there was a nonpareil spaceband, it wouldn't be no bigger than the blade of a pocketknife. Now, go on back."

Since that day I have witnessed the perpetration of innumerable practical jokes. I could write a book about practical jokes and I'd do it except that I am a physical coward and have no appetite for being hanged. There is an immense popular prejudice against practical jokes.

Kindly people look upon playful hoaxing as criminal and classify the practical joke with the pun. I'm not altogether in agreement with them. I won't undertake to defend the practical joke, but I will speak for the pun. Its enemies usually employ the old aphorism: a pun is the lowest form of wit. Yet the pun has had some distinguished champions. Charles Lamb, for example, wrote:

"A pun is a noble thing *per se*. It fills the mind; it is as perfect as a sonnet: better. I never knew an enemy to puns who was not an ill-natured man."

A practical joke can be wantonly cruel—as in the case of Battling Ben Chiffriller—and again it can be an innocuous work of genius. Years after the affair of the nonpareil spaceband it was my privilege to make the acquaintance of the most accomplished practical joker of the contemporary scene. He is an artist named Hugh Troy, and was about thirty-five years old at that time. At the present writing he is in the Army. I began hearing vague stories about him almost from the moment of my arrival in New York, but I didn't meet him until ten years had passed.

Hugh Troy stands five inches above six feet, which may account for his becoming one of New York's leading muralists. The day I first met him I lunched with him beneath one of his murals in the café lounge of the Savoy-Plaza and I noticed that the headwaiter scrutinized him carefully as we entered the room, as though he expected Hugh to break forth a bundle of Roman candles or turn loose a chipmunk.

At first Hugh tried to argue me out of a project I had in mind—writing an article about his career as a practical joker. He was well aware of the stigma that seems to attach itself to the business.

"My reputation as a practical joker," he said, "is affecting my reputation as an artist. I get a commission from some big company to do a mural, and then the president of the company finds out about me. They have me under suspicion from that moment on. When I get through with a job they come around in committees and go over my paintings with magnifying glasses, looking for gags. I've always tried to soft-pedal my extracurricular activities."

Later he changed his mind and spent the afternoon with me, remembering some of his exploits.

Hugh Troy's father was a professor at Cornell and Hugh's penchant for pranks dates back to his boyhood in Ithaca.

"When I was a kid," he said, "the people next door closed their house and went off to Europe for six months. They had a big cherry tree in their back yard. We heard they were coming back two weeks before their arrival in Ithaca. My brother and I spent those two weeks hard at work. We filled that cherry tree full of apples, fastening them onto the limbs with bits of wire. We used two barrels of apples, and when the people came home and saw their cherry tree bearing apples, they called in half the town to look at the miracle before they found out it was a hoax."

Hugh's parents usually spent a couple of months away from Ithaca each year, leaving the two boys home with Grandma and a maid. Grandma Troy, whose great age kept her indoors, was pure Irish and believed implicitly in the little people. She became the victim of a game which Hugh invented, called Getting Grandma Behind.

"As soon as my father and mother left," Hugh explained, "I would begin on Grandma. Chiefly by manipulating the newspapers, I would mix up her calendar, first getting her a day behind so that she believed Friday was really Thursday and finally getting her to the point where Sunday, at our house, was actually Wednesday.

"On Wednesday morning my brother and I would bring out the Sunday papers, which we had kept hidden for four days. The maid would cook up a chicken dinner and Grandma would lead us in prayer. It was even more difficult to bring Grandma back up to date when the time approached for the return of my mother and father. But we always managed to do it, and Grandma never found out."

Hugh attended Cornell, and his years at the university were made up of a succession of gags. The skipper of a dinky trolley car came to resent Hugh's presence in town. Whenever the car approached, Hugh would step forward and signal it to stop. Then, with easy nonchalance, he would place one foot on the car step, tie his shoelace, utter his thanks to the motorman, and wave the trolley on its way.

A certain professor of architecture at Cornell—prototype of the absent-minded pundit—habitually wore rubber overshoes to class if the weather report even hinted at rain. One very wet day Hugh purloined the rubbers for a few hours and painted them to resemble human feet. He then covered them with lampblack and put them back in the locker room. That afternoon the unsuspecting professor started home in the rain. He had walked no more than a block before the lampblack was washed away and such citizens as happened to be abroad were startled to see him sloshing along, so it appeared, in his bare feet.

When he had finished college Hugh Troy came to New York to

make a name for himself as an artist. Usually he shared living quarters with other college men and usually they were up to no good.

Early one morning Troy led four companions down Fifty-fourth Street to Fifth Avenue. They wore overalls, carried picks and shovels, and had provided themselves with red lanterns and "Men Working" signs.

Opposite the old Rockefeller town house they set to work ripping up the pavement. They labored through the morning and by noon had dug quite a hole in the street. Hugh posted flags and signs and they knocked off for lunch. He led his fellow laborers into the dining room of a fashionable hotel near by. The headwaiter was horrified as the grimy workmen tramped into his sedate precincts. Hugh quickly identified himself and whispered:

"It's all right. It's a little joke the manager wants us to put over."

After a hearty meal, during which many of the other guests sniffed in the general direction of the chandeliers and then stamped out of the place, Hugh led his boys back to the diggings. They worked through the afternoon until they had a hole big enough to drop a Buick into, then they put up their lanterns and signs and quit. Their gaping excavation was not officially discovered to be a fake until night-fall of the following day, and a couple of years went by before the identity of the gang foreman became known, by which time anger had abated and there was no prosecution.

Another time Hugh and one of his friends were sitting on a bench in Central Park. They sat quietly until they saw a policeman approaching. Then they got up, picked up the bench, and started walking away with it. The cop, to be sure, came charging down on them, demanding to know what in the name of heaven they thought they were doing with that bench.

"Oh," said Hugh Troy airily, "we're just taking it home."

"Takin' it home, are ya!" roared the cop. "Well, I'm takin' ya to the station house."

At the Arsenal Precinct in the Park the lieutenant changed color when Hugh placidly produced a bill of sale showing that the bench actually belonged to him, that it had been built to order for him and he had paid for it.

The lieutenant was in a fury but could do nothing beyond sending Hugh and his friend away with their bench. They hurried at once to the north end of the Park. This time they hid in the shrubbery with their bench until they saw a cop ambling in their direction. They came out of the bushes carrying the bench, but this time they were running, looking furtively in all directions except that where the startled cop was standing. He caught them.

Back in the station house they again faced the livid lieutenant. He blasted them with profanity and assigned an officer to escort them out of the Park and to their home.

"I don't know what the law says about it," the lieutenant declared, "but I know that if you come back in this Park with that bench, I'll make a personal issue out of it, and I'll tear that bench up and beat your brains out with the planks."

In those days Troy lived in Greenwich Village and often patronized Loew's Sheridan Theatre, where he preferred to sit in the rear of the balcony. He is so extraordinarily tall that one day his head got in the way of the beam from the projection room, messing up the picture on the screen. The audience hooted and stamped and the manager came on the run. He gave Hugh an expert tongue-lashing, which was an error.

A week or so later the film in which Garbo first talked opened at the Sheridan. Hugh took a seat off to one side of the balcony. He waited until the picture was well started, then he quietly opened a small can he had been carrying in his pocket. Out flew a dozen moths, and they made directly for the beam of light and stayed there. Garbo not only talked—she blemished.

Hugh has baffled and confused many citizens who have had the misfortune to call a telephone number and get his phone by mistake. If they were calling the druggist, he'd be the druggist. Or the butcher, or the boy friend, or the Committee for the Protection of the Holders of Bonds Sold through G. L. Miller & Co., Inc. (Rector 2-3289). Hugh always played all the parts ad lib.

During one period he was continually getting calls intended for a bookmaker. Hugh accepted bets and quoted odds and had a magnificent time inventing horse names.

"Who win the fifth at Belmont?" a caller would ask.

"Belt Buckle," Hugh would say.

"Who?"

"Belt Buckle win it."

"I don't get it. Sounds like you said Belt Buckle."

"I did say Belt Buckle. Belt Buckle win the fifth at Belmont."

Then Hugh would hang up—leaving the horse player bewildered and convinced that, at last, he had begun to hear strange noises.

There was a woman in Queens who repeatedly got Troy on the phone when she was seeking some other number. For a while he tried arguing with her, but she was stubborn, insisting that she had the right number. Hugh tried all sorts of things, but the nuisance would not abate. At last he resolved on vengeance. He considered the thing for a long time before he acted.

"I'll drive her crazy," he said. "I'll drive her crazy on one single subject."

He chose turkeys as the subject and he set out deliberately to make the woman turkey-conscious. He knew her identity and her address. He bought a huge carton of Thanksgiving Day greeting cards all bearing turkey illustrations. He began mailing these so she would receive one in every mail delivery. He showered her with reams of literature concerning poultry shows, with entry blanks for prize turkeys. He sent her, now and then, a cheap roasting pan with instructions on how to cook a turkey. And about once a week he'd dispatch a telegram to her, saying:

GOBBLE GOBBLE GOBBLE

"I kept it up for six months," he said, "and then I began to get sick of turkeys myself. I don't know what effect it ever had on her."

On election night in 1932 Hugh was walking through Times Square when his eyes fell on a stack of tabloid extras carrying big black headlines:

ROOSEVELT

ELECTED

He could think of nothing to do with the papers at the moment, but the notion struck him that someday they might be useful. He bought a dozen copies, took them home, and stowed them away in a closet.

Three years later he invited a few friends to his apartment for a New Year's Eve party. After a few cocktails the crowd decided to range around town in quest of adventure. There were no definite plans and at the last minute Hugh remembered his election extras. He got them out, gave a copy to each of his guests, and they hurried to the nearest subway station.

For three hours they rode the subways, always standing in the aisles, each with a copy of the old newspaper. Passengers in the seats would look up and see a man reading a newspaper which proclaimed, ROOSEVELT ELECTED. Farther down the car would be another man reading the same paper. It was confusing no end.

Being one of the tallest men in New York City, Hugh Troy has a little trick that often startles his companions. All over town he has twenty-five-cent pieces hidden on ledges. He'll be walking in Times Square with some acquaintance. Suddenly he'll say:

"Excuse me just a moment."

Then he'll step over to the wall of a theater or a hotel, reach up to a ledge, and pluck a quarter from it. I suppose he collected his hidden wealth before he went off to war.

"If I ever get rich," he told me that afternoon of the long talk, "I'm going to buy a yacht and call it the *Great White Also*. When I was in elementary school, back in Ithaca, I came upon a line in my geography which said:

"The Arctic is inhabited by the brown bear, the black bear, and the great white also.

"It worried me. At home I asked about the Great White Also. The family let me go on believing that a Great White Also was some horrible, child-eating beast, and whenever I misbehaved they used to tell me that the Great White Also would get me. I think it would be a wonderful name for a boat."

He confessed to one great frustration.

He was walking on Fifth Avenue one day when the window display in a fashionable beauty salon caught his eye. It was a representation of a "Temple de Beauté." In the foreground was a single flickering flame—the flame of eternal beauty or some such thing. For a long time Hugh schemed and plotted ways of getting into the salon window unobserved, but he never made it. He wanted to hang a frankfurter over the eternal flame.

ACKNOWLEDGMENTS

The editor and the publisher have made every effort to trace the ownership of all material contained herein. It is their belief that the necessary permissions from publishers, authors, and authorized agents have been obtained in all cases. In the event of any question arising as to the use of any material, the editor and publisher, while expressing regret for any error unconsciously made, will be pleased to make the necessary correction in future editions of this book.

Thanks are due the following authors, publishers, publications, and agents for permission to use the material indicated.

Franklin P. Adams for "A Pair of Sexes," from *A Treasury of Laughter*, edited by Louis Untermeyer, copyright, 1911, by Doubleday & Company, Inc.

Emily Amber for "Rules for Writing to Camp Noosa Woosa," reprinted by permission of the author and *The New York Times*, copyright, 1953, by The New York Times Company.

Roger Angell for "Living with a Dog," from *Holiday* magazine, copyright, 1951, by Roger Angell.

Dick Ashbaugh for "Just Leave a Note, Honey," and "You, too, can be Nervous," copyrighted by Dick Ashbaugh.

John Bailey, the author, for "It Isn't the Heat and It Isn't the Humidity, Either," copyright, 1956, by The Curtis Publishing Company.

William Birmingham for "Don't Bother with the Ants," from his Beach Combings column in *The Fire Islander*, copyright, 1955, by Fire Island Publishing Corporation.

Morris Bishop for "I Am the Corporal of My Soul," from *Spilt Milk*, copyright, 1942, by Morris Bishop.

Lurton Blassingame for "Your Talk Tells Your Age," by Perry Laukhauf, copyright, 1956, by United Newspaper Magazine Corporation.

Brandt and Brandt for "Soaring," from *Penrod*, by Booth Tarkington, published by Doubleday & Company, Inc., copyright, 1914, 1942, by Booth Tarkington.

Brandt and Brandt and *The New Yorker* magazine, for "B. Sc.," by Emily Hahn, copyright, 1946, by The New Yorker Magazine, Inc.

Curtis Brown, Ltd., the author, and The New Yorker Magazine, Inc., for "Slurvian Self-Taught," by John Davenport, copyright © 1949 by The New Yorker Magazine, Inc.

Carl A. Buchele for "Housekeeping Tips," from *The Saturday Evening Post*, copyright, 1950, by The Curtis Publishing Company.

Patrick Campbell for "The Intrepid Airman," from *The Sunday Dispatch*, London, 1949.

Bennett Cerf for "Take My Word for It" from The Cerfboard, *This Week Magazine*, copyright, 1956, by United Newspapers Magazine Corporation.

Mrs. Laura Baker Cobb, c/o Buhler, King & Buhler, 274 Madison Avenue, New York, N.Y., for "Speaking of Operations," by Irvin S. Cobb, copyright, 1917, by Laura Baker Cobb.

Jack Conroy for "The High Divers," from the Chicago Industrial Folklore Manuscripts of the Federal Writers Project of the W.P.A. for the State of Illinois.

Cowles Magazine, Inc., for "Life with Sears Roebuck," from the 1953 Flair Annual.

Parke Cummings for "I Say It's False," reprinted from *Esquire*, copyright, 1939, by Esquire, Inc.; "Double That Order," reprinted from *The Rotarian Magazine*, copyright, 1950, by The Rotarians.

Parke Cummings and Crowell-Collier Publishing Company for "In One Ear and Upside Down" by Parke Cummings, copyright, 1950, by Crowell-Collier Publishing Company; also the author and *The Saturday Evening Post* for "Summer is Icumen In," copyright, 1949, by The Curtis Publishing Company.

Paul de Vergie for "Mother Married an Oboe Player," by Paul de Vergie, copyright, 1949, by Paul de Vergie.

Dial Press, Inc., The New Yorker Magazine, Inc., and the author for "The Crusty Professor's Song," from *A Bowlful of Bishop*, by Morris Bishop, copyright, 1953, by The New Yorker Magazine, Inc., and copyright, 1954, by Morris Bishop.

Dodd, Mead & Company, Inc., for "Ring Out, Wild Bells," by Wolcott Gibbs, from *A Bed of Neuroses*, copyright © 1936, by Wolcott Gibbs; "Grandfather's New Automobile," from *How Dear to My Heart*, by Emily Kimbrough, copyright © 1944, by Dodd, Mead & Company, Inc.; "How We Kept Mother's Day," from *Laugh With Leacock*, by Stephen Leacock, copyright © 1930, by Dodd, Mead & Company, Inc.

Doubleday & Company, Inc., for the following by O. Henry: "By Courier," from *The Four Million*, copyright, 1902, by Doubleday & Company, Inc.; "Jeff Peters as a Personal Magnet," from *The Gentle Grafter*, copyright, 1907, by Doubleday & Company, Inc.; "The Ransom of Red Chief," from *Whirligigs*, copyright, 1910, by Doubleday & Company, Inc.

Doubleday & Company, Inc., for "Chiefly About Hugh Troy," from *Life in a Putty Knife Factory*, by H. Allen Smith, copyright, 1943, by H. Allen Smith.

Doubleday & Company, Inc., and Franklin Watts, Inc., for the following games from *The Real Book of Games* by Joseph Leeming (edited by Helen Hoke); copyright, 1953, by Franklin Watts, Inc.

Harry Dubin and Barthold Fles for "Scene 1 from Hail, Alma Pater," by Harry Dubin, copyright, 1954, by Harry Dubin.

Clifton Fadiman and *The New Yorker* for "How to Attract the Attention of a Schrafft's Hostess," by Clifton Fadiman, copyright, 1937, by The New Yorker Magazine, Inc. (formerly The F.-R. Publishing Corp.)

Farrar, Straus & Cudahy, Inc., for selections from *Life Among the Savages*, by Shirley Jackson, copyright, 1953, by Shirley Jackson.

Robert Fontaine for "God Hit a Home Run," from *The Happy Time*, by Robert Fontaine, copyright, 1945, by Robert Fontaine.

Wilfred Funk for "The Black Magic of Words," by Wilfred Funk, copyrighted.

Galaxy Publishing Corporation for an article by H. L. Gold from his columns entitled "Look Now" and "Now Look," in Galaxy Science Fiction Magazine, copyright, 1956, by Galaxy Publishing Corporation, Inc.

Greenberg: Publisher for selections from *Big Fun Book*, copyright, 1940, by Greenberg: Publisher; *Fun for the Family*, copyright, 1937, by Greenberg: Publisher; and *More Fun for the Family*, copyright, 1938, by Greenberg: Publisher.

Harcourt, Brace and Company, Inc., for "Chivalry is Born," by Heywood Broun, from the *Collected Edition of Heywood Broun*, copyright, 1941, by Harcourt, Brace and Company, Inc.

Harper & Brothers for a selection from *The Innocents Abroad* and "Huckleberry Finn Joins Tom Sawyer's Gang," from *The Adventures of Tom Sawyer*, by Mark Twain; for "A Plethora of Sergeants," from *From Here to Shimbashi*, by John Sack, copyright, 1955, by John Sack; for "Help! Help! Au Secours!" from *Far, Far from Home*, by Ruth McKenny, copyright, 1952, by Curtis Publishing Company; for "Your Boy and His Dog," from *Chips Off the Old Benchley*, by Robert Benchley, copyright, 1932, by Liberty Magazine, Inc.; and for "Center Shot," from *Native American Humor*, edited by James Aswell.

Harold Helfer for "Initiative," by Harold Helfer, copyright, 1945, Gourmet Magazine.

Eleanor Hollister for "To a Frog . . . and a Man," by Eleanor Hollister, from *Columbia Poetry 1932*, copyright, 1932, by Columbia University Press.

Henry Holt & Company for "Araminta and the Automobile," by Charles Battell Loomis, from *Cheerful Americans*, copyright, 1904, by Henry Holt & Company.

Charlotte C. Jackson for two stories by Joseph Henry Jackson: "Weasels in the Cornmeal," copyright, 1953, by Charlotte Jackson; and "Marta the Dog Lover," copyright, 1955, by Charlotte Jackson.

Norman R. Jaffray for "Where's Everybody Gone?" reprinted from *The Saturday Evening Post*, copyright, 1957, by The Curtis Publishing Company.

Moritz Jagendorf for "The Saints of Kansas," "Marvels o' the West," "A Tale for Texas," and "Olden Days Fishing," copyright © 1957, by Moritz Jagendorf.

C. S. Jennison for "Wonder Fabrics Make Me Wonder," reprinted from *The Atlantic Monthly*, copyright, 1955, by The Atlantic Monthly Company, Boston 16, Mass.

Ralf Kircher for "If it was a Snake," reprinted from *The Saturday Evening Post*, copyright by The Curtis Publishing Company; for "Kitty, Kitty, Kitty," "Silence, Bottles," and "Your Best Friend is Your Father," from *There's a Fly in This Room*, copyright, 1946, by Ralf Kircher.

Alfred A. Knopf, Inc., for "Father Sews on a Button," from *Life With Father* by Clarence Day, copyright, 1934, 1935, by Clarence Day; and for "Middle East Calls Middle West," from *From Pillar to Post*, by Anne Sinclair Mehdevi, copyright, 1956, by Anne Sinclair Mehdevi.

J. B. Lippincott Company for "Butch Minds the Baby," from *Guys and Dolls*, by Damon Runyon, copyright, 1930, by Damon Runyon; excerpts from "Onions in the Stew," by Betty MacDonald, copyright, 1955, by Betty MacDonald; and for "Roofsitter," from *There's One in Every Family*," by Frances Eisenberg, copyright, 1941, by Frances Eisenberg.

The Macmillan Company for "When Father Carves the Duck," by E. V. Wright, from *A Treasury of the Familiar*, edited by Ralph L. Woods (1955 The Macmillan Company), copyright, 1942, by Ralph L. Woods; excerpt from *The Behavior Book, A Manual for Ladies*, by Eliza Leslie; and for "Toidy Days" and "First Books," from *Baby Book*, by Stanley and Janice Berenstain, copyright, 1931, by Stanley and Janice Berenstain.

J. P. McEvoy for "McEvoy in Nurseryland," copyright, 1946, by The Reader's Digest Association, Inc.

Mavis McIntosh-Elizabeth McKee for "The All-Purpose Fishing Story" and the "All-Purpose Ghost Story," by Charles W. Morton, copyright, 1952, by Charles W. Morton.

Mademoiselle, and the author's agent, Mavis McIntosh-Elizabeth McKee, for "How to be Happy Though Fired," by Sylvia Wright, copyright, 1956, by Sylvia Wright.

Philip Minoff for "My Wife Never Looks at Gauges," copyright, 1955, by Archbold van Beuren; and "Strictly Business," by Philip Minoff, copyright, 1956, by Archbold van Beuren. Both reprinted from *Cue Magazine*.

Howard Moorepark for "On Being Translated into English," by Lesley Conger, copyright, 1956, by F & W Publishing Corp., and "Things," by Lesley Conger, copyright © 1957, by Shirley Suttles; for "The Night the Station Got Lost," by Hugh A. Mulligan, copyright, 1956, by Hugh A. Mulligan; and for "Luke and the Lord's Work," by Paul T. Sturges, from *The Farm Journal*, copyright, 1956, by The Curtis Publishing Company.

Mt. Holyoke College for "The Real Fire Laws of Mt. Holyoke Female Seminary of About 1857, and the Burlesque of Them by Students of Mt. Holyoke College in the 1870's."

New Statesman and Nation (London, England) for "Cheap Clothes for Fat Old Women," by Marghanita Laski, reprinted from the *New Statesman and Nation* of November 15, 1948.

Douglas Newton for "Our Shared (?) Language." Hitherto unpublished. Copyright © 1957, by Helen Hoke Associates.

The New Yorker for "Farewell, My Lovely!" by Lee Strout White (E. B. White and Richard Lee Strout), from *Farewell to Model T*, published by Putnam's, copyright, 1936, by The New Yorker Magazine, Inc.; and for "Nothing Over Ten Cents," by Mary Heaton Vorse, copyright, 1932, by The New Yorker Magazine, Inc. (formerly The F.-R. Publishing Corp.)

New York Herald Tribune for "Take Two Cans of Tuna," by Byron Fish from *Today's Living*, copyright © 1956, by New York Herald Tribune, Inc.

The New York Times and the author for "Grasshoppers a la Mode," by Jean Condit, copyright, 1956, by The New York Times Company.

Leonard A. Paris for "Help Wanted," by Leonard A. Paris, copyright, 1950, by The Curtis Publishing Company.

G. P. Putnam's Sons for "The Whisperer," by Ironquill, copyright, 1902, by G. P. Putnam's Sons.

Punch (London) for three articles from *H.J. Talking*, by R. G. G. Price.

Eugene Rachlis and *The New York Times* for "How Not to Do-It-Yourself," by Eugene Rachlis, copyright, 1954, by The New York Times Company.

Boris Randolph for the puzzles used in this volume, and hitherto unpublished. Copyright © 1957, by Boris Randolph.

Paul R. Reynolds & Son for "Letter to a Manufacturer," by H. F. Ellis, copyright, 1951, by The Curtis Publishing Company.

Edward J. Riebe for "Whatever Happened to Plop?" by Edward J. Riebe, copyright, 1950, by The Curtis Publishing Company.

Berry Rockwell for "Complaint Department," by Katherine Best, from *Old Life*, copyrighted by Berry Rockwell.

Charles Scribner's Sons for "The Transferred Ghost," by Frank Stockton.

John D. Sheridan for "Dressing the Baby," from *I Can't Help Laughing*, by John D. Sheridan (Talbot Press, Ireland).

Larry Siegel for "Private Wumperdopp of the New Army," by Larry Siegel, copyright, 1949, by *American Legion Magazine*.

Simon & Schuster, Inc., for "New Yorkese," from *Almanac for New Yorkers 1937*, compiled by Workers of the Federal Writers' Project of the Works Progress Administration in New York City, copyright, 1936, by Simon & Schuster, Inc.; for "A Man's Television Set is His Castle," from *The Book of Little Knowledge*, by Goodman Ace, copyright, 1951, 1952, 1953, 1954, 1955, by Saturday Review Associates, Inc., and copyright, 1955, by Goodman Ace; and for "The Flea Position" and "Whatever Happened to the Bad Boy," from *Out of the Blue*, by John Crosby, copyright, 1946, 1947, 1948, 1949, 1950, 1951, by New York Herald Tribune, Inc., and © 1952, by John Crosby.

Caskie Stinnett for "Let Me Handle This In My Own Way," from *The Saturday Evening Post*, copyright, 1951, by The Curtis Publishing Company; and for "A Night to Remember or I'll Try Tomorrow," "And If Elected, and I Think I Will Be," "May We See You a Moment Outside?", "It May Cost a Little More" and "Where's the Studio Audience," from *Speaking of Holiday*, copyright, 1955, 1956, by The Curtis Publishing Company.

United Features Syndicate, Inc., for "Doctor Doll," by Inez Robb, first published in the *World Telegram and Sun*, copyright, 1956, by United Features Syndicate, Inc.

Vanguard Press, Inc., for "It Makes Me No Difference," an excerpt from *Mil-*

waukee: *Old Lady Thrift*, by Richard S. Davis, copyright, 1947, by Vanguard Press, Inc.

Viking Press, Inc., for "Yvonne," from *In One Ear*, by Frank Sullivan, copyright, 1933, by Frank Sullivan; for "The Thing," from *The Boys and Their Mother*, by Keith W. Jennison, copyright, 1955, 1956, by Keith W. Jennison.

A. P. Watt & Son, the author, *Punch Magazine* and Methuen & Co. Ltd. of London, England, for "Giving Up Smoking," from *Mild and Bitter*, by A. P. Herbert.

John D. Weaver and Margot Johnson for "Woman's Work," copyright, 1951, by Crowell-Collier Publishing Company.

Willis Kingsley Wing for "No Nutburgers for Me," by Robert de Roos, from *Collier's*, copyright, 1955, by Crowell-Collier Publishing Company; for "Coward in the Congo," by Art Buchwald, copyright, 1955, by Art Buchwald; for "Women Have no Sense of Humor," "I Don't Want to Play," "How to Slay Them with Small Talk," "Daddy Won't Listen to Reason" and "What Makes Children Laugh," all by Robert Thomas Allen, reprinted by permission of Mr. Wing, the agent, and *MacLean's Magazine* and *Mayfair* of Canada; and for the following by Scott Corbett: "Daddy's a Private Eye!" from *This Week Magazine*, copyright, 1943, by United Newspapers Magazine Corp.; "Floorwalker Impersonator" and "Mr. Frisbie Leads the Way," from *This Week Magazine*, both copyright, 1942, by United Newspapers Magazine Corp.; "Score This, Guiseppe!" from *The Atlantic Monthly*, copyright, 1954, by The Atlantic Monthly Co., and "You Can't Cure an Epicure," from *The Saturday Evening Post*, copyright, 1954, by The Curtis Publishing Company.

Robert M. Yoder and The Curtis Publishing Company for "Is There a Life After Forty?" (*The Saturday Evening Post* and the *Post Treasury*), "Evensong: or Be There, Sandman, You Bum," (*The Saturday Evening Post* and *Postscripts*) and "How Gay Was Our Credit" (*The Saturday Evening Post* and *Postscripts*), all three copyright, 1947, by The Curtis Publishing Company.

Cartoons

Frank Adams for a Greyhound bus cartoon reprinted from *Family Circle Magazine*.

Argosy Magazine for "I wouldn't stand over there, son," by Dana Fradon, copyright, 1954, Popular Publications, Inc.

Stanley and Janice Berenstain for "A copy of a Paris original what?" from *Marital Blitz*, by the Berenstains, published by Dell Publishing Co., copyright; 1955, by Stanley and Janice Berenstain; and for "I'll try to explain why you can't play your Old MacDonald record" from *Collier's Magazine*, copyright by Stanley and Janice Berenstain.

Al Boime for "Earth, Please," copyright, 1955, by Crowell-Collier Publishing Company.

Chon Day for "Will the trousers hold a press?" reprinted from *This Week Magazine*, copyright, 1953, by United Newspaper Magazine Corp.; "The first time I get a strike . . ." from *Collier's Magazine*, copyright, 1954, by Crowell-Collier Publishing Company; and "Ladies! Borrow up to $1500 on your husband's signature," from *Collier's Magazine*, copyright, 1955, by Crowell-Collier Publishing Company.

John Dempsey for "Just one more question . . ." from *Look Magazine*, copyright, 1955, by Cowles Magazine, Inc.; and for "What do you mean, when is the slack season?" from *Look Magazine*, copyright, 1955, by Cowles Magazine, Inc.

Dick Ericson for "Do you have something that will cause crab grass a very slow and painful death?" from *Collier's Magazine*, copyright, 1955, by Crowell-Collier Publishing Company.

George Feyer and *MacLean's Magazine* (Canada) for "Skier being carried on a stretcher," copyright, 1954, by MacLean-Hunter Publishing Company, Limited.

Stan Fine for "Well, maybe I don't know what I'm talking about, but . . ." from *Look Magazine*, copyright, 1954, by Cowles Magazine, Inc.

Roy L. Fox for "Don't slam . . . the door," from *The Saturday Evening Post*, copyright by Curtis Publishing Company.

John Gallagher for "Did you see what the moths did to my overcoat?" from *The Saturday Evening Post*, copyright by The Curtis Publishing Company.

Dave Gerard for "While you're up, would you look at the roast . . ." from *The Saturday Evening Post*, copyright by The Curtis Publishing Company; and for "Well, here she is! Dead Man's Slide, we used to call it—" from *The Saturday Evening Post*, copyright, 1947, by The Curtis Publishing Company.

Mary Gibson for "Someone in Tourist Class whistled at me!" from *Collier's Magazine*, copyright, 1955, by Crowell-Collier Publishing Company.

Sid Gordin for "Can you do anything besides graduate?" from *Collier's Magazine*, copyright, 1955, by Crowell-Collier Publishing Company.

Larry Harris for "Boy! This next phase we go through is a dilly!" from *Look Magazine*, copyright, 1956, by Cowles Magazine, Inc.

Ray Helle for "It's all fixed. His pants fall down in the second round," from *The Saturday Evening Post*, copyright, 1952, by The Curtis Publishing Company.

Ned Hilton for "Anything I can do to help?" and for "Says here a child can assemble this . . ." both from *Look Magazine*, and both copyright, 1954, by Cowles Magazine, Inc.; for "Fifty years ago people would just have . . ." from *Look Magazine*, copyright, 1955, by Cowles Magazine, Inc.; and for "I'm sorry, John, the decorator says you'll have to go," from *This Week Magazine*, copyright, 1952, by the United Newspapers Magazine Corp.

David Huffine for "I wish they'd hurry and finish building," from *Collier's Magazine*, copyright, 1950, by Crowell-Collier Publishing Company.

Alfred W. Isler for "There goes the left rear!" from *Collier's Magazine*, copyright, 1956, by Crowell-Collier Publishing Company.

Al Johns for "Everyone in there is on the wrong train, Frank . . ." from *Collier's Magazine*, copyright, 1954, by Crowell-Collier Publishing Company.

Al Kaufman for "Are you sure you're taking that vitamin prescription?" from *The Saturday Evening Post*, copyright, 1955, by The Curtis Publishing Company; and "In case you're interested, we're no longer keeping up with the Joneses . . ." from *The Saturday Evening Post*, copyright, 1956, by The Curtis Publishing Company.

Lion Books, Inc., for Robert LaRocca's cartoon, "There you have the rest of them, T-U-V-W-X-Y-Z," from *Stories for Stags*, copyright, 1956, by Eddie Davis and reprinted by permission of Lion Library Editions.

Clyde Lamb for "Yessir . . . thirty-seven percent less nicotine," from *This Week Magazine*, copyright, 1953, by the United Newspaper Magazine Corp.

Edwin Lepper for "Now for heaven's sake, don't act silly," from *Collier's Magazine*, copyright, 1955, by Crowell-Collier Publishing Company.

Harry Mace for "It's very generous of you, Russell . . ." from *The Saturday Evening Post*, copyright, 1957, by The Curtis Publishing Company.

New York Herald Tribune for the "Miss Peach" comic strip of February 8, by Mell, copyright, 1957, by New York Herald Tribune, Inc.; and for the following H. T. Webster cartoons: "Life's Darkest Moment" (I bet you're glad to see an American girl), "How to Torture Your Husband" (Oh, Sugar! Did you take a clean handkerchief? and Here's a pretty good story . . .) and "Fishing" (The best Fly-fisherman in the State); copyright, 1940, 1941, 1944, New York Herald Tribune, Inc.

Kate Osann for "The main thing is not to let ourselves be fooled . . ." from *Collier's Magazine*, copyright, 1954, by Crowell-Collier Publishing Company; and "It's simple economics, George . . ." from *Collier's Magazine*, copyright, 1956, by Crowell-Collier Publishing Company.

Virgil F. Partch for "Of course it's a police dog," from *Collier's Magazine*, copyright, 1956, by Crowell-Collier Publishing Company.

Al Ross for "Don't think she won't hear about this . . ." from *This Week Magazine*, copyright, 1953, by the United Newspapers Magazine Corp.

Vahan Shirvanian for "Tell you what . . . I'll hold him and you give him the needle," from *The Saturday Evening Post*, copyright, 1957, by The Curtis Publishing Company.

Henry Syverson for "Mother with triplets about to photograph Father . . ." from *This Week Magazine*, copyright, 1951, by the United Newspapers Magazine Corp.

Mort Temes for "Nine times six is seventy-two . . ." from *The Saturday Evening Post*, copyright, 1956, by The Curtis Publishing Company.

Jack Tyrrell for "If there's one song I hate, it's 'Tiger Rag,'" from *The Saturday Evening Post*, copyright, 1957, by The Curtis Publishing Company.

Veterans of Foreign Wars of the United States for "It helps keep the married men from getting homesick," by Marvin Townsend. Reprinted from *V.F.W. Magazine*.

Walt Wetterberg for "Your allergy tests suggest that you may have been intended for some other planet" from *The Saturday Evening Post*, copyright, 1954, by The Curtis Publishing Company.

Fritz Wilkinson for "This is my big surprise—I'm going to make all our furniture," from *Look Magazine*, copyright, 1954, by Cowles Magazine, Inc.

Gahan Wilson for "The map ends here, too," copyright, 1954, by Crowell-Collier Publishing Company; and "Sometimes I think the kid'll never get the hang of it," copyright, 1957, by Crowell-Collier Publishing Company. Both from *Collier's Magazine*.

INDEX OF AUTHORS

INDEX OF TITLES